Small Engines Service Manual

(11th Edition)

W9-AOR-740

Only engines of less than 15 cubic inch displacement are contained in this manual.

CONTENTS

GENERAL

ENGINE SHOP MANUALS

Published by

TECHNICAL PUBLICATIONS DIV.
INTERTEC PUBLISHING CORPORATION

P.O. Box 12901, Overland Park, Kansas 66212

A subsidiary of Howard W. Sams & Co., Inc.
Copyright 1976 by Intertec Publishing Corp., Overland Park, Kansas. Printed in the United States of America.

FUNDAMENTALS SECTION

ENGINE FUNDAMENTALS

OPERATING PRINCIPLES

The small engines used to power lawn mowers, garden tractors and many other items of power equipment in use today are basically similar. All are technically known as "Internal Combustion Reciprocating Engines."

The source of power is heat formed by the burning of a combustible mixture of petroleum products and air. In a reciprocating engine, this burning takes place in a closed cylinder containing a piston. Expansion resulting from the heat of combustion applies pressure on the piston to turn a shaft by means of a crank and connecting rod.

The fuel-air mixture may be ignited by means of an electric spark (Otto Cycle Engine) or by heat formed from compression of air in the engine cylinder (Diesel Cycle Engine). The complete series of events which must take place in order for the engine to run may occur in one revolution of the crankshaft (two strokes of the piston in cylinder) which is referred to as a "Two-Stroke Cycle Engine," or in two revolutions of the crankshaft (four strokes of the piston in cylinder) which is referred to as a "Four-Stroke Cycle Engine."

OTTO CYCLE. In a spark ignited engine, a series of five events is required in order for the engine to provide power. This series of events is called the "Cycle" (or "Work Cycle") and is repeated in each cylinder of the engine as long as work is being done. This series of events which comprise the "Cycle" is as follows:

1. The mixture of fuel and air is pushed into the cylinder by atmospheric pressure when the pressure within the engine cylinder is reduced by the piston moving downward in the cylinder (or by applying pressure to the fuel-air mixture as by crankcase compression in the crankcase of a "Two-Stroke Cycle Engine" which is described in a later paragraph).

2. The mixture of fuel and air is compressed by the piston moving upward in the cylinder.

3. The compressed fuel-air mixture is ignited by a timed electric spark.

4. The burning fuel-air mixture expands, forcing the piston downward in the cylinder thus converting the chemical energy generated by combustion into mechanical power.

5. The gaseous products formed by the burned fuel-air mixture are exhausted from the cylinder so that a new "Cycle" can begin.

The above described five events which comprise the work cycle of an engine are commonly reffered to as (1), INTAKE; (2), COMPRESSION; (3), IGNITION; (4), EXPANSION (POWER); and (5), EXHAUST.

DIESEL CYCLE. The Diesel Cycle differs from the Otto Cycle in that air alone is drawn into the cylinder during the intake period. The air is heated from being compressed by the piston moving upward in the cylinder, then a finely atomized charge of fuel is injected into the cylinder where it mixes with the air and is ignited by the heat of the compressed air. In order to create sufficient heat to ignite the injected fuel, an engine operating on the Diesel Cycle must compress the air to a much greater degree than an engine operating on the Otto Cycle where the fuel-air mixture is ignited by an electric spark. The power and exhaust events of the Diesel Cycle are similar to the power and exhaust events of the Otto Cycle.

TWO-STROKE CYCLE ENGINES. Two stroke cycle engines may be of the Otto Cycle (spark ignition) or Diesel Cycle (compression ignition) type. However, since the two-stroke cycle engines listed in the repair section of this manual are all of the Otto Cycle type, operation of two-stroke Diesel Cycle engines will not be discussed in this section.

In two-stroke cycle engines, the piston is used as a sliding valve for the cylinder intake and exhaust ports. The intake and exhaust ports are both open when the piston is at the bottom of its downward stroke (bottom dead center or "B.D.C."). The exhaust port is open to atmospheric pressure; therefore, the fuel-air mixture must be elevated to a higher than atmospheric pressure in order for the mixture to enter the cylinder. As the crankshaft is turned from B.D.C. and the piston starts on its upward stroke, the intake and exhaust ports are closed and the fuel-air mixture in the cylinder is compressed. When the piston is at or near the top of its upward stroke (top dead center or "T.D.C."), an electric spark across the electrode gap of the spark plug ignites the fuel air mixture. As the crankshaft turns past T.D.C. and the piston starts on its downward stroke, the rapidly burning fuel-air mixture expands and

forces the piston downward. As the piston nears bottom of its downward stroke, the cylinder exhaust port is opened and the burned gaseous products from combustion of the fuel-air mixture flows out the open port. Slightly further downward travel of the piston opens the cylinder intake port and a fresh charge of fuel-air mixture is forced into the cylinder. Since the exhaust port remains open, the incoming flow of fuel-air mixture helps clean (scavenge) any remaining burned gaseous products from the cylinder. As the crankshaft turns past B.D.C. and the piston starts on its upward stroke, the cylinder intake and exhaust ports are closed and a new cycle begins.

Since the fuel-air mixture must be elevated to a higher than atmospheric pressure to enter the cylinder of a two-stroke cycle engine, a compressor pump must be used. Coincidentally, downward movement of the piston decreases the volume of the engine crankcase. Thus, a compressor pump is made available by sealing the engine crankcase and connecting the carburetor to a port in the crankcase. When the piston moves upward, volume of the crankcase is increased which lowers pressure within the crankcase to below atmospheric. Air will then be forced through the carburetor, where fuel is mixed with the air, and on into the engine crankcase. In order for downward movement of the piston to compress the fuel-air mixture in the crankcase, a valve must be provided to close the carburetor to crankcase port. Three different types of valves are used. In Fig. 1-1, a reed type inlet valve is shown in the schematic diagram of the two-stroke cycle engine. Spring steel reeds (R) are forced open by atmospheric pressure as shown in view "B" when the piston is on its upward stroke and pressure in the crankcase is below atmospheric. When the piston reaches T.D.C., the reeds close as shown in view "A" and fuel-air mixture is trapped in the crankcase to be compressed by downward movement of the piston. In Fig. 1-2, a schematic diagram of a two-stroke cycle engine is shown in which the piston is utilized as a sliding carburetor-crankcase port (third port) valve. In Fig. 1-3, a schematic diagram of a two-stroke cycle engine is shown in which a slotted disc (rotary valve) attached to the engine crankshaft opens the carburetor-crankcase port when the piston is on its upward stroke. In each of the three basic designs shown, a transfer port (TP—Fig. 1-2) connects the crankcase compression chamber to the cylinder; the transfer port is the cylinder intake port through which the compressed fuel-air mixture in the crankcase is transferred to the cylinder when the piston is at bottom of stroke as shown in view "A."

Due to rapid movement of the fuel-air mixture through the crankcase, the crankcase cannot be used as a lubricating oil sump because the oil would be carried into the cylinder. Lubrication is accomplished by mixing a small amount of oil with the fuel; thus, lubricating oil for the engine moving parts is carried into the crankcase with the fuel-air mixture. Normal lubricating oil to fuel mixture ratios vary from one part of oil mixed with 16 to 20 parts of fuel by volume. In all instances, manufacturer's recommendations for fuel-oil mixture ratio should be observed.

FOUR-STROKE CYCLE. In a four-stroke cycle engine operating on the Otto Cycle (spark ignition), the five events of the cycle take place in four strokes of the piston, or in two revolutions of the engine crankshaft. Thus, a power stroke occurs only on alternate downward strokes of the piston.

In view "A" of Fig. 1-4, the piston is on the first downward stroke of the cycle. The mechanically operated intake valve has opened the intake port

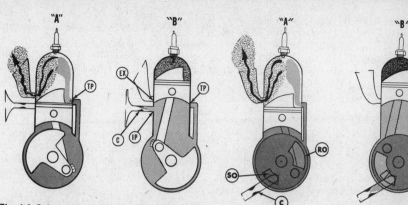

Fig. 1-2–Schematic diagram of two-stroke cycle engine operating on Otto Cycle. Engine differs from that shown in Fig. 1-1 in that piston is utilized as a sliding valve to open and close intake (carburetor to crankcase) port (IP) instead of using reed valve (R–Fig. 1-1).

C. Carburetor
EX. Exhaust port
IP. Intake port (carburetor to crankcase)
TP. Transfer port (crankcase to cylinder)

Fig. 1-3–Schematic diagram of two-stroke cycle engine similar to those shown in Figs. 1-1 and 1-2 except that a rotary carburetor to crankcase port valve is used. Disc driven by crankshaft has rotating opening (RO) which uncovers stationary opening (SO) in crankcase when piston is on upward stroke. Carburetor is (C).

and, as the downward movement of the piston has reduced the air pressure in the cylinder to below atmospheric pressure, air is forced through the carburetor, where fuel is mixed with the air, and into the cylinder through the open intake port. The intake valve remains open and the fuel-air mixture continues to flow into the cylinder until the piston reaches the bottom of its downward stroke. As the piston starts on its first upward stroke, the mechanically operated intake valve closes and, since the exhaust valve is closed, the fuel-air mixture is compressed as in view "B."

Just before the piston reaches the top of its first upward stroke, a spark at the spark plug electrodes ignites the compressed fuel-air mixture. As the engine crankshaft turns past top center, the burning fuel-air mixture expands rapidly and forces the piston downward on its power stroke as shown in view "C". As the piston reaches the bottom of the power stroke, the mechanically operated exhaust valve starts to open and as the pressure of the burned fuel-air mixture is higher than atmospheric pressure, it starts to flow out the open exhaust port. As the engine crankshaft turns past bottom center, the exhaust

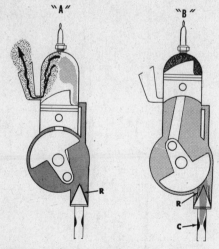

Fig. 1-1–Schematic diagram of a two-stroke engine operating on the Otto Cycle (spark ignition). View "B" shows piston near top of upward stroke and atmospheric pressure is forcing air through carburetor (C), where fuel is mixed with the air, and the fuel-air mixture enters crankcase through open reed valve (R). In view "A", piston is near bottom of downward stroke and has opened the cylinder exhaust and intake ports; fuel-air mixture in crankcase has been compressed by downward stroke of engine and flows into cylinder through open port. Incoming mixture helps clean burned exhaust gases from cylinder.

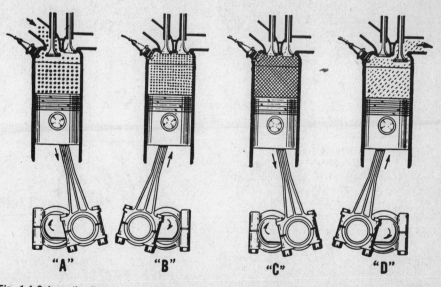

Fig. 1-4–Schematic diagram of four-stroke cycle engine operating on the Otto (spark ignition) cycle. In view "A", piston is on first downward (intake) stroke and atmospheric pressure is forcing fuel-air mixture from carburetor into cylinder through the open intake valve. In view "B", both valves are closed and piston is on its first upward stroke compressing the fuel-air mixture in cylinder. In view "C", spark across electrodes of spark plug has ignited fuel-air mixture and heat of combustion rapidly expands the burning gaseous mixture forcing the piston on its second downward (expansion or power) stroke. In view "D", exhaust valve is open and piston on its second upward (exhaust) stroke forces the burned mixture from cylinder. A new cycle then starts as in view "A".

valve is almost completely open and remains open during the upward stroke of the piston as shown in view "D." Upward movement of the piston pushes the remaining burned fuel-air mixture out of the exhaust port. Just before the piston reaches the top of its second upward or exhaust stroke, the intake valve opens and the exhaust valve closes. The cycle is completed as the crankshaft turns past top center and a new cycle begins as the piston starts downward as shown in view "A."

In a four-stroke cycle engine oper-ating on the Diesel Cycle, the sequence of events of the cycle is similar to that described for operation on the Otto Cycle, but with the following exceptions: On the intake stroke, air only is taken into the cylinder. On the com-pression stroke, the air is highly com-pressed which raises the temperature of the air. Just before the piston reaches top dead center, fuel is injected into the cylinder and is ignited by the heated, compressed air. The remainder of the cycle is similar to that of the Otto Cycle.

the carburetor choke plate or disc, a small hole or notch is cut in the plate so that some air can flow through the plate when it is in closed position to provide air for the starting fuel-air mixture. In some instances after starting a cold engine, it is advanta-geous to leave the choke plate in a partly closed position as the restriction of air flow will decrease the air pres-sure in carburetor venturi, thus causing more fuel to flow from the nozzle, resulting in a richer fuel-air mixture. The choke plate or disc should be in fully open position for normal engine operation.

If, after the engine has been started, the throttle plate is in the wide-open position as shown by the solid line in Fig. 2-2, the engine can obtain enough fuel and air to run at dangerously high speeds. Thus, the throttle plate or disc must be partly closed as shown by the dotted lines to control engine speed. At no load, the engine requires very little air and fuel to run at its rated speed and the throttle must be moved on toward the closed position as shown by the dash lines. As more load is placed on the engine, more fuel and air are required for the engine to operate at its rated speed and the throttle must be moved closer to the wide open position as shown by the solid line. When the engine is required to develop max-imum power or speed, the throttle must be in the wide open position.

CARBURETOR FUNDAMENTALS

OPERATING PRINCIPLES

Function of the carburetor on a spark-ignition engine is to atomize the fuel and mix the atomized fuel in proper proportions with air flowing to the engine intake port or intake mani-fold. Carburetors used on engines that are to be operated at constant speeds and under even loads are of simple design since they only have to mix fuel and air in a relatively constant ratio. On engines operating at varying speeds and loads, the carburetors must be more complex because different fuel-air mixtures are required to meet the varying demands of the engine.

FUEL-AIR MIXTURE RATIO REQUIREMENTS. To meet the de-mands of an engine being operated at varying speeds and loads, the car-buretor must mix fuel and air at dif-ferent mixture ratios. Fuel-air mixture ratios required for different operating conditions are approximately as fol-lows:

	Fuel	Air
Starting, cold weather	1 lb.	7 lbs.
Accelerating	1 lb.	9 lbs.
Idling (no load)	1 lb.	11 lbs.
Part open throttle	1 lb.	15 lbs.
Full load, open throttle	1 lb.	13 lbs.

BASIC DESIGN. Carburetor design is based on the venturi principle which simply means that a gas or liquid flowing through a necked-down section (venturi) in a passage undergoes an increase in velocity (speed) and a de-crease in pressure as compared to the velocity and pressure in full size sec-tions of the passage. The principle is illustrated in Fig. 2-1, which shows air passing through a carburetor venturi. The figures given for air speeds and vacuum are approximate for a typical wide-open throttle operating condition. Due to low pressure (high vacuum) in the venturi, fuel is forced out through the fuel nozzle by the atmospheric pres-sure (0 vacuum) on the fuel; as fuel is emitted from the nozzle, it is atomized by the high velocity air flow and mixes with the air.

In Fig. 2-2, the carburetor choke plate and throttle plate are shown in relation to the venturi. Downward pointing arrows indicate air flow through the carburetor.

At cranking speeds, air flows through the carburetor venturi at a slow speed; thus, the pressure in the venturi does not usually decrease to the extent that atmospheric pressure on the fuel will force fuel from the nozzle. If the choke plate is closed as shown by dotted line in Fig. 2-2, air cannot enter into the carburetor and pressure in the carburetor decreases greatly as the engine is turned at cranking speed. Fuel can then flow from the fuel nozzle. In manufacturing

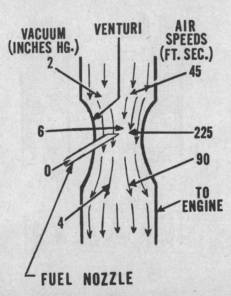

Fig. 2-1–Drawing illustrating the venturi prin-ciple upon which carburetor design is based. Figures at left are inches of mercury vacuum and those at right are air speeds in feet per second that are typical of conditions found in a carburetor operating at wide open throttle. Zero vacuum in fuel nozzle corresponds to atmospheric pressure.

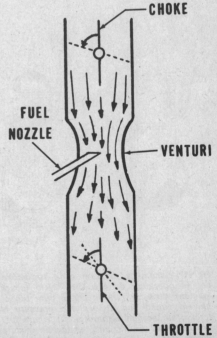

Fig. 2-2–Drawing showing basic carburetor design. Text explains operation of the choke and throttle valves. In some carburetors, a primer pump may be used instead of the choke valve to provide fuel for the starting fuel-air mixture.

Although some carburetors may be as simple as the basic design just described, most engines require more complex design features to provide variable fuel-air mixture ratios for different operating conditions. These design features will be described in the following paragraphs which outline the different carburetor types.

CARBURETOR TYPES

Carburetors used on small engines are usually classified by types as to method of delivery of fuel to the carburetor fuel nozzle. The following paragraphs describe the features and operating principles of the different type carburetors from the most simple suction lift type to the more complex float and diaphragm types.

SUCTION LIFT CARBURETOR. A cross-sectional drawing of a typical suction lift carburetor is shown in Fig. 2-4. Due to the low pressure at the orifice (O) of the fuel nozzle and to atmospheric pressure on the fuel in fuel supply tank, fuel is forced up through the fuel pipe and out of the nozzle into the carburetor venturi where it is mixed with the air flowing through the venturi. A check ball is located in the lower end of the fuel pipe to prevent pulsations of air pressure in the venturi from forcing fuel back down through the fuel pipe. The lower end of the fuel pipe has a fine mesh screen to prevent foreign material or dirt in fuel from entering the fuel nozzle. Fuel-air ratio can be adjusted by opening or closing the adjusting needle (N) slightly; turning the needle in will decrease flow of fuel out of nozzle orifice (O).

In Fig. 2-3, a cut-away view is shown of a suction type carburetor used on several models of a popular make small engine. This carburetor features an idle fuel passage, jet and adjustment

screw. When carburetor throttle is nearly closed (engine is at low idle speed), air pressure is low (vacuum is high) at inner side of throttle plate. Therefore, atmospheric pressure in fuel tank will force fuel through the idle jet and adjusting screw orifice where it is emitted into the carburetor throat and mixes with air passing the throttle plate. The adjustment screw is turned in or out until an optimum fuel-air mixture is obtained and engine runs smoothly at idle speed. When the throttle is opened to increase engine speed, air velocity through the venturi increases, air pressure in the venturi decreases and fuel is emitted from the nozzle. Power adjustment screw (high speed fuel needle) is turned in or out to obtain proper fuel-air mixture for engine running under operating speed and load.

FLOAT TYPE CARBURETOR. The principle of float type carburetor operation is illustrated in Fig. 2-5. Fuel is delivered at inlet (I) by gravity with fuel tank placed above carburetor, or by a fuel lift pump when tank is located below carburetor inlet. Fuel flows into the open inlet valve (V) until fuel level (L) in bowl lifts float against fuel valve needle and closes the valve. As fuel is emitted from the nozzle (N) when engine is running, fuel level will drop, lowering the float and allowing valve to open so that fuel will enter the carburetor to meet the requirements of the engine.

In Fig. 2-6, a cut-away view of a well known make of small engine float type carburetor is shown. Atmospheric pressure is maintained in fuel bowl through passage (20) which opens into carburetor air horn ahead of the choke plate (21). Fuel level is maintained at just below level of opening (O) in nozzle (22) by float (19) actuating inlet valve needle (8). Float height can be adjusted by bending float tang (5).

When starting a cold engine, it is necessary to close the choke plate (21) as shown by dotted lines so as to lower the air pressure in carburetor venturi (18) as engine is cranked. Then, fuel will flow up through nozzle (22) and will be emitted from openings (O) in nozzle. When an engine is hot, it will start on a leaner fuel-air mixture than when cold and may start without the

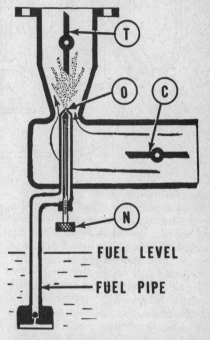

Fig. 2-4–Principle of suction lift carburetor is illustrated in above drawing. Atmospheric pressure on fuel forces fuel up through pipe and out nozzle orifice (O). Needle (N) is used to adjust amount of fuel flowing from nozzle to provide correct fuel-air mixture for engine operation. Choke (C) and throttle (T) valves are shown in wide open position.

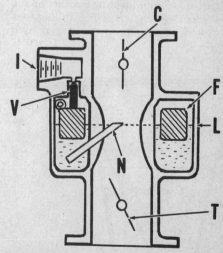

Fig. 2-5–Drawing showing basic float type carburetor design. Fuel must be delivered under pressure either by gravity or by use of fuel pump, to the carburetor fuel inlet (I). Fuel level (L) operates float (F) to open and close inlet valve (V) to control amount of fuel entering carburetor. Also shown are the fuel nozzle (N), throttle (T) and choke (C).

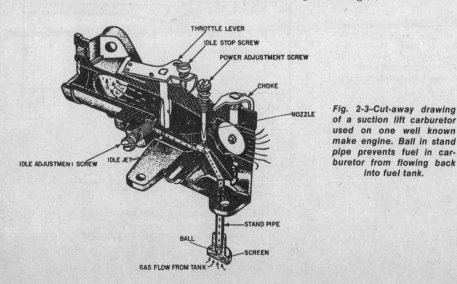

Fig. 2-3–Cut-away drawing of a suction lift carburetor used on one well known make engine. Ball in stand pipe prevents fuel in carburetor from flowing back into fuel tank.

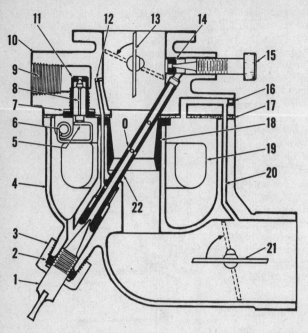

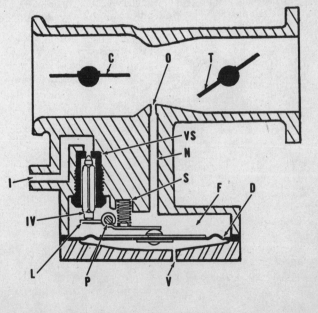

Fig. 2-6–Cross-sectional drawing of float type carburetor used on a popular small engine.

0. Orifice
1. Main fuel needle
2. Packing
3. Packing nut
4. Carburetor bowl
5. Float tang
6. Float hinge pin
7. Gasket
8. Inlet valve
9. Fuel inlet
10. Carburetor body
11. Inlet valve seat
12. Vent
13. Throttle plate
14. Idle orifice
15. Idle fuel needle
16. Plug
17. Gasket
18. Venturi
19. Float
20. Fuel bowl vent
21. Choke
22. Fuel nozzle

Fig. 2-9–Operating principle of diaphragm type fuel pump is illustrated in above drawings. Pump valves (A & B) are usually a part of diaphragm (D). Pump inlet is (I) and outlet is (O). Chamber above diaphragm is connected to engine crankcase by passage (C). When piston is on upward stroke, vacuum (V) at crankcase passage allows atmospheric pressure to force fuel into pump fuel chamber as shown in middle drawing. When piston is on downward stroke, pressure (P) expands diaphragm downward forcing fuel out of pump as shown in lower drawing.

choke plate being closed.

When engine is running at slow idle speed (throttle plate nearly closed as indicated by dotted lines in Fig. 2-6), air pressure above the throttle plate is low and atmospheric pressure in fuel bowl forces fuel up through the nozzle and out through orifice in seat (14) where it mixes with air passing the throttle plate. The idle fuel mixture is adjustable by turning needle (15) in or out as required. Idle speed is adjustable by turning the throttle stop screw (not shown) in or out to control amount of air passing the throttle plate.

When throttle plate is opened to increase engine speed, velocity of air flow through venturi (18) increases, air pressure at venturi decreases and fuel will flow from openings (O) in nozzle instead of through orifice in idle seat (14). When engine is running at high speed, pressure in nozzle (22) is less than at vent (12) opening in carburetor throat above venturi. Thus, air will enter vent and travel down the vent into the nozzle and mix with the fuel in the nozzle. This is referred to as air bleeding and is illustrated in Fig. 2-7.

Many different designs of float type carburetors will be found when servicing the different makes and models of small engines. Reference should be made to the engine repair section of this manual for adjustment and overhaul specifications. Refer to carburetor servicing paragraphs in fundamentals sections for service hints.

DIAPHRAGM TYPE CARBURETOR. Refer to Fig. 2-8 for cross-sectional drawing showing basic design of a diaphragm type carburetor. Fuel is delivered to inlet (I) by gravity with fuel tank above carburetor, or under pressure from a fuel pump. Atmospheric pressure is maintained on lower side of diaphragm (D) through vent hole (V). When choke plate (C) is closed and engine is cranked, or when engine is running, pressure at orifice (O) is less than atmospheric pressure; this

Fig. 2-7–Illustration of air bleed principle explained in text.

Fig. 2-8–Cross-section drawing of basic design diaphragm type carburetor. Atmospheric pressure actuates diaphragm (D).

C. Choke
D. Diaphragm
F. Fuel chamber
I. Fuel inlet
IV. Inlet valve needle
L. Lever
N. Nozzle
O. Orifice
P. Pivot pin
S. Spring
T. Throttle
V. Vent
VS. Valve seat

low pressure, or vacuum, is transmitted to fuel chamber (F) above diaphragm through nozzle channel (N). The higher (atmospheric) pressure at lower side of diaphragm will then push the diaphragm upward compressing spring (S) and allowing inlet valve (IV) to open and fuel will flow into the fuel chamber.

Some diaphragm type carburetors are equipped with an integral fuel pump. Although design of the pump may vary as to type of check valves, etc., all operate on the principle shown in Fig. 2-9. A channel (C) (or pulsation passage) connects one side of the diaphragm to the engine crankcase. When engine piston is on upward stroke, vacuum (V) (lower than atmospheric pressure) is present in channel; thus atmospheric pressure on fuel forces inlet valve (B) open and fuel flows into chamber below the diaphragm as shown in middle view. When piston is on downward stroke, pressure (P) (higher than atmospheric pressure) is present in channel (C); thus, the pressure forces the diaphragm downward closing the inlet valve (B) and causes

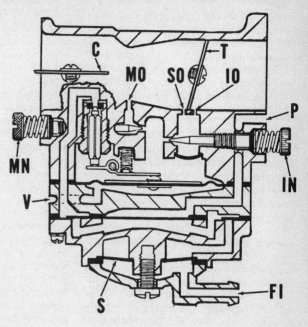

Fig. 2-10 – Cross-sectional view of a popular make diaphragm type carburetor with integral fuel pump. Refer to Fig. 2-8 for view of basic diaphragm carburetor and to Fig. 2-9 for views showing operation of the fuel pump.

C. Choke
FI. Fuel inlet
IN. Idle fuel adjusting needle
IO. Idle orifice
MN. Main fuel adjusting needle
MO. Main orifice
P. Pulsation channel (fuel pump)
S. Screen
SO. Secondary orifice
T. Throttle
V. Vent (atmosphere to carburetor diaphragm)

the fuel to flow out by the outlet valve (A) as shown in lower view.

In Fig. 2-10, a cross-sectional view of

a popular make diaphragm type carburetor, with integral diaphragm type pump, is shown.

IGNITION SYSTEM FUNDAMENTALS

The ignition system provides a properly timed surge of extremely high voltage electrical energy which flows across the spark plug electrode gap to create the ignition spark. Small engines may be equipped with either a magneto or battery ignition system. A magneto ignition system generates electrical energy, intensifies (transforms) this electrical energy to the extremely high voltage required and delivers this electrical energy at the proper time for the ignition spark. In a battery ignition system, a storage battery is used as a source of electrical energy and the system transforms the relatively low electrical voltage from the battery into the high voltage required and delivers the high voltage at proper time for the ignition spark. Thus, the function of the two systems is somewhat similar except for the basic source of electrical energy. The fundamental operating principles of ignition systems are explained in the following paragraphs.

MAGNETISM AND ELECTRICITY

The fundamental principles upon which ignition systems are designed are presented in this section. As the study of magnetism and electricity is an entire scientific field, it is beyond the scope of this manual to fully explore these subjects. However, the following information will impart a working knowledge of basic principles which should be of value in servicing small engines.

MAGNETISM. The effects of magnetism can be shown easily while the theory of magnetism is too complex to be presented here. The effects of magnetism were discovered many years ago when fragments of iron ore were found to attract each other and also attract other pieces of iron. Further, it was found that when suspended in air, one end of the iron ore fragment would always point in the direction of the North Star. The end of the iron ore fragment pointing north was called the "north pole" and the opposite end the "south pole." By stroking a piece of steel with a "natural magnet," as these iron ore fragments were called, it was found that the magnetic properties of the natural magnet could be transferred or "induced" into the steel.

Steel which will retain magnetic properties for an extended period of time after being subjected to a strong magnetic field are called "permanent magnets;" iron or steel that loses such magnetic properties soon after being subjected to a magnetic field are called "temporary magnets." Soft iron will lose magnetic properties almost immediately after being removed from a magnetic field, and so is used where

this property is desirable.

The area affected by a magnet is called a "field of force." The extent of this field of force is related to the strength of the magnet and can be determined by use of a compass. In practice, it is common to illustrate the field of force surrounding a magnet by lines as shown in Fig. 3-1 and the field of force is usually called "lines of force" or "flux." Actually, there are no "lines;" however, this is a convenient method of illustrating the presence of the invisible magnetic forces and if a certain magnetic force is defined as a "line of force," then all magnetic forces may be measured by comparison. The number of "lines of force" making up a strong magnetic field is enormous.

Most materials when placed in a magnetic field are not attracted by the magnet, do not change the magnitude or direction of the magnetic field, and so are called "non-magnetic materials." Materials such as iron, cobalt, nickel or their alloys, when placed in a magnetic field will concentrate the field of force and hence are magnetic conductors or "magnetic materials." There are no materials known in which magnetic fields will not penetrate and magnetic lines of force can be deflected only by magnetic materials or by another magnetic field.

Alnico, an alloy containing aluminum, nickel and cobalt, retains magnetic properties for a very long period of time after being subjected to a strong magnetic field and is extensively used as a permanent magnet. Soft iron, which loses magnetic properties quickly, is used to concentrate magnetic fields as in Fig. 3-1.

ELECTRICITY. Electricity, like magnetism, is an invisible physical force whose effects may be more readily explained than the theory of what electricity consists of. All of us are familiar with the property of electricity to produce light, heat and mechanical power. What must be explained for the purpose of understanding ignition system operation is the inter-relationship of magnetism and electricity and how the ignition spark is produced.

Electrical current may be defined as a flow of energy in a conductor which, in some ways, may be compared to flow of water in a pipe. For electricity to flow, there must be a pressure (voltage) and a complete circuit (closed path) through which the electrical energy may return, a comparison being a water pump and a pipe that receives water from the outlet (pressure) side of the pump and returns the water to the inlet side of the pump. An electrical circuit may be completed by electricity flowing through the earth (ground), or through the metal framework of an engine or other equipment ("grounded" or "ground" connections). Usually, air is an insulator through which electrical energy will not flow. However, if the force (voltage) becomes great, the resistance of air to the flow of electricity is broken down and a current will flow, releasing energy in the form of a spark. By high voltage electricity breaking down the resistance of the air gap between the spark plug electrodes, the ignition spark is formed.

ELECTRO-MAGNETIC INDUCTION. The principle of electro-magnetic induction is as follows: When a wire (conductor) is moved through a field of magnetic force so as to cut across the lines of force (flux), a potential voltage or electromotive force (emf) is induced in the wire. If the wire is a part of a completed electrical circuit, current will flow through the circuit as illustrated in Fig. 3-2. It should be noted that the movement of the wire through the lines of magnetic force is a relative motion; that is, if the lines of force of a moving magnetic field cut across a wire, this will also induce an emf to the wire.

The direction of an induced current is related to the direction of magnetic force and also to the direction of movement of the wire through the lines of force, or flux. The voltage of an induced current is related to the strength, or concentration of lines of force, of the magnetic field and to the rate of speed at which the wire is moved through the flux. If a length of wire is wound into a coil and a section of the coil is moved through magnetic lines of force, the voltage induced will be proportional to the number of turns of wire in the coil.

ELECTRICAL MAGNETIC FIELDS. When a current is flowing in a wire, a magnetic field is present around the wire as illustrated in Fig. 3-3. The direction of lines of force of this magnetic field is related to the direction of current in the wire. This is known as the right hand rule and is stated as follows: If a wire carrying a current is grasped in the right hand with thumb pointing in direction current is flowing, the curved fingers will point the direction of lines of magnetic force (flux) encircling the wire.

If a current is flowing in a wire that is wound into a coil, the magnetic flux surrounding the wire converge to form

a stronger magnetic field as shown in Fig. 3-4. If the coils of wire are very close together, there is little tendency for magnetic flux to surround individual loops of the coil and a strong magnetic field will surround the entire coil. The strength of this field will vary with the current flowing through the coil.

STEP-UP TRANSFORMERS (IGNITION COILS). In both battery and magneto ignition systems, it is necessary to step-up, or transform, a relatively low primary voltage to the 15,000 to 20,000 volts required for the ignition spark. This is done by means of an ignition coil which utilizes the inter-relationship of magnetism and electricity as explained in preceding paragraphs.

Basic ignition coil design is shown in Fig. 3-5. The coil consists of two separate coils of wire which are called the

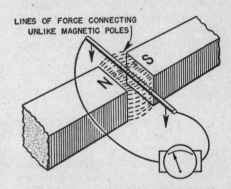

Fig. 3-2–When a conductor is moved through a magnetic field so as to cut across lines of force, a potential voltage will be induced in the conductor. If the conductor is a part of a completed electrical circuit, current will flow through the circuit as indicated by the gage.

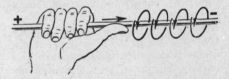

Fig. 3-3–A magnetic field surrounds a wire carrying an electrical current. The direction of magnetic force is indicated by the "right hand rule"; that is, if thumb of right hand points in direction that electrical current is flowing in conductor, fingers of right hand will indicate direction of magnetic force.

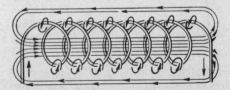

Fig. 3-4–When a wire is wound in a coil, the magnetic force created by a current in the wire will tend to converge in a single strong magnetic field as illustrated. If the loops of the coil are wound closely together, there is little tendency for lines of force to surround individual loops of the coil.

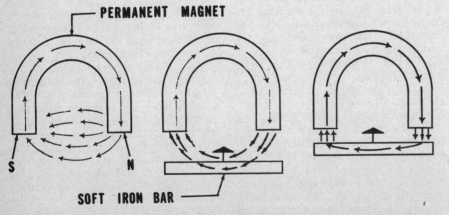

PERMANENT MAGNET

S   N

SOFT IRON BAR

Fig. 3-1–In left view, field of force of permanent magnet is illustrated by arrows showing direction of magnetic force from north pole (N) to south pole (S). In center view, lines of magnetic force are being attracted by soft iron bar that is being moved into the magnetic field. In right view, the soft iron bar has been moved close to the magnet and the field of magnetic force is concentrated within the bar.

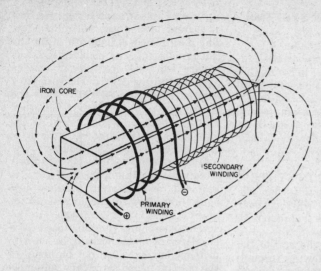

Fig. 3-5–Drawing showing principles of ignition coil operation. A current in primary winding will establish a magnetic field surrounding both the primary and secondary windings and the field will be concentrated by the iron core. When primary current is interrupted, the magnetic field will "collapse" and the lines of force will cut the coil windings inducing a very high voltage in the secondary winding.

primary coil winding and the secondary coil winding, or simply the primary winding and secondary winding. The primary winding as indicated by the heavy, black line is of larger diameter wire and has a smaller number of turns when compared to the secondary winding indicated by the light line.

A current passing through the primary winding creates a magnetic field (as indicated by the "lines of force") and this field, concentrated by the soft iron core, surrounds both the primary and secondary windings. If the primary winding current is suddenly interrupted, the magnetic field will collapse and the lines of force will cut through the coil windings. The resulting induced voltage in the secondary winding is greater than the voltage of the current that was flowing in the primary winding and is related to the number of turns of wire in each winding. Thus:

Induced secondary voltage = primary voltage ×

$$\frac{\text{No. of turns in secondary winding}}{\text{No. of turns in primary winding}}$$

For example, if the primary winding of an ignition coil contained 100 turns of wire and the secondary winding contained 10,000 turns of wire, a current having an emf of 200 volts flowing in the primary winding, when suddenly interrupted, would result in an emf of:

$$200 \text{ Volts} \times \frac{10,000 \text{ turns of wire}}{100 \text{ turns of wire}}$$
$$= 20,000 \text{ volts}$$

SELF-INDUCTANCE. It should be noted that the collapsing magnetic field resulting from the interrupted current in the primary winding will also induce a current in the primary winding. This effect is termed "self-inductance." This self-induced current is such as to oppose any interruption of current in the primary winding, slowing the collapse of the magnetic field and reducing the efficiency of the coil. The self-induced primary current flowing across the slightly open breaker switch, or contact points, will damage the contact surfaces due to the resulting spark.

To momentarily absorb, then stop the flow of current across the contact

points, a capacitor or, as commonly called, a condenser is connected in parallel with the contact points. A simple condenser is shown in Fig. 3-6a; however, the capacity of such a condenser to absorb current (capacitance) is limited by the small surface area of the plates. To increase capacity to absorb current, the condenser used in ignition systems is constructed as shown in Fig. 3-7.

EDDY CURRENTS. It has been found that when a solid soft iron bar is used as a core for an ignition coil, stray electrical currents are formed in the core. These stray, or "eddy currents," create opposing magnetic forces causing the core to become hot and also decrease the efficiency of the coil. As a means of preventing excessive formation of eddy currents within the core, or other magnetic field carrying parts of a magneto, a laminated plate construc-

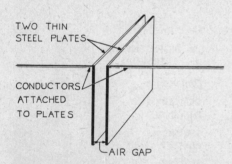

Fig. 3-6a–Drawing showing construction of a simple condenser. Capacity of such a condenser to absorb current is limited due to the relatively small surface area. Also, there is a tendency for current to arc across the air gap. Refer to Fig. 3-7 for construction of typical ignition system condenser.

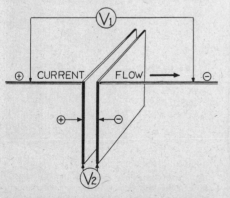

Fig. 3-6b–A condenser in an electrical circuit will absorb flow of current until an opposing voltage (V2) is built up across condenser plates which is equal to the voltage (V1) of the electrical current.

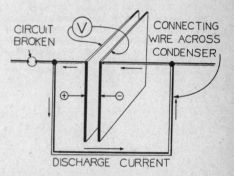

Fig. 3-6c–When flow of current is interrupted in circuit containing condenser (circuit broken), the condenser will retain a potential voltage (V). If a wire is connected across the condenser, a current will flow in reverse direction of charging current until condenser is discharged (voltage across condenser plates is zero).

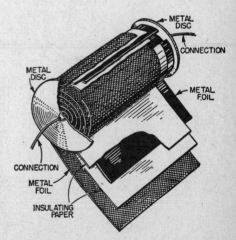

Fig. 3-7–Drawing showing construction of typical ignition system condenser. Two layers of metal foil, insulated from each other with paper, are rolled tightly together and a metal disc contacts each layer, or strip, of foil. Usually, one disc is grounded through the condenser shell.

tion as shown in Fig. 3-8 is used instead of solid material. The plates, or laminations, are insulated from each other by a natural oxide coating formed on the plate surfaces or by coating the plates with varnish. The cores of some ignition coils are constructed of soft iron wire instead of plates and each wire is insulated by a varnish coating. This type construction serves the same purpose as laminated plates.

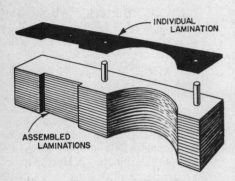

Fig. 3-8–To prevent formation of "eddy currents" within soft iron cores used to concentrate magnetic fields, core is assembled of plates or "laminations" that are insulated from each other. In a solid iron core, there is a tendency for counteracting magnetic forces to build up from stray currents induced in the core.

BATTERY IGNITION SYSTEMS

Some small engines are equipped with a battery ignition system. A schematic diagram of a typical battery ignition system for a single cylinder engine is shown in Fig. 3-9. Designs of battery ignition systems may vary, especially as to location of breaker points and method for actuating the points; however, all operate on the same basic principles.

BATTERY IGNITION SYSTEM PRINCIPLES. Refer to the schematic diagram in Fig. 3-9. When the timer cam is turned so that the contact points are closed, a current is established in the primary circuit by the emf of the battery. This current flowing through the primary winding of the ignition coil establishes a magnetic field concentrated in the core laminations and surrounding the windings. A cut-away view of a typical ignition coil is shown in Fig. 3-10. At the proper time for the ignition spark, the contact points are opened by the timer cam and the primary ignition circuit is interrupted. The condenser, wired in parallel with the breaker contact points between the timer terminal and ground, absorbs the self-induced current in the primary cir-

cuit for an instant and brings the flow of current to a quick, controlled stop. The magnetic field surrounding the coil rapidly cuts the primary and secondary windings creating an emf as high as 250 volts in the primary winding and up to 25,000 volts in the secondary winding. Current absorbed by the condenser is discharged as the cam closes the breaker points, grounding the condenser lead wire.

Due to resistance of the primary winding, a certain period of time is required for maximum primary current flow after the breaker contact points are closed. At high engine speeds, the points remain closed for a smaller interval of time, hence the primary current does not build up to the maximum and secondary voltage is somewhat less than at low engine speed. However, coil design is such that the minimum voltage available at high engine speed exceeds the normal maximum voltage required for the ignition spark.

MAGNETO IGNITION SYSTEMS

By utilizing the principles of magnetism and electricity as outlined in previous paragraphs, a magneto generates an electrical current of relatively

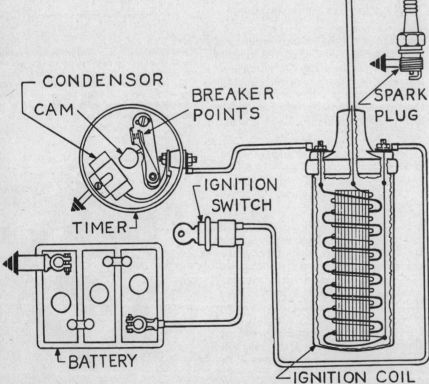

Fig. 3-9–Schematic diagram of typical battery ignition system. On unit shown, breaker points are actuated by timer cam; on some units, the points may be actuated by cam on engine camshaft. Refer to Fig. 3-10 for cut-away view of typical battery ignition coil. In view above, primary coil winding is shown as heavy black line (outside coil loops) and secondary winding is shown by lighter line (inside coil loops).

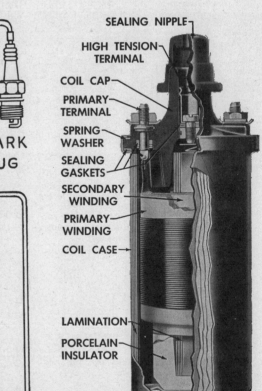

Fig. 3-10–Cut-away view of typical battery ignition system coil. Primary winding consists of approximately 200-250 turns (loops) of heavier wire; secondary winding consists of several thousand turns of fine wire. Laminations concentrate the magnetic lines of force and increase efficiency of the coil.

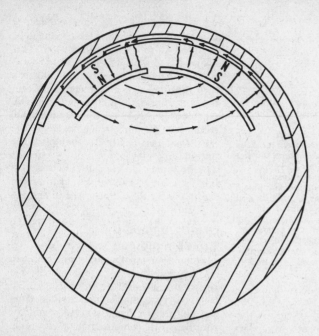

Fig. 3-11–Cut-away view of typical engine flywheel used with flywheel magneto type ignition system. The permanent magnets are usually cast into the flywheel. For flywheel type magnetos having the ignition coil and core mounted to outside of flywheel, magnets would be flush with outer diameter of flywheel.

the magnets moved into this position, their magnetic field was attracted by the armature core as illustrated in Fig. 3-1 and a potential voltage (emf) was induced in the coil windings. However, this emf was not sufficient to cause current to flow across the spark plug electrode gap in the high tension circuit and the points were open in the primary circuit.

In Fig. 3-13, the flywheel magnets have moved to a new position to where their magnetic field is being attracted by the center and right legs of the armature core, and is being withdrawn from the left and center legs. As indicated by the heavy black arrows, the lines of force are cutting up through the section of coil windings between the left and center legs of the armature

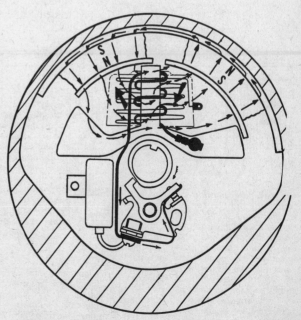

low voltage, then transforms this voltage into the extremely high voltage necessary to produce the ignition spark. This surge of high voltage is timed to create the ignition spark and ignite the compressed fuel-air mixture in the engine cylinder at the proper time in the Otto cycle as described in the paragraphs on fundamentals of engine operation principles.

Two different types of magnetos are used on small engines and, for discussion in this section of the manual, will be classified as "flywheel type magnetos" and "self-contained unit type magnetos." The most common type of ignition system found on small engines is the flywheel type magneto.

Flywheel Type Magnetos

The term "flywheel type magneto" is derived from the fact that the engine flywheel carries the permanent magnets and is the magneto rotor. In some similar systems, the magneto rotor is mounted on the engine crankshaft as is the flywheel, but is a part separate from the flywheel.

FLYWHEEL MAGNETO OPERATING PRINCIPLES. In Fig. 3-11, a cross-sectional view of a typical engine flywheel (magneto rotor) is shown. The arrows indicate lines of force (flux) of the permanent magnets carried by the flywheel. As indicated by the arrows, direction of force of the magnetic field is from the north pole (N) of the left magnet to the south pole (S) of the right magnet.

Figs. 3-12, 3-13, 3-14, and 3-15 illustrate the operational cycle of the flywheel type magneto. In Fig. 3-12, the flywheel magnets have moved to a position over the left and center legs of the armature (ignition coil) core. As

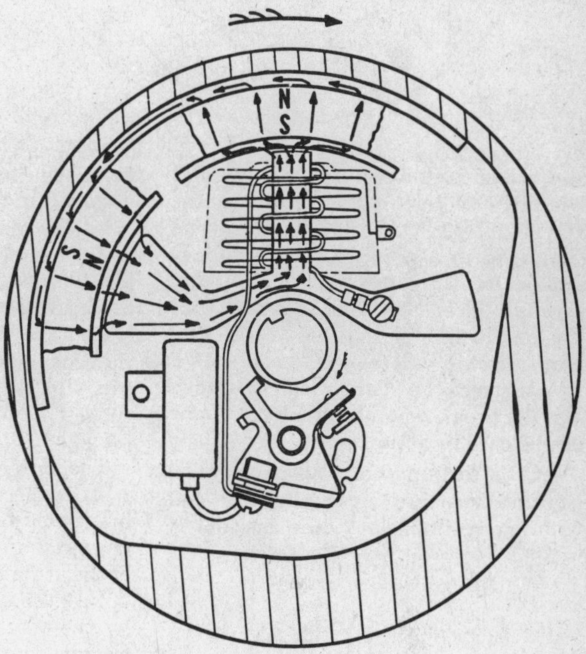

Fig. 3-12–View showing flywheel turned to a position so that lines of force of the permanent magnets are concentrated in the left and center core legs and are interlocking the coil windings.

Fig. 3-13–View showing flywheel turned to a position so that lines of force of the permanent magnets are being withdrawn from the left and center core legs and are being attracted by the center and right core legs. While this event is happening, the lines of force are cutting up through the coil windings section between the left and center legs and are cutting down through the section between the right and center legs as indicated by the heavy black arrows. As the breaker points are now closed by the cam, a current is induced in the primary ignition circuit as the lines of force cut through the coil windings.

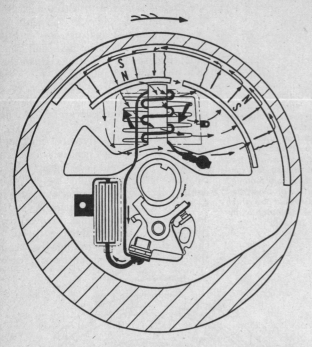

Fig. 3-14—The flywheel magnets have now turned slightly past the position shown in Fig. 3-13 and the rate of movement of lines of magnetic force cutting through the coil windings is at the maximum. At this instant, the breaker points are opened by the cam and flow of current in the primary circuit is being absorbed by the condenser, bringing the flow of current to a quick, controlled stop. Refer now to Fig. 3-15.

points were it not for the condenser absorbing the flow of current and bringing it to a controlled stop. This allows the electro-magnetic field to collapse at such a rapid rate to induce a very high voltage in the coil high tension or secondary windings. This voltage, in the order of 15,000 to 25,000 volts, is sufficient to break down the resistance of the air gap between the spark plug electrodes and a current will flow across the gap. This creates the ignition spark which ignites the compressed fuel-air mixture in the engine cylinder.

Self-Contained Unit
Type Magnetos

Some four-stroke cycle engines are equipped with a magneto which is a self-contained unit as shown in Fig. 3-20. This type magneto is driven from the engine timing gears via a gear or coupling. All components of the magneto are enclosed in one housing and the magneto can be removed from the engine as a unit.

UNIT TYPE MAGNETO OPERATING PRINCIPLES. In Fig. 3-21, a schematic diagram of a unit type magneto is shown. The magneto rotor is

and are cutting down through the coil windings section between the center and right legs. If the right hand rule, as explained in a previous paragraph, is applied to the lines of force cutting through the coil sections, it is seen that the resulting emf induced in the primary circuit will cause a current to flow through the primary coil windings and the breaker points which have now been closed by action of the cam.

At the instant the movement of the lines of force cutting through the coil winding sections is at the maximum

rate, the maximum flow of current is obtained in the primary circuit. At this time, the cam opens the breaker points interrupting the primary circuit and, for an instant, the flow of current is absorbed by the condenser as illustrated in Fig. 3-14. An emf is also induced in the secondary coil windings, but the voltage is not sufficient to cause current to flow across the spark plug gap.

The flow of current in the primary windings created a strong electro-magnetic field surrounding the coil windings and up through the center leg of the armature core as shown in Fig. 3-15. As the breaker points were opened by the cam, interrupting the primary circuit, this magnetic field starts to collapse cutting the coil windings as indicated by the heavy black arrows. The emf induced in the primary circuit would be sufficient to cause a flow of current across the opening breaker

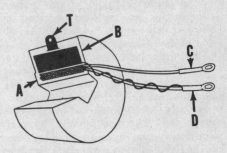

Fig. 3-16—Drawing showing construction of a typical flywheel magneto ignition coil. Primary winding (A) consists of about 200 turns of wire. Secondary winding (B) consists of several thousand turns of fine wire. Coil primary and secondary ground connection is (D); primary connection to breaker point and condenser terminal is (C); and coil secondary (high tension) terminal is (T).

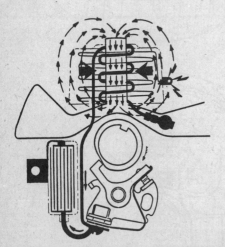

Fig. 3-15—View showing magneto ignition coil, condenser and breaker points at same instant as illustrated in Fig. 3-14; however, arrows shown above illustrate lines of force of the electro-magnetic field established by current in primary coil windings rather than the lines of force of the permanent magnets. As the current in the primary circuit ceases to flow, the electro-magnetic field collapses rapidly, cutting the coil windings as indicated by heavy arrows and inducing a very high voltage in the secondary coil winding resulting in the ignition spark.

Fig. 3-17—Exploded view of a flywheel type magneto in which the breaker points (14) are actuated by a cam on engine camshaft. Push rod (9) rides against cam to open and close points. In this type unit, an ignition spark is produced only on alternate revolutions of the flywheel as the camshaft turns at one-half engine speed.

1. Flywheel
2. Ignition coil
3. Coil clamps
4. Coil ground lead
5. Breaker point lead
6. Armature core (laminations)
7. Crankshaft bearing retainer
8. High tension lead
9. Push rod
10. Bushing
11. Breaker box cover
12. Point lead strap
13. Breaker point spring
14. Breaker point assembly
15. Condenser
16. Breaker box
17. Terminal bolt
18. Insulators
19. Grounding (stop) spring

driven through an impulse coupling (shown at right side of illustration). The function of the impulse coupling is to increase the rotating speed of the rotor, thereby increasing magneto efficiency, at engine cranking speeds.

A typical impulse coupling for a single cylinder engine magneto is shown in Fig. 3-22. When the engine is turned at cranking speed, the coupling hub pawl engages a stop pin in the magneto housing as the engine piston is coming up on compression stroke. This stops rotation of the coupling hub assembly and magneto rotor. A spring within the coupling shell (see Fig. 3-23) connects the shell and coupling hub; as the engine continues to turn, the spring winds up until the pawl kickoff contacts the pawl and disengages it from the stop pin. This occurs at the time an ignition spark is required to ignite the compressed fuel-air mixture in the engine cylinder. As the pawl is released, the spring connecting the coupling shell and hub unwinds and rapidly spins the magneto rotor.

The magneto rotor (see Fig. 3-21) carries permanent magnets. As the rotor turns, alternating the position of the magnets, the lines of force of the magnets are attracted, then withdrawn from the laminations. In Fig. 3-21, arrows show the magnetic field concentrated within the laminations, or armature core. Slightly further rotation of the magnetic rotor will place the magnets to where the laminations will have greater attraction for opposite poles of the magnets. At this instant, the lines of force as indicated by the arrows will suddenly be withdrawn and an opposing field of force will be established in the laminations. Due to this rapid movement of the lines of force, a current will be induced in the primary magneto circuit as the coil

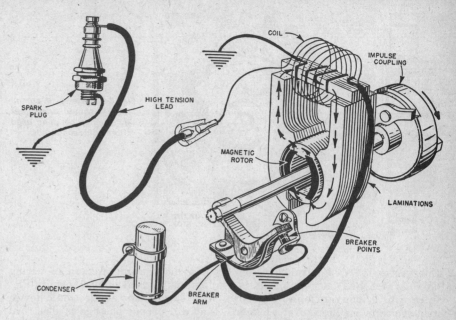

Fig. 3-21–Schematic diagram of typical unit type magneto for single cylinder engine. Refer to Figs. 3-22, 3-23 and 3-23A for views showing construction of impulse couplings.

Fig. 3-22–Views of typical impulse coupling for magneto driven by engine shaft with slotted drive connection. Coupling drive spring is shown in Fig. 3-23. Refer to Fig. 3-23A for view of combination magneto drive gear and impulse coupling used on some magnetos.

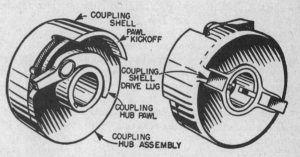

windings are cut by the lines of force. At the instant the maximum current is induced in the primary windings, the breaker points are opened by a cam on the magnetic rotor shaft interrupting the primary circuit. The lines of magnetic force established by the primary current (refer to Fig. 3-5) will cut through the secondary windings at such a rapid rate to induce a very high voltage in the secondary (or high tension) circuit. This voltage will break down the resistance of the spark plug electrode gap and a spark across the electrodes will result.

At engine operating speeds, centrifugal force will hold the impulse coupling hub pawl (See Fig. 3-22) in a position so that it cannot engage the stop pin in magneto housing and the magnetic rotor will be driven through the spring (Fig. 3-23) connecting the coupling shell to coupling hub. The impulse coupling retards the ignition spark, at cranking speeds, as the engine piston travels closer to top dead center while the magnetic rotor is held stationary by the pawl and stop pin. The difference in degrees of impulse coupling shell rotation between the position of retarded spark and normal

running spark is known as the impulse coupling lag angle.

SOLID STATE IGNITION SYSTEM

BREAKERLESS MAGNETO SYSTEM. The solid state (breakerless) magneto ignition system operates somewhat on the same basic principles as the conventional type flywheel magneto previously described. The main difference is that the breaker contact points are replaced by a solid

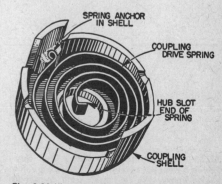

Fig. 3-23–View showing impulse coupling shell and drive spring removed from coupling hub assembly. Refer to Fig. 3-22 for views of assembled unit.

Fig. 3-20–Some engines are equipped with a unit type magneto having all components enclosed in a single housing (H). Magneto is removable as a unit after removing retaining nuts (N). Stop button (B) grounds out primary magneto circuit to stop engine. Timing window is (W).

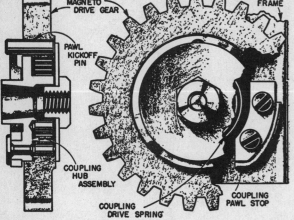

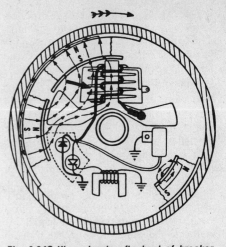

Fig. 3-23A–Views of combination magneto drive gear and impulse coupling used on some magnetos.

Fig. 3-24C–View showing flywheel of breakerless magneto system at instant of rotation where lines of force of ignition coil magnets are being drawn into left and center legs of magneto armature. The diode (see Fig. 3-24) acts as a closed set of breaker points in completing the primary ignition circuit at this time.

state electronic Gate Controlled Switch (GCS) which has no moving parts. Since, in a conventional system breaker points are closed over a longer period of crankshaft rotation than is the "GCS", a diode has been added to the circuit to provide the same characteristics as closed breaker points.

BREAKERLESS MAGNETO OPERATING PRINCIPLES. The same basic principles for electro-magnetic induction of electricity and formation of magnetic fields by electrical current as outlined for the conventional flywheel type magneto also apply to the solid state magneto. Therefore the principles of the different components (diode and GCS) will complete the operating principles of the solid state magneto.

The diode is represented in wiring diagrams by the symbol shown in Fig. 3-24. The diode is an electronic device that will permit passage of electrical current in one direction only. In electrical schematic diagrams, current flow is opposite direction the arrow part of symbol is pointing.

The symbol shown in Fig. 3-24A is used to represent the gate controlled switch (GCS) in wiring diagrams. The GCS acts as a switch to permit passage of current from cathode (C) terminal to anode (A) terminal when in "ON" state and will not permit electric current to flow when in "OFF" state. The GCS can be turned "ON" by a positive surge of electricity at the gate (G) terminal and will remain "ON" as long as current remains positive at the gate terminal

or as long as current is flowing through the GCS from cathode (C) terminal to anode (A) terminal.

The basic components and wiring diagram for the solid state breakerless magneto are shown schematically in Fig. 3-24B. In Fig. 3-24C, the magneto rotor (flywheel) is turning and the ignition coil magnets have just moved into position so that their lines of force are cutting the ignition coil windings and producing a negative surge of current in the primary windings. The diode

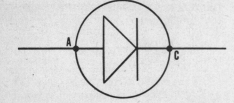

Fig. 3-24–In a diagram of an electrical circuit, the diode is represented by the symbol shown above. The diode will allow current to flow in one direction only, from cathode (C) to anode (A).

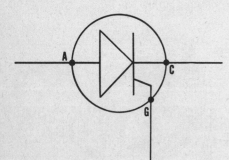

Fig. 3-24A–The symbol used for a Gate Controlled Switch (GCS) in an electrical diagram is shown above. The GCS will permit current to flow from cathode (C) to anode (A) when "turned on" by a positive electrical charge at gate (G) terminal.

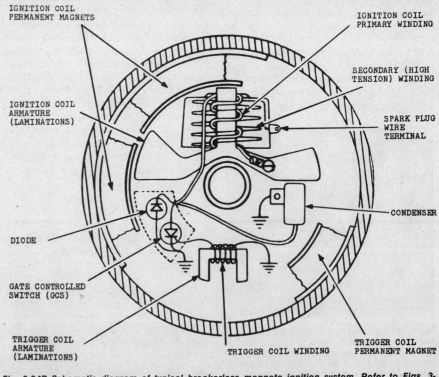

Fig. 3-24B–Schematic diagram of typical breakerless magneto ignition system. Refer to Figs. 3-24C, 3-24D and 3-24E for schematic views of operating cycle.

allows current to flow opposite to the direction of diode symbol arrow and action is same as conventional magneto with breaker points closed. As rotor (flywheel) continues to turn as shown in Fig. 3-24D, direction of magnetic flux lines will reverse in the armature center leg. Direction of current will change in the primary coil circuit and the previously conducting diode will be shut off. At this point, neither diode is conducting. As voltage begins

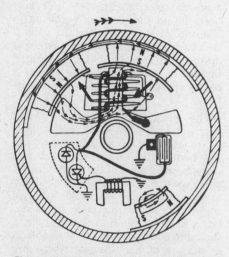

Fig. 3-24D–Flywheel is turning to point where magnetic flux lines through armature center leg will reverse direction and current through primary coil circuit will reverse. As current reverses, diode which was previously conducting will shut off and there will be no current. When magnetic flux lines have reversed in armature center leg, voltage potential will again build up, but since GCS is in "OFF" state, no current will flow. To prevent excessive voltage build up, the condenser acts as a buffer.

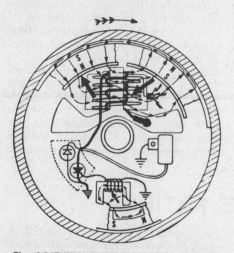

Fig. 3-24E–With flywheel in the approximate position shown, maximum voltage potential is present in windings of primary coil. At this time the triggering coil armature has moved into the field of a permanent magnet and a positive voltage is induced on the gate of the GCS. The GCS is triggered and primary coil current flows resulting in the formation of an electromagnetic field around the primary coil which inducts a voltage of sufficient potential in the secondary windings to "fire" the spark plug.

to build up as rotor continues to turn, the condenser acts as a buffer to prevent excessive voltage build up at the GCS before it is triggered.

When the rotor reaches the approximate position shown in Fig. 3-24E, maximum flux density has been achieved in the center leg of the armature. At this time the GCS is triggered. Triggering is accomplished by the triggering coil armature moving into the field of a permanent magnet which induces a positive voltage on the gate of the GCS. Primary coil current flow results in the formation of an electromagnetic field around the primary coil which inducts a voltage of sufficient potential in the secondary coil windings to "fire" the spark plug.

When the rotor (flywheel) has moved the magnets past the armature, the GCS will cease to conduct and revert to the "OFF" state until it is triggered. The condenser will discharge during the time that the GCS was conducting.

CAPACITOR DISCHARGE SYSTEM. The capacitor discharge (CD) ignition system uses a permanent magnet rotor (flywheel) to induce a current in a coil, but unlike the conventional flywheel magneto and solid state breakerless magneto described previously, the current is stored in a capacitor (condenser). Then the stored current is discharged through a transformer coil to create the ignition spark. Refer to Fig. 3-24F for a schematic of a typical capacitor discharge ignition system.

CAPACITOR DISCHARGE OPERATING PRINCIPLES. As the permanent flywheel magnets pass by the input generating coil (1—Fig. 3-24F), the current produced charges capacitor (6). Only half of the generated current passes through diode (3) to charge the capacitor. Reverse current is blocked by diode (3) but passes through Zener diode (2) to complete the reverse circuit. Zener diode (2) also limits maximum voltage of the forward current. As the flywheel continues to turn and magnets pass the trigger coil (4), a

small amount of electrical current is generated. This current opens the gate controlled switch (5) allowing the capacitor to discharge through the pulse transformer (7). The rapid voltage rise in the transformer primary coil induces a high voltage secondary current which forms the ignition spark when it jumps the spark plug gap.

THE SPARK PLUG

In any spark ignition engine, the spark plug (See Fig. 3-25) provides the means for igniting the compressed fuel-air mixture in the cylinder. Before an electric charge can move across an air gap, the intervening air must be charged with electricity, or ionized. If the spark plug is properly gapped and the system is not shorted, not more than 7,000 volts may be required to initiate a spark. Higher voltage is required as the spark plug warms up, or if compression pressures or the distance of the air gap is increased. Compression pressures are highest at full throttle and relatively slow engine speeds, therefore, high voltage requirements or a lack of available secondary voltage most often shows up as a miss during maximum acceleration from a slow engine speed.

There are many different types and sizes of spark plugs which are designed for a number of specific requirements.

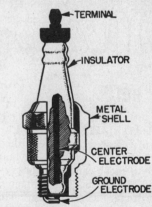

Fig. 3-25–Cross-sectional drawing of spark plug showing construction and nomenclature.

Fig. 3-24F–Schematic diagram of a typical capacitor discharge ignition system.

1. Generating coil
2. Zener diode
3. Diode
4. Trigger coil
5. Gate controlled switch
6. Capacitor
7. Pulse transformer (coil)
8. Spark plug

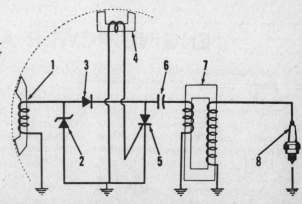

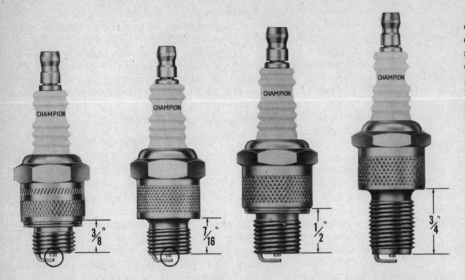

Fig. 3-26–Views showing spark plugs with various "reaches" available; small engines are usually equipped with a spark plug having a ⅜-inch reach. A ⅜-inch reach spark plug measures ⅜-inch from firing end of shell to gasket surface of shell. The two plugs at left side illustrate the difference in plugs normally used in two-stroke cycle and four-stroke cycle engines; refer to the circled electrodes. Spark plug at left has a shortened ground electrode and is specifically designed for two-stroke cycle engines. Second spark plug from left is normally used in four-stroke cycle engines although some two-stroke cycle engines may use this type plug.

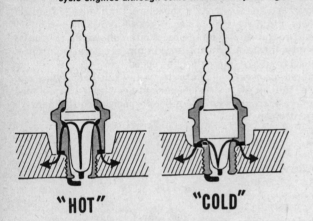

"HOT"   "COLD"

Fig. 3-27–Spark plug tip temperature is controlled by the length of the path heat must travel to reach cooling surface of the engine cylinder head.

HEAT RANGE. During engine operation, part of the heat generated during combustion is transferred to the spark plug, and from the plug to the cylinder through the shell threads and gasket. The operating temperature of the spark plug plays an important part in engine operation. If too much heat is retained by the plug, the fuel-air mixture may be ignited by contact with the heated surface before the ignition spark occurs. If not enough heat is retained, partially burned combustion products (soot, carbon and oil) may build up on the plug tip resulting in "fouling" or shorting out of the plug. If this happens, the secondary current is dissipated uselessly as it is generated instead of bridging the plug gap as a useful spark, and the engine will misfire.

The operating temperature of the plug tip can be controlled, within limits, by altering the length of the path the heat must follow to reach the threads and gasket of the plug. Thus, a plug with a short, stubby insulator around the center electrode will run cooler than one with a long, slim insulator. Refer to Fig. 3-27. Most plugs in the more popular sizes are available in a number of heat ranges which are interchangeable within the group. The proper heat range is determined by engine design and the type of service. Refer to SPARK PLUG SERVICING FUNDAMENTALS for additional information on spark plug selection.

SPECIAL TYPES. Sometimes, engine design features or operating conditions call for special plug types designed for a particular purpose. Of special interest when dealing with two-cycle engines is the spark plug shown in the left hand view, Fig. 3-26. In the design of this plug, the ground electrode is shortened so that its end aligns with center of insulated electrode rather than completely overlapping as with the conventional plug. This feature reduces the possibility of the gap bridging over by carbon formations.

THREAD SIZE. The threaded, shell portion of the spark plug and the attaching hole in the cylinder are manufactured to meet certain industry established standards. The diameter is referred to as "Thread Size." Those commonly used are: 10 mm, 14 mm, 18 mm, ⅞ inch and ½ inch pipe. The 14 mm plug is almost universal for small engine use.

REACH. The length of thread, and the thread depth in cylinder head or wall are also standardized throughout the industry. This dimension is measured from gasket seat of plug to cylinder end of thread. See Fig. 3-26. Four different reach plugs commonly used are: ⅜-inch, 7/16-inch, ½-inch and ¾-inch. The first two mentioned are the ones commonly used in small engines.

ENGINE POWER AND TORQUE RATINGS

The following paragraphs discuss the terms used in expressing engine horsepower and torque ratings and explains the methods for determining the different ratings. Some small engine repair shops are now equipped with a dynamometer for measuring engine torque and/or horsepower and the mechanic should be familiar with terms, methods of measurement and how actual power developed by an engine can vary under different conditions.

GLOSSARY OF TERMS

FORCE. Force is an action against an object that tends to move the object from a state of rest, or to accelerate the movement of an object. For use in calculating torque or horsepower, force is measured in pounds.

WORK. When a force moves an object from a state of rest, or accelerates the movement of an object, work is done. Work is measured by multiplying the force applied by the distance the force moves the object, or:

$$\text{work} = \text{force} \times \text{distance}.$$

Thus, if a force of 50 pounds moved an object 50 feet, work done would equal 50 pounds times 50 feet, or 2500 pounds-feet (or as it is usually expressed, 2500 foot-pounds).

POWER. Power is the rate at which work is done; thus, if:

work = force × distance,

then:

power = force × distance.

————————————

time

From the above formula, it is seen that power must increase if the time in which work is done decreases.

HORSEPOWER: Horsepower is a unit of measurement of power. Many years ago, James Watt, a Scotsman noted as the inventor of the steam engine, evaluated one horsepower as being equal to doing 33,000 foot-pounds of work in one minute. This evaluation has been universally accepted since that time. Thus, the formula for determining horsepower is:

$$horsepower = \frac{pounds \times feet}{33,000 \times minutes}$$

When referring to engine horsepower ratings, one usually finds the rating expressed as brake horsepower or rated horsepower, or sometimes as both.

BRAKE HORSEPOWER. Brake horsepower is the maximum horsepower available from an engine as determined by use of a dynamometer, and is usually stated as maximum observed brake horsepower or as corrected brake horsepower. As will be noted in a later

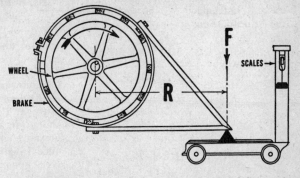

Fig. 4-4–Diagram showing a prony brake on which the torque being developed by an engine can be measured. By also knowing the RPM of the engine output shaft, engine horsepower can be calculated.

paragraph, observed brake horsepower of a specific engine will vary under different conditions of temperature and atmospheric pressure. Corrected brake horsepower is a rating calculated from observed brake horsepower and is a means of comparing engines tested at varying conditions. The method for calculating corrected brake horsepower will be explained in a later paragraph.

RATED HORSEPOWER. An engine being operated under a load equal to the maximum horsepower available (brake horsepower) will not have reserve power for overloads and is subject to damage from overheating and rapid wear. Therefore, when an engine is being selected for a particular load, the engine's brake horsepower rating should be in excess of the expected normal operating load. Usually, it is recommended that the engine not be operated in excess of 80% of the engine maximum brake horsepower rating; thus, the "rated horsepower" of an engine is usually equal to 80% of maximum horsepower that the engine will develop.

TORQUE. In many engine specifications, a "torque rating" is given. Engine torque can be defined simply as the turning effort exerted by the engine output shaft when under load. Thus, it is possible to calculate engine horsepower being developed by measuring torque being developed and engine output speed. Refer to the following paragraphs.

MEASURING ENGINE TORQUE AND HORSEPOWER

THE PRONY BRAKE. The prony brake is the most simple means of testing engine performance. Refer to diagram in Fig. 4-4. A torque arm is attached to a brake on wheel mounted on engine output shaft. The torque arm, as the brake is applied, exerts a force (F) on scales. Engine torque is computed by multiplying the force (F) times the length of the torque arm radius (R), or:

engine torque = F × R.

If, for example, the torque arm radius (R) is 2 feet and the force (F) being exerted by the torque arm on the scales is 6 pounds, engine torque would be 2 feet x 6 pounds, or 12 foot-pounds.

To calculate engine horsepower being developed by use of the prony brake, we must also count revolutions of the engine output shaft for a specific length of time. In the formula for calculating horsepower:

$$horsepower = \frac{feet \times pounds}{33,000 \times minutes};$$

feet will equal the circumference transcribed by the torque arm radius multiplied by the number of engine output shaft revolutions. Thus:

feet = 2 × 3.14 × radius × revolutions.

Pounds in the formula will equal the force (F) of the torque arm. If, for example, the force (F) is 6 pounds,

Fig. 4-1–A force, measured in pounds, is defined as an action tending to move an object or to accelerate movement of an object.

Fig. 4-2–If a force moves an object from a state of rest or accelerates movement of an object, then work is done.

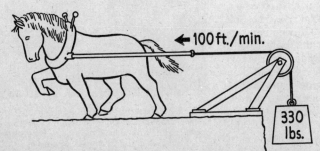

Fig. 4-3–This horse is doing 33,000 foot-pounds of work in one minute, or one horsepower.

torque arm radius is 2 feet and engine output shaft speed is 3300 revolutions per minute, then:

$$horsepower = \frac{2 \times 3.14 \times 2 \times 3300 \times 6}{33,000 \times 1}$$

or,

$$horsepower = 7.54$$

DYNAMOMETERS. Some commercial dynamometers for testing small engines are now available, although the cost may be prohibitive for all but the larger small engine repair shops. Usually, these dynamometers have a hydraulic loading device and scales indicating engine speed and load; horsepower is then calculated by use of a slide rule type instrument. For further information on commercial dynamometers, refer to manufacturers listed in special service tool section of this manual.

HOW ENGINE HORSEPOWER OUTPUT VARIES

Engine efficiency will vary with the amount of air taken into the cylinder on each intake stroke. Thus, air density has a considerable effect on the horsepower output of a specific engine. As air density varies with both temperature and atmospheric pressure, any change in air temperature, barometric pressure, or elevation will cause a variance in observed engine horsepower. As a general rule, engine horsepower will:

A. Decrease approximately 3% for each 1000 foot increase above 1000 ft. elevation;
B. Decrease approximately 3% for each 1 inch drop in barometric pressure; or,
C. Decrease approximately 1% for each 10° rise in temperature (Farenheit).

Thus, to fairly compare observed horsepower readings, the observed readings should be corrected to standard temperature and atmospheric pressure conditions of 60° F., and 29.92 inches of mercury. The correction formula specified by the Society of Automotive Engineers is somewhat involved; however, for practical purposes, the general rules stated above can be used to approximate the corrected brake horsepower of an engine when the observed maximum brake horsepower is known.

For example, suppose the engine horsepower of 7.54 as found by use of the prony brake was observed at an altitude of 3000 feet and at a temperature of 100 degrees. At standard atmospheric pressure and temperature conditions, we could expect an increase of 4% due to temperature (100°. – 60° × 1% per 10°) and an increase of 6% due to altitude (3000 ft. – 1000 ft. × 3% per 1000 ft.) or a total increase of 10%. Thus, the corrected maximum horsepower from this engine would be approximately 7.54 + .75, or approximately 8.25 horsepower.

TROUBLESHOOTING

When servicing an engine to correct a specific complaint, such as engine will not start, is hard to start, etc., a logical step-by-step procedure should be followed to determine cause of trouble before performing any service work. This procedure is "TROUBLE-SHOOTING."

Of course, if an engine is received in your shop for a normal tune up or specific repair work is requested, troubleshooting procedure is not required and the work should be performed as requested. It is wise, however, to fully check the engine before repairs are made and recommend any additional repairs or adjustments necessary to ensure proper engine performance.

The following procedures, as related to a specific complaint or trouble, have proven to be a satisfactory method for quickly determining cause of trouble in a number of small engine repair shops. NOTE: It is not suggested that the trouble shooting procedure as outlined in following paragraphs be strictly adhered to at all times. In many instances, customer's comments on when trouble was encountered will indicate cause of trouble. Also, the mechanic will soon develop a diagnostic technique that can only come with experience. In addition to the general troubleshooting procedure, reader should also refer to special notes following this section and to the information included

Fig. 5-1–Diagnosing cause of trouble, or "trouble-shooting" is an important factor in servicing small engines.

in the engine, carburetor and magneto servicing fundamentals sections.

If Engine Will Not Start— Or Is Hard To Start

1. If engine is equipped with a rope or crank starter, turn engine slowly. As the engine piston is coming up on compression stroke, a definite resistance to turning should be felt on rope or crank. See Fig. 5-2. This resistance should be noted every other crankshaft revolution on a single cylinder four-stroke cycle engine and on every revolution of a two-stroke cycle engine crankshaft. If alternate hard and easy turning is noted, the engine compression can be considered as not the cause of trouble at this time. NOTE: Compression

Fig. 5-2–Checking engine compression by slowly cranking engine; a definite resistance should be felt on starter rope each time piston comes up on compression stroke.

gages for small gasoline engines are available and are of value in trouble-shooting engine service problems. Where available from engine manufacturer, specifications will be given for engine compression pressure in the engine service sections of this manual. On engines having electric or impulse starters, remove spark plug and check engine compression with gage; if gage is not available, hold thumb so that spark plug hole is partly covered. An alternating blowing and suction action should be noted as the engine is cranked.

If very little or no compression is noted, refer to appropriate engine repair section for repair of engine. If check indicates engine is developing compression, proceed to step 2.

2. Remove spark plug wire and hold wire terminal about ⅛-inch away from cylinder. (On wires having rubber spark plug boot, insert a small screw or bolt in terminal.) Note: If available, use of a test plug is recommended. See Fig. 5-3. While cranking engine, a bright blue spark should snap across the ⅛-inch gap. If spark is weak or yellow, or if no spark occurs while cranking engine, refer to IGNITION SYSTEM SERVICE FUNDAMENTALS for information on appropriate type system. NOTE: A test plug with ⅛-inch gap is available or a test plug can be made by adjusting the electrode gap of a new 18 mm. spark plug to 0.125.

If spark is satisfactory, remove and inspect spark plug. Refer to SPARK PLUG SERVICE FUNDAMENTALS. If in doubt about spark plug condition, install a new plug. NOTE: Before installing plug, be sure to check electrode gap with proper gage and, if necessary, adjust to value given in engine repair section of this manual. DO NOT guess or check gap with a "thin dime"; a few thousandths variation from correct spark plug electrode gap can make an engine run unsatisfactorily, or under

some conditions, not start at all. See Fig. 5-4.

If ignition spark is satisfactory and engine will not start with new plug, proceed with step 3.

3. If engine compression and ignition spark seem to be OK, trouble within the fuel system should be suspected. Remove and clean or renew air cleaner or cleaner element. Check fuel tank (See Fig. 5-5) and be sure it is full of fresh gasoline (four-stroke cycle engines) or fresh gasoline and lubricating oil mixture (two-stroke cycle engines) as prescribed by engine manufacturer. Refer to LUBRICATION paragraph in each two-cycle engine service (engine repair) section for proper fuel-oil mixture for each make and model. If equipped with a fuel shut-off valve, be sure valve is open.

If engine is equipped with remote throttle controls that also operate carburetor choke plate, check to be sure that when controls are placed in choke position, carburetor choke plate is fully closed. If not, adjust control linkage so that choke will fully close; then, try to start engine. If engine does not start after several turns, remove air cleaner assembly; carburetor throat should be wet with gasoline. If not, check for reason fuel is not getting to carburetor. On models with gravity feed from fuel tank to carburetor (fuel tank above carburetor), disconnect fuel line at carburetor to see that fuel is flowing through the line. If no fuel is flowing, remove and clean fuel tank, fuel line and any fuel filters or shut-off valve.

On models having a fuel pump separate from carburetor, remove fuel line at carburetor and crank engine through several turns; fuel should spurt from open line. If not, disconnect fuel line from tank to fuel pump at pump connection. If fuel will not run from open line, remove and clean the fuel tank, line and if so equipped, fuel filter and/or shut-off valve. If fuel runs from open line, remove and overhaul or renew the fuel pump.

After making sure that clean, fresh fuel is available at carburetor, again try to start engine. If engine will not start, refer to recommended initial adjustments for carburetor in appropriate engine repair section of this manual and adjust carburetor idle and/or main fuel needles.

If engine will not start when compression and ignition test OK and clean, fresh fuel is available to carburetor, remove and clean or overhaul carburetor as outlined in CARBURETOR SERVICING FUNDAMENTALS section of this manual.

4. The preceding troubleshooting techniques are based on the fact that to run, an engine must develop compression, have an ignition spark and receive the proper fuel-air mixture. In some instances, there are other factors involved. Refer to the special notes following this section for service hints on finding common causes of engine trouble that may not be discovered in normal troubleshooting procedure.

If Engine Starts, Then Stops

This complaint is usually due to fuel starvation, but may be caused by a faulty ignition system. Recommended troubleshooting procedure is as follows:

1. Remove and inspect fuel tank cap; on all except a few early two-stroke cycle engines, fuel tank is vented through breather in fuel tank cap so that air can enter the tank as fuel is used. If engine stops after running several minutes, a clogged breather should be suspected. On some engines, it is possible to let the engine run with fuel tank cap removed and if this permits engine to run without stopping, clean or renew the cap. Caution: Be sure to observe safety precautions before attempting to run engine without fuel tank cap in place. If there is any danger of fuel being spilled on engine or spark entering open tank, **do not** attempt to run engine without fuel tank cap in place. If in doubt, try a new cap.

2. If clogged breather in fuel tank cap is eliminated as cause of trouble, a partially clogged fuel filter or fuel line should be suspected. Remove and clean fuel tank and line and if so equipped, clean fuel shut-off valve and/or fuel tank filter. On some engines, a screen or felt type fuel filter is located in the carburetor fuel inlet; refer to engine repair section for appropriate engine make and model for carburetor construction.

3. After cleaning fuel tank, line, filters, etc., if trouble is still encountered, a sticking or faulty carburetor inlet needle valve, float or diaphragm may be cause of trouble. Remove, disas-

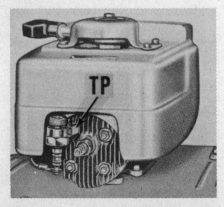

Fig. 5-3–Checking ignition spark across gap of special test plug (TP).

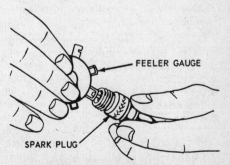

Fig. 5-4–Be sure to check spark plug electrode gap with proper size feeler gage and adjust gap to specification recommended by manufacturer.

semble and clean carburetor using data in engine repair section and in CARBURETOR SERVICE FUNDAMENTALS as a guide.

4. If fuel system is eliminated as cause of trouble by performing procedure outlined in steps 1, 2 and 3, check magneto or battery ignition coil on tester if such equipment is available. If not, check for ignition spark immediately after engine stops. Renew coil, condenser and breaker points if no spark is noted. Also, on four-stroke cycle engines, check for engine compression immediately after engine stops; trouble may be caused by sticking intake or exhaust valve or cam followers (tappets). If no or little compression is noted immediately after engine stops, refer to ENGINE SERVICE FUNDAMENTALS section and to engine repair data in the appropriate engine repair section of this manual.

Engine Overheats

When air cooled engines overheat, check for:

1. Air inlet screen in blower housing plugged with grass, leaves, dirt or other debris.

2. Remove blower housing and shields and check for dirt or debris accumulated on or between cooling fins on cylinder.

3. Missing or bent shields or blower housing. (Never attempt to operate an air cooled engine without all shields and blower housing in place.)

4. A too lean main fuel-air adjustment of carburetor.

5. Improper ignition spark timing. Check breaker point gap, and on engine with unit type magneto, check magneto to engine timing. On battery ignition units with timer, check for breaker points opening at proper time.

6. Engines being operated under loads in excess of rated engine horsepower or at extremely high ambient (surrounding) air temperatures may overheat.

7. Two-cycle engines being operated with an improper fuel-lubricating oil mixture may overheat due to lack of lubrication; refer to appropriate engine service section in this manual for recommended fuel-lubricating oil mixture.

Engine Surges When Running

Trouble with an engine surging is usually caused by improper carburetor adjustment or improper governor adjustment.

1. Refer to CARBURETOR paragraphs in the appropriate engine repair section and adjust carburetor as outlined.

2. If adjusting carburetor did not correct the surging condition, refer to GOVERNOR paragraph and adjust governor linkage.

3. If any wear is noted in governor linkage and adjusting linkage did not correct problem, renew worn linkage parts.

4. If trouble is still not corrected, remove and clean or overhaul carburetor as necessary. Also check for any possible air leaks between the carburetor to engine gaskets or air inlet elbow gaskets.

Engine Misses Out When Running (Two-Stroke Cycle Engines)

1. If engine misses out only at no load high idle speed, first be sure that engine is not equipped with an ignition cut-out governor. (If so equipped, engine will miss out at high speed due to cut-out action.) If not so equipped, refer to appropriate engine repair section and adjust carburetor as outlined in CARBURETOR paragraph. Some two-stroke cycle engines will miss out (four-cycle) when not under load, even though carburetor is adjusted properly. If a two-cycle engine fires evenly under normal load, it can usually be considered OK.

Special Notes on Engine Troubleshooting

ROTARY LAWN MOWER ENGINES. On most rotary lawn mower engines, the flywheel is of light weight and the mower blade provides the addi-

Fig. 5-5—Condensation can cause water and rust to form in fuel tank even though only clean fuel has been poured into tank.

tional inertia required for providing power to turn the engine through the compression stroke. Therefore, such engines will not start without the blade being solidly attached. When checking rotary mower engines for hard starting or will not start complaint, first be sure that blade is mounted and that it is solidly attached. Disconnect spark plug wire, hold engine shaft from turning and see if blade can be turned on shaft; if so, the slip clutch must be tightened or the shear key renewed.

TWO-STROKE CYCLE ENGINES WITH REED VALVE. On two-stroke cycle engines, the incoming fuel-air mixture must be compressed in engine crankcase in order for the mixture to properly reach the engine cylinder. On engines utilizing reed type carburetor to crankcase intake valve, a bent or broken reed will not allow compression build up in the crankcase. Thus, if such an engine seems otherwise OK, remove and inspect the reed valve unit. Refer to appropriate engine repair section in this manual for information on individual two-stroke cycle engine models.

TWO-STROKE CYCLE ENGINE EXHAUST PORTS. Two-stroke cycle engines, and especially those being operated on an overly rich fuel-air mixture or with too much lubricating oil mixed with the fuel, will tend to build up carbon in the cylinder exhaust ports. It is recommended that the muffler be removed on two-stroke cycle engines periodically and the carbon removed from the exhaust ports. Recommended procedure varies somewhat with different makes of engines; therefore, refer to CARBON paragraph of maintenance instructions in appropriate engine repair section of this manual.

On two-stroke cycle engines that are hard to start, or where complaint is loss of power, it is wise to remove the muffler and inspect the exhaust ports for carbon build up.

FOUR-STROKE CYCLE ENGINES WITH COMPRESSION RELEASE. Several different makes of four-stroke cycle engines now have a compression release that reduces compression pressure at cranking speeds, thus making it easier to crank the engine. Most models having this feature will develop full compression when turned in a reverse direction. Refer to the appropriate engine repair section in this manual for detailed information concerning the compression release used on different makes and models.

IGNITION SYSTEM SERVICE

The fundamentals of servicing ignition systems are outlined in the following paragraphs. Refer to appropriate heading for type ignition system being inspected or overhauled.

BATTERY IGNITION SERVICE FUNDAMENTALS

Service of battery ignition systems used on small engines is somewhat simplified due to the fact that no distribution system is required as on automotive type ignition systems. Usually all components are readily accessible and while use of test instruments is sometimes desirable, condition of the system can be determined by simple checks. Refer to following paragraphs.

GENERAL CONDITION CHECK.

Remove spark plug wire and if terminal is rubber covered, insert small screw or bolt in terminal. Hold uncovered end of terminal, or bolt inserted in terminal about ⅛-inch away from engine or connect spark plug wire to test plug as shown in Fig. 5-3. Crank engine while observing gap between spark plug wire terminal and engine; if a bright blue spark snaps across the gap, condition of the system can be considered satisfactory. However, ignition timing may have to be adjusted. Refer to timing procedure in appropriate engine repair section.

VOLTAGE, WIRING AND SWITCH CHECK.

If no spark, or a weak yellow-orange spark occurred when checking system as outlined in preceding paragraph, proceed with following checks:

Test battery condition with hydrometer or voltmeter. If check indicates a dead cell, renew the battery; recharge battery if a discharged condition is indicated. Note: On models with electric starter or starter-generator unit, battery can be assumed in satisfactory condition if the starter cranks the engine freely. If battery checks OK, but starter unit will not turn engine, a faulty starter unit is indicated and ignition trouble may be caused by excessive current draw of such a unit. If battery and starting unit, if so equipped, are in satisfactory condition, proceed as follows:

Remove battery lead wire from ignition coil and connect a test light of same voltage as the battery between the disconnected lead wire and engine ground. Light should go on when ignition switch is in "on" position and go off when switch is in "off" position. If not,

renew switch and/or wiring and recheck for satisfactory spark. If switch and wiring check OK, but no spark is obtained, proceed as follows:

BREAKER POINTS AND CONDENSER. Remove breaker box cover and, using small screwdriver, separate and inspect breaker points. If burned or deeply pitted, renew breaker points and condenser. If point contacts are clean to grayish in color and are only slightly pitted, proceed as follows: Disconnect condenser and ignition coil lead wires from breaker point terminal and connect a test light and battery between terminal and engine ground. Light should go on when points are closed and should go out when points are open. If light fails to go out when points are open, breaker arm insulation is defective and breaker points must be renewed. If light does not go on when points are in closed position, clean or renew the breaker points. In some instances, new breaker point contact surfaces may have an oily or wax coating or have foreign material between the surfaces so that proper contact is prevented. Check ignition timing and breaker point gap as outlined in appropriate engine repair section of this manual.

Connect test light and battery between condenser lead and engine ground; if light goes on, condenser is shorted out and should be renewed. Capacity of condenser can be checked if test instrument is available. It is usually good practice to renew the condenser whenever new breaker points

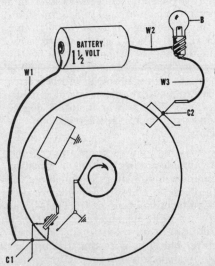

Fig. 5-6—Drawing showing a simple test lamp for checking ignition timing and/or breaker point opening.

B. 1½ volt bulb
C1. Spring clamp
C2. Spring clamp

W1. Wire
W2. Wire
W3. Wire

are being installed if tester is not available.

IGNITION COIL. If a coil tester is available, condition of coil can be checked. However, if tester is not available, a reasonably satisfactory performance test can be made as follows:

Disconnect high tension wire from spark plug. Turn engine so that cam has allowed breaker points to close. With ignition switch on, open and close points with small screwdriver while holding high tension lead about ⅛ to ¼-inch away from engine ground. A bright blue spark should snap across the gap between spark plug wire and ground each time the points are opened. If no spark occurs, or spark is weak and yellow-orange, renewal of the ignition coil is indicated.

Sometimes, an ignition coil may perform satisfactorily when cold, but fail after engine has run for some time and coil is hot. Check coil when hot if this condition is indicated.

FLYWHEEL MAGNETO SERVICE FUNDAMENTALS

In servicing a flywheel magneto ignition system, the mechanic is concerned with trouble shooting, service adjustments and testing magneto components. The following paragraphs outline the basic steps in servicing a flywheel type magneto. Refer to the appropriate engine section for adjustment and test specifications for a particular engine.

Trouble Shooting

If the engine will not start and malfunction of the ignition system is suspected, make the following checks to find cause of trouble.

Check to be sure that the ignition switch (if so equipped) is in the "On" or "Run" position and that the insulation on the wire leading to the ignition switch is in good condition. The switch can be checked with the timing and test light as shown in Fig. 5-6. Disconnect the lead from the switch and attach one clip of the test light to the switch terminal and the other clip to the engine. The light should go on when the switch is in the "Off" or "Stop" position, and should go off when the switch is in the "On" or "Run" position.

Inspect the high tension (spark plug) wire for worn spots in the insulation or breaks in the wire. Frayed or worn insulation can be repaired temporarily with plastic electrician's tape.

If no defects are noted in the ignition

switch or ignition wires, remove and inspect the spark plug as outlined in the SPARK PLUG SERVICING section. If the spark plug is fouled or is in questionable condition, connect a spark plug of known quality to the high tension wire, ground the base of the spark plug to engine and turn engine rapidly with the starter. If the spark across the electrode gap of the spark plug is a bright blue, the magneto can be considered in satisfactory condition. NOTE: Some engine manufacturers specify a certain type spark plug and a specific test gap. Refer to appropriate engine service section; if no specific spark plug type or electrode gap is recommended for test purposes, use spark plug type and electrode gap recommended for engine make and model. If spark across the gap of the test plug is weak or orange colored, or no spark occurs as engine is cranked, magneto should be serviced as outlined in the following paragraphs.

Magneto Adjustments

BREAKER CONTACT POINTS. Adjustment of the breaker contact points affects both ignition timing and magneto edge gap. Therefore, the breaker contact point gap should be carefully adjusted according to engine manufacturer's specifications. Before adjusting the breaker contact gap, inspect contact points and renew if condition of contact surfaces is questionable. It is sometimes desirable to check the condition of points as follows: Disconnect the condenser and primary coil leads from the breaker point terminal. Attach one clip of a test light (See Fig. 5-6) to the breaker point terminal and the other clip of the test light to magneto ground. The light should be out when contact points are open and should go on when the engine is turned

Fig. 5-7—On some engines, timing is adjustable by moving magneto stator plate in slotted mounting holes. Marks should be applied to stator plate and engine after engine is properly timed; marks usually appear on factory assembled stator plate and engine cylinder block.

to close the breaker contact points. If the light stays on when points are open, insulation of breaker contact arm is defective. If light does not go on when points are closed, contact surfaces are dirty, oily or are burned.

Adjust breaker point gap as follows unless manufacturer specifies adjusting breaker gap to obtain correct ignition timing. First, turn engine so that points are closed to be sure that the contact surfaces are in alignment and seat squarely. Then, turn engine so that breaker point opening is maximum and adjust breaker gap to manufacturer's specification. A wire type feeler gage is recommended for checking and adjusting the breaker contact gap. Be sure to recheck gap after tightening breaker point base retaining screws.

IGNITION TIMING. On some engines, ignition timing is non-adjustable and a certain breaker point gap is specified. On other engines, timing is adjustable by changing the position of the magneto stator plate (See Fig. 5-7) with a specified breaker point gap or by simply varying the breaker point gap to obtain correct timing. Ignition timing is usually specified either in degrees of engine (crankshaft) rotation or in piston travel before the piston reaches top dead center position. In some instances, a specification is given for ignition timing even though the timing may be non-adjustable; if a check reveals timing is incorrect on these engines, it is an indication of incorrect breaker point adjustment or excessive wear of breaker cam. Also, on some engines, it may indicate that a wrong breaker cam has been installed or that the cam has been installed in a reversed position on engine crankshaft.

Some engines may have a timing mark or flywheel locating pin to locate the flywheel at proper position for the ignition spark to occur (breaker points begin to open). If not, it will be necessary to measure piston travel as illustrated in Fig. 5-8 or install a degree indicating device on the engine crankshaft.

A timing light as shown in Fig. 5-6 is a valuable aid in checking or adjusting engine timing. After disconnecting the ignition coil lead from the breaker point terminal, connect the leads of the timing light as shown. If timing is adjustable by moving the magneto stator plate, be sure that the breaker point gap is adjusted as specified. Then, to check timing, slowly turn engine in normal direction of rotation past the point at which ignition spark should occur. The timing light should be on, then go out (breaker points open) just

as the correct timing location is passed. If not, turn engine to proper timing location and adjust timing by relocating the magneto stator plate or varying the breaker contact gap as specified by engine manufacturer. Loosen the screws retaining the stator plate or breaker points and adjust position of stator plate or points so that points are closed (timing light is on). Then, slowly move adjustment until timing light goes out (points open) and tighten the retaining screws. Recheck timing to be sure adjustment is correct.

ARMATURE AIR GAP. To fully concentrate the magnetic field of the flywheel magnets within the armature core, it is necessary that the flywheel magnets pass as closely to the armature core as possible without danger of metal to metal contact. The clearance between the flywheel magnets and the legs of the armature core is called the armature air gap.

On magnetos where the armature and high tension coil are located outside of the flywheel rim, adjustment of the armature air gap is made as follows: Turn the engine so that the flywheel magnets are located directly under the legs of the armature core and check the clearance between the armature core and flywheel magnets. If the measured clearance is not within manufacturers specifications, loosen the armature core mounting screws and place shims of thickness equal to minimum air gap specification between the magnets and armature core (Fig. 5-9). The magnets will pull the armature core against the shim stocks. Tighten the armature core mounting screws, remove the shim stock and turn the engine through several revolutions to be sure the flywheel does not contact the armature core.

Where the armature core is located under or behind the flywheel, the following methods may be used to check and adjust armature air gap: On some

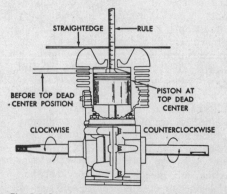

Fig. 5-8—On some engines, it will be necessary to measure piston travel with rule, dial indicator or special timing gage when adjusting or checking ignition timing.

engines, slots or openings are provided in the flywheel through which the armature air gap can be checked. Some engine manufacturers provide a cutaway flywheel that can be installed temporarily for checking the armature air gap. A test flywheel can be made out of a discarded flywheel (See Fig. 5-10), or out of a new flywheel if service volume on a particular engine warrants such expenditure. Another method of checking the armature air gap is to remove the flywheel and place a layer of plastic tape equal to the minimum specified air gap over the legs of the armature core. Reinstall flywheel and turn engine through several revolutions and remove flywheel; no evidence of contact between the flywheel magnets and plastic tape should be noticed. Then cover the legs of the armature core with a layer of tape of thickness equal to the maximum specified air gap; then, reinstall flywheel and turn engine through several revolutions. Indication of the flywheel magnets contacting the plastic tape should be noticed after the flywheel is again removed. If the magnets contact the first thin layer of tape applied to the armature core legs, or if they do not

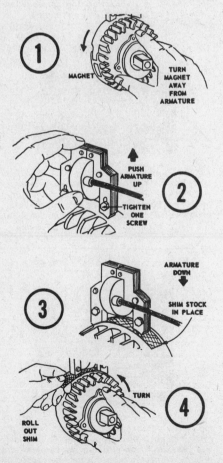

Fig. 5-9–Views showing adjustment of armature air gap when armature is located outside flywheel. Refer to Fig. 5-10 for engines having armature located inside flywheel.

contact the second thicker layer of tape, armature air gap is not within specifications and should be adjusted.

NOTE: Before loosening armature core mounting screws, scribe a mark on mounting plate against edge of armature core so that adjustment of air gap can be gaged.

In some instances, it may be necessary to slightly enlarge the armature core mounting holes before proper air gap adjustment can be made.

MAGNETO EDGE GAP. The point of maximum acceleration of the movement of the flywheel magnetic field through the high tension coil (and therefore, the point of maximum current induced in the primary coil windings) occurs when the trailing edge of the flywheel magnet is slightly past the left hand leg of the armature core. The exact point of maximum primary current is determined by using electrical measuring devices, the distance between the trailing edge of the flywheel magnet and the leg of the armature core at this point is measured and becomes a service specification. This distance, which is stated either in thousandths of an inch or in degrees of flywheel rotation, is called the Edge Gap or "E" Gap.

For maximum strength of the ignition spark, the breaker points should just start to open when the flywheel magnets are at the specified edge gap position. Usually, edge gap is non-adjustable and will be maintained at the proper dimension if the contact breaker points are adjusted to the recommended gap and the correct breaker cam is installed. However magneto edge gap can change (and spark intensity thereby reduced) due to the following:

a. Flywheel drive key sheared
b. Flywheel drive key worn (loose)
c. Keyway in flywheel or crankshaft worn (oversized)
d. Loose flywheel retaining nut which can also cause any above listed difficulty
e. Excessive wear on breaker cam
f. Breaker cam loose on crankshaft
g. Excessive wear on breaker point rubbing block or push rod so that points cannot be properly adjusted.

Unit Type Magneto Service Fundamentals

Improper functioning of the carburetor, spark plug or other components often causes difficulties that are thought to be an improperly functioning magneto. Since a brief inspec-

tion will often locate other causes for engine malfunction, it is recommended that one be certain the magneto is at fault before opening the magneto housing. Magneto malfunction can easily be determined by simple tests as outlined in following paragraph.

Trouble Shooting

With a properly adjusted spark plug in good condition, the ignition spark should be strong enough to bridge a short gap in addition to the actual spark plug gap. With engine running, hold end of spark plug wire not more than 1/16-inch away from spark plug terminal. Engine should not misfire.

To test the magneto spark if engine will not start, remove ignition wire from magneto end cap socket. Bend a short piece of wire so that when it is inserted in the end cap socket, other end is about ⅛-inch from engine casting. Crank engine slowly and observe gap between wire and engine; a strong blue spark should jump the gap the instant that the impulse coupling trips. If a strong spark is observed, it is recommended that the magneto be eliminated as the source of engine difficulty and that the spark plug, ignition wire and terminals be thoroughly inspected.

If, when cranking the engine, the impulse coupling does not trip, the magneto must be removed from the engine and the coupling overhauled or renewed. It should be noted that if the impulse coupling will not trip, a weak spark will occur.

Magneto Adjustments and Service

BREAKER POINTS. Breaker points are accessible for service after removing the magneto housing end cap. Examine point contact surfaces for pitting or pyramiding (transfer of

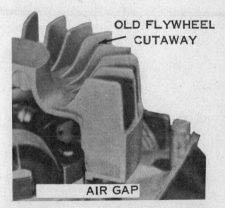

Fig. 5-10–Where armature core is located inside flywheel, check armature gap by using a cut-away flywheel unless other method is provided by manufacturer; refer to appropriate engine repair section. Where possible, an old discarded flywheel should be used to cut-away section for checking armature air gap.

metal from one surface to the other); a small tungsten file or fine stone may be used to resurface the points. Badly worn or badly pitted points should be renewed. After points are resurfaced or renewed, check breaker point gap with rotor turned so that points are opened maximum distance. Refer to MAGNETO paragraph in appropriate engine repair section for point gap specifications.

When replacing the magneto end cap, both the end cap and housing mating surfaces should be thoroughly cleaned and a new gasket be installed.

CONDENSER. Condenser used in unit type magneto is similar to that used in other ignition systems. Refer to MAGNETO paragraph in appropriate engine repair section for condenser test specifications. Usually, a new condenser should be installed whenever the breaker points are being renewed.

COIL. The ignition coil can be tested without removing the coil from the housing. The instructions provided with coil tester should have coil test specifications listed.

ROTOR. Usually, service on the magneto rotor is limited to renewal of bushings or bearings, if damaged. Check to be sure rotor turns freely and does not drag or have excessive end play.

MAGNETO INSTALLATION. When installing a unit type magneto on an engine, refer to MAGNETO paragraph in appropriate engine repair section for magneto to engine timing information.

SOLID STATE IGNITION SERVICE FUNDAMENTALS

Because of differences in solid state ignition construction, it is impractical to outline a general procedure for solid state ignition service. Refer to the specific engine section for testing, overhaul notes and timing of solid state ignition systems.

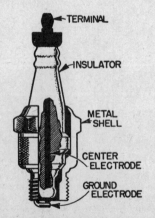

Fig. 5-11–Cross-sectional drawing of spark plug showing construction and nomenclature.

SPARK PLUG SERVICING

ELECTRODE GAP. The spark plug electrode gap should be adjusted by bending the ground electrode. Refer to Fig. 5-11. The recommended gap is listed in the SPARK PLUG paragraph in appropriate engine repair section of this manual.

CLEANING AND ELECTRODE CONDITIONING. Spark plugs are most usually cleaned by abrasive action commonly referred to as "sand blasting." Actually, ordinary sand is not used, but a special abrasive which is nonconductive to electricity even when melted, thus the abrasive cannot short out the plug current. Extreme care should be used in cleaning the plugs after sand blasting, however, as any particles of abrasive left on the plug may cause damage to piston rings, piston or cylinder walls. Some engine

Fig. 5-12–Normal plug appearance in four-stroke cycle engine. Insulator is light tan to gray in color and electrodes are not burned. Renew plug at regular intervals as recommended by engine manufacturer.

Fig. 5-13–Appearance of four-stroke cycle spark plug indicating cold fouling. Cause of cold fouling may be use of a too-cold plug, excessive idling or light loads, carburetor choke out of adjustment, defective spark plug wire or boot, carburetor adjusted too "rich" or low engine compression.

Fig. 5-14–Appearance of four-stroke cycle spark plug indicating wet fouling; a wet, black oily film is over entire firing end of plug. Cause may be oil getting by worn valve guides, worn oil rings or plugged breather or breather valve in tappet chamber.

Fig. 5-15–Appearance of four-stroke cycle spark plug indicating overheating. Check for plugged cooling fins, bent or damaged blower housing, engine being operated without all shields in place or other causes of engine overheating. Also can be caused by too lean a fuel-air mixture or spark plug not tightened properly.

Fig. 5-16–Normal appearance of plug removed from a two-stroke cycle engine. Insulator is light tan to gray in color, few deposits are present and electrodes not burned.

Fig. 5-17–Appearance of plug from two-stroke cycle engine indicating wet fouling. A damp or wet black carbon coating is formed over entire firing end. Could be caused by a too-cold plug, excessive idling, improper fuel-lubricating oil mixture or carburetor adjustment too rich.

Fig. 5-18–Appearance of plug from two-stroke cycle engine indicating overheating. Insulator has gray or white blistered appearance and electrodes may be burned. Could be caused by use of a too-hot plug, carburetor adjustment too lean, "sticky" piston rings, engine overloaded, or cooling fins plugged causing engine to run too hot.

manufacturers recommend that the spark plug be renewed rather than cleaned because of possible engine damage from cleaning abrasives.

After plug is cleaned by abrasive, and before gap is set, the electrode surfaces between the grounded and insulated electrodes should be cleaned and returned as nearly as possible to original shape by filing with a point file. Failure to properly dress the electrodes can result in high secondary voltage requirements, and misfire of the plug.

PLUG APPEARANCE DIAGNOSIS. The appearance of a spark plug will be altered by use, and an examination of the plug tip can contribute useful information which may assist in obtaining better spark plug life. It must be remembered that the contributing factors differ in two-cycle and four-cycle engine operation and although the appearance of two spark plugs may be similar, the corrective measures may depend on whether the engine is of two-cycle or four-cycle design. Figs. 5-12 through 5-18 are provided by Champion Spark Plug Company to illustrate typical observed conditions. Refer to Figs. 5-12 through 5-15 for four-stroke cycle engines and to Figs. 5-16 through 5-18 for two-cycle engines. Listed in captions are the probable causes and suggested corrective measures.

CARBURETOR SERVICING FUNDAMENTALS

The bulk of carburetor service consists of cleaning, inspection and adjustment. After considerable service it may become necessary to overhaul the carburetor and renew worn parts to restore original operating efficiency. Although carburetor condition affects engine operating economy and power, ignition and engine compression must also be considered to determine and correct causes of poor performance.

Before dismantling carburetor for cleaning or overhaul, clean all external surfaces and remove accumulated dirt and grease. Refer to appropriate engine repair section for carburetor exploded or cross-sectional views. Dismantle carburetor and note any discrepancies to assure correction during overhaul. Thoroughly clean all parts and inspect for damage or wear. Wash jets and passages and blow clear with clean, dry compressed air. Do not use a drill or wire to clean jets as the possible enlargement of calibrated holes will disturb operating balance. The measurement of jets to determine the extent of wear is difficult and new parts are usually installed to assure satisfactory results.

Carburetor manufacturers provide for many of their models an assortment of gaskets and other parts usually needed to do a correct job of cleaning and overhaul. These assortments are usually catalogued as Gasket Kits and Overhaul Kits respectively.

On float type carburetors, inspect float pin and needle valve for wear and renew if necessary. Check metal floats for leaks and where a dual type float is installed, check alignment of float sections. Check cork floats for loss of protective coating and absorption of fuel. NOTE: Do not attempt to recoat cork floats with shellac or varnish or to resolder leaky metal floats. Renew part if defective.

Check the fit of throttle and choke valve shafts. Excessive clearance will cause improper valve plate seating and

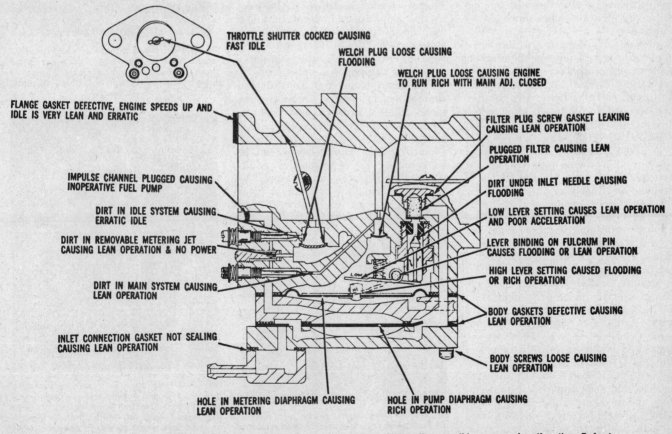

Fig. 5-20–Schematic cross-sectional view of a diaphragm type carburetor illustrating possible causes of malfunction. Refer to appropriate engine repair section for adjustment information and for exploded and/or cross-sectional view of actual carburetors used.

will permit dust or grit to be drawn into the engine. Air leaks at throttle shaft bores due to wear will upset carburetor calibration and contribute to uneven engine operation. Rebush valve shaft holes where necessary and renew dust seals. If rebushing is not possible, renew the body part supporting the shaft. Inspect throttle and choke valve plates for proper installation and condition.

Power or idle adjustment needles must not be worn or grooved. Check condition of needle seal packing or "O" ring and renew packing or "O" ring if necessary.

Reinstall or renew jets, using correct size listed for specific model. Adjust power and idle settings as described for specific carburetors in engine service section of manual.

It is important that the carburetor bore at the idle discharge ports and in the vicinity of the throttle valve be free of deposits. A partially restricted idle port will produce a "flat spot" between idle and mid-range rpm. This is because the restriction makes it necessary to open to throttle wider than the designed opening to obtain proper idle speed. Opening the throttle wider than the design specified amount will uncover more of the port than was intended in the calibration of the carburetor. As a result an insufficient amount of the port will be available as a reserve to cover the transition period (idle to the mid-range rpm) when the high speed system begins to function.

Refer to Fig. 5-20 for service hints on diaphragm type carburetors.

When reassembling float type carburetors, be sure float position is properly adjusted. Refer to CARBURETOR paragraph in appropriate engine repair section for float level adjustment specifications.

sandpaper or lapping compound. Use a figure-eight motion with minimum pressure, and remove only enough metal to eliminate the imperfection. Bearing clearances, if any, must not be lessened by removing metal from the joint.

Use only the specified gaskets when re-assembling, and use an approved gasket cement or sealing compound unless the contrary is stated. Seal all exposed threads and repaint or retouch with an approved paint.

REPAIRING DAMAGED THREADS

Damaged threads in castings can be renewed by use of thread repair kits which are recommended by a number of equipment and engine manufac-

Fig. 5-22–Damaged threads in casting before repair. Refer to Figs. 5-23, 5-24 and 5-25 for steps in installing thread insert. (Series of photos provided by Heli-Coil Corp., Danbury, Conn.)

ENGINE SERVICE

DISASSEMBLY AND ASSEMBLY

Special techniques must be developed in repair of engines of aluminum alloy or magnesium alloy construction. Soft threads in aluminum or magnesium castings are often damaged by carelessness in overtightening fasteners or in attempting to loosen or remove seized fasteners. Manufacturer's recommended torque values for tightening screw fasteners should be followed closely. Note: If damaged threads are encountered, refer to following paragraph, "REPAIRING DAMAGED THREADS."

A given amount of heat applied to aluminum or magnesium will cause it to expand a greater amount than will steel under similar conditions. Because of the different expansion characteristics, heat is usually recommended for easy installation of bearings, pins, etc., in aluminum or magnesium castings. Sometimes, heat can be used to free parts that are seized or where an interference fit is used. Heat, therefore, becomes a service tool and the application of heat one of the required service techniques. An open flame is not usually advised because it destroys the paint and other protective coatings and because a uniform and controlled temperature with open flame is difficult to obtain. Methods commonly used are heating in oil or water, with a heat lamp, electric hot plate, or in an oven or kiln. See Fig. 5-21. The use of water or oil gives a fairly accurate temperature control but is somewhat limited as

to the size and type of part than can be handled. Thermal crayons are available which can be used to determine the temperature of a heated part. These crayons melt when the part reaches a specified temperature, and a number of crayons for different temperatures are available. Temperature indicating crayons are usually available at welding equipment supply houses.

The crankcase and combustion chambers of a two-cycle engine must be sealed against pressure and vacuum. To assure a perfect seal, nicks, scratches and warpage are to be avoided. Slight imperfections can be removed by using a fine-grit sandpaper. Flat surfaces can be lapped by using a surface plate or a smooth piece of plate glass, and a sheet of 120-grit

Fig. 5-21–In small engine repair, heat can be used efficiently as a disassembly and assembly tool. Heating crankcase halves on electric hot plate (above) will allow bearings to be easily removed.

Fig. 5-23–First step in repairing damaged threads is to drill out old threads using exact size drill recommended in instructions provided with thread repair kit. Drill all the way through an open hole or all the way to bottom of blind hole, making sure hole is straight and that centerline of hole is not moved in drilling process.

turers. Use of thread repair kits is not difficult, but instructions must be carefully followed. Refer to Figs. 5-22 through 5-25 which illustrate the use of Heli-Coil thread repair kits that are manufactured by the Heli-Coil Corporation, Danbury, Connecticut.

Heli-Coil thread repair kits are available through the parts departments of most engine and equipment manufacturers; the thread inserts are available in all National Coarse (USS) sizes from #4 to 1½ inch and National Fine (SAE) sizes from #6 to 1½ inch. Also, sizes for repairing 14mm. and 18mm. spark plug ports are available.

VALVE SERVICE FUNDAMENTALS
(Four-Stroke Cycle Engines)

When overhauling small four-stroke

Fig. 5-24–Special drill taps are provided in thread repair kit for threading drilled hole to correct size for outside of thread insert. A standard tap cannot be used.

Fig. 5-25–A thread insert and a completed repair are shown above. Special tools are provided in thread repair kit for installation of thread insert.

cycle engines, obtaining proper valve sealing is of primary importance. The following paragraphs cover the fundamentals of servicing the intake and exhaust valves, valve seats and valve guides.

REMOVING AND INSTALLING VALVES. A valve spring compressor, one type of which is shown in Fig. 5-26, is a valuable aid in removing and installing the intake and exhaust valves. This tool is used to hold the spring compressed while removing or installing the pin, collars or retainer from the valve stem. Refer to Fig. 5-27 for views showing some of the different methods of retaining valve spring to valve stem.

VALVE REFACING. If the valve face (See Fig. 5-28) is slightly worn, burned or pitted, the valve can usually be refaced providing proper equipment is available. Many small engine shops will usually renew the valves, however, rather to invest in somewhat costly valve refacing tools.

Before attempting to reface a valve, refer to specifications in appropriate engine repair section for valve face angle. On some engines, manufacturer recommends grinding the valve face to an angle of ½ to 1 degree less than that

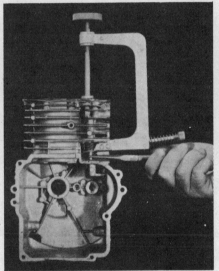

Fig. 5-26–View showing one type of valve spring compressor being used to remove keeper. (Block is cut-away to show valve spring.)

Fig. 5-27–Drawing showing three types of valve spring keepers used.

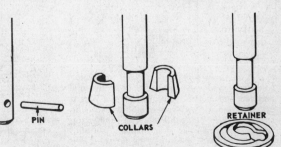

of the valve seat. Refer to Fig. 5-29. Also, nominal valve face angle may be either 30 or 45 degrees.

After valve is refaced, check thickness of valve "margin" (See Fig. 5-28). If margin is less than manufacturer's minimum specification (refer to specifications in appropriate engine repair section), or is less than one-half the

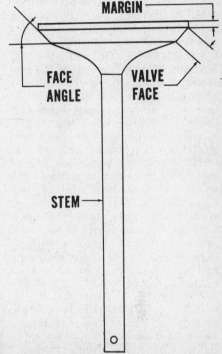

Fig. 5-28–Drawing showing typical four-stroke cycle engine valve. Face angle is usually 30° or 45°. On some engines, valve face is ground to an angle of ½ or 1 degree less than seat angle.

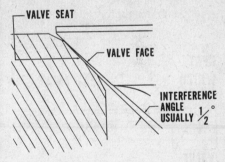

Fig. 5-29–Drawing showing line contact of valve face with valve seat when valve face is ground at smaller angle than valve seat; this is specified on some engines.

margin of a new valve, renew the valve. Valves having excessive material removed in refacing operation will not give satisfactory service.

When refacing or renewing a valve, the seat should also be reconditioned, or in engines where valve seat is renewable, a new seat should be installed. Refer to following paragraph "RESEATING OR RENEWING VALVE SEATS." Then, the seating surfaces should be lapped in using a fine valve grinding compound.

RESEATING OR RENEWING VALVE SEATS. On engines having the valve seat machined in the cylinder block casting, the seat can be reconditioned by using a correct angle seat grinding stone or valve seat cutter. When reconditioning valve seat, care should be taken that only enough material is removed to provide a good seating or valve contact surface. The width of the seat should then be measured (See Fig. 5-30) and if width exceeds manufacturer's maximum specifications, the seat should be narrowed by using one stone or cutter with an angle 15° greater than valve seat angle and a second stone or cutter with an angle 15° less than seat angle. When narrowing the seat, coat seat lightly with Prussian blue and check where seat contacts valve face by inserting valve in guide and rotating valve lightly against seat. Seat should contact approximate center of valve face. By using only the narrow angle seat narrowing stone or cutter, seat contact will be moved towards outer edge of valve face.

On engines having renewable valve seats, refer to appropriate engine re-

pair section in this manual for recommended method of removing old seat and installing new seat. Refer to Fig. 5-31 for one method of installing new valve seats. Seats are retained in cylinder block bore by an interference fit; that is, seat is slightly larger than the bore in block. It sometimes occurs that the valve seat will become loose in the bore, especially on engines with aluminum crankcase. Some manufacturers provide oversize valve seat inserts (insert O.D. larger than standard part) so that if standard size insert fits loosely, the bore can be cut oversize and a new insert be tightly installed. After installing valve seat insert in engines of aluminum construction, the metal around the seat should be peened as shown in Fig. 5-32. Where a loose insert is encountered and an oversize insert is not available, the loose insert can usually be tightened by center-punching the cylinder block material at three equally spaced points around the insert, then peening completely around the insert as shown in Fig. 5-32.

For some engines with cast iron cylinder blocks, a service valve seat insert is available for reconditioning the valve seat, and is installed by counter-boring the cylinder block to specified dimensions, then driving insert into place. Refer to appropriate engine repair section in this manual for information on availability and installation of service valve seat inserts for cast iron engines.

INSTALLING OVERSIZE PISTON AND RINGS

Some small engine manufacturers

have over-size piston and ring sets available for use in repairing engines in which the cylinder bore is excessively worn and standard size piston and rings cannot be used. If care and approved procedure are used in oversizing the cylinder bore, installation of an oversize piston and ring set should result in a highly satisfactory overhaul.

The cylinder bore may be oversized by using either a boring bar or a hone; however, if a boring bar is used, it is usually recommended the cylinder bore be finished with a hone. Refer to Fig. 5-33.

Where oversize piston and rings are available, it will be so noted in the appropriate engine repair section of this manual. Also, the standard bore diameter will also be given. Before attempting to rebore or hone the cylinder to oversize, carefully measure the cylinder bore to be sure that standard size piston and rings will not fit within tolerance. Also, it may be possible that the cylinder is excessively worn or damaged and that reboring or honing to largest oversize will not clean up the worn or scored surface.

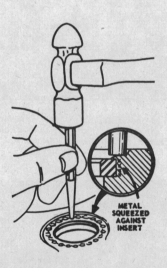

Fig. 5-32–It is usually recommended that on aluminum block engines, metal be peened around valve seat insert after insert is installed.

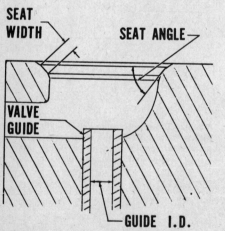

Fig. 5-30–Cross-sectional drawing of typical valve seat and valve guide as used on small engines. Valve guide may be integral part of cylinder block; on some models so constructed, valve guide I.D. may be reamed out and an oversize valve stem installed. On other models, a service guide may be installed after counter-boring cylinder block.

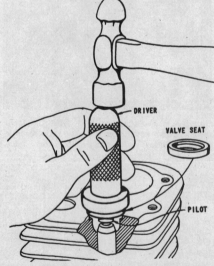

Fig. 5-31–View showing one method used to install valve seat insert. Refer to appropriate engine repair section for manufacturer's recommended method.

Fig. 5-33–A cross-hatch pattern as shown should be obtained when honing cylinder. Pattern is obtained by moving hone up and down cylinder bore as it is being turned by slow speed electric drill.

TRACK TUNING YOUR KART CARBURETOR

The only way to accurately tune kart carburetors is to make all adjustments "ON THE TRACK." Track tuning enables an accurate adjustment taking into consideration track conditions, weather conditions and different fuel-oil mixtures.

Fig. 7-1, 7-2 and 7-3 show the location of adjusting needles on most diaphragm carburetors. Several companies offer kits which provide remote adjustment of the mixture needles.

First obtain an initial setting by turning both adjusting needles in (clockwise) until needles lightly contact seat; then, open needles (turn counter-clockwise) about 1-1½ turns.

NOTE: Be careful when turning needles toward seat and **DO NOT FORCE,** or damage to the needle and/or seat may result. Generally this primary adjustment is too rich; but, starting with a rich mixture won't cause engine to overheat, and seize before you get it tuned.

Take the kart out on the track and run several laps until the engine reaches operating temperature. Final carburetor adjustment shouldn't be made until the engine is warm even though engine will probably miss out ("four-cycle" or "blubber") part of the time.

After the engine is warm, lean (close) the high speed needle, by turning in a clockwise direction, a little at a time until the engine runs smoothly all the way to the end of the longest straight away. After a couple of more laps, richen (open) high speed needle just slightly. If after richening just slightly the engine starts to miss out (four-cycle) at the end of the straight away, the setting is very close to correct. The needle should be set so that engine runs smoothly all the way to the end of the straight away, but, if setting is richened just **SLIGHTLY** it will start to miss (four-cycle) at the end of the straight away.

Now run a few laps at low speed (about the speed traveled when lining up for the green flag). If the engine has

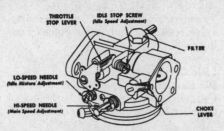

Fig. 7-2–View showing location of adjustment points on some Tillotson carburetors. Location of adjustment points on McCulloch Kart carburetors are similar.

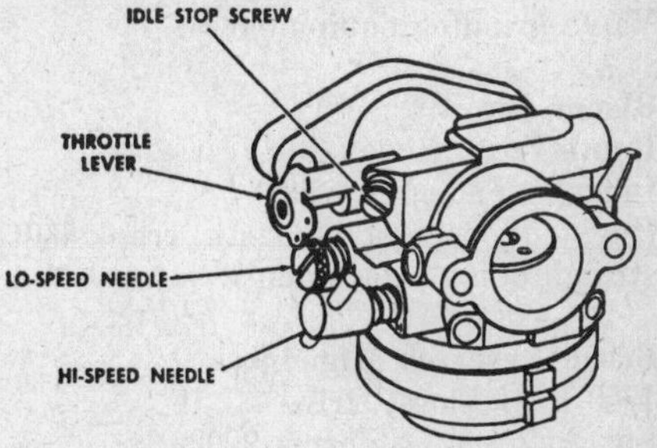

Fig. 7-3–Typical Brown carburetor showing points of adjustment.

a tendency to load up (run too rich) when you first start to accelerate after running slowly, the low speed needle is set too rich. Lean the low speed needle by turning clockwise (about ⅛ turn); then, recheck the high speed performance as described in the previous paragraph. **Changing the low speed needle setting will change the high speed performance also.** Usually if the low speed needle is leaned, the high speed needle will need to be set slightly richer. Again recheck the slow speed performance. If the kart is sluggish coming out of the turns but doesn't "four-cycle," the low speed needle is probably set too lean.

The important thing is: When one needle is changed, the other should be checked.

Carburetor adjustment should be checked several times in a day of racing because many things that affect the setting are changed. If adjustment was made in the morning, the temperature will probably change several degrees before afternoon. The warmer temperature will cause the engine to run warmer; which will require a richer setting. If adjustment was made with high humidity and later in the day there is less humidity, the mixture should be richened. Engine vibrations, gear ratio, brand of oil, viscosity (thickness of oil), amount of oil, type of fuel and additives all affect carburetor adjustment.

Adjustment of the carburetor with the rear wheels raised means nothing (except that the engine will run). Don't waste time attempting to tune anywhere but on the track.

SERVICE SHOP TOOL BUYER'S GUIDE

This listing of Service Shop Tools is solely for the convenience of users of this manual and does not imply endorsement or approval by Technical Publications, Inc. of the tools and equipment listed. The listing is in response to many requests for information on sources for purchasing special tools and equipment. Every attempt has been made to make the listing as complete as possible at time of publication and each entry is made from latest material available.

Special engine service tools such as seal drivers, bearing drivers, etc., which are available from the engine manufacturer are not listed in this section of the manual. Where a special service tool is listed in the engine service section of this manual, the tool is available from the central parts or service distributors listed at the end of

most engine service sections, or from the manufacturer.

NOTE TO MANUFACTURERS AND NATIONAL SALES DISTRIBUTORS OF SMALL ENGINE SERVICE TOOLS AND RELATED SERVICE EQUIPMENT. To obtain either a new listing for your products, or to change or add to an existing listing, write to Technical Publications, 1014 Wyandotte, Kansas City, Mo. 64105.

Engine Service Tools

Ammco Tools, Inc.
2100 Commonwealth Ave.
North Chicago, Illinois 60064
Valve spring compressor, torque wrenches, cylinder hones, ridge reamers, piston ring compressors, piston ring expanders.

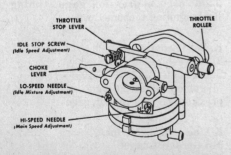

Fig. 7-1–View showing location of adjustment points on some Tillotson carburetors.

Black & Decker Mfg. Co.
701 East Joppa Road
Towson, Maryland 21204
Valve grinding equipment

Bloom, Inc.
Route Four, Hiway 20 West
Independence, Iowa 50644
Engine repair stand with crankshaft straightening attachment.

Brush Research Mfg. Inc.
4353 East Floral Drive
Los Angeles, California 90022
Cylinder hones

Carr Lane Mfg. Co.
4200 Carr Lane Court
Saint Louis, Missouri 63119
Thread inserts

Cedar Rapids Engineering
902 17th Street NE
Cedar Rapids, Iowa 52402
Cylinder boring equipment, valve refacing machines, valve seat grinders.

Frederick Mfg. Co., Inc.
1400 C, Agnes Avenue
Kansas City, Missouri 64127
Crankshaft straightener

Heli-Coil Products Division
Heli-Coil Corporation
Shelter Rock Lane
Danbury, Connecticut 06810
Thread repair kits, thread inserts, installation tools.

K-D Manufacturing Co.
Lancaster, Pennsylvania 17604
Thread repair kits, valve spring compressors, reamers.

Keystone Reamer & Tool Co.
Post Office Box 310
Millersburg, Pennsylvania 17061
Valve seat cutter & pilots, adjustable reamers.

Ki-Sol Corporation
3134 Washington Ave.
Saint Louis, Missouri 63103
Cylinder hone, ridge reamer, ring compressor, ring expander, ring groove cleaner, torque wrenches, valve spring compressor, valve refacing equipment.

K-Line Industries, Inc.
315 Garden Avenue
Holland, Michigan 49423
Cylinder hone, ridge reamer, ring compressor, valve guide tools, valve spring compressor, reamers.

Lawnmower Parts Mfg. Co., Inc.
16400 Truman Road
Independence, Missouri 64050
Crankshaft straightener.

K. O. Lee Company
Post Office Box 970
Aberdeen, South Dakota 57401
Valve refacing, valve seat grinding, valve reseating and valve guide reaming tools.

Lisle Corporation
807 East Main
Clarinda, Iowa 51632
Cylinder hones.

Little Brute Company
317 East First Street
Monticello, Iowa 52310
Crankshaft straightener, engine (crankshaft) seal puller, flywheel knocker, test flywheel for checking rotary mower engines, carburetor adjusting tools.

Mighty Midget Mfg. Co. Div. of
Kansas City Screw Thread Co.
1423 Kansas
Kansas City, Missouri 64127
Crankshaft straightener.

Neway Manufacturing, Inc.
1013 No. Shiawassee
Corunna, Michigan 48817
Valve seat cutters.

Owatonna Tool Company
436 Eisenhower Drive
Owatonna, Minnesota 55060
Valve tools, spark plug tools, piston ring tools, cylinder hones.

The Precision Manufacturing Co., Inc.
509 D Street, P.O. Box 218
Clearwater, Florida 33517
Cylinder boring equipment.

Sunnen Products Company
7910 Manchester Avenue
Saint Louis, Missouri 63143
Cylinder reconditioning hones, honing machine.

Vulcan Tools
2300 Kenmore Avenue
Buffalo, New York 14207
Cylinder hones, reamers, ridge removers, valve spring compressors, valve spring testers, ring compressor, ring groove cleaner.

Waters-Dove Manufacturing
Post Office Box 40
Skiatook, Oklahoma 74070
Crankshaft straightener, crankshaft cleaner, oil seal remover.

Test Equipment and Gages

Allen Test Products
2101 North Pitcher Street
Kalamazoo, Michigan 49007
Coil and condenser testers, compression gages.

AW Dynamometer, Inc.
131½ East Main Street
Colfax, Illinois 61728
Engine test dynamometer.

B. C. Ames Company
131 Lexington
Waltham, Massachusetts 02081
Micrometer dial gages and indicators.

The Bendix Corporation
Delaware Avenue
Sidney, New York 13838
Condenser tester, magneto test equipment, timing light.

Burco
Box 26125
Charlotte, North Carolina 28213
Coil and condenser tester, compression gage, carburetor tester.

Perry Davis Equipment
21353 Endsley Avenue
Rocky River, Ohio 44116
Flywheel magneto tester, 0-160 psi compression gage, condenser and coil tester.

Dixon, Inc.
Post Office Box 1449
Grand Junction, Colorado 81501
Tachometer, compression gage, timing light.

Fox Valley Instrument Co.
Route 5, Box 390
Cheboygan, Michigan 49721
Coil and condenser tester, ignition actuated tachometer.

Graham-Lee Electronics, Inc.
4220 Central Avenue NE
Minneapolis, Minnesota 55421
Coil and condenser tester.

K-D Manufacturing Co.
Lancaster, Pennsylvania 17604
Diode tester & installation tools, compression gage, timing light.

King Electronics Company
6892 Snowville
Brecksville, Ohio 44141
Magneto coil and condenser tester, 0-250 psi compression gage, timing light, ignition tachometer.

Ki-Sol Corporation
3134 Washington Avenue
Saint Louis, Missouri 63103
Micrometers, telescoping gages, compression gages, cylinder gages.

K-Line Industries, Inc.
315 Garden Avenue
Holland, Michigan 49423
Compression gage, tachometers.

Little Brute Company
317 East First Street
Monticello, Iowa 52310
Flywheel magneto tester, compression gage, condenser and coil tester.

Marquette Div., Applied Power, Inc.
3800 North Dunlap Street
Saint Paul, Minnesota 55112
Compression gage, condenser tester, tachometer, timing light and ignition analyzer.

Merc-O-Tronic Instruments Corporation
215 Branch Street
Almont, Michigan 48003
Electronic tachometer, magneto ignition analyzer, power timing light, combination (tune-up) tester.

C. E. Niehoff & Company
4925 Lawrence Avenue
Chicago, Illinois 60630
Ignition test equipment.

Owatonna Tool Company
436 Eisenhower Drive
Owatonna, Minnesota 55060
Feeler gages, hydraulic test gages.

Peerless Instrument Company
6101 Gross Point Road
Chicago, Illinois 60648
Timing lights, tachometers, gages, compression testers.

Simpson Electric Company
853 Dundee Avenue
Elgin, Illinois 60120
Electronic test equipment, coil and condenser tester.

Proto Tool Div., Ingersoll-Rand
2600 East Nutwood Avenue
Fullerton, California 92613
Engine tune-up equipment

L. S. Starrett Company
1-165 Crescent Street
Athol, Massachusetts 01331
Micrometers, dial gages

Stevens Company, Inc.
Post Office Box 193
Waukegan, Illinois 60085
Ignition analyzers, timing lights, tachometers, volt-ohmmeters, spark checkers, CD ignition testers.

Stewart-Warner Corporation
1826 Diversey Parkway
Chicago, Illinois 60614
Compression gage, ignition tachometer, timing light ignition analyzer.

P. A. Sturtevant Co., Div. Dresser Ind.
3201 North Wolf Road
Franklin Park, Illinois 60131
Torque wrenches.

Sun Electric Corporation
3011 East Route 176
Crystal Lake, Illinois 60014
Compression gage, hydraulic test gages, coil and condenser tester, ignition tachometer, ignition analyzer.

Weidenhoff Corp., Subs. Snap-On Tools Corp.
Post Office Box 220
Algona, Iowa 50511
Coil and condenser testers.

Westberg Manufacturing Company
3400 Westach Way
Sonoma, California 95476
Ignition tachometer, magneto test equipment, ignition system analyzer.

Wico Div., Prestolite Company
Post Office Box 931
Toledo, Ohio 43694
Ignition coil analyzer.

Shop Tools and Equipment

A-C Delco Div., General Motors Corp.
3044 West Grand Boulevard
Detroit, Michigan 48202
Spark plug cleaning and test equipment.

Air Electric Machine Co., Inc.
Post Office Box 215
Lohrville, Iowa 51453
Universal engine positioner (repair stand)

Black & Decker Mfg. Co.
701 East Joppa Road
Towson, Maryland 21204
Air and electric powered tools

Bloom, Inc.
Route 4, Hiway 20 West
Independence, Iowa 50644
Lawn mower repair bench with built-in engine cranking mechanism.

Campbell Chain Company
Post Office Box 1667
York, Pennsylvania 17405
Chain type engine and utility slings.

Champion Pneumatic Machinery Co.
825 North Pleasant Street
Princeton, Illinois 61356
Air compressors.

Champion Spark Plug Co.
Post Office Box 910
Toledo, Ohio 43661
Spark plug cleaning and testing equipment, gap tools and wrenches.

Chicago Pneumatic Tool Co.
Oneida County Airport
Utica, New York 13503
Air compressors, air and electric impact wrenches, air hammers, air drills and grinders, jacks.

Clayton Manufacturing Company
415 North Temple City Boulevard
El Monte, California 91731
Steam cleaning equipment.

Coastal Abrasive and Tool Co.
Trumbull Industrial Park
Trumbull, Connecticut 06611
Power tool accessories.

Comet Industries
25 Washington Avenue
Richmond, Indiana 47374
Lightweight 1-ton hoist.

G & H Products, Inc.
Post Office Box 770
St. Paris, Ohio 43072
Motorized lawnmower stand.

General Scientific Equipment Company
Limekiln Pike & Williams Ave.
Box 3038
Philadelphia, Pennsylvania 19150
Safety equipment.

Goodall Div. of Bunton Company
1405 Bunton Road
Louisville, Kentucky 40258
Floor-mounted lift-workstand for mowers.

Graymills Corporation
3705 North Lincoln Avenue
Chicago, Illinois 60613
Parts washing stand.

Heli-Coil Products Div., Heli-Coil Corp.
Shelter Rock Lane
Danbury, Connecticut 06810
Thread repair kits, thread inserts and installation tools.

Ingersoll-Rand
200 Chestnut Ridge Road
Woodcliff Lake, New Jersey 07675
Air and electric impact wrenches, electric drills and screwdrivers.

Jaw Manufacturing Co.
39 Mulberry Street, P.O. Box 213
Reading, Pennsylvania 19603
Files for renewal of damaged threads, hex nut size rethreader dies, flexible shaft drivers and extensions, screw extractors, impact drivers.

Jenny Div. of Homestead Ind., Inc.
11 Johnson Street
Coraopolis, Pennsylvania 15108
Steam cleaning equipment

Keystone Reamer & Tool Co.
Post Office Box 310
Millersburg, Pennsylvania 17061
Adjustable reamers, twist drills, taps, dies, etc.

K-Line Industries, Inc.
315 Garden Avenue
Holland, Michigan 49423
Air and electric impact wrenches

Marquette Div., Applied Power, Inc.
3800 North Dunlap Street
Saint Paul, Minnesota 55112
Arc and gas welding equipment, welding rods, accessories, battery service equipment.

Millers Falls Company
57 Wells Street
Greenfield, Massachusetts 01301
Impact wrenches, portable electric tools.

Owatonna Tool Company
436 Eisenhower Drive
Owatonna, Minnesota 55060
Bearing and gear pullers, hydraulic shop presses.

Proto Tool Div. Ingersoll-Rand
2600 East Nutwood Avenue
Fullerton, California 92613
Torque wrenches, precision measuring tools, portable air and electric wrenches.

Shure Manufacturing Corp.
1601 South Hanley Road
Saint Louis, Missouri 63144
Steel shop benches, desks, engine overhaul stand.

Sioux Tools, Inc.
2801-2999 Floyd Blvd.
Sioux City, Iowa 51102
Portable air and electric tools.

Skil Corporation
5033 Elston Avenue
Chicago, Illinois 60630
Air and electric impact wrenches.

Vulcan Tools
2300 Kenmore Avenue
Buffalo, New York 14207
Air and electric impact wrenches.

Sharpening and Maintenance Equipment for Small Engine Powered Implements

Bell Industries, Saw & Machine Div.
Post Office Box 2510
Eugene, Oregon 97402
Saw chain grinder.

Belsaw Machinery Co.
315 Westport Road
Kansas City, Missouri 64111
Handsaw filer, circular saw grinder, reel mower sharpener, chain saw sharpener, blade balancer.

Desa Industries, Inc.
25000 South Western Ave.
Park Forest, Illinois 60466
Saw chain breakers and rivet spinners, chain files, file holder and filing guide.

Foley Manufacturing Co.
3300 Fifth Street NE
Minneapolis, Minnesota 55418
Circular, band and hand saw filers, heavy duty grinders, saw setters, retoothers, circular saw vises, lawn mower sharpener.

Granberg Industries
201 Nevin Ave., Box 1549
Richmond, California 94801
Saw chain grinder, file guides, chain breakers and rivet spinners, chain saw lumber cutting attachments.

Ki-Sol Corporation
3134 Washington Avenue
Saint Louis, Missouri 63103
Mower blade balancer.

Magna-Matic Division, A. J. Karrels Co.
Port Washington, Wisconsin 53074
Rotary mower blade balancer, "track" checking tool.

Omark Industries, Inc.
9701 SE McLoughlin Blvd.
Portland, Oregon 97222
Saw chain and saw bar maintenance equipment, to include file holders, filing vises, rivet spinners, chain breakers, filing depth gages, bar groove gages, grinding wheels and dressing bricks.

S.I.P. Grinding Machine Company
722 Porter
Lansing, Michigan 48905
Lawn mower sharpeners, saw chain grinders, lapping machine, ice skate sharpener, hand saw grinder.

Smith's Implements & Parts
419 Main Street
Carthage, Illinois 62321
Rotary mower blade balancer.

Specialty Motors
Post Office Box 171
Longview, Washington 98632
Chain saw bar rebuilding equipment

Mechanic's Hand Tools

Channellock, Inc.
South Main Street
Meadville, Pennsylvania 16335

Dresser Industries
Post Office Box 407
Defiance, Ohio 43512

John H. Graham & Company, Inc.
617 Oradell Avenue
Oradell, New Jersey 07649

Jaw Manufacturing Company
39 Mulberry Street
Reading, Pennsylvania 19603

K-D Manufacturing Company
Lancaster,
Pennsylvania 17604

K-Line Industries, Inc.
315 Garden Avenue
Holland, Michigan 49423

Millers Falls Company
57 Wells Street
Greenfield, Massachusetts 01301

The New Britain Machine Company
Hand Tools Division
492 Cedar Street
Newington, Connecticut 06111

Owatonna Tool Company
436 Eisenhower Drive
Owatonna, Minnesota 55060

Proto Tool Div., Ingersoll-Rand
2600 East Nutwood Avenue
Fullerton, California 92613

Snap-On Tools
2801 80th Street
Kenosha, Wisconsin 53140

Triangle Corporation - Tool Division
Cameron Road
Orangeburg, South Carolina 29115

Vulcan Tools
2300 Kenmore Avenue
Buffalo, New York 14207

J. H. Williams Div. of TRW, Inc.
400 Vulcan Street
Buffalo, New York 14207

Shop Supplies (Chemicals, Metallurgy Products, Seals, Sealers, Common Parts Items, etc.)

Amsco Div. of ABEX Corp.
Chicago Heights, Illinois 60411
Hardfacing alloys.

Atlas Tool & Manufacturing Co.
5151 Natural Bridge Road
Saint Louis, Missouri 63115
Rotary mower blades

Bendix Automotive Aftermarket
1094 Bendix Drive
Jackson, Tennessee 38301
Cleaning chemicals.

CR Industries
900 North State Street
Elgin, Illinois 60120
Shaft & bearing seals.

Clayton Manufacturing Company
415 North Temple City Blvd.
El Monte, California 91731
Steam cleaning compounds and solvents

Eutectic Welding Alloys Corp.
40-40 172nd Street
Flushing, New York 11358
Low temperature welding alloys and processes.

The Federal Process Company
704 Citizens Building
Cleveland, Ohio 44114
Varnish type and heavy duty sealers (Gasolia).

Frederick Manufacturing Co., Inc.
1400 C Agnes Street
Kansas City, Missouri 64127
Throttle controls and parts.

Gunk Laboratories, Inc.
1001 South Harlem Ave.
Forest Park, Illinois 60130
Cleaning chemicals.

Heli-Coil Products Division
Heli-Coil Corporation
Shelter Rock Lane
Danbury, Connecticut 06810
Thread repair kits, thread inserts and installation tools.

Hans Johnsen Company
8901 Chancellor Row
Dallas, Texas 75247
Mower and small engine parts.

King Cotton Cordage
Oradell, New Jersey 07649
Starter rope, nylon cord.

Loctite Corporation
705 North Mountain Road
Newington, Connecticut 06111
Thread locking compounds, bearing mounting compounds, retaining compounds and sealants.

McCord Corporation
2850 West Grand Boulevard
Detroit, Michigan 48202
Gaskets, seals.

Morgal Machine Tool Company
Stamped Sprocket Division
2100 South Yellow Springs Road
Springfield, Ohio 45501
Gears, sprockets.

Permatex Company, Inc.
Post Office Box 1350
West Palm Beach, Florida 33402
Cleaning chemicals, gasket sealers

Union Carbide Corporation
Consumer Products Division
270 Park Avenue
New York, New York 10017
Cleaning chemicals, engine starting fluid.

Whirltronics, Inc.
900 East Hennepin Avenue
Minneapolis, Minnesota 55414
Rotary mower blades.

BRIGGS & STRATTON

BRIGGS & STRATTON CORPORATION
Milwaukee, Wisconsin 53201

Basic Model	Bore	Stroke	Displacement
5	2	1½	4.71
6 & N	2	2	6.28
8	2¼	2	7.95
9	2¼	2¼	8.95
14	2⅜	2⅜	14.21

All Briggs & Stratton engines covered in this section are of cast iron construction.

MAINTENANCE

SPARK PLUG. Recommended spark plug for all models is a Champion J-8, Autolite A-71 or an AC GC46. Set electrode gap to 0.030 for all models. Note: If a resistor type plug is necessary to reduce radio interference, use Champion XJ-8 or equivalent. Briggs & Stratton Corporation does not recommend cleaning spark plugs by abrasive blasting method as this may introduce some abrasive material into the engine which could cause extensive damage.

CARBURETOR AND FUEL SYSTEM. Unless the model designation is followed by the suffix "S", the engine is equipped with a float type carburetor shown in Fig. B1. Engines with model designation followed by the suffix "S" are equipped with suction type carburetors shown in Fig. B2.

FLOAT TYPE CARBURETORS. Float type carburetors are equipped with adjusting needles for both idle and power fuel mixtures. Counter-clockwise rotation of the adjusting needles richens the fuel mixtures as shown in Fig. B3. Initial adjustment of the carburetor is ¾-turn open on the idle needle valve and 1½ turns open on the power needle valve. This will allow the engine to start and run, but final adjustment should be made with the engine running and hot. Run the engine under full load at operating speed and turn the power needle valve counter-clockwise until the engine begins to run unevenly. Then turn the power needle valve clockwise slowly until the engine runs smoothly. Return the engine to idle speed and adjust the idle speed screw on the throttle shaft so that the engine is running at 1200 rpm on models 9 and 14 engines and at 1750 rpm on all other models. Then, adjust the idle needle valve until the engine runs smoothly. Check the idle speed again after adjusting the idle needle valve and reset the speed adjusting screw if necessary.

After making the above adjustments, the engine should accelerate to full speed from idle position without sputtering or hesitation. If it does not accelerate properly, turn the power needle valve slightly counter-clockwise to provide a richer fuel mixture.

Correct float settings are shown in Fig. B4. Bend the float tang that contacts float valve to bring the float setting within the specifications shown.

The throttle shaft and bushings should be checked for wear, and if a diametral clearance of 0.010 or more can be found, installation of a new shaft and/or bushings is required. On carburetors not having bushings on the throttle shaft, the upper body must be renewed if installation of a new shaft does not reduce the clearance to under 0.010. Check the upper body for being warped with a 0.002 feeler gage. If the gage can be inserted between the upper and lower bodies as shown in Fig. B5, a new upper body should be installed. Install new inlet float valve and seat if any wear is visible.

CAUTION: The upper and lower bodies of float type carburetors are locked together by the main nozzle. Be sure to remove the power needle valve and main nozzle before attempting to separate the upper body from the lower body. (See Fig. B6)

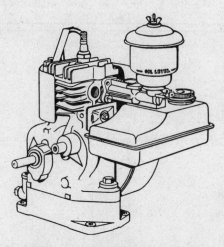

Fig. B2–Typical suction carburetor installation on B&S engine. Fuel is drawn by vacuum from fuel tank.

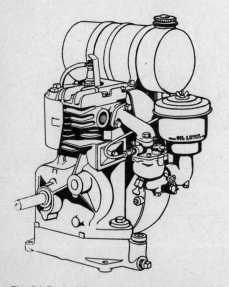

Fig. B1–Typical float carburetor installation on B&S engine. Fuel feed to carburetor may be either by gravity as shown or by fuel pump.

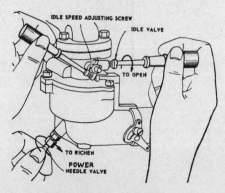

Fig. B3–Adjustment of fuel mixtures and idle speed on float type carburetor.

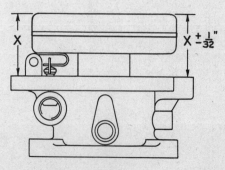

Fig. B4–Checking float setting on float type carburetor.

SUCTION TYPE CARBURETORS. Suction type carburetors (See Fig. B7) are much simpler than the float type and have only one fuel mixture adjusting needle. Turning the needle clockwise leans the fuel mixture. Initial adjustment is 1½ turns open. Final adjustment should be made with the engine warm and running, and with the fuel tank about ½ full. Run the engine at operating speed with no load and turn the needle valve clockwise until the engine starts to lose speed. Then turn the needle valve counterclockwise slowly until the engine begins to run unevenly. This should result in a fuel mixture rich enough for full load operation. If the engine does not pull its load satisfactorily, it may help to turn the needle valve counterclockwise a slight amount, but this richer mixture may cause the engine to idle unevenly. Adjust the idle speed screw until the engine idles at 1750 rpm.

FUEL TANK OUTLET. Figs. B8 and B9 illustrate two typical fuel tank outlets for engines with float type carburetors. The tank outlet shown in Fig. B8 is used on smaller engines and the fuel screen is within the fuel tank. The tank outlet shown in Fig. B9 is used on larger engines and incorporates a sediment bowl; the fuel screen is located in the bowl. Any dirt or lint should be brushed from the screen and the glass bowl cleaned. Varnish or other deposits may be removed with a suitable solvent. If the shut-off valve leaks, tighten the packing nut. If this does not stop the leak, remove the packing nut and install new packing.

The fuel tank outlet used with earlier suction type carburetors is shown in Fig. B10. Sectional views in this figure show two different types of check valves used in the fuel tank outlet. On later type suction carburetors, the fuel tank is mounted directly under the carburetor and the fuel tank outlet is a part of the carburetor. It is essential that the check valves operate to allow fuel to flow to the carburetor, but prevent fuel from returning to the tank. The valve should open when air is blown through the screen end of the outlet, and close tightly when air is blown through the connection end. If the check valve does not operate properly, it may be cleaned in a solvent. If cleaning does not allow the valve to operate properly, install a new fuel tank outlet. Refer to Fig. B11 for method of removing and installing a fuel tank outlet on models where it is a part of the carburetor.

FUEL PUMP. The fuel pump that is used on some engines is actuated by a lever which rides in a groove on the crankshaft. The lever should be greased at the point shown in Fig. B12 before the fuel pump is installed. The fuel pump diaphragm can be renewed. Refer to FUEL PUMP paragraph in SERVICING BRIGGS & STRATTON ACCESSORIES section for fuel pump service information.

AUTOMATIC CHOKE. Exploded view of automatic choke is shown in Fig. B13. To adjust the automatic choke unit, refer to Fig. B14 and B15, and proceed as follows: Loosen set screw (S) on the lever of the thermostat assembly and slide the lever on the

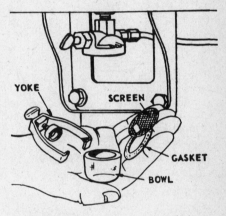

Fig. B9–Fuel tank outlet used on larger models of B&S engines with float type carburetors.

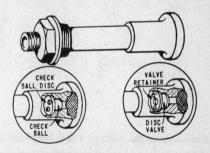

Fig. B10–Fuel tank outlet used with suction type carburetors on B&S engines. Sectional views show two different types of check valves used in this type outlet. (Outlet may be part of carburetor as in Fig. B11)

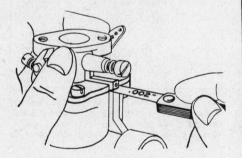

Fig. B5–Checking upper body for warpage on float type carburetor.

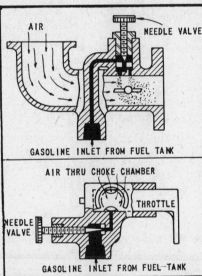

Fig. B7–Cross section views of two typical B&S suction type carburetors. Idle speed adjusting screw on throttle shaft not shown in these views.

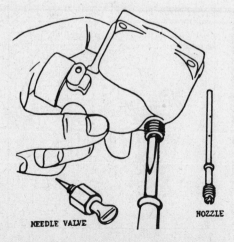

Fig. B6–Remove main nozzle before separating upper and lower bodies of float type carburetor.

Fig. B8–Fuel tank outlet used on smaller B&S engines that are equipped with float type carburetors.

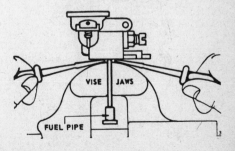

Fig. B11–Removing check valve and fuel pipe assembly from carburetor on models so constructed.

shaft to insure free movement of the choke unit. Turn the thermostat shaft clockwise until the stop screw strikes the tube as shown in Fig. B14. While holding the thermostat shaft in this position, move the shaft lever until the choke is open exactly ⅛-inch and tighten the lever set screw. Turn the thermostat shaft counter-clockwise until the stop screw strikes the tube as

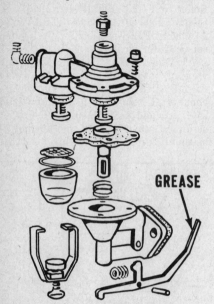

Fig. B12—Exploded view of fuel pump used on some models.

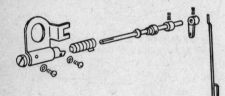

Fig. B13—Exploded view of automatic choke unit that is used on some models.

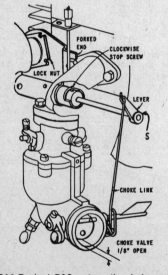

Fig. B14—Typical B&S automatic choke unit in "Hot" position.

shown in Fig. B15. Manually open the choke valve until it stops against the choke link opening. At this time, the choke valve should be open at least 3/32, but not more than 5/32-inch. Hold choke valve in horizontal position (wide-open) and check position of the counterweight lever. Lever should also be in a horizontal position with free end toward right.

GOVERNORS. Governors may be either the gear driven mechanical type, with linkage as shown in Figs. B22 through B26 or the air vane type with linkage as shown in Figs. B16 through B21 and Fig. B27. All slack due to wear must be removed from governor linkage to prevent "hunting" of the throttle.

Three types of remote control of engine speed are used on these engines: (A) remote throttle control whereby only the top speed of the engine is controlled by the governor, the intermediate speeds being controlled by the remote throttle lever; (B) remote gov-

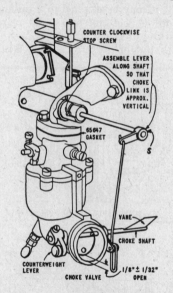

Fig. B15—Typical B&S automatic choke unit in "Cold" position.

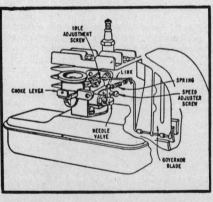

Fig. B16—Model 5S and 6S suction type carburetor. Model 6HS is similar. Air vane governor hook-up shown. Turn the speed adjuster screw clockwise to increase engine speed.

ernor control whereby the governed speed is adjusted by movement of a remote control lever to provide (within the range of the governor) the effect of a variable speed governor; or (C) remote idle control, whereby the engine may be slowed to idle speed by movement of the remote control lever.

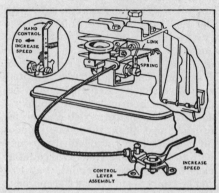

Fig. B17—Same as Fig. B16 except remote governor control is shown. Speed on some engines is changed by moving hand control lever. (See inset)

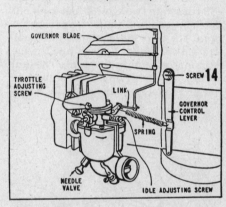

Fig. B18—B&S models 6H (except 6HS) and 8H pneumatic (air-vane) governor, showing hookup and clamp screw (14). To increase speed, loosen screw (14) and move control lever to right.

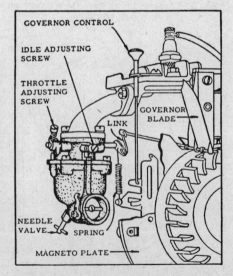

Fig. B19—B&S model 5 pneumatic governor linkage and governor control. To increase speed, pull up on governor control.

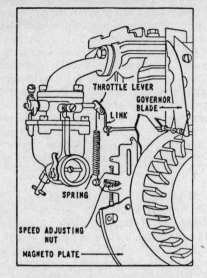

Fig. B20–B&S models N (except NS) and 8 (except 8H) pneumatic governor linkage and speed adjusting nut. To increase speed, turn speed adjusting nut down.

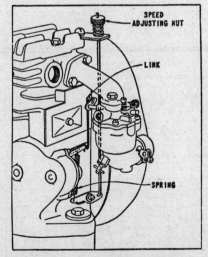

Fig. B21–Models N (except NS) and 8 (except 8H) pneumatic governor hook-up with remote control. Speed is changed by moving the remote lever as shown.

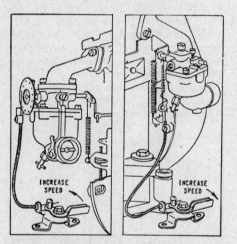

Fig. B22–B&S models N (except NS) and 8 (except 8H) mechanical governor linkage, showing points of adjustment. To increase speed, turn adjusting nut down.

SPEED ADJUSTMENT. On air vane governors with fixed speed control as shown in Fig. B20, the speed adjusting nut should be turned down to increase the governed engine speed. On installation shown in Fig. B16, used with suction type carburetors, turn the speed adjusting screw clockwise to increase engine speed. On installations as shown in Fig. B18, loosen screw (14) on the blower housing, then move the governor control lever to the right to increase the engine speed. On installations shown in Fig. B27, turn speed adjusting screw down or move remote control lever to increase the engine speed.

On installation shown in Fig. B22, turn the speed adjusting nut down to increase engine speed. The governor spring on these installations should be installed in the hole in the governor lever where the speed variation between load and no load is smallest without producing hunting or unsteady running. Moving the springs closer to the governor shaft lowers no load speed, but tends to produce hunting; moving it away from the shaft increases the no load speed, but tends to

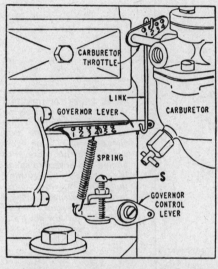

Fig. B23–B&S models N (except NS) and 8 (except 8H) with mechanical governor showing hook-up and speed adjusting screw (S). To increase speed, loosen locknut and turn screw (S) down.

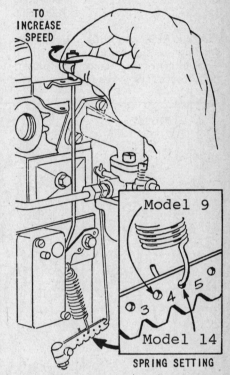

Fig. B24–On models 9 and 14, connect governor spring as shown in insert. To increase speed on standard governor control, turn thumb nut as shown.

Fig. B25–Views showing methods of connecting different remote governor controls on models 9 and 14. Moving the control lever will vary the governor spring tension, thus varying engine governed speeds. Refer also to Fig. B26.

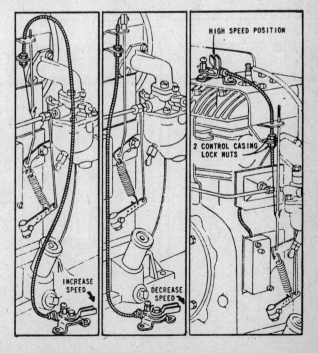

reduce hunting. On installations shown in Fig. B25, turn the governor adjusting nut clockwise to increase engine speed.

Briggs & Stratton recommended operating speed ranges are as follows:

MODELS	ENGINE RPM*
5S, 6S, 6HFB & 6HS	2200-3200
Other 5 & 6 models	2600-3600
8 & N	2600-3600
9	1800-3600
14	1800-3600

*Engine RPM may differ slightly depending on the equipment in which B&S engines are used. Equipment manufacturers recommendations should be followed in all cases.

VANE CLEARANCE. On air vane governors, make sure the air vane clears the magneto armature core and screws when the linkage is moved through its full range of travel. It can be made to clear by bending the bracket as shown in Fig. B28, or by filing the vane slightly.

LINKAGE. On mechanical type governors, if the carburetor to governor linkage has been disturbed, it should be reset by first loosening the nut or bolt which clamps the governor lever to the governor shaft. After moving carburetor throttle to wide open position and turning governor shaft so that governor weights are in (as far clockwise as the shaft will turn), then tighten the governor lever clamp bolt or nut.

On early N model engines, obtain the ¼-inch distance from top of carburetor throttle lever (See Fig. B29) to bottom of throttle spring hole by bending the lever tang. Solder the neck of tang if it cracks in bending. The loop at the lower end of the throttle spring on these engines should not be spread. Refer to right and wrong views in Fig. B29.

MAGNETO. Two different types of magnetos are used on this series of Briggs & Stratton engines. Refer to appropriate following paragraph heading listing engine model or series number for service information on a particular engine.

MODELS N, 5, 6 & 8 MAGNETO. The magneto breaker mechanism is located in back of, and is enclosed by, the flywheel. Breaker gap on all models is 0.020 and condenser capacity for all models is 0.18-0.24 mfd. The timing on these engines is fixed and non-adjustable.

To renew the breaker points and condenser, first remove flywheel, then disconnect and remove breaker points

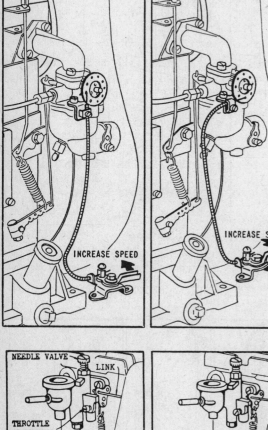

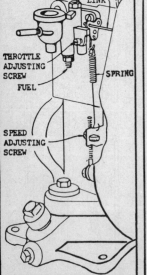

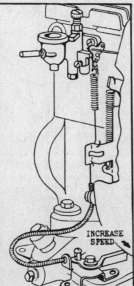

Fig. B26–Views showing methods of connecting remote throttle controls on models 9 and 14. When control lever is in high speed position, the governor controls speed of engine and governed speed is adjusted by turning thumb nut. Moving control lever to slow speed position moves carburetor throttle shaft stop to slow down the engine.

Fig. B27–B&S model NS pneumatic governor hook-up. Speed is increased by turning the speed adjusting screw down or moving the remote control lever as shown.

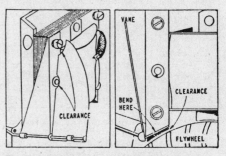

Fig. B28–B&S air vane governor adjustment.

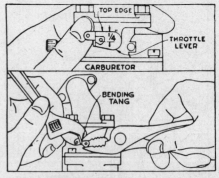

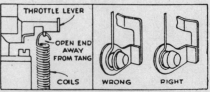

Fig. B29–Checking throttle spring and tang on early B&S model N engines.

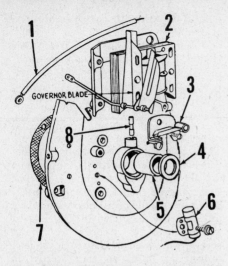

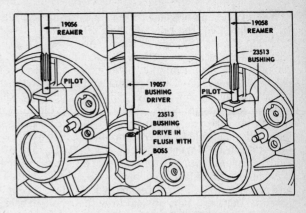

Fig. B33—Views showing reaming plunger bore to accept bushing (left view), installing bushing (center view) and finish reaming bore in bushing (right view).

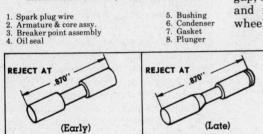

Fig. B30—Magneto back plate used on models N, 5, 6 and 8 engines. Gasket (7) is available in thicknesses of 0.005, 0.009 and 0.015.

1. Spark plug wire
2. Armature & core assy.
3. Breaker point assembly
4. Oil seal
5. Bushing
6. Condenser
7. Gasket
8. Plunger

REJECT AT .870"

(Early)

REJECT AT .870"

(Late)

Fig. B31—Early and late type breaker point plungers used on models N, 5, 6, and 8 engines. Refer to text.

stall flywheel and tighten nut to a torque of 57 ft.-lbs.

Check air gap between armature legs and magnets on flywheel. Air gap should be 0.012-0.016. To adjust the air gap, loosen armature mounting screws and move armature away from flywheel. Place feeler gages or correct thickness shim stock between armature legs and magnets on flywheel. Hold armature tight against feeler gages or shim stock, then tighten mounting screws.

MODELS 9 and 14 MAGNETO. Refer to exploded view in Fig. B34 for typical magneto used on these models. Breaker points and condenser are mounted externally in a breaker box located on carburetor side of engine and are accessible after removing breaker box cover (18). Adjust breaker point gap to 0.020. Condenser capacity is 0.18-0.24 mfd.

and condenser. Before installing breaker points, remove breaker plunger (8—Fig. B30) and check plunger and plunger bore for excessive wear. Refer to Fig. B31 and renew breaker plunger if worn to a length of 0.870 or less. Check plunger bore with B&S plug gage #19055 as shown in Fig. B32. If plug gage will enter bore ¼-inch or more, bore should be reamed and a bushing installed. Refer to Fig. B33 for steps in reaming bore and installing bushing. Early plunger (Fig. B31) can be installed either end up. Late type plunger must be installed with groove end at top.

Install new breaker points and condenser. Rotate crankshaft until plunger is in fully out position, then adjust breaker point gap to 0.020. In-

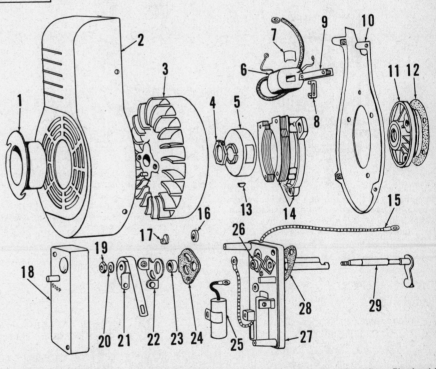

Fig. B34—Exploded view of magneto ignition system used on models 9 and 14 engines. Flywheel is not keyed to crankshaft and may be installed in any position; however, on crank start models, flywheel should be installed as shown in Fig. B42. Breaker arm (21) is mounted on shaft (29) which is actuated by cam on engine cam gear; see Fig. B43. Two different methods of attaching magneto rotor (5) to engine crankshaft have been used; refer to Figs. B38 and B39.

1. Starter pulley
2. Blower housing
3. Flywheel
4. Rotor clamp
5. Magneto rotor
6. Coil clip
7. Ignition coil
8. Core retainer
9. Coil core
10. Back plate
11. Bearing support
12. Shim gasket
13. Rotor key
14. Armature
15. Primary coil lead
16. Shaft seal
17. Eccentric
18. Breaker box cover
19. Nut
20. Washer
21. Breaker point arm
22. Breaker point base
23. Pivot
24. Insulator
25. Condenser
26. Seal retainer
27. Breaker box
28. Gasket
29. Shaft

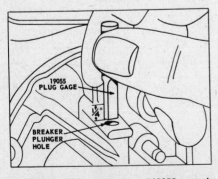

Fig. B32—If B&S plug gage #19055 can be inserted in breaker plunger bore a distance of ¼-inch or more, bore is worn and must be rebushed.

Briggs & Stratton

When renewing breaker points, or if oil leak is noted, the breaker shaft oil seal (16) should be renewed. To renew points and/or seal, proceed as follows: Turn engine so that breaker point gap is at maximum. Remove terminal and breaker spring screws and loosen breaker arm retaining nut (19) so that it is flush with end of shaft (29). Tap loosened nut lightly to free breaker arm (21) from taper on shaft, then remove breaker arm, breaker plate (22), pivot (23), insulating plate (24), and eccentric (17). Pry oil seal out with ice pick and press new oil seal in with metal side out. Place breaker plate on insulating plate with dowel on breaker plate entering hole in insulator, then install unit with edges of plates parallel with breaker box as shown in Fig. B35. Turn breaker shaft clockwise as far as possible and install breaker arm while holding shaft in this position. Adjust breaker point gap to 0.020.

Breaker box can be removed without removing points or condenser. Refer to Fig. B36. Disassembly of unit is evident after removal from engine.

To renew ignition coil, the engine flywheel must be removed. Disconnect coil ground and primary wires and pull spark plug wire from hole in back plate. Disengage clips (8—Fig. B34) retaining coil core (9) to armature (14), then push core from coil. Insert core in new coil with rounded side of core towards spark plug wire. On model 9 engines, shorten spark plug wire by tying knot a distance (D) of 1½ inches from coil as shown in Fig. B37. Place coil and core on armature with retainer (7—Fig. B34) between coil and armature. Reinstall core retaining clips, connect coil ground and primary wires and insert spark plug wire through hole in back plate.

Two types of magnetic rotors have been used; refer to Fig. B38 for view of rotor retained by set screw and to Fig. B39 for rotor retained by clamp ring. If rotor is as shown in Fig. B39, refer to

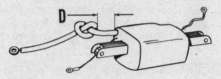

Fig. B37–When installing new ignition coil on model 9 engine, tie a knot a distance (D) of 1½ inches from coil to shorten spark plug wire.

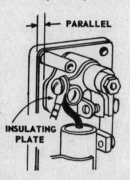

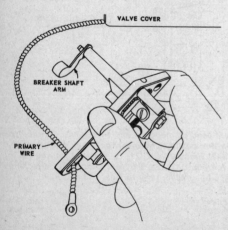

Fig. B35–When installing new breaker points on models 9 and 14 engines, be sure dowel on breaker point base enters hole in insulator and place sides of base and insulating plate parallel with edge of breaker box.

Fig. B36–Removing the breaker box on models 9 and 14 engines. It is not necessary to remove points and condenser as the unit can be removed as an assembly.

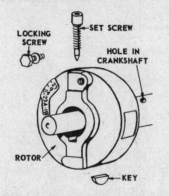

Fig. B38–On some models, magneto rotor is fastened to crankshaft by set screw which enters hole in shaft; set screw is locked in place by a second screw. Refer to Fig. B39 for alternate method of fastening rotor to crankshaft.

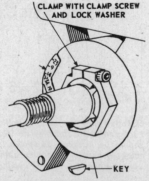

Fig. B39–View showing magneto rotor fastened to crankshaft with clamp; be sure split in clamp is between two slots in rotor as shown and check clearance between rotor and shoulder on crankshaft as shown in Fig. B40. Refer to Fig. B38 for alternate method of fastening rotor to crankshaft.

Fig. B40 when installing rotor on crankshaft.

If armature core has been loosened or removed, rotor timing must be readjusted as follows: With point gap adjusted to 0.020, connect a static timing light from breaker point terminal to ground (coil primary wire must be disconnected) and turn engine in normal direction of rotation until light goes on. Then, turn engine very slowly in same direction until light just goes out (breaker points start to open). At that time, engine model number on magneto rotor should be aligned with arrow on armature as shown in Fig. B41; if not, loosen armature core retaining cap screws and turn armature in slotted mounting holes so that arrow is aligned with appropriate engine model number on rotor. Tighten the armature mounting screws.

When installing flywheel on models with crank starter, place flywheel on crankshaft as shown in Fig. B42 with magneto timing marks aligned as in previous paragraph. On models not having a crank starter, flywheel may be installed in any position.

Magneto breaker points are actuated by a cam on a centrifugal weight mounted on engine camshaft; refer to Fig. B43. When engine is being overhauled, or cam gear is removed, check action of the advance spring and centri-

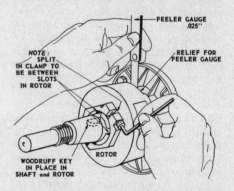

Fig. B40–On models having magneto rotor clamped to crankshaft, position rotor 0.025 from shoulder on shaft and split in clamp between slots of rotor, then tighten clamping screw.

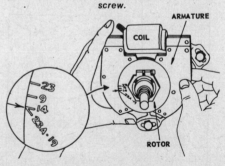

Fig. B41–With engine turned so that points are just starting to open, align model number line on rotor with arrow on armature by rotating armature in slotted mounting holes.

fugal weight unit by holding cam gear in position shown and pressing weight down. When weight is released, spring should return weight to its original position. If weight does not return to its original position, check weight for binding and renew the spring.

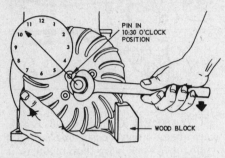

Fig. B42–On models 9 and 14 with crank starter, mount flywheel with pin in position shown and with armature timing marks aligned as shown in Fig. B41.

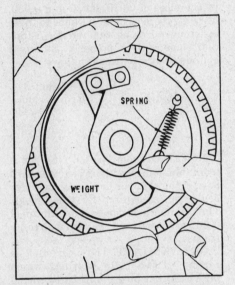

Fig. B43–Checking timing advance weight and spring on models 9 and 14. Refer to text.

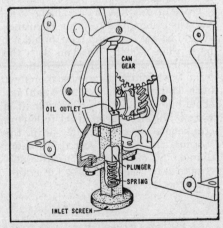

Fig. B44–View showing one type of oil pump used on some horizontal crankshaft models. Pump plunger is actuated by camshaft and oil sprays from outlet in plunger to lubricate engine. A second type of plunger type pump is similar, but oil is delivered via a tube connected to pump.

LUBRICATION. Model N engines from Serial No. 205000 to 205499 are lubricated by an ejector type pump (Fig. B44) wherein the pump squirts oil onto the internal moving parts. A similar system using a gear type pump is used on model N engines Serial No. 205500 to 205999 and all horizontal cylinder engines. Refer to Fig. B45. All other engines are lubricated by a plain splash system.

Use oil marked for "Service MS." For temperatures above 40° F., use SAE 30 or 10W-30 oil; for temperatures below 40°, use SAE 10 or 5W-20 oil. Fill crankcase to top of filler cap opening on vertical cylinder engines and to the "F" mark on sump dip stick for horizontal cylinder engines.

OIL RETURN VALVE. Some engines are equipped with an oil return valve located under the magneto end main bearing. See Fig. B53. If engine

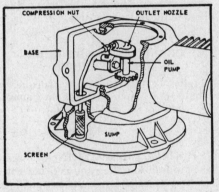

Fig. B45–Oil pump installation on horizontal cylinder engines.

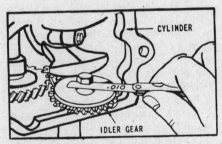

Fig. B46–Idler gear installation on models 6AH, 8AH and 6AHS. The idler gear should have .010 end play on the shoulder screw when cold.

Fig. B47–Old style (cast-in) type oil return valve in B&S engines should be milled off and the new removable type installed.

leaks oil at the main bearing, remove and clean or install a new oil return valve. Early production engines were equipped with a cast-in type of oil return valve and late production engines have a removable oil return valve. When overhauling early production engines, mill off the cast-in type and install the removable type. See Fig. B47.

CRANKCASE BREATHER. Outside type breathers should be cleaned and the filter element renewed. Some breathers are located inside the engine in the valve spring compartment as shown in Fig. B48. Disassemble, clean, and reassemble the parts in sequence shown.

REPAIRS

CYLINDER HEAD. When removing cylinder head, note position from which different length cap screws were removed. If they are not used in same position when installing head, it will result in some screws bottoming in holes and not enough thread engagement on others. When installing cylinder head, tighten all screws lightly and then retighten them in sequence shown in Fig. B49 or B50 to the fol-

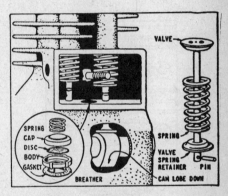

Fig. B48–Some B&S engines have internal breathers as shown. Insert shows assembly sequence.

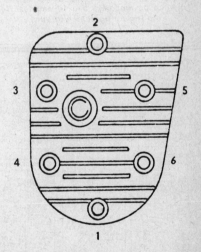

Fig. B49–Cylinder head cap screw tightening sequence on models N, 5, 6 and 8 engines. Refer to text for tightening torque.

lowing torques: 140 in.-lbs. on model 9, 165 in.-lbs. on model 14 and 140 in.-lbs. on all other models.

Start engine and allow it to run for five minutes or until warm; then, retighten cap screws using same sequence and torque values as before.

CONNECTING ROD. Rod and piston assembly is removed from cylinder head end of block. The aluminum alloy connecting rod rides directly on the induction hardened crankpin. Connecting rod should be rejected if crankpin hole is out-of-round 0.0007 or more, if piston pin hole is out-of-round 0.0005 or more or if worn to reject size.

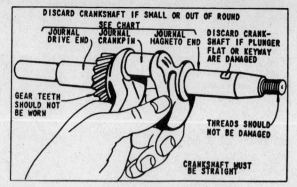

Fig. B52–Check points to determine if crankshaft should be reused or rejected.

REJECT SIZES FOR CONNECTING ROD

Basic Model	Crankpin Hole	Piston Pin Hole
5	0.7523	0.492
N, 6 & 8	0.751	0.49125
9	0.876	0.5633
14	1.0007	0.6735

NOTE: If rod is otherwise serviceable except for piston pin hole, rod and piston can be reamed and a 0.005 oversize piston pin installed.

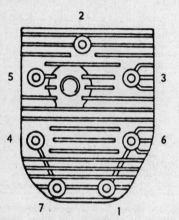

Fig. B50–Cylinder head cap screw tightening sequence on models 9 and 14 engines. Refer to text for tightening torques.

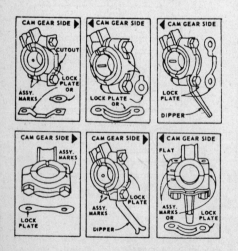

Fig. B51–B&S rod position is determined by clearance flats or assembly marks as shown.

Recommended clearance of rod to crankpin is 0.0015-0.0045 and recommended rod to piston pin clearance is 0.0005-0.0015.

Rod position in the crankcase is determined by the clearance flat, or assembly marks. See Fig. B51. Tighten connecting rod bolts to the torque specified in the following table.

CONNECTING ROD TORQUE SPECIFICATIONS

Engine Model	Torque, Inch-Pounds	Torque, Foot-Pounds
N, 5, 6 & 8 ..	90-110	7.7-9.1
9	130-150	10.8-12.5
14	175-200	14.5-16.6

PISTON, PIN AND RINGS. Piston is of aluminum alloy and is fitted with two compression rings and one oil ring. If piston shows visible signs of wear, scoring or scuffing, it should be renewed. Also, renew piston if side clearance of new ring in top ring groove exceeds 0.005 on models N, 5, 6 and 8 or 0.007 on models 9 and 14. Reject piston or hone piston pin hole to 0.005 oversize if pin hole is 0.0005 or more out-of-round or worn to a diameter of 0.563 on model 9, 0.673 on model 14 or 0.491 on models N, 5, 6 and 8.

Renew piston pin if 0.0005 out-of-round, or if worn to a diameter of 0.561 on model 9, 0.671 on model 14 or 0.489 on models N, 5, 6 and 8.

Pistons with an "X" mark on a pin boss are installed with this mark towards magneto side of engine. Pistons not having this mark may be installed either way.

Reject piston rings having an end gap of 0.030 for compression rings and 0.035 for the oil ring. If top ring has groove on inside, install with groove up. If second compression ring has groove on outside, install with groove down. Oil ring may be installed either side up.

Pistons and rings are available in 0.010, 0.020 and 0.030 oversizes. A chrome ring set is available for slightly worn standard bore cylinders. Refer to note in CYLINDER paragraph.

CYLINDER Cylinder and crankcase are an integral cast iron casting. If cylinder is worn more than 0.003, or is more than 0.0015 out-of-round, it should be rebored and the next larger oversize piston and ring set be installed. Pistons and rings are furnished in oversizes of 0.010, 0.020 and 0.030; always rebore or hone cylinder to these exact oversizes so that stock pistons and rings will fit properly. Standard cylinder bore sizes are as follows:

Engine Model	Standard Cylinder Bore
5, 6 & N	1.999-2.000
8 & 9	2.249-2.250
14	2.624-2.625

NOTE: A chrome piston ring set is available for slightly worn standard bore cylinders. No honing or cylinder deglazing is required for these rings. The cylinder bore can be a maximum of 0.005 oversize when using chrome rings.

CRANKSHAFT. The crankshaft is carried in two main bearings which may be either bushing or ball bearing type, or be one bushing and one ball bearing, depending upon the engine model or special type.

On engines having bushing type main bearings, the running clearance should be not less than 0.0015 and not more than 0.0045. Wear on both the crankshaft and bushings will determine the running clearance; therefore, both the crankshaft and bushings should be checked. If the crankshaft is worn to the sizes given in the following crankshaft rejection chart, or if the journals are rough, scored, or more than 0.0007 out-of-round, install a new crankshaft. (See Fig. B52 for crankshaft check points.)

CRANKSHAFT REJECTION SIZES

Engine Model	Crankpin Journal	Magneto End Journal	Drive End Journal
N, 5, 6 & 8 .	0.7433	0.8726	0.8726
9	0.8726	0.9832	0.9832
14	0.9964	1.1790	1.1790

On plain bushing equipped models 9 and 14, main bearing bushings are not available separately from bearing plates. Renew bearing plates if bushing is 0.0007 or more out-of-round or if worn to a diameter of 0.9875 on model 9 or 1.1850 on model 14.

On models N, 5, 6 and 8 equipped with plain bushings, renew bushings if they are rough, scored, out-of-round 0.0007 or are worn to the reject size of 0.878.

When pressing or driving old main bearing bushings from block or crankcase, always support the crankcase wall with a Briggs & Stratton Crankcase Support or a pipe of suitable diameter to prevent damage to the casting.

When new main bushings are installed on models N, 5, 6 and 8, ream bushings to an inside diameter of 0.8764 to 0.877.

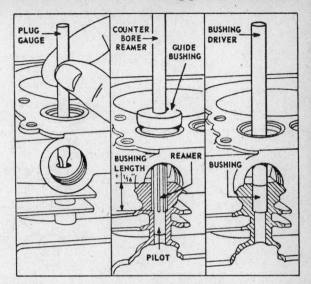

Fig. B56—Views showing checking valve guide, reaming guide to accept bushing and installing valve guide bushing.

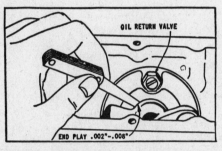

Fig. B53—Checking end play between bearing plate and crankshaft thrust face. Also note oil return valve used on some B&S engines.

On engines equipped with ball bearing mains, check ball bearings for wear or roughness. If bearing is loose or noisy, renew the bearing. Ball bearings are a press fit on crankshaft and must be removed by pressing crankshaft out of bearings. Expand new bearings by heating them in oil to a maximum temperature of 325° F., and install them on crankshaft with shielded side towards crankpin journal.

Recommended crankshaft end play for all models is 0.002-0.008. End play is controlled by use of different thickness shim gaskets between the flywheel end main bearing plate and crankcase. End play can be checked by clamping dial indicator to crankshaft and resting indicator button against crankcase. On plain bushing models only, end play can be checked with engine base removed by using a feeler gage as shown in Fig. B53. Shim gaskets are available in thicknesses of 0.005, 0.009 and 0.015 for models N, 5, 6, 8 and 9 and 0.005, 0.009 and 0.020 for model 14.

CAM GEAR. On all models timing gear and lobes are an integral part and is referred to as the "cam gear". The

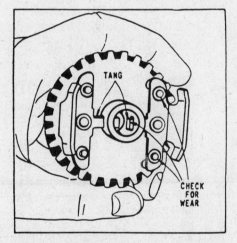

Fig. B54—B&S governor tangs. Tangs should be square and smooth; if not, renew gear and weights assembly.

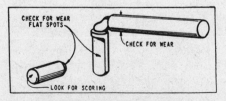

Fig. B55—B&S governor crank and plunger. Renew crank and plunger if either shows wear at points indicated.

Fig. B57—Exploded view of model 6 engine assembly. Models N, 5 and 8 are similar. Refer to Fig. B30 for view of magneto back plate and flywheel end crankshaft bearing. Some models are equipped with ball bearing mains.

1. Shields
2. Bushing
3. Oil seal
4. Piston pin
5. Snap rings
6. Output drive key
7. Crankshaft
8. Rod bolt lock
9. Oil dipper
10. Connecting rod
11. Piston
12. Piston rings
13. Crankcase
14. Gasket
15. Breather body and valve assembly
16. Spring
17. Oil spray shield
18. Cylinder head gasket
19. Cylinder head
20. Spark plug
21. Grounding spring
22. Tappet chamber cover
23. Valves
24. Valve springs
25. Spring retainers
26. Retainer pins
27. Tappets
28. Plug
29. Camshaft
30. Cam gear
31. Gasket
32. Engine base
33. Dowel
34. Flywheel nut
35. Starter cup
36. Flywheel
37. Flywheel key

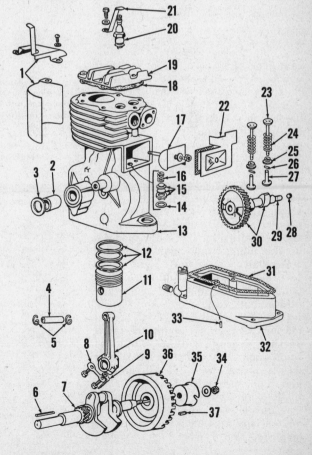

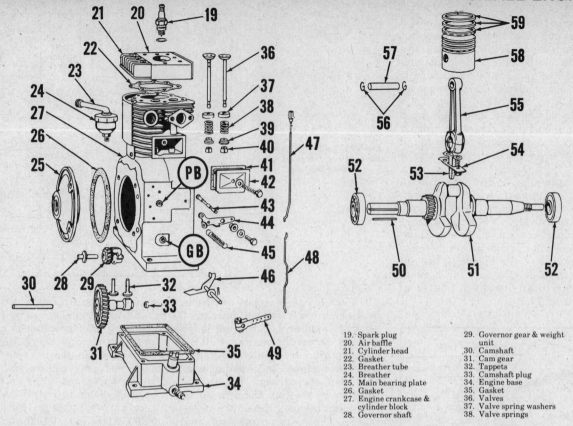

19. Spark plug
20. Air baffle
21. Cylinder head
22. Gasket
23. Breather tube
24. Breather
25. Main bearing plate
26. Gasket
27. Engine crankcase & cylinder block
28. Governor shaft
29. Governor gear & weight unit
30. Camshaft
31. Cam gear
32. Tappets
33. Camshaft plug
34. Engine base
35. Gasket
36. Valves
37. Valve spring washers
38. Valve springs

Fig. B58–Exploded view of model 9 or 14 engine assembly not having "Magna-Matic" ignition system; for Magna-Matic ignition models, refer to Fig. B59. Breaker plunger bushing (PB) and governor crank bushing (GB) in engine crankcase (27) are renewable. Breaker plunger (43) rides against a cam on cam gear (31).

39. Spring retainers (or "Roto-Caps")
40. Keepers
41. Gasket
42. Tappet chamber cover
43. Breaker point plunger

44. Governor control lever
45. Governor spring
46. Governor crank
47. Governor control rod
48. Governor link
49. Governor lever

50. Output drive key
51. Crankshaft
52. Ball bearings (on models so equipped)
53. Oil dipper
54. Rod bolt lock

55. Connecting rod
56. Piston pin retaining rings
57. Piston pin
58. Piston
59. Piston rings

cam gear turns on a stationary shaft which is referred to as the "camshaft". Reject camshaft if it is worn to a diameter of 0.3719 on models N, 5, 6, 8 and 9 engines or 0.4968 on model 14. Reject cam gear if lobes are worn to a diameter of 0.875 on models N, 5, 6 and 8, 1.124 on model 9 or 1.115 on model 14.

On models with "Magna-Matic" ignition system, cam gear is equipped with an ignition advance weight (Fig. B43); a tang on the advance weight contacts breaker arm (29—Fig. B34) each camshaft revolution. On other models, breaker plunger rides against a cam on crankshaft.

On all models, align timing marks on crankshaft gear and cam gear when reassembling engine.

GOVERNOR WEIGHT UNIT. On mechanical type governors, the tangs on the governor weights should be square and smooth. If they are worn or do not operate freely, renew the gear and weights assembly. See Fig. B54.

Governor weight unit is removed from inside of crankcase on models 9 and 14, and from outside of crankcase on models N, 5, 6 and 8.

Fig. B59–Exploded view of engine crankcase and cylinder block on models with "Magna-Matic" ignition system; note ignition advance weight (AW). Refer to Fig. B58 for rod, piston and crankshaft.

AW. Advance weight
20. Air baffle
21. Cylinder head
22. Gasket
25. Bearing plate, plain bushing
25B. Bearing plate, ball bearing
26. Gasket
27. Crankcase & cylinder
28. Governor shaft
29. Governor gear & weight unit
30. Camshaft
31. Cam gear
32. Tappets
33. Camshaft plug
34. Engine base
35. Gasket
36. Valves
37. Valve spring washers
38. Valve springs
39. Spring retainers (or "Roto-Caps")
40. Keepers
41. Gasket
42. Tappet chamber cover
44. Governor control lever
45. Governor spring
46. Governor crank
49. Governor lever

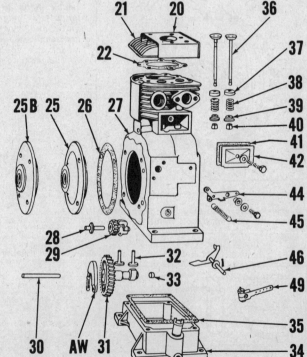

GOVERNOR CRANK. On mechanical type governors, the governor crank should be a free fit in the bushing with only perceptible shake. If new crank fits the old bushing loosely, install a new bushing. On models 9 and 14, ream bushing, after installation, to 0.2385-0.239. Reject crank if it shows wear spots. See Fig. B55.

VALVE SYSTEM. Tappet (valve) clearance is adjusted by grinding ends of valve stems squarely. Check clearance with engine cold; clearance on all models should be 0.007-0.009 on intake valve and 0.014-0.016 on exhaust valve.

Valve face and valve seat angle is 45 degrees; desired seat width is 3/64 to 1/16-inch. Renew valve if margin is 1/64-inch or less after refacing. All models are equipped with exhaust valve seat insert and an intake valve seat insert is available for service. Renewal of exhaust valve seat insert and installation of intake valve seat insert requires use of special tools which are available from Briggs & Stratton Central Service Distributors. Refer to Briggs & Stratton Special Service Tool List following engine repair section.

If Briggs & Stratton plug gage #19151 (models 9 and 14) or #19122 (models N, 5, 6 and 8) can be inserted a distance of 5/16-inch or more into valve guide, guide should be rebushed with a service bushing, Briggs & Stratton part #230655 (models 9 and 14) or #63709 (models N, 5, 6 and 8), as follows: Ream guide a depth of 1/16-inch longer than bushing with Briggs & Stratton reamer 19183 and reamer guide 19192 on models 9 and 14 or reamer 19064 and reamer guide 19191 on models N, 5, 6 and 8; then press bushing in flush with top of guide. Bushing is pre-sized and should not require reaming for new standard size valve.

VALVE TIMING. When reassembling engine, align timing mark on cam gear with timing mark on crankshaft gear or crankshaft collar. Valve to piston timing will then be correct.

BRIGGS & STRATTON

BRIGGS & STRATTON CORPORATION
Milwaukee, Wisconsin 53201

Basic Model (Series)	Bore	Stroke	Displacement
6B & Early 6000	2-5/16	1½	6.3
Late 60000	2-3/8	1½	6.65
8B & 80000	2-3/8	1¾	7.75
82000	2-3/8	1¾	7.75
92000	2-9/16	1¾	9.02
100000	2½	2-1/8	10.42
110900	2-25/32	1-7/8	11.44
130000	2-9/16	2-7/16	12.57
140000	2¾	2-3/8	14.11

All engines covered in this section have aluminum cylinder blocks with either plain aluminum cylinder bore or with a cast iron sleeve integrally cast into the block.

Early production of the 60000 model engines were of the same bore and stroke as the model 6B engine. The bore on the 60000 engines was changed from 2 5/16 to 2⅜ inches at Serial No. 5810060 on engines with plain aluminum bore, and at Serial No. 5810030 on engines with a cast iron sleeve.

MAINTENANCE

SPARK PLUG. Use AC GC46, Autolite A71, Champion J-8 or equivalent plug. If resistor type plugs are necessary to decrease radio interference, use Champion XJ-8 or equivalent. Set gap to 0.030 on all models. Briggs & Stratton Corporation recommends that plugs not be cleaned by abrasive blasting method as this may introduce some abrasive material into the engine which could cause extensive damage.

FLOAT TYPE (FLO-JET) CARBURETORS. Three different float type carburetors are used. They are called a "two-piece" (See Fig. B60), a small "one-piece" (See Fig. B64) or a large "one-piece" (See Fig. B66) carburetor depending upon the type of construction.

Float type carburetors are equipped with adjusting needles for both idle and power fuel mixtures. Counter-clockwise rotation of the adjusting needles richens the mixture. For initial starting adjustment, open the main needle valve (power fuel mixture) 1½ turns on the two-piece carburetor and 2½ turns on the small one-piece carburetor. Open the idle needle valve ½ to ¾-turn on the two-piece carburetor and 1½ turns on the small one-piece carburetor. On the large one-piece carburetor, open both needle valves 1⅛ turns. Start the engine and when it is

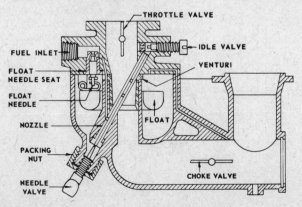

Fig. B60–Cross-sectional view of typical B&S "two-piece" carburetor. Before separating upper and lower body sections, loosen packing nut and unscrew nut and needle valve as unit. Then, using special screwdriver, remove nozzle.

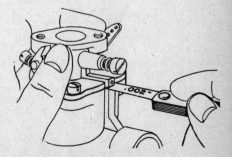

Fig. B61–Checking upper body of "two-piece" carburetor for warpage.

warm, make final adjustments as follows: Set the speed control for desired operating speed, turn main needle clockwise until engine misses, and then turn it counter-clockwise just past the smooth operating point until the engine begins to run unevenly. Return the speed control to idle position and adjust the idle speed stop screw until the engine idles at 1750 RPM. Then adjust the idle needle valve until the engine runs smoothly. Reset the idle speed stop screw if necessary. The engine should then accelerate without hesitation or sputtering. If it does not accelerate properly, turn the main needle valve counter-clockwise slightly to provide a richer fuel mixture.

The float setting on all float type car-

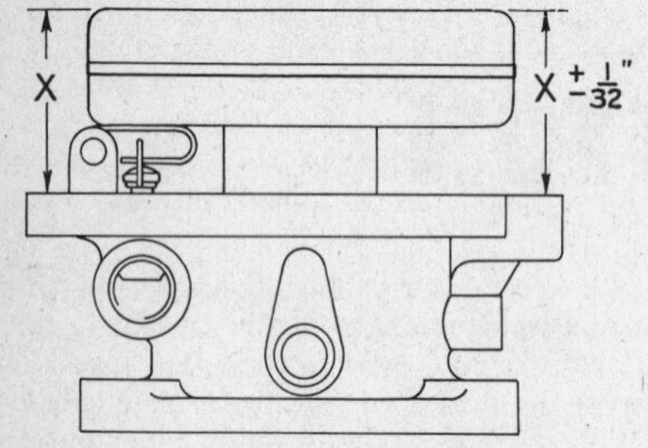

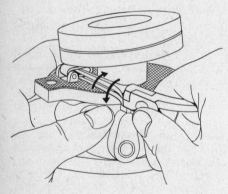

Fig. B62–Carburetor float setting should be within specifications shown. To adjust float setting, bend tang with needle nose pliers as shown in Fig. B63.

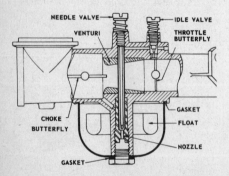

Fig. B63–Bending tang with needle nose pliers to adjust float setting. Refer to Fig. B62 for method of checking float setting.

Fig. B64–Cross-sectional view of typical B&S small "one-piece" float type carburetor. Refer to Fig. B65 for disassembly views.

buretors should be within dimensions shown in Fig. B62. If not, bend the tang on float as shown in Fig. B63 to adjust float setting. If any wear is visible on the inlet valve or the inlet valve seat, install a new valve and seat assembly. On large one-piece carburetors, the renewable inlet valve seat is pressed into the carburetor body until flush with the body.

NOTE: The upper and lower bodies of the two-piece float type carburetor are locked together by the main nozzle. Refer to cross-sectional view of carburetor in Fig. B60. Before attempting to separate the upper body from the lower body, loosen packing nut and unscrew nut and needle valve. Then, using special screwdriver (B&S tool No. 19061 or 19062), remove nozzle.

If a 0.002 feeler gage can be inserted between upper and lower bodies of the two-piece carburetor as shown in Fig. B61, the upper body is warped and should be renewed.

Check the throttle shaft for wear on all float type carburetors. If 0.010 or more free play (shaft to bushing clearance) is noted, install new throttle shaft and/or throttle shaft bushings. To remove worn bushings, turn a ¼-inch x

Fig. B65–Disassembling the small "one-piece" float type carburetor. Pry out welch plug, remove choke butterfly (disc), remove choke shaft and needle valve; venturi can then be removed as shown in left view.

Fig. B66–Cross-sectional view of B&S large "one-piece" float type carburetor.

20 tap into bushing and pull bushing from body casting with the tap. Press new bushings into casting by using a vise and, if necessary, ream bushings with a 7/32-inch drill bit.

SUCTION TYPE (VACU-JET) CARBURETORS. A typical suction type (Vacu-Jet) carburetor is shown in Fig. B67. This type carburetor has only one fuel mixture adjusting needle. Turning the needle clockwise leans the fuel-air mixture. Adjust suction type carburetors with fuel tank approximately one-half full and with the engine warm and running at approximately 3000 RPM at no load. Turn needle valve clockwise until engine begins to lose speed; then, turn needle slowly counter-clockwise until engine begins to run unevenly from a too-rich fuel-air mixture. This should result in a correct adjustment for full load operation. Adjust idle speed to 1750 RPM.

To remove the suction type carburetor, first remove carburetor and fuel tank as an assembly, then remove carburetor from fuel tank. When reinstalling carburetor on fuel tank, use a new gasket and tighten retaining screws evenly.

The suction type carburetor has a

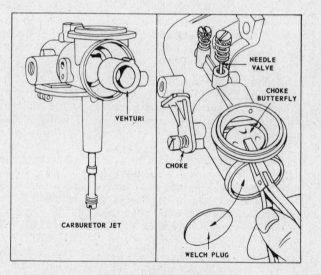

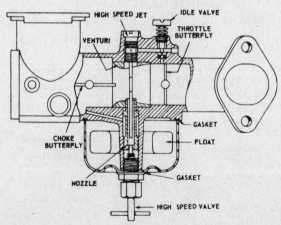

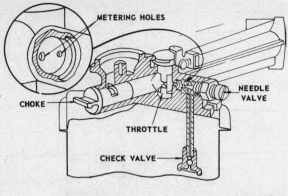

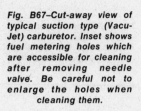

Fig. B67–Cut-away view of typical suction type (Vacu-Jet) carburetor. Inset shows fuel metering holes which are accessible for cleaning after removing needle valve. Be careful not to enlarge the holes when cleaning them.

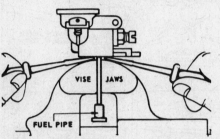

Fig. B68–Removing brass fuel feed pipe from suction type carburetor. Press new brass pipe into carburetor until it projects 2 9/32 to 2 5/16 inch from carburetor face. Nylon fuel feed pipe is threaded into carburetor.

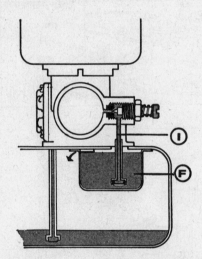

Fig. B69–Fuel flow in Pulsa-Jet carburetor. Fuel pump incorporated in carburetor fills constant level sump below carburetor (F) and excess fuel flows back into tank. Fuel is drawn from sump through inlet (1) past fuel mixture adjusting needle by vacuum in carburetor.

fuel feed pipe extending into fuel tank. The pipe has a check valve to allow fuel to feed up into the carburetor but prevents fuel from flowing back into the tank. If check valve is inoperative and cleaning in alcohol or acetone will not free the check valve, renew the fuel feed pipe. If feed pipe is made of brass, remove as shown in Fig. B68. Using a vise, press new pipe into carburetor so that it extends from 2 9/32 to 2 5/16 inches from carburetor body. If pipe is made of nylon (plastic), screw pipe out of carburetor body with wrench. When installing new nylon feed pipe, be careful not to overtighten.

NOTE: If soaking carburetor in cleaner for more than one-half hour, be sure to remove all nylon parts and "O" ring, if used, before placing the carburetor in cleaning solvent.

PUMP TYPE (PULSA-JET) CARBURETORS. The pump type (Pulsa-Jet) carburetor is basically a suction type carburetor incorporating a fuel pump to fill a constant level fuel sump in top of fuel tank. Refer to schematic view in Fig. B69. This makes a constant fuel-air mixture available to engine regardless of fuel level in tank. Adjustment of the pump type carburetor fuel mixture needle valve is the same as outlined for suction type carburetors in previous paragraph, except that fuel level in tank is not important.

To remove the pump type carburetor, first remove the carburetor and fuel tank as an assembly; then, remove carburetor from fuel tank. When rein-

stalling carburetor on fuel tank, use a new gasket or pump diaphragm as required and tighten retaining screws evenly.

Fig. B70 shows an exploded view of the pump unit used on all carburetors except those for models 82900, 92900 and 110900. On engine models 82900, 92900 and 110900, the pump diaphragm is placed between the carburetor and fuel tank as shown in Fig. B71.

The pump type carburetor has two fuel feed pipes; the long pipe feeds fuel into the pump portion of the carburetor from which fuel then flows to the constant level fuel sump. The short pipe extends into the constant level sump and feeds fuel into the carburetor venturi via the fuel mixture needle valve. As check valves are incorporated in the pump diaphragm, fuel feed pipes on pump type carburetors do not have a check valve. However, if the fuel screen in lower end of pipe is broken or clogged and cannot be cleaned, the pipe or screen housing can be renewed. If pipe is made of nylon, unscrew old pipe and install new pipe with a wrench; be careful not to overtighten new pipe. If pipe is made of brass, clamp pipe lightly in a vise and drive old screen housing from pipe with a screwdriver or small chisel as shown in Fig. B72. Drive a new screen housing onto pipe with a soft faced hammer.

NOTE: If soaking carburetor in cleaner for more than one-half hour, be sure to remove all nylon parts and "O" ring, if used, before placing carburetor in cleaning solvent.

NOTE: On engine models 82900,

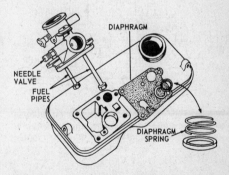

Fig. B71—On models 82900, 92900 and 110900, pump type (Pulsa-Jet) carburetor diaphragm is installed between carburetor and fuel tank.

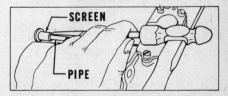

Fig. B72–To renew screen housing on pump type carburetors with brass feed pipes, drive old screen housing from pipe as shown. To hold pipe, clamp lightly in a vise.

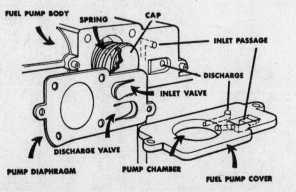

Fig. B70—Exploded view of fuel pump that is incorporated in Pulsa-Jet carburetor except those used on 82900, 92900 and 110900 models; refer to Fig. B71.

92900 and 110900, be sure air cleaner retaining screw is in place if engine is being operated (during tests) without air cleaner installed. If screw is not in place, fuel will lift up through the screw hole and enter carburetor throat as the screw hole leads directly into the constant level fuel sump.

INTAKE TUBE. Models 82000, 92000, 100900, 110900 and 130900 have an intake tube between carburetor and engine intake port; carburetor is sealed to intake tube with an "O" ring as shown in Fig. B73.

On model 82000 engines, the intake tube is threaded into the engine intake port. A gasket is used between the engine intake port cover and engine casting; refer to Fig. B74.

On model 92000 and 110900 engines, the intake tube is bolted to the engine intake port and a gasket is used

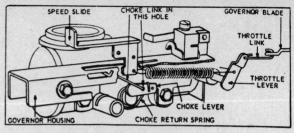
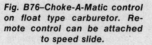

Fig. B76–Choke-A-Matic control on float type carburetor. Remote control can be attached to speed slide.

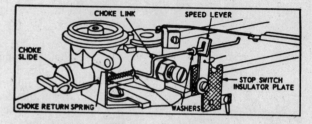

Fig. B77–Typical Choke-A Matic control on suction type carburetor. Remote control can be attached to speed lever.

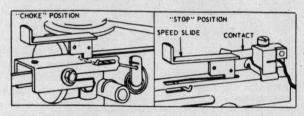

Fig. B78–Choke-A-Matic control in choke and stop positions on float carburetor.

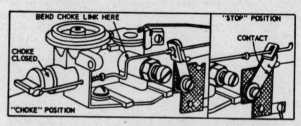

Fig. B79–Choke-A-Matic control in choke and stop positions on suction carburetor. Bend choke link if necessary to adjust control.

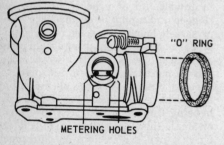

Fig. B73–Metering holes in pump type carburetors are accessible for cleaning after removing fuel mixture needle valve. On models with intake pipe, carburetor is sealed to pipe with "O" ring.

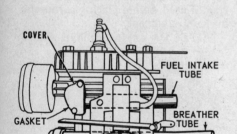

Fig. B74–On Series 82000 models, intake tube is threaded into intake port of engine; a gasket is placed between intake port cover and intake port.

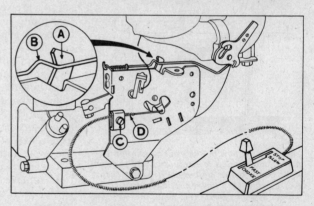

Fig. B80–On Choke-A-Matic controls shown, choke actuating lever (A) should just contact choke link or shaft (B) when control is at "FAST" position. If not, loosen screw (C) and move control wire housing (D) as required.

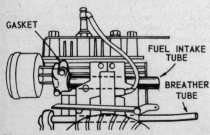

Fig. B75– On series 92000 and 110900 models, fuel intake tube is bolted to engine intake port and a gasket is placed between tube and engine. On Series 100000 and 130000 vertical crankshaft models, intake tube and gasket are similar.

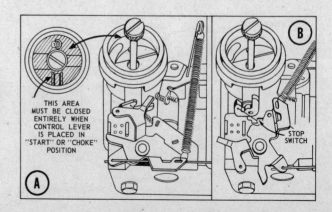

Fig. B81–When Choke-A-Matic control is in "START" or "CHOKE" position, choke must be completely closed as shown in view A. When control is in "STOP" position, arm should contact stop switch (view B).

between the intake tube and engine casting; refer to Fig. B75. On models 100900 and 130900 intake tubes are attached to engine in similar manner.

CHOKE-A-MATIC CARBURETOR CONTROLS. Engines equipped with float, suction or pump type carburetors may be equipped with a control unit with which the carburetor choke and throttle and the magneto

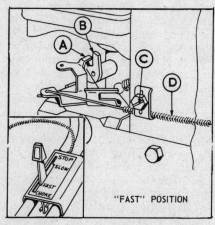

Fig. B82–On Choke-A-Matic controls shown, lever (A) should just contact choke shaft arm (B) when control is in "FAST" position. If not, loosen screw (C) and move control wire housing (D) as required, then tighten screw.

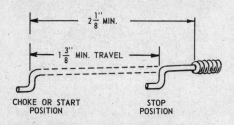

Fig. B83–For proper operation of Choke-A-Matic controls, remote control wire must extend to dimension shown and have a minimum travel of 1⅜ inches.

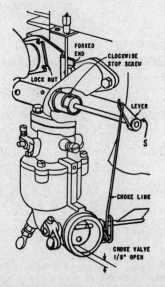

Fig. B84–Automatic choke used on some models equipped with two-piece Flo-Jet carburetor showing unit in "Hot" position.

grounding switch are operated from a single lever (Choke-A-Matic carburetors). Refer to Figs. B76 through B82 for views showing the different types of Choke-A-Matic carburetor controls.

To check operation of Choke-A-Matic carburetor controls, move control lever to "CHOKE" position; carburetor choke slide or plate must be completely closed. Then, move control lever to "STOP" position; magneto grounding switch should be making contact. With the control lever in "RUN", "FAST", or "SLOW" position, carburetor choke should be completely open. On units with remote controls, synchronize movement of remote lever to carburetor control lever by loosening screw (C—Fig. B80 or Fig. B82) and moving control wire housing (D) as required; then, tighten screw to clamp the housing securely. Refer to Fig. B83 to check remote control wire movement.

AUTOMATIC CHOKE (THERMOSTAT TYPE). A thermostat operated choke is used on some models equipped with the two-piece carburetor. To adjust choke linkage, hold choke shaft so thermostat lever is free. At room temperature, stop screw in thermostat collar should be located midway between thermostat stops. If not, loosen stop screw, adjust the collar and tighten stop screw. Loosen set screw (S—Fig. B84) on thermostat lever. Then, slide lever on shaft to insure free movement of choke unit. Turn thermostat shaft clockwise until stop screw contacts thermostat stop. While holding shaft in this position, move shaft lever until choke is open exactly ⅛-inch and tighten lever set screw. Turn thermostat shaft counterclockwise until stop screw contacts thermostat stop as shown in Fig. B85. Manually open choke valve until it stops against top of choke link opening. At this time, choke valve should be open at least 3/32-inch, but not more than 5/32-inch. Hold choke valve in wide open position and check position

of counterweight lever. Lever should be in a horizontal position with free end towards right.

AUTOMATIC CHOKE (VACUUM TYPE). A spring and vacuum operated automatic choke is used on some series 92000 and 110900 vertical crankshaft engines. A diaphragm under carburetor is connected to the choke shaft by a link. The compression spring works against the diaphragm, holding choke in closed position when engine is not running. See Fig. B86. As engine starts, increased vacuum works against the spring and pulls the diaphragm and choke link down, holding choke in open (running) position shown in Fig. B87.

During operation, if a sudden load is applied to engine or a lugging condition develops, a drop in intake vacuum occurs, permitting choke to close partially. This provides a richer fuel mixture to meet the condition and keeps the engine running smoothly. When the load condition has been met, increased vacuum returns choke valve to normal running (fully open) position.

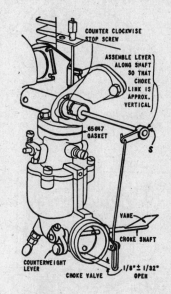

Fig. B85–Automatic choke on two-piece Flo-Jet carburetor in "Cold" position.

Fig. B86—Diagram showing vacuum operated automatic choke used on some series 92000 and 110900 vertical crankshaft engines in closed (engine not running) position.

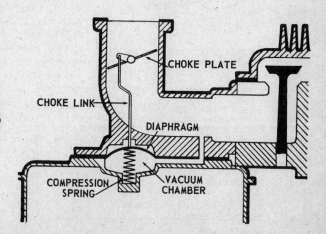

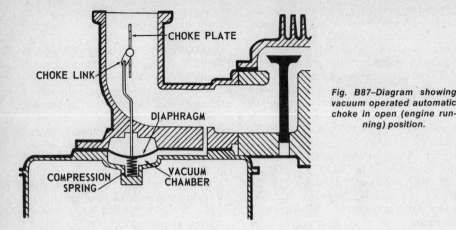

Fig. B87–Diagram showing vacuum operated automatic choke in open (engine running) position.

FUEL TANK OUTLET. Small models with float type carburetors are equipped with a fuel tank outlet as shown in Fig. B88. On larger engines, a fuel sediment bowl is incorporated with the fuel tank outlet as shown in Fig. B89. Clean any lint and dirt from tank outlet screens with a brush. Varnish or

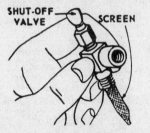

Fig. B88–Fuel tank outlet used on smaller engines with float type carburetor.

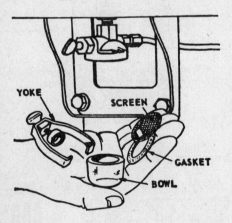

Fig. B89–Fuel tank outlet used on larger B&S engines.

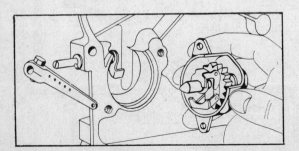

Fig. B90–Removing governor unit (except on Series 100000, 130000, and late 140000) from inside crankcase cover on horizontal crankshaft models. Refer to Fig. B91 for exploded view of governor.

other gasoline deposits may be removed by use of a suitable solvent. Tighten packing nut or remove nut and shut-off valve, then renew packing if leakage occurs around shut-off valve stem.

FUEL PUMP. A fuel pump is available as optional equipment on some models. Refer to SERVICING BRIGGS & STRATTON ACCESSORIES section in this manual for fuel pump servicing information.

GOVERNOR. All models are equipped with either a mechanical (fly-weight type) or an air vane (pneumatic) governor. Refer to following appropriate paragraph for service and adjustment information on the governor unit being serviced.

MECHANICAL GOVERNOR. Three different designs of mechanical governors are used.

On all engines except Series 100000, 130000 and all late Series 140000 models, a governor unit as shown in Fig. B90 is used. An exploded view of this governor unit is shown in Fig. B91. The governor housing is attached to inner side of crankcase cover and the governor gear is driven from the engine camshaft gear. Use Figs. B90 and B91 as a disassembly and assembly guide. Renew any parts that bind or show excessive wear. After governor is assembled, refer to Fig. B92 and adjust linkage as follows: Loosen screw clamping governor lever to governor crank. Turn governor lever counter-clockwise so that carburetor throttle is in wide open position and while

holding lever, turn governor crank as far counter-clockwise as possible and tighten screw clamping lever to crank. Governor crank can be turned with screwdriver. Check linkage to be sure it is free and that the carburetor throttle will move from idle to wide open position.

On Series 100000, 130000 and late Series 140000 horizontal crankshaft models, the governor gear and weight unit (G—Fig. B93) is supported on a pin in engine crankcase cover and the governor crank is installed in a bore in the engine crankcase. A thrust washer (W) is placed between governor gear and crankcase cover. When assembling crankcase cover to crankcase, be sure governor crank (C) is in position shown in Fig. B93. After governor unit and crankcase cover is installed, refer to Fig. B94 for installation of linkage. Before attempting to start engine, refer to Fig. B95 and adjust linkage as follows: Loosen bolt clamping governor lever to governor crank. Set control lever in high speed position, then, using screwdriver, turn governor crank as far clockwise as possible and tighten

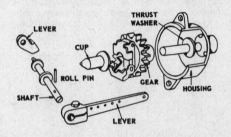

Fig. B91–Exploded view of governor unit used on all horizontal crankshaft models (except Series 100000, 130000 and late 140000) with mechanical governor. Refer also to Figs. B90 and B92.

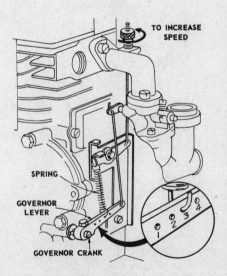

Fig. B92–View of governor linkage used on horizontal crankshaft mechanical governor models except Series 100000, 130000 and late 140000. Governor spring should be hooked in governor lever as shown in inset.

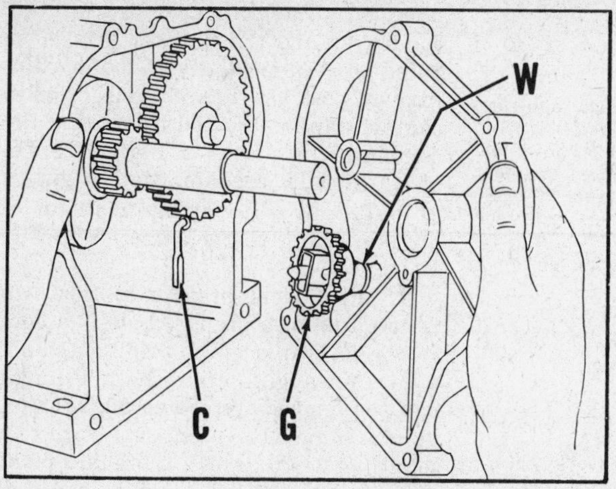

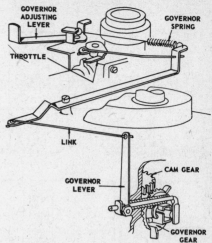

Fig. B93–Installing crank-case cover on Series 100000, 130000 and late 140000 with mechanical governor. Governor crank (C) must be in position shown. A thrust washer (W) is placed between governor (G) and crankcase cover.

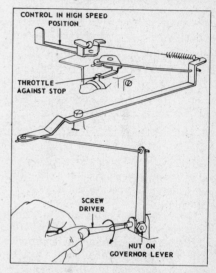

Fig. B97–Schematic drawing of Series 100000, 130000 and 140000 mechanical governor and linkage used on vertical crankshaft mechanical governed models.

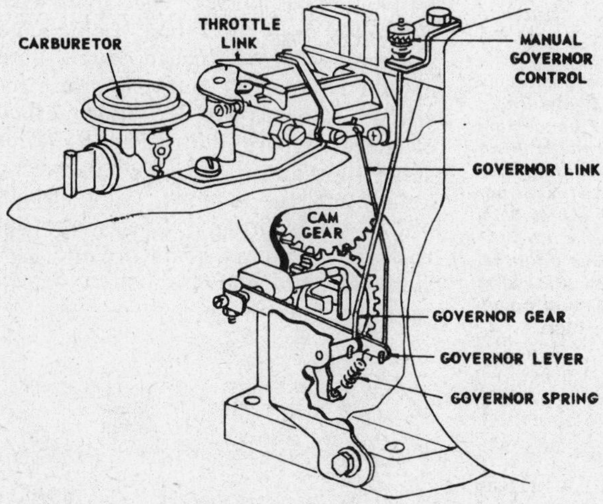

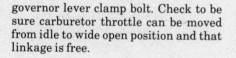

Fig. B94–Cut-away drawing of governor and linkage used on Series 100000, 130000 and late 140000 horizontal crankshaft models.

Fig. B98–View showing adjustment of Series 100000, 130000 and 140000 vertical crankshaft mechanical governor; refer to text for procedure.

governor lever clamp bolt. Check to be sure carburetor throttle can be moved from idle to wide open position and that linkage is free.

On vertical crankshaft Series 100000, 130000 and 140000 having a mechanical governor, the governor weight unit is integral with the lubricating oil slinger and is mounted on lower end of camshaft gear as shown in Fig. B96. With engine upside down, place governor and slinger unit on camshaft gear as shown, place spring washer (Series 100000 and 130900 only) on camshaft gear and assemble engine base to crankcase. Assemble linkage as shown in Fig. B97; then, refer to Fig. B98 and adjust linkage as follows: With bolt clamping governor lever to governor crank loose and con-

trol lever in high speed position, turn governor crank with screwdriver as far clockwise as possible and tighten governor lever clamping bolt.

AIR VANE (PNEUMATIC) GOVERNORS. Many models are equipped with

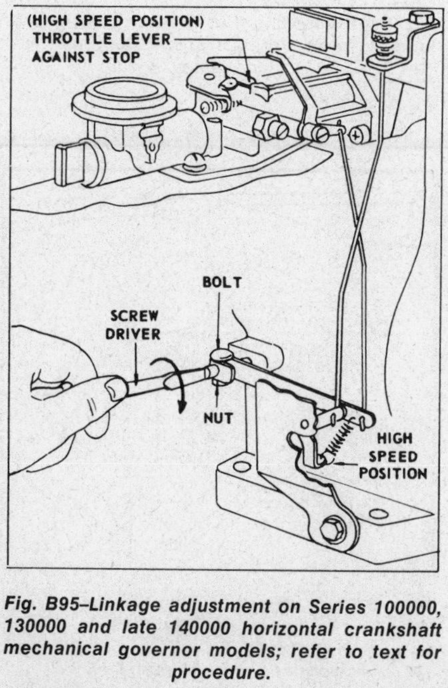

Fig. B95–Linkage adjustment on Series 100000, 130000 and late 140000 horizontal crankshaft mechanical governor models; refer to text for procedure.

Fig. B96–View showing Series 100000, 130000 and 140000 vertical crankshaft mechanical governor unit. Drawing is of lower side of engine with oil sump (engine base) removed; note spring washer location used on Series 100000 and 130000 only.

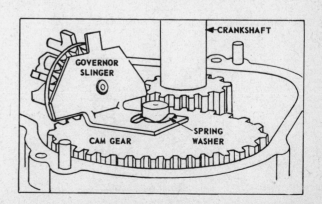

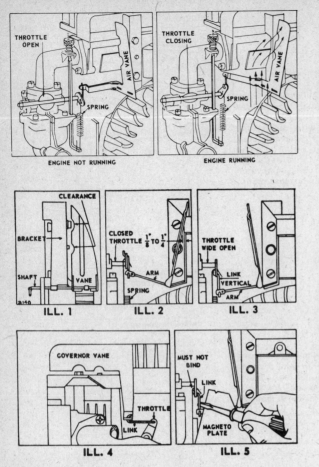

Fig. B99–Views showing operating principle of air vane (pneumatic) governor. Air from flywheel fan acts against air vane to overcome tension of governor spring; speed is adjusted by changing spring tension.

Fig. B100–Air vane governors and linkage. ILL. 1, The governor vane should be checked for clearance in all positions. ILL. 2, the vane should stop at ⅛ to ¼-inch from the magneto coil. ILL. 3, With wide open throttle, the link connecting vane arm to throttle lever should be in a vertical position on vertical cylinder engines and in a horizontal position (ILL. 4) on horizontal cylinder engines. Bend link slightly (ILL. 5) to remove any binding condition in linkage.

an air vane governor; refer to Fig. B99 for schematic operational views of a typical unit.

The vane should stop at ⅛ to ¼-inch from the magneto coil (See Fig. B100, Ill. 2) when the linkage is assembled and attached to carburetor throttle shaft. If necessary to adjust, spring the vane while holding the shaft. With wide open throttle, the link from the air vane arm to the carburetor throttle should be in a vertical position on horizontal crankshaft models and in a horizontal position on vertical crankshaft models. (See Fig. B100, illustration 3 and 4). Check linkage for binding; if binding condition exists, bend links

slightly to correct. Refer to Fig. B100, illustration 5.

NOTE: Some engines are equipped with a nylon governor vane which does not require adjustment.

MAGNETO. The breaker contact gap is 0.020 on all models. Condenser capacity on all models is 0.18-0.24 mfd.

On all except "Sonoduct" (vertical crankshaft with flywheel below engine) models, breaker points and condenser are accessible after removing engine flywheel and breaker cover. On "Sonoduct" models, breaker points are located below breaker cover on top side of engine. Refer to Fig. B114.

On some models, one breaker contact

point is an integral part of the ignition condenser and the breaker arm is pivoted on a knife edge retained in a slot in pivot post. On these models, breaker contact gap is adjusted by moving the condenser as shown in Fig. B101. On other models, breaker contact gap is adjusted by relocating position of breaker contact bracket; refer to Fig. B102.

On all models, breaker contact arm is actuated by a plunger held in a bore in engine crankcase and riding against a cam on engine crankshaft. Plunger can be removed after removing breaker points. Renew the plunger if worn to a length of 0.870 or less. If breaker point plunger bore in crankcase is worn, oil will leak past plunger. Check bore with B&S plug gage No. 19055; if plug gage will enter bore ¼-inch or more, bore should be reamed and a bushing installed. Refer to Fig. B103 for method of checking bore and to Fig. B104 for steps in reaming bore and installing bushing if bore is worn. To ream bore and install bushing, it is necessary that the breaker points, armature and ignition coil and the crankshaft be removed.

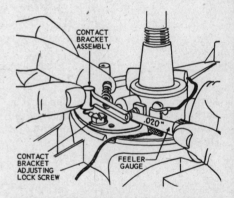

Fig. B102–Adjustment of breaker point gap on models having breaker point separate from condenser.

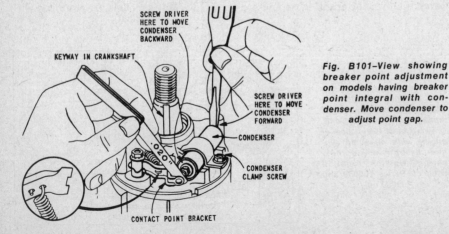

Fig. B101–View showing breaker point adjustment on models having breaker point integral with condenser. Move condenser to adjust point gap.

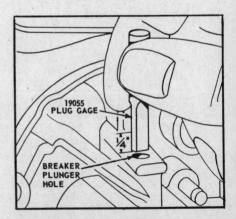

Fig. B103–If Briggs & Stratton plug gage #19055 can be inserted in breaker plunger bore a distance of ¼-inch or more, bore is worn and must be rebushed.

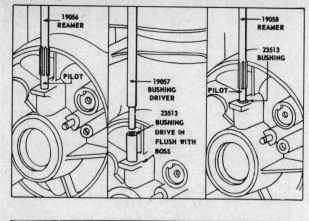

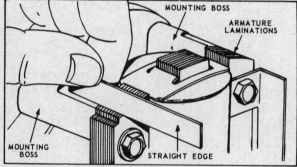

Fig. B104–Views showing reaming plunger bore to accept bushing (left view), installing bushing (center) and finish reaming bore (right) of bushing.

Fig. B105–On "Sonoduct" models, align armature core with mounting boss for proper magneto air gap.

Series 140000:
Two Leg Armature 0.010-0.014
Three Leg Armature . . .0.016-0.019

LUBRICATION. Vertical crankshaft engines are lubricated by an oil slinger wheel driven by the cam gear. On early 6B and 8B models, the oil slinger wheel was mounted on a bracket attached to the crankcase. Renew the bracket if pin on which gear rotates is worn to 0.490; renew steel bushing in hub of gear if worn. On later model vertical crankshaft engines, the oil slinger wheel, pin and bracket are an integral unit with the bracket being retained by the lower end of the engine camshaft. On Series 100000 and 130000 models, a spring washer is placed on lower end of camshaft between bracket and oil sump boss. Renew the oil slinger assembly if teeth

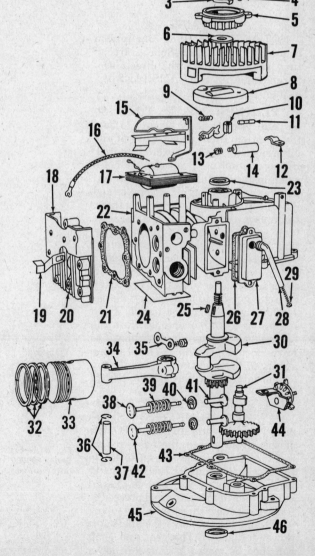

On "Sonoduct" models, armature and ignition coil are inside flywheel on bottom side of engine. Armature air gap is correct if armature is installed flush with mounting boss as shown in Fig. B105. On all other models, armature and ignition coil are located outside flywheel and armature to flywheel air gap should be as follows:
Models 6B & 8B 0.012-0.016
Series 60000 & 80000:
  Two Leg Armature 0.006-0.010
  Three Leg Armature . . .0.012-0.016
Series 92000 & 110900 . . . . . .0.006-0.010
Series 100000:
  Two Leg Armature 0.010-0.014
  Three Leg Armature . . .0.012-0.016
Series 130000 . . . . .0.010-0.014

1. Snap ring
2. Washer
3. Ratchet
4. Steel balls
5. Starter clutch
6. Washer
7. Flywheel
8. Breaker cover
9. Breaker point spring
10. Breaker arm & pivot
11. Breaker plunger
12. Condenser clamp
13. Coil spring (primary wire retainer)
14. Condenser
15. Governor air vane & bracket assembly
16. Spark plug wire
17. Armature & coil assy.
18. Air baffle
19. Spark plug grounding switch
20. Cylinder head
21. Cylinder head gasket
22. Cylinder block
23. Crankshaft oil seal
24. Cylinder shield
25. Flywheel key
26. Gasket
27. Breather & tappet chamber cover
28. Breather tube assembly
29. Coil spring
30. Crankshaft
31. Cam gear and shaft
32. Piston rings
33. Piston
34. Connecting rod
35. Rod bolt lock
36. Piston pin retaining rings
37. Piston pin
38. Intake valve
39. Valve springs
40. Valve spring keepers
41. Tappets (cam followers)
42. Exhaust valve
43. Gasket (0.005, 0.009 or 0.015)
44. Oil slinger assembly
45. Oil sump (engine base)
46. Crankshaft oil seal

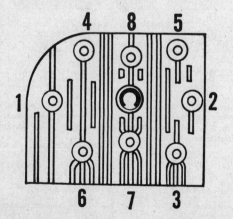

Fig. B106–Cylinder head screw tightening sequence. Long screws are used in positions 2, 3 and 7.

Fig. B107–Exploded view of typical vertical crankshaft model with air vane (pneumatic) governor. To remove flywheel, remove blower housing and starter unit; then, remove snap ring (1), lift off ratchet (3) and washer (2), extract steel balls (4) and unscrew starter clutch housing (5). Flywheel can then be pulled from crankshaft.

are worn on slinger gear or gear is loose on bracket. On horizontal crankshaft engines, a splash system (oil dipper on connecting rod) is used for engine lubrication.

Use oils labeled "For Service MS, SC or SD" only. (Use of higher or lower API classification oils is not recommended.) SAE-30, 10W-30 or 10W-40 oil is recommended for temperatures above 40° F., SAE 10W or 5W-20 for temperatures below 40° F., or 10W oil diluted with 10% kerosene for below 0° F. Fill crankcase to point of overflowing or to FULL mark on dipstick when engine is level.

CRANKCASE BREATHER. The crankcase breather is built into the engine valve cover. The mounting holes are offset so the breather can only be installed one way. Rinse breather in solvent and allow to drain. A vent tube connects the breather to the carburetor air horn on certain model engines for extra protection against dusty conditions.

REPAIRS

NOTE: When checking compression on models with "Easy-Spin" starting, turn engine opposite the direction of normal rotation. See CAMSHAFT paragraph.

CYLINDER HEAD. When removing cylinder head, be sure to note the position from which each of the different length screws were removed. If they are not used in the same holes when installing the head, it will result in screws bottoming in some holes and not enough thread contact in others. Lubricate the cylinder head screws with graphite grease before installation. Do not use sealer on head gasket. When installing cylinder head, tighten all screws lightly and then retighten them in sequence shown in Fig. B106 to a torque of 165 in.-lbs. on Series 140000 engines and to a torque of 140 in.-lbs. on all other engines. Run the engine for 2 to 5 minutes to allow it to warm up and retighten the head screws again following the sequence and torque values mentioned above.

OIL SUMP REMOVAL, AUXILIARY PTO MODELS. On Series 92000 models with auxiliary PTO, one of the oil sump (engine base) to cylinder retaining screws is installed in the recess in sump for the PTO auxiliary drive gear. To remove the oil sump, refer to Fig. B108 and proceed as follows: Remove the cover plate (upper view) and then remove the shaft stop (lower left view). The gear and shaft can then be moved as shown in lower right view to allow removal of the retaining screws. Reverse procedure to reassemble.

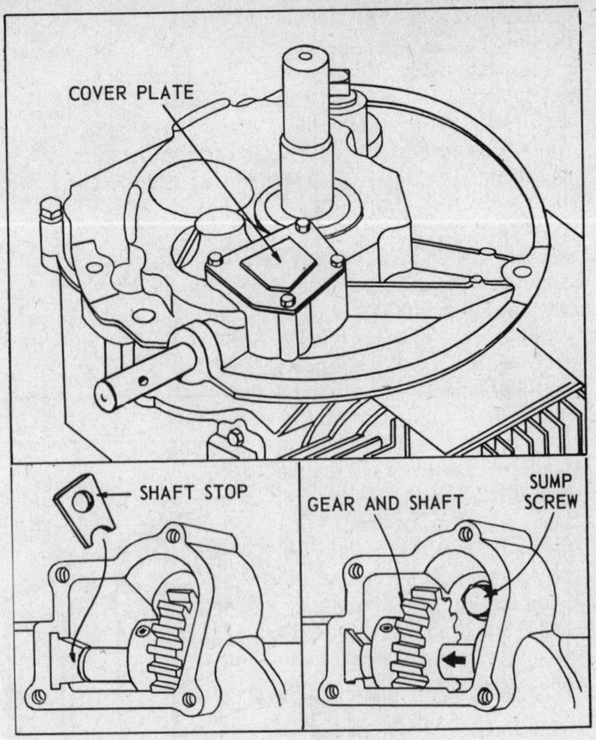

Fig. B108–To remove oil sump (engine base) on Series 92000 models with auxiliary PTO, remove cover plate, shaft stop and retaining screw as shown.

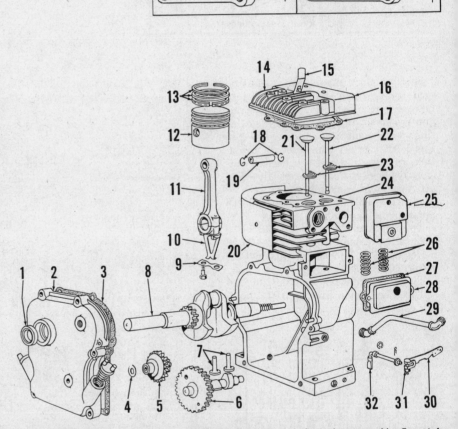

Fig. B109–Exploded view of Series 100000 horizontal crankshaft engine assembly. Except for Series 130000 and late Series 140000 models, other horizontal crankshaft models with mechanical governor will have governor unit as shown in Fig. B90; otherwise, construction of all other horizontal crankshaft models is similar.

1. Crankshaft oil seal	11. Connecting rod	23. Valve spring retainers
2. Crankcase cover	12. Piston	24. Cylinder block
3. Gasket (0.005, 0.009 or 0.015)	13. Piston rings	25. Muffler
4. Thrust washer	14. Cylinder head	26. Valve springs
5. Governor assembly	15. Spark plug ground switch	27. Gasket
6. Cam gear and shaft	16. Air baffle	28. Breather & tappet chamber cover
7. Tappets (cam followers)	17. Cylinder head gasket	29. Breather pipe
8. Crankshaft	18. Piston pin retaining rings	30. Governor lever
9. Rod bolt lock	19. Piston pin	31. Clamping bolt
10. Oil dipper	20. Air baffle	32. Governor crank
	21. Exhaust valve	
	22. Intake valve	

OIL BAFFLE PLATE, SERIES 140000 ENGINES. Series 140000 engines with mechanical governor have a baffle located in the cylinder block (crankcase). When servicing these engines, it is important that the baffle be correctly installed. The baffle must fit tightly against the valve tappet boss in the crankcase; check for this before installing oil sump (vertical crankshaft models) or crankcase cover (horizontal crankshaft models).

CONNECTING ROD. The connecting rod and piston are removed from cylinder head end of block as an assembly. The aluminum alloy connecting rod rides directly on the induction hardened crankpin. The rod should be rejected if the crankpin hole is scored or out-of-round over 0.0007 or if the piston pin hole is scored or out-of-round over 0.0005. Wear limit sizes are given in the following chart. Reject the connecting rod if either the crankpin or piston pin hole is worn to or larger than the sizes given in the chart.

REJECT SIZES FOR CONNECTING ROD

Basic Model	Crankpin Hole	*Piston Pin Hole
6B, 60000 . . .	0.876	0.492
8B, 80000 . . .	1.0013	0.492
82000, 92000	1.0013	0.492
100000	1.0013	0.555
110900, 130000	1.0013	0.492
140000	1.0949	0.674

*NOTE: Piston pins of 0.005 oversize are available for service. Piston pin hole in rod can be reamed to this size if crankpin hole is O.K.

Torque connecting rod cap screws to 165 in.-lbs. on Series 140000 and 100 in.-lbs. on all other engines.

PISTON, PIN AND RINGS. Pistons for use in engines having aluminum bore are not interchangeable with those for use in cylinders having cast-iron sleeve. Pistons may be identified as follows: Those for use in cast-iron sleeve cylinders have a plain, dull aluminum finish, have an "L" stamped on top and use an oil ring expander. Those for use in aluminum bore cylinders are chrome plated (shiny finish), do not have an identifying letter and do not use an oil ring expander.

Reject pistons showing visible signs of wear, scoring or scuffing. If, after cleaning carbon from top ring groove, a new top ring has a side clearance of 0.007 or more, reject the piston. Reject piston or hone piston pin hole to 0.005 oversize if pin hole is 0.005 or more out-of-round, or is worn to a diameter of 0.491 on 6B, 8B, 60000, 80000, 82000, 92000, 110900 and 130000 engines, 0.554 on 100000 engines or 0.673 on 140000 engines.

If the piston pin is 0.0005 or more out-of-round, or is worn to a diameter of 0.489 or smaller on 6B, 8B, 60000, 80000, 82000, 92000, 110900 and 130000 models, 0.552 or smaller on 100000 models, or 0.671 or smaller on 140000 models, reject the pin.

The piston ring gap for new rings should be from 0.010-0.025 on models with aluminum cylinder bore and 0.010-0.018 with cast iron cylinder bore. Reject compression rings having an end gap of 0.035 or more and reject oil rings having an end gap of 0.045 or more.

Pistons and rings are available in 0.010, 0.020 and 0.030 oversizes as well as standard size.

A chrome ring set is available for slightly worn standard bore cylinders. Refer to note in CYLINDER paragraph.

CYLINDER. If cylinder bore wear is 0.003 or more or is 0.0025 or more out-of-round, cylinder must be rebored to next larger oversize.

The standard bore sizes for each basic model series are given below:

STANDARD CYLINDER BORE SIZES

Basic Model	Cylinder Bore
6B, early 60000	2.3115-2.3125
Other 60000	2.374-2.375
8B, 80000, 82000	2.374-2.375
92000, 130000	2.5615-2.5625
100000	2.499-2.500
110900	2.7802-2.7812
140000	2.749-2.750

It is recommended that a hone be used for resizing cylinders. Operate hone at 300-700 RPM and with an up and down movement that will produce a 45° crosshatch pattern. Clean cylinder after honing with oil or soap suds. Always resize to exact 0.010, 0.020 or 0.030 oversize from given dimensions. Approved hones are as follows: For aluminum bore, use Ammco No. 3956 for rough and finishing or Sunnen No. AN200 for rough and Sunnen AN500 for finishing; and for sleeved bores, use Ammco No. 4324 for rough and finishing, or Sunnen No. AN100 for rough and Sunnen No. AN300 for finishing.

Note: A chrome piston ring set is available for slightly worn standard bore cylinders. No honing or cylinder deglazing is required for these rings. The cylinder bore can be a maximum of 0.005 oversize when using chrome rings.

CRANKSHAFT AND MAIN BEARINGS. Except where equipped with ball bearings, the main bearings are an integral part of the crankcase and cover or sump. The bearings are renewable by reaming out the crankcase and cover or sump bearing bores and installing service bushings. The tools for reaming the crankcase and cover or sump, and for installing the service bushings are available from Briggs & Stratton. If the bearings are scored, out-of-round 0.0007 or more, or are worn to or larger than the reject sizes given below, ream the bearings and install service bushings.

MAIN BEARING REJECT SIZES

Basic Model	Bearing Magneto	Bearing Drive
6B, 60000 . . .	0.878	0.878*
8B, 80000 . . .	0.878	0.878*
82000, 92000	0.878	0.878
110900	0.878	0.878
100000, 130000	0.878	1.003
140000	1.0036	1.185

*Drive bearing reject size is 1.003 on 8B-HA and 60000 and 80000 horizontal crankshaft models that are equipped with auxiliary power take-off. Bushings are not available for servicing the drive end bearings on these models; therefore, the sump must be renewed if necessary to renew the bearing.

Rejection sizes for the crankshaft bearing journals are given in the following chart. Figures given for main bearing journals would apply to plain bearing applications only.

CRANKSHAFT REJECTION SIZES

Basic Model	Magneto Journal	Crankpin Journal	Drive End Journal
6B, 60000	0.873	0.870	0.873*
8B, 80000	0.873	0.996	0.873*
82000, 92000 . .	0.873	0.996	0.873
110900 . . .	0.873	0.997	0.873
100000, 130000 .	0.873	0.996	0.998
140000 . . .	0.997	1.090	1.179

*0.998 on model 8B-HA and 60000 and 80000 models equipped with auxiliary power take-off.

Ball bearing mains are a press fit on the crankshaft, and must be removed by pressing the crankshaft out of the bearing. Reject ball bearing if worn or rough. Expand new bearing by heating it in oil (325° F. maximum) and install it on crankshaft with seal side towards crankpin journal.

Crankshaft end play on all models is 0.002-0.008. (With at least one 0.015 cover or sump gasket in place.) Additional sump or cover gaskets of 0.005 and 0.009 thickness are available if end play is less than 0.002. If end play is over 0.008, metal shims are available for use on crankshaft between crankshaft gear and cylinder.

CAMSHAFT. The camshaft and camshaft gear are an integral part which rides in journals at each end of the camshaft. The camshaft and gear should be inspected for wear on the journals, cam lobes and gear teeth. Rejection sizes for the journals and cam lobes are given in the chart below.

CAMSHAFT REJECTION SIZES

Basic Model	Journal Reject Size	Lobe Reject Size
6B, 60000 . . .	0.498	0.883
8B, 80000 . . .	0.498*	0.883
82000, 92000	0.498	0.883
110900	**	0.870
100000, 130000	0.498	0.950
140000	0.498	0.977

*On auxiliary pto models, the camshaft journal rejection size is 0.498 on the magneto end and 0.751 on the pto end.

**On model 110900 journal reject size is 0.436 on magneto end and 0.498 on pto end.

On models with "Easy-Spin" starting, the intake cam lobe is designed to hold the intake valve slightly open on a part of the compression stroke. Therefore, to check compression, the engine must be turned backwards.

"Easy-Spin" camshafts (cam gears) can be identified by two holes drilled in the web of the gear. Where part number of an older cam gear and an "Easy-Spin" cam gear are the same (except for an "E" following the "Easy-Spin" part number), the gears are interchangeable.

VALVE SYSTEM. Intake valve tappet clearance is 0.005-0.007 and exhaust valve tappet clearance is 0.009-0.011 when engine is cold. The valve seat angle is 45°. Regrind or renew valve seat insert if the seat width is 5/64-inch or wider. Regrind to width of 3/64 to 1/16-inch. Obtain specified valve tappet clearance by grinding end of valve stem squarely. Renew valve if margin is 1/64-inch or less after refacing.

The valve guides on all engines with aluminum blocks are an integral part of the cylinder block. To renew the valve guides, they must be reamed out and a bushing installed. Reamers and bushings are available from Briggs & Stratton. The part numbers are as follows:

Engine Model	Reamer Part No.	Bushing Part No.
6B, 8B, 60000, 80000, 82000, 92000, 100000,110900 & 130000 . . .	19064, 19066 (Driver— 19065)	63709
140000	19183	230655

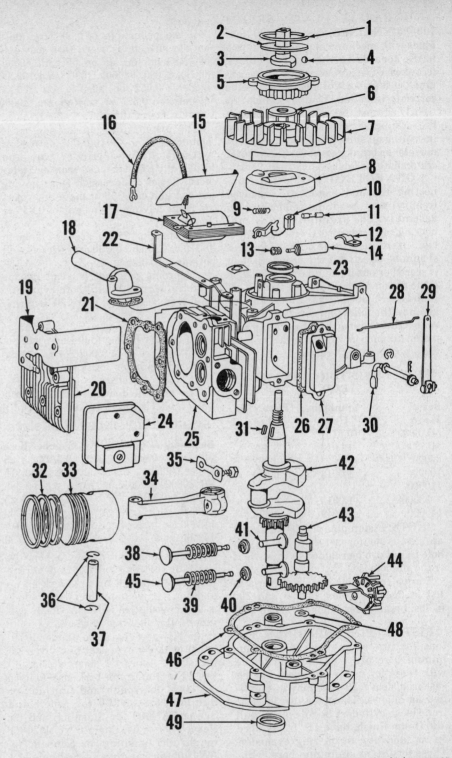

Fig. B110–Exploded view of Series 100000 vertical crankshaft engine with mechanical governor. Series 130000 and 140000 vertical crankshaft models with mechanical governor are similar. Refer to Fig. B107 for typical vertical crankshaft model with air vane governor.

1. Snap ring
2. Washer
3. Starter ratchet
4. Steel balls
5. Starter clutch
6. Washer
7. Flywheel
8. Breaker cover
9. Breaker arm spring
10. Breaker arm & pivot
11. Breaker plunger
12. Condenser clamp
13. Primary wire retainer spring
14. Condenser
15. Air baffle
16. Spark plug wire
17. Armature & coil assy.
18. Intake pipe
19. Air baffle
20. Cylinder head
21. Cylinder head gasket
22. Linkage lever
23. Crankshaft oil seal
24. Muffler
25. Cylinder block
26. Gasket
27. Breather & tappet chamber cover
28. Governor link
29. Governor lever
30. Governor crank
31. Flywheel key
32. Piston rings
33. Piston
34. Connecting rod
35. Rod bolt lock
36. Piston pin retaining rings
37. Piston pin
38. Intake valve
39. Valve springs
40. Valve spring retainers
41. Tappets (cam followers)
42. Crankshaft
43. Cam gear
44. Governor & oil slinger assembly
45. Exhaust valve
46. Gasket (0.005, 0.009 0.015)
47. Oil sump (engine base)
48. Crankshaft oil seal

On 6B, 8B, 60000, 80000, 82000, 92000, 100000, 110900 and 130000 models, use Reamer No. 19064 with oil to ream worn guide. Ream only about 1/16-inch deeper than length of bushing. Press in bushing with Driver No. 19065 until it is flush with top of guide bore. Finish ream the bushing with Reamer No. 19066.

On 140000 models, use Reamer No. 19183 to ream worn valve guide. Ream only about 1/16-inch deeper than top end of flutes on reamer. Press in bushing with soft driver as bushing is finish reamed at the factory.

VALVE TIMING. On engines equipped with ball bearing mains,

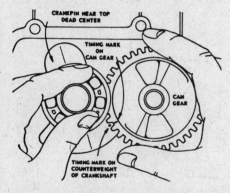

Fig. B111–Align timing marks on cam gear with mark on crankshaft counterweight on ball bearing equipped models.

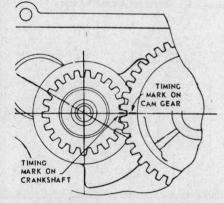

Fig. B112–Align timing marks on cam gear and crankshaft gear on plain bearing models.

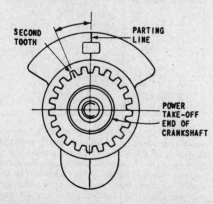

Fig. B113–Location of tooth to align with timing mark on cam gear if mark is not visible on crankshaft gear.

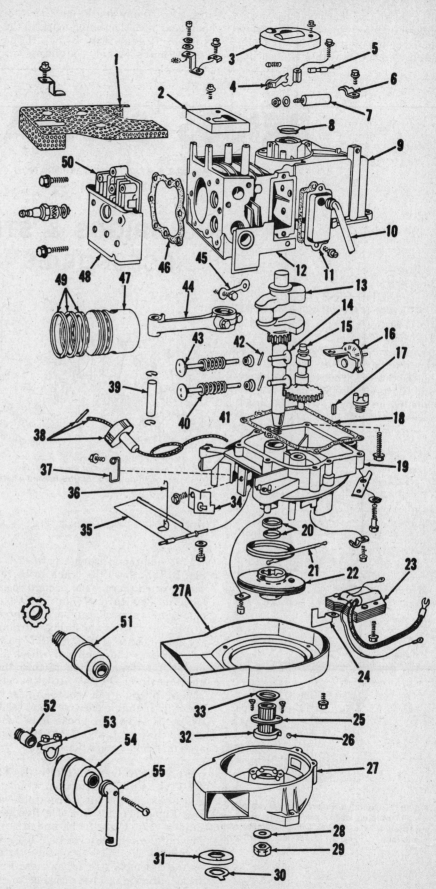

Fig. B114–Exploded view of typical "Sonoduct" vertical crankshaft engine. Flywheel (27) is located on lower end of crankshaft to lower the center of gravity and provide a low profile appearance. Cooling air is drawn through the screen (1) and ejected below the mower deck out through ducted flywheel.

align the timing mark on the cam gear with the timing mark on the crankshaft counterweight as shown in Fig. B111. On engines with plain bearings,

align the timing marks on the camshaft gear with the timing mark on the crankshaft gear (Fig. B112). If the timing mark is not visible on the

crankshaft gear, align the timing mark on the camshaft gear with the second tooth to the left of the crankshaft counterweight parting line as in Fig. B113.

BRIGGS & STRATTON

BRIGGS & STRATTON CORPORATION
Milwaukee, Wisconsin 53201

SERVICING BRIGGS & STRATTON ACCESSORIES

WIND-UP STARTER

STARTER OPERATION (EARLY UNITS). Refer to Figs. B115 and B116. Turning the knob (17) to "CRANK" position holds the engine flywheel stationary. Turning the crank (1) winds up the power spring within the spring and cup assembly (8). Spring tension is held by the clutch ratchet (15) and the crank ratchet pawl (2). On some start-

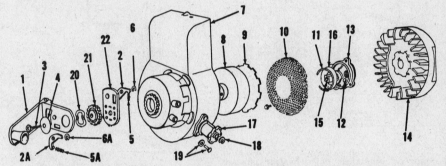

Fig. B116–Exploded view of typical Briggs & Stratton wind-up starter equipped with ratchet type wind-up crank. Starter is used where space does not permit full turn of crank.

1. Crank	6. Snap ring
2. Pawl	6A. Snap ring
2A. Pawl	7. Blower housing
3. Screw	8. Power spring & cup assy.
4. Washer	9. Retainer plate
5. Spring	10. Screen
5A. Spring	

11. Snap ring	17. Flywheel holder
12. Clutch balls	18. Snap ring
13. Clutch housing	19. Rivet & burr
14. Flywheel	20. Wave washer
15. Clutch ratchet	21. Ratchet
16. Ratchet cover	22. Pawl housing

ers, an additional ratchet pawl (2A—Fig. B116) allows the crank to be reversed when there is not enough room for a full 360° turn of crank. Approximately 5½ turns of crank are required to fully wind the power spring. Turning the holding knob (17) to "START" position releases the engine flywheel allowing the power spring to turn the engine. Note: Do not turn knob to "CRANK" position when engine is running. If engine does not start readily, check to be sure choke is in fully closed position and that ignition system is delivering a hot spark.

STARTER OPERATION (LATE UNITS). Late production wind-up starter assemblies have a control lever (see Fig. B117) instead of a flywheel holder (17—Figs. B115 and B116). Moving the control lever to "CRANK" position locks the hub of the starter spring assembly (see lower view, Fig. B117) allowing starter spring to be wound up by turning crank. Moving the control lever to "START" position releases the spring assembly hub; the spring unwinds, engaging the starter

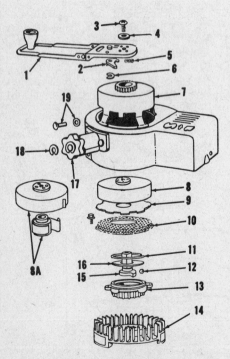

Fig. B115–Exploded view of typical early production wind-up starter. Refer to Fig. B116 for exploded view of starter using a ratchet type crank and to Fig. B117 for late production starter.

1. Crank	10. Screen
2. Pawl	11. Snap ring
3. Screw	12. Clutch balls
4. Washer	13. Clutch housing
5. Spring	14. Flywheel
6. Snap ring	15. Starter ratchet
7. Blower housing	16. Ratchet cover
8. Power spring & cup assy.	17. Flywheel holder
8A. Power spring & cup assy.	18. Snap ring
9. Retainer plate	19. Rivet & burr

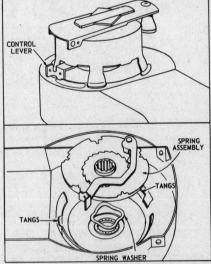

Fig. B117–On late production units, control lever (top view) locks hub of spring assembly (bottom) to allow spring to be wound up by turning crank. To remove spring assembly, first remove screw (3–Fig. B118), washer (4) and crank (1); then, bend tangs of blower housing out as shown in bottom view and lift cup, spring and control lever assembly from housing. Note spring washer placed between cup and washer.

ratchet, and cranks up engine.

CAUTION: Never work on engine or driven machinery if starter is wound up. If attached machinery such as mower blade is jammed up so that starter will not turn engine, remove blower housing and starter assembly from engine to allow starter to unwind.

OVERHAUL (EARLY UNITS). Remove starter and blower housing from engine. Check condition of flywheel and flywheel holder assembly. Check action of clutch ratchet (15—Fig. B115 or B116); remove snap ring (11) to disassemble clutch unit. Bend tangs of blower housing back to remove retainer (9). Remove screw (3) retaining crank and ratchet assembly to power spring cup (8).

Flywheel holder assembly may be renewed as a unit using new rivets and washers (19) after cutting old assembly from blower housing. Knob (17) and snap ring (18) are available separately.

On early models, power spring and cup (8A) are available separately; on later units, spring and cup (8) are available only as an assembly.

Renew parts as necessary and reas-

semble as follows: Place ratchet (15) in cup (13), drop the balls (12) in beside ratchet and install washer (16) and snap ring (11). Reassemble blower housing and starter unit in reverse of disassembly procedure.

OVERHAUL (LATE UNITS). Refer to Fig. B118 and proceed as follows: Move control lever (L) to "START" position; if starter is wound up and will not turn engine, hold crank (1) securely and loosen screw (3). Remove blower housing and starter unit from engine and, if not already done, remove screw (3) and crank (1). Turn blower housing over and bend tangs outward as shown in bottom view of Fig. B117; then lift cup, spring and control lever assembly from the blower housing. CAUTION: DO NOT attempt to disassemble the cup and spring assembly; unit is serviced as a complete assembly only.

When reassembling unit, renew the spring washer (8—Fig. B118) if damaged in any way. Grease the mating surfaces of spring cup and blower housing and stick spring washer in place with grease. Renew pawl (2) or pawl spring (5) on crank assembly (1) if necessary. Check condition of ratchet teeth on blower housing; renew housing if teeth are broken or worn off. Reassemble by reversing disassembly procedure.

Starter ratchet cover (14) and ratchet (13) can be removed after removing the Sems screws (10) and rotating screen (11). Be careful not to lose the steel balls (15). Clutch housing (16) also is the flywheel retaining nut. To

remove housing, hold flywheel and turn housing counter-clockwise. A special wrench (B & S tool No. 19114) is available for removing and installing housing.

To reassemble, first be sure spring washer is in place on crankshaft with cup (hollow) side towards the flywheel. Install starter clutch housing and tighten securely. Place starter ratchet on crankshaft and drop the steel balls in place in housing. Reinstall ratchet cover with new seal (12) if required. Reinstall the rotating screen and install blower housing and starter assembly.

REWIND STARTERS

OVERHAUL. To renew broken rewind spring, proceed as follows: Grasp free outer end of spring (S—Fig. B120) and pull broken end from starter housing. With blower housing removed, bend nylon bumpers (N) up and out of the way and remove starter pulley from housing. Untie knot in rope (R) and remove rope and inner end of broken spring from pulley. Apply a small amount of grease on inner face of pulley, thread inner end of new spring through notch in starter housing, engage inner end of spring in pulley hub (on older models, install retainer in hub with split side of retainer away from spring hook) and place pulley in housing. Renew nylon bumpers if necessary and bend bumpers down to within ⅛-inch of the pulley. Insert a ¾-inch square bar in pulley hub and turn pulley approximately 13½ turns in a counter-clockwise direction as shown in Fig. B121. Tie wrench to blower housing with wire to hold pulley so that hole (H) in pulley is aligned with rope guide (G) in housing as shown in

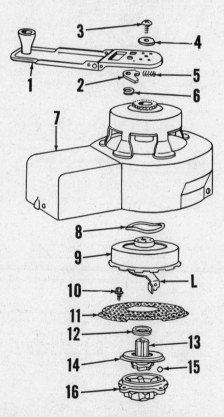

Fig. B118—Exploded view of late production wind-up starter assembly. Control lever (L) locks ratchet drive hub to allow starter to be wound up and releases hub to crank engine.

L. Control lever	9. Cup, spring & release
1. Crank	assembly
2. Pawl	10. Sems screws
3. Screw	11. Rotating screen
4. Washer	12. Seal
5. Spring	13. Starter ratchet
6. Snap ring	14. Ratchet cover
7. Blower housing	15. Steel balls
8. Spring washer	16. Clutch housing

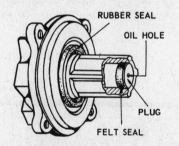

Fig. B119—Cut-away view of late type starter ratchet showing sealing felt and plug in outer end. Oil ratchet through hole in plug. A rubber seal is also used at ratchet cover.

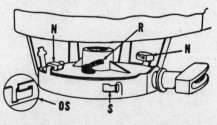

Fig. B120—View of Briggs & Stratton rewind starter assembly.

N. Nylon bumpers   R. Starter rope
OS. Old style spring   S. Rewind spring

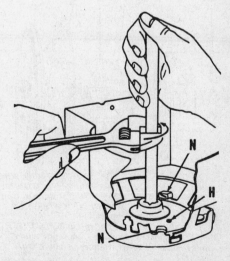

Fig. B121—Using square shaft and wrench to wind up the rewind starter spring. Refer to text.

H. Hole in starter pulley
N. Nylon bumpers

Fig. B122. Hook a wire in inner end of rope and thread rope through guide and hole in pulley; then, tie a knot in rope and release the pulley allowing the spring to wind the rope into the pulley groove.

To renew starter rope only, it is not generally necessary to remove starter pulley and spring. Wind up the spring and install new rope as outlined in preceding paragraph.

Two different types of starter clutches have been used; refer to exploded view of early production unit in Fig. B123 and exploded view of late production unit in Fig. B124. The outer end of the late production ratchet (refer to cutaway view in Fig. B125) is sealed with a felt and a retaining plug and a rubber ring is used to seal ratchet to ratchet cover.

To disassemble early type starter clutch unit, refer to Fig. B123 and proceed as follows: Remove snap ring (3) and lift ratchet (5) and cover (4) from starter housing (7) and crankshaft. Be careful not to lose the steel balls (6). Starter housing (7) is also flywheel retaining nut; to remove housing, first remove screen (2) and using Briggs & Stratton flywheel

wrench No. 19114, unscrew housing from crankshaft in counter-clockwise direction. When reinstalling housing, be sure spring washer (8) is placed on crankshaft with cup (hollow) side towards flywheel, then install starter housing and tighten securely. Reinstall rotating screen. Place ratchet on crankshaft and into housing and insert the steel balls. Reinstall cover and retaining snap ring.

To disassemble late starter clutch unit, refer to Fig. B124 and proceed as follows: Remove rotating screen (2) and starter ratchet cover (4). Lift ratchet (5) from housing and crankshaft and extract the steel balls (6). If necessary to remove housing (7), hold flywheel and unscrew housing in counter-clockwise direction using Briggs & Stratton flywheel wrench No. 19114. When installing housing, be sure spring washer (8) is in place on crankshaft with cup (hollow) side towards flywheel; then, tighten housing securely. Inspect felt seal and plug in outer end of ratchet; renew ratchet if seal or plug are damaged as these parts are not serviced separately. Lubricate the felt with oil and place ratchet on crankshaft. Insert the steel balls and install ratchet cover, rubber seal and rotating screen.

NOTE: Crankshafts used with early and late starter clutches differ; refer to Fig. B126. If renewing early (long) crankshaft with late (short) shaft, also install late type starter clutch unit. If renewing early starter clutch with late type unit, the crankshaft must be shortened to the dimension shown for short shaft in Fig. B126; also, hub of starter rope pulley must be shortened to ½-inch dimension shown in Fig.

B127. Bevel end of crankshaft after removing the approximate ⅜-inch from shaft.

When installing blower housing and starter assembly, turn starter ratchet so that word "TOP" on ratchet is toward engine cylinder head.

VERTICAL PULL STARTER

OVERHAUL. To renew rope or spring, first remove all spring tension from rope. Using a screwdriver as shown in Fig. B129, pull rope up about one foot. Wind rope and pulley counter-clockwise 3 turns as shown in Fig. B130 to remove all tension. Carefully pry off the plastic spring cover. Refer to Fig. B131 and remove anchor bolt and spring anchor. Carefully remove spring from housing. Unbolt and remove rope guide. Note position of the friction link in Fig. B132. Remove old rope from pulley.

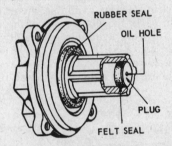

Fig. B125–Cut-away view showing felt seal and plug in end of late production starter ratchet (5–Fig. B124).

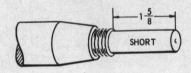

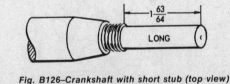

Fig. B126–Crankshaft with short stub (top view) must be used with late production starter clutch assembly. Early crankshaft (bottom view) can be modified by cutting off stub end to the dimension shown in top view and beveling end of shaft to allow installation of late type clutch unit.

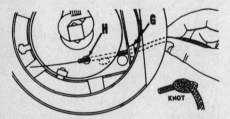

Fig. B122–Threading starter rope through guide (G) in blower housing and hole (H) in starter pulley with wire hooked in end of rope. Tie knot in end of rope as shown.

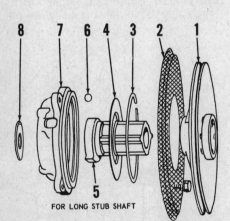

Fig. B123–Exploded view of early production starter clutch unit; refer to Fig. B126 for view of "long stub shaft". A late type unit (Fig. B125) should be installed when renewing "long" crankshaft with "short" (late production) shaft.

Fig. B124–View of late production sealed starter clutch unit. Late unit can be used with "short stub shaft" only; refer to Fig. B126. Refer to Fig. B125 for cut-away view of ratchet (5).

1. Starter rope pulley
2. Rotating screen
3. Snap ring
4. Ratchet cover
5. Starter ratchet
6. Steel balls
7. Clutch housing (flywheel nut)
8. Spring washer

1. Starter rope pulley
2. Rotating screen
3. Rubber seal
4. Ratchet cover
5. Starter ratchet
6. Steel balls
7. Clutch housing (flywheel nut)
8. Spring washer

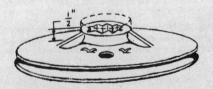

Fig. B127–When installing a late type starter clutch unit as replacement for early type, either install new starter rope pulley or cut hub of old pulley to dimension shown.

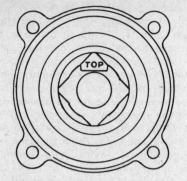

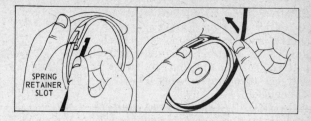

Fig. B133–Hook outer end of spring in retainer slot, then coil the spring counter-clockwise in the housing.

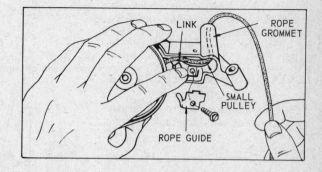

Fig. B128–When reinstalling blower housing and starter assembly, turn starter ratchet so that word "TOP" stamped on outer end of ratchet is towards engine cylinder head.

Fig. B134–When installing pulley assembly in housing, make sure friction link is positioned as shown, then install rope guide.

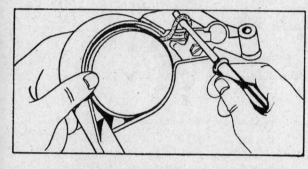

Fig. B129–Use a screwdriver to pull rope up to provide about one foot of slack.

It is not necessary to remove the gear retainer unless pulley or gear is damaged and renewal is necessary. Clean and inspect all parts. The friction link should move the gear to both extremes of its travel. If not, renew the linkage assembly.

Install new spring by hooking end in retainer slot and winding until spring is coiled in housing. See Fig. B133. Insert new rope through the housing and into the pulley. Tie a small knot, heat seal the knot and pull it tight into the recess in pulley. Install pulley assembly in the housing with friction link in pocket of casting as shown in Fig. B134. Install rope guide. Rotate pulley counter-clockwise until rope is fully wound. Hook free end of spring to anchor, install screw and tighten to a torque of 75-90 in.-lbs. Lubricate spring with a small amount of engine oil. Snap the plastic spring cover in place. Pre-load spring by pulling rope up about one foot, then winding rope and pulley 2 or 3 turns clockwise.

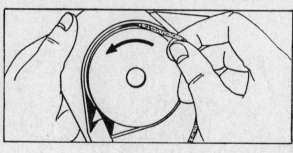

Fig. B130–Rotate pulley and rope 3 turns counter-clockwise to remove spring tension from rope.

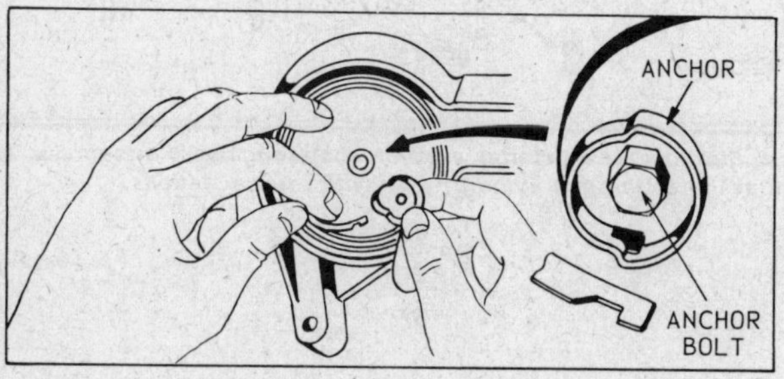

110-VOLT ELECTRIC STARTERS (CHAIN AND BELT DRIVE)

Early production 110-volt electric starter with chain drive is shown in Fig. B135; later type with belt drive is shown in Fig. B136. Starters for horizontal crankshaft engines are similar to units shown for vertical shaft engines.

Fig. B131–Remove anchor bolt and spring anchor to release inner end of spring.

Chain (2—Fig. B135) on early models is adjusted by changing position of nuts on adjusting stud (11) so that chain deflection is approximately ¼-inch between sprockets. There should be about 1/32-inch clearance between spring (8) and sprocket (9) when unit is assembled. Clutch unit (7, 8 & 9) should disengage when engine starts.

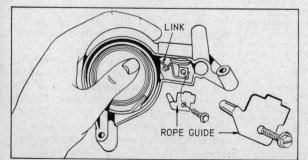

Fig. B132–Rope guide removed from Vertical Pull starter. Note position of friction link.

Belt (8—Fig. B136) tension is adjusted by shifting starter motor in slotted mounting holes so that clutch unit (3) on starter motor will engage belt and turn engine, but so that belt will not turn starter when clutch is disengaged.

CAUTION: Always connect starter cord to starter before plugging cord into 110-volt outlet and disconnect cord from outlet before removing cord from starter connector. Do not run the electric starter for more than 60 seconds at a time.

12-VOLT STARTER-GENERATOR UNITS

The combination starter-generator functions as a cranking motor when

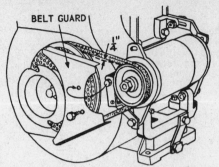

Fig. B137–View showing starter-generator belt adjustment on models so equipped. Refer to text.

the starting switch is closed. When engine is operating and with starting switch open, the unit operates as a generator. Generator output and circuit voltage for the battery and various operating requirements are controlled by a current-voltage regulator. On units where voltage regulator is mounted separately from generator unit, do not mount regulator with cover down as regulator will not function in this position. To adjust belt tension, apply approximately 30 pounds pull on generator adjusting flange and tighten mounting bolts. Belt tension is correct

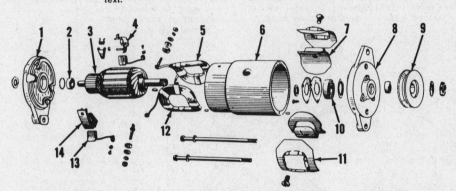

Fig. B138–Exploded view of Delco-Remy starter-generator unit used on some B&S engines.

1. Commutator end frame	6. Frame	10. Bearing
2. Bearing	7. Pole shoe	11. Field coil insulator
3. Armature	8. Drive end frame	12. Field coil R.H.
4. Ground brush holder	9. Pulley	13. Brush
5. Field coil L.H.		14. Insulated brush holder

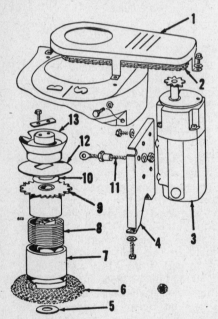

Fig. B135–Exploded view of early production 110-volt electric starter used on vertical crankshaft models. Starter used on horizontal crankshaft models was similar.

1. Chain shield	8. Spring
2. Drive chain	9. Sprocket & hub
3. Electric motor	10. Thrust washer
4. Mounting bracket	11. Adjusting screw
5. Washer	12. Guard washer
6. Rotating screen	13. Rope starter pulley
7. Shaft adapter	

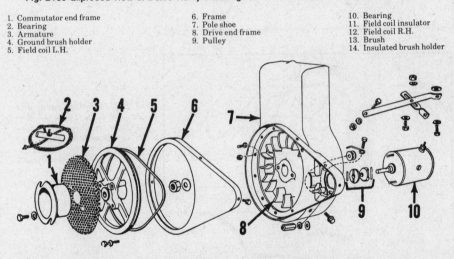

Fig. B139–Exploded view of Briggs & Stratton 12-volt starter used on some engines. Parts and/or service on starter motor are available through authorized Autolite service stations.

1. Rope pulley	6. Belt guard
2. Starter rope	7. Blower housing
3. Rotating screen	8. Flywheel
4. Starter driven pulley	9. Starter clutch
5. Drive belt	10. Starter motor

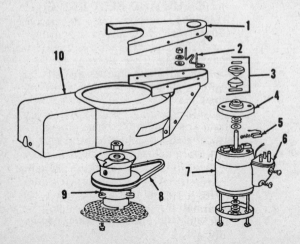

Fig. B136–Exploded view of late production 110-volt electric starter unit. Starters for horizontal crankshaft models are similar.

1. Belt shield
2. Belt guide
3. Clutch assembly
4. Cover
5. Commutator brush assy.
6. Connector plug
7. Electric motor
8. Drive belt
9. Drive pulley
10. Blower housing

when a pressure of 10 pounds applied midway between pulleys will deflect belt ¼-inch. See Fig. B137. On units equipped with two drive belts, always renew belts in pairs. A 50-ampere capacity battery is recommended. Starter-generator units are intended for use in temperatures above 0° F. Refer to Fig. B138 for exploded view of starter-generator. Parts and service on the starter-generator are available at authorized Delco-Remy service stations.

12-VOLT ELECTRIC STARTER
(BELT DRIVE)

Refer to Fig. B139. Adjust position of starter motor (10) so that clutch will engage belt and turn engine when starter is operated, but so that belt will not turn starter motor when engine is running. The 12-volt electric starter is intended for use in temperatures above 15° F. Driven equipment should be disengaged before using starter. Parts and service on starter motor are available at Autolite service agencies.

CAUTION: Do not use automotive jumper (booster) battery as this may result in damage to starter motor.

GEAR-DRIVE STARTERS

Two types of gear drive starters may be used, a 110 volt AC starter or a 12 volt DC starter. Refer to Fig. B140 for an exploded view of starter motors. A properly grounded receptacle should be used with power cord connected to 110 volt AC starter motor. A 32 ampere hour capacity battery is recommended for use with 12 volt DC starter motor.

To renew a worn or damaged flywheel ring gear, drill out retaining rivets using a 3/16-inch drill. Attach new ring gear using screws provided with new ring gear.

To check for correct operation of starter motor, remove starter motor from engine and place motor in a vise or other holding fixture. Install a 0-5 amp ammeter in power cord to 110 volt AC starter motor. On 12 volt DC motor,

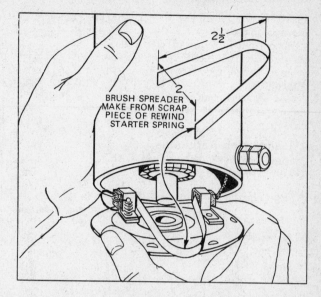

Fig. B142–Tool shown may be fabricated to hold brushes when installing motor end cap.

connect a 6 volt battery to motor with a 0-50 amp ammeter in series with positive line from battery to starter motor. Connect a tachometer to drive end of starter. With starter activated on 110 volt motor, starter motor should turn at 5200 rpm minimum with a maximum current draw of 3½ amps. The 12 volt motor should turn at 5000 rpm minimum with a current draw of 25 amps maximum. If starter motor does not operate satisfactorily, check operation of rectifier or starter switch. If rectifier and starter switch are good, disassemble and inspect starter motor.

To check the rectifier used on the 110 volt AC starter motor, remove rectifier

unit from starter motor. Solder a 10,000 ohm 1 watt resistor to the DC internal terminals of the rectifier as shown in Fig. B141. Connect a 0-100 range DC voltmeter to resistor leads. Measure the voltage of the AC outlet to be used. With starter switch in "OFF" position, a zero reading should be shown on DC voltmeter. With starter switch in "ON" position, the DC voltmeter should show a reading that is 0-14 volts lower than AC line voltage measured previously. If voltage drop exceeds 14 volts, renew rectifier unit.

Disassembly of starter motor is self-evident after inspection of unit and referral to Fig. B140. Note position of bolts (9) during disassembly so that they can be installed in their original positions during reassembly. When reassembling motor, lubricate end cap bearings with #20 oil. Be sure to match the drive cap keyway to the stamped key in the housing when sliding the armature into the motor housing. Brushes may be held in their holders during installation by making a brush spreader tool from a piece of metal as shown in Fig. B142. Splined end of helix (2—Fig. B140) must be towards end of armature shaft as shown in Fig. B143. Tighten armature shaft nut to 170 inch-lbs.

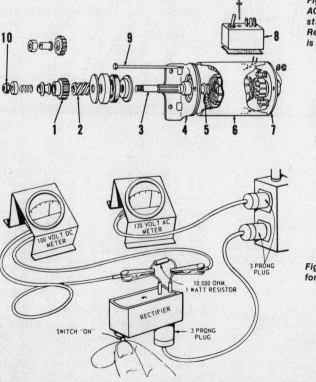

Fig. B140–View of 110 volt AC starter motor. 12 volt DC starter motor is similar. Rectifier and switch unit (8) is used on 110 volt motor only.

1. Pinion gear
2. Helix
3. Armature shaft
4. Drive cap
5. Thrust washer
6. Housing
7. End cap
8. Rectifier & switch
9. Bolt
10. Nut

Fig. B141–Test connections for 110 volt rectifier. Refer to text for procedure.

FLYWHEEL ALTERNATOR
Early Type External

Refer to Fig. B144 for assembled view and to Fig. B145 for exploded view of alternator. The 12-volt flywheel alternator is designed for use with the 12-volt electric starter and a 20 to 24 ampere-hour capacity battery.

Armature air gap should be 0.005-0.016. Rectifiers (diodes) are available separately from the armature and coil unit which is available as an assembly only. When renewing the condenser or fuses, be sure to use the correct Briggs & Stratton parts.

No cut-out is required with this alternator as the rectifiers (6) prevent reverse flow of electricity through the alternator.

CAUTION: Do not short across alternator terminals as rectifiers may be damaged.

1½ Amp. Non-Regulated

Some engines are equipped with a 1½ ampere non-regulated flywheel al-

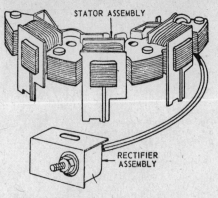

Fig. B146–Stator and rectifier assembly used on the 1½ ampere non-regulated flywheel alternator.

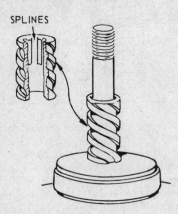

Fig. B143–Install helix on armature so that splines of helix are to the outer end as shown.

Fig. B147 – Disconnect charging lead and connect load lamp to test alternator output.

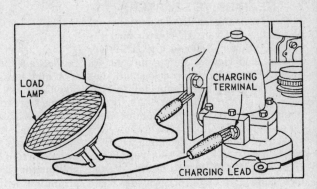

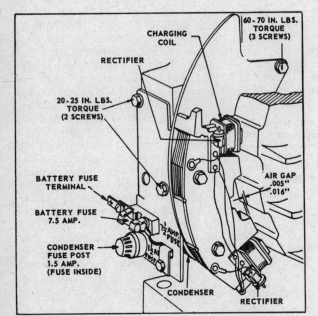

Fig. B144–Assembled and installed view of early type 12-volt flywheel alternator; refer to Fig. B145 for exploded view of unit.

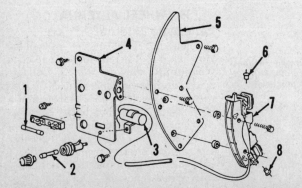

Fig. B145–Exploded view of early type 12-volt flywheel alternator designed for use with the 12-volt starter motor unit shown in Fig. B139.

1. Fuse (3AG—7½ amps.)
2. Fuse (AG—1½ amps.)
3. Condenser
4. Support plate
5. Alternator plate
6. Rectifier
7. Armature & coil assy.
8. Rectifier

ternator. This alternator (Fig. B146) with a solid state rectifier, is designed for use with a compact battery. A 12 ampere hour battery is suggested for warm temperature operation and a 24 ampere hour battery should be used in cold service. The alternator is rated at 3600 rpm. At lower speeds, available output is reduced.

To test for alternator output, disconnect charging lead from charging terminal. Connect a 12 volt lamp between charging terminal and ground as shown in Fig. B147. Start engine. If lamp lights, alternator is functioning. If lamp does not light, alternator is defective.

To check for faulty stator, disconnect charging lead from battery and rectifier. Remove rectifier box mounting screw. Turn box to expose eyelets to which red and black stator leads are soldered. Start engine and with engine operating, touch load lamp leads to eyelets as in Fig. B148. If lamp does not light, stator or flywheel is defective. Remove flywheel and check to be sure magnet ring is in place and has magnetism. Check wires from stator to rectifier. If flywheel and wiring is good, renew stator assembly which includes new rectifier. If the load lamp lights, stator is satisfactory. Check for faulty rectifier as follows: With engine stopped and charging lead disconnected from charging terminal, connect one ohmmeter lead to charging terminal and other lead to engine block. See Fig. B149. Check for continuity, then reverse ohmmeter leads and again check for continuity. Ohmmeter should show a continuity reading for one direction only. If tests show no continuity in either direction or continuity in both directions, rectifier is faulty and must be renewed. Rectifier assembly is serviced separately.

4 Amp. Non-Regulated

Some engines are equipped with the 4 ampere non-regulated flywheel alternator shown in Fig. B150. A solid state rectifier and 7½ amp fuse is used with this alternator.

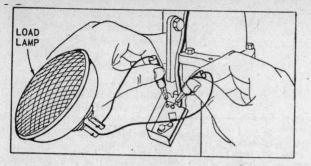

Fig. B148—Use 12 volt load lamp to test for defective stator. Refer to text.

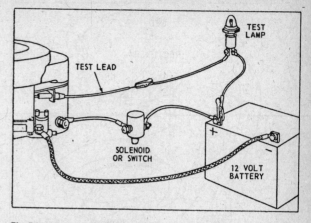

Fig. B152—Connect a test lamp as shown to test for shorted stator or defective rectifier. Refer to text.

If battery is run down and no output from alternator is suspected, first check the 7½ amp fuse. If fuse is good, clean and tighten all connections. Disconnect charging lead and connect an ammeter as shown in Fig. B151. Start engine and check for alternator output.

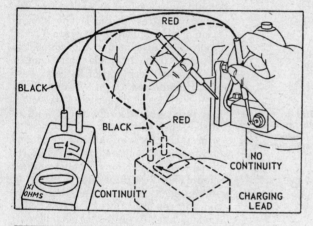

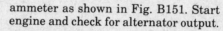

Fig. B149—When checking rectifier with an ohmmeter, and meter shows continuity both directions or neither direction, rectifier is defective.

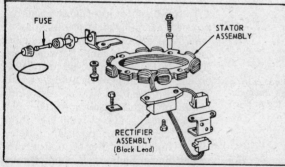

Fig. B150—Stator and rectifier assemblies used on the 4 ampere non-regulated flywheel alternator. Fuse is 7½ amp AGC or 3AG.

If ammeter shows no charge, stop engine, remove ammeter and install a test lamp as shown in Fig. B152. Test lamp should not light. If it does light, stator or rectifier is defective. Unplug rectifier plug under blower housing. If test lamp goes out, rectifier is defective. If test lamp does not go out, stator is shorted.

If shorted stator is indicated, use an ohmmeter and check continuity as follows: Touch one test lead to lead inside of fuse holder as shown in Fig. B153. Touch the other test lead to each of the four pins in rectifier connector. Unless the ohmmeter shows continuity at each of the four pins, stator winding is open and stator must be renewed.

If defective rectifier is indicated, unbolt and remove the flywheel blower housing with rectifier. Connect one ohmmeter test lead to blower housing and other test lead to the single pin connector in rectifier connector. See Fig. B154. Check for continuity, then reverse leads and again test for continuity. If tests show no continuity in either direction or continuity in both directions, rectifier is faulty and must be renewed.

7 Amp. Regulated

A 7 amp regulated flywheel alter-

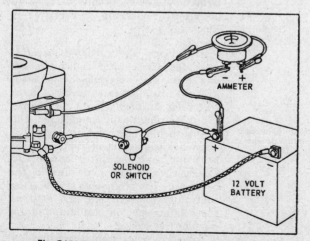

Fig. B151—Install ammeter as shown for output test.

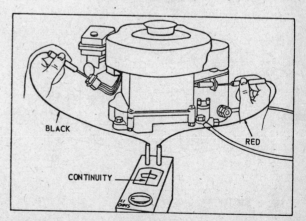

Fig. B153—Use an ohmmeter to check condition of stator. Refer to text.

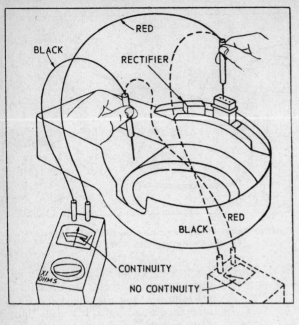

Fig. B154—If ohmmeter shows continuity in both directions or in neither direction, rectifier is defective.

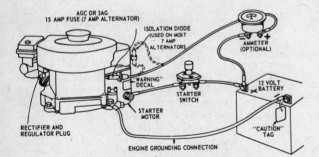

Fig. B155—Stator, rectifier and regulator assemblies used on the 7 ampere regulated flywheel alternator.

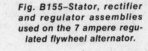

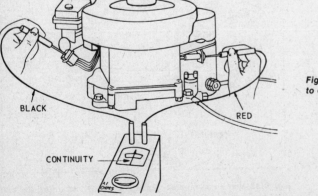

Fig. B156—Typical wiring used on engines equipped with 7 ampere flywheel alternator.

Fig. B157—Use an ohmmeter to check condition of stator. Refer to text.

nator is used with the 12 volt gear drive starter motor. The alternator is equipped with a solid state rectifier and regulator. An isolation diode is also used on most models.

If engine will not start, using electric start system, and trouble is not in starting motor, install an ammeter in circuit as shown in Fig. B156. Start engine manually. Ammeter should indicate charge. If ammeter does not show battery charging taking place, check for defective wiring and if necessary proceed with troubleshooting.

If battery charging occurs with engine running, but battery does not retain charge, then isolation diode may be defective. The isolation diode is used to prevent battery drain if alternator circuit malfunctions. After troubleshooting diode, remainder of circuit should be inspected to find reason for excessive battery drain. To check operation of diode, disconnect white lead of diode from fuse holder and connect a test lamp from the diode white lead to the negative terminal of battery. Test lamp should not light. If test lamp lights, diode is defective. Disconnect test lamp and disconnect red lead of diode. Test continuity of diode with ohmmeter by connecting leads of ohmmeter to leads of diode, then reverse lead connections. The ohmmeter should show continuity in one direction and an open circuit in the other direction. If readings are incorrect, then diode is defective and must be renewed.

To troubleshoot alternator assembly, proceed as follows: Disconnect white lead of isolation diode from fuse holder and connect a test lamp between positive terminal of battery and fuse holder on engine. Engine must not be started. With connections made, test lamp should not light. If isolation diode operates correctly and test lamp does light, stator, regulator or rectifier is defective. Unplug rectifier-regulator plug under blower housing. If lamp remains lighted, stator is grounded. If lamp goes out, regulator or rectifier is shorted.

If previous test indicated stator is grounded, check stator leads for defects and repair if necessary. If shorted leads are not found, renew stator. Check stator for an open circuit as follows: Using an ohmmeter, connect red lead to fuse holder as shown in Fig. B157 and black lead to one of the pins in the rectifier and regulator connector. Check each of the four pins in the connector. The ohmmeter should show continuity at each pin; if not, then there is an open in stator and stator must be renewed.

To test rectifier, unplug rectifier and

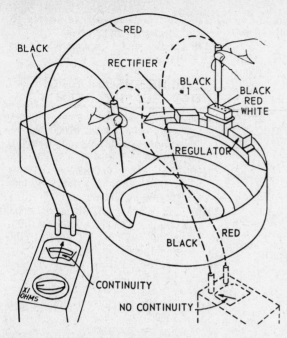

RED

BLACK

RECTIFIER

BLACK #1

BLACK
RED
WHITE

REGULATOR

BLACK   RED

CONTINUITY

NO CONTINUITY

X1 OHMS

Fig. B158–Be sure good contact is made between ohmmeter test lead and metal cover when checking rectifier and regulator.

ment. Refer to Fig. B159 for exploded view of pump.

To disassemble pump, refer to Figs. B159 and B160; then, proceed as follows: Remove clamp (1), fuel bowl (2), gasket (3) and screen (4). Remove screws retaining upper body (9) to lower body (16). Pump valves (5) and gaskets (6) can now be removed. Drive the pin (14) out to either side of body (16), then press diaphragm (10) against spring (11) as shown in view A, Fig. B160, and remove lever (13). Diaphragm and spring (11—Fig. B159) can now be removed.

To reassemble, place diaphragm spring in lower body and place diaphragm on spring, being sure that spring enters cup on bottom side of diaphragm and that slot in shaft is at right angle to pump lever. Then, compressing diaphragm against spring as in view A, Fig. B160, insert hooked end of lever into slot in shaft. Align hole in lever with hole in lower body and drive pin into place. Then, insert lever spring (15) into body and push outer end of spring into place over hook on arm of lever as shown in view B. Hold lever downward as shown in view C while tightening screws holding upper body to lower body. When installing pump on engine, apply a liberal amount of grease on lever (13) at point where it contacts groove in crankshaft.

regulator connector plug and remove blower housing from engine. Using an ohmmeter, check for continuity between connector pins connected to black wires and blower housing as shown in Fig. B158. Be sure good contact is made with metal of blower housing. Reverse ohmmeter leads and check continuity again. The ohmmeter should show a continuity reading for one direction only on each plug. If either pin shows a continuity reading

for both directions, or if either pin shows no continuity for either direction, then rectifier must be renewed.

To test regulator unit, repeat procedure used to test rectifier unit, except connect ohmmeter lead to pins connected to red wire and white wire. If ohmmeter shows continuity in either direction for red lead pin, regulator is defective and must be renewed. White lead pin should read as an open on the ohmmeter in one direction and a weak reading in the other direction. Otherwise, the regulator is defective and must be renewed.

FUEL PUMP

A diaphragm type fuel pump is available on many models as optional equip-

BRIGGS & STRATTON SPECIAL TOOLS

The following special tools are available from Briggs & Stratton Central Service Distributors.

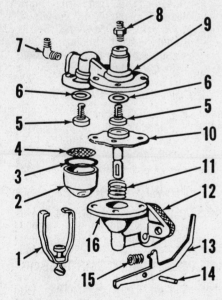

Fig. B159–Exploded view of diaphragm type fuel pump used on some Briggs & Stratton engines. Refer to Fig. B160 for assembly and disassembly views.

1. Yoke assembly
2. Filter bowl
3. Gasket
4. Filter screen
5. Pump valves
6. Gaskets
7. Elbow fitting
8. Connector
9. Fuel pump head
10. Pump diaphragm
11. Diaphragm spring
12. Gasket
13. Pump lever
14. Lever pin
15. Lever spring
16. Fuel pump body

Fig. B160–Views showing disassembly and reassembly of diaphragm type fuel pump. Refer to text for procedure and to Fig. B159 for exploded view of pump and for legend.

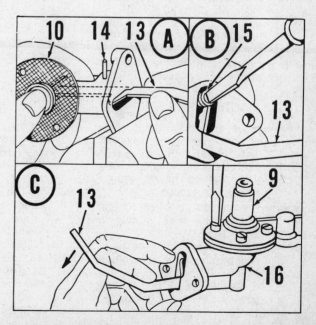

TOOL KITS

19158—Main bearing service kit for engine models 5, 6, 8, N, 6B, 8B and for engine Series 60000, 61000, 80000, 81000, 82000, 92000, 100000, 110900 and 130000. Includes tool numbers 19094, 19095, 19096, 19099, 19100, 19101, 19123, 19124 and 19166.

19184—Main bearing service kit for Series 140000. Includes tool numbers 19096, 19168, 19169, 19170, 19171, 19172, 19173, 19174, 19175, 19178, 19179 and 19201.

291661—Dealer service tool kit. Includes tool numbers 19051, 19055, 19056, 19057, 19058, 19061, 19062, 19063, 19064, 19065, 19066, 19068, 19069, 19070, 19114, 19122, 19151, 19165, 19167 and 19191.

PLUG GAGES

19055—Check breaker plunger hole on models 5, 6, 8, N, 6B, 8B and Series 60000, 61000, 80000, 81000, 82000, 92000, 100000, 110900, 130000 and 140000.

19117—Check main bearing bore on models 9 and 14.

19122—Check valve guide bore on models 5, 6, 8, N, 6B, 8B, and Series 60000, 61000, 80000, 81000, 82000, 92000, 100000, 110900, and 130000.

19151—Check valve guide bore on models 9, 14 and Series 140000.

19164—Check camshaft bearings on models 6B, 8B, and Series 60000, 61000, 80000, 81000, 82000, 92000, 100000, 110900, 130000 and 140000.

19166—Check main bearing bore on models 5, 6, 8, N, 6B, 8B and on engine Series 60000, 61000, 80000, 81000, 82000, 92000, 100000, 110900 and 130000.

19178—Check main bearing bore on engine Series 140000.

REAMERS

19056—Ream hole to install breaker plunger bushing on models 5, 6, 8, N, 6B, 8B, and Series 60000, 61000, 80000, 81000, 82000, 92000, 100000, 110900, 130000 and 140000.

19058—Finish ream breaker plunger bushing on same models as 19056 Reamer.

19064—Ream valve guide bore to install bushing on models 5, 6, 8, N, 6B, 8B, and Series 60000, 61000, 80000, 81000, 82000, 92000, 100000, 110900 and 130000.

19066—Finish ream valve guide bushing on same models as listed for 19064 Reamer.

19095—Finish ream main bearings on same models as listed for 19064 Reamer.

19099—Ream counterbore for main bearings on models 6B and 8B, and Series 60000, 61000, 80000, 81000, 82000, 92000, 100000, 110900 and 130000.

19172—Ream counterbore for main bearing on Series 100000, 130000 and 140000.

19173—Finish reamer for main bearing on Series 100000, 130000 and 140000.

19174—Ream counterbore for main bearing on Series 140000.

19175—Finish ream main bearing on Series 140000.

19183—Ream valve guide bore to install bushing on models 9, 14, and Series 140000.

GUIDE BUSHINGS FOR VALVE GUIDE REAMERS

19191—For models 5, 6, 8, N, 6B, 8B, and Series 60000, 61000, 80000, 81000, 82000, 92000, 100000, 110900 and 130000.

19192—For models 9, 14, and Series 140000.

PILOTS

19096—Pilot for main bearing reamer on models 5, 6, 8, N, 6B, 8B, and Series 60000, 61000, 80000, 81000, 82000, 92000, 100000, 110900, 130000 and 140000.

19126—Expansion pilot for valve seat counterbore cutter on models 5, 6, 8, N, 6B, 8B, and Series 60000, 61000, 80000, 81000, 82000, 92000, 100000, 110900 and 130000.

19127—Expansion pilot for valve seat counterbore cutter on models 9, 14, and Series 140000.

DRIVERS

19057—To install breaker plunger bushing on models 5, 6, 8, N, 6B, 8B, and Series 60000, 61000, 80000, 81000, 82000, 92000, 100000, 110900, 130000 and 140000.

19065—To install valve guide bushings on models 5, 6, 8, N, 6B, 8B and Series 60000, 61000, 80000, 81000, 82000, 92000, 100000, 110900 and 130000.

19124—To install main bearing bushings on models 5, 6, 8, N, 6B, 8B, and Series 60000, 61000, 80000, 81000, 82000, 92000, 100000, 110900 and 130000.

19136—To install valve seat inserts on all models and Series.

19179—Install main bearing on Series 140000.

GUIDE BUSHINGS FOR MAIN BEARING REAMERS

19094—For models 5, 6, 8, N, 6B, 8B, and Series 60000, 61000, 80000, 81000, 82000, 92000, 100000, 110900 and 130000.

19100—For models 6B, 8B, and Series 60000, 80000, 81000, 82000, 92000 and 110900.

19101—For models 6B, 8B, and Series 60000, 61000, 80000, 81000, 82000, 92000, 100000, 110900 and 130000.

19168—For Series 100000, 130000 and 140000.

19169—For Series 140000.

19170—For Series 100000, 130000 and 140000.

19171—For Series 140000.

19186—For Series 100000 and 130000.

COUNTERBORE CUTTERS

19131—To install intake valve seat on model 14.

19132—To install intake valve seat insert on models 8 and 9.

19133—To install intake valve seat on models 5, 6 and N.

CRANKCASE SUPPORT JACK

19123—To support crankcase when removing and installing main bearing bushings on models 5, 6, 8, N, 6B, 8B, and Series 60000, 61000, 80000, 81000, 82000, 92000, 100000, 110900, 130000 and 140000.

FLYWHEEL PULLERS

19068—For models 9 and 14.

19069—For models 6B, 8B, and Series 60000, 61000, 80000, 81000, 82000, 92000 and 110900.

19165—For Series 140000.

FLYWHEEL HOLDER

19167—For models 6B, 8B and Series 60000, 61000, 80000, 81000, 82000, 92000 and 110900.

VALVE SPRING COMPRESSOR

19063—For all models and Series.

PISTON RING COMPRESSOR

19070—For all models and Series

STARTER WRENCH

19114—All models with rewind or wind-up starters.

19161—All models with rewind or wind-up starters.

IGNITION SPARK TESTER
19051—For all models and Series.

VALVE SEAT REPAIR TOOLS
19129—Planer shank-driver for counterbore cutter on all models and Series.

19130—T-handle for planer shank

19129 on all models and Series.

19135—Knockout pin to remove counterbore cutter from planer shank.

19137—T-handle for expansion pilots.

19138—Insert puller to remove valve seats on all models and Series

(when puller nut 19140, included with 19138, is ground to 1/32-inch thick for pulling insert on aluminum alloy models).

19182—Puller nut to adapt 19138 puller to aluminum alloy models.

BRIGGS & STRATTON CENTRAL SERVICE DISTRIBUTORS

(Alphabetically by States)

These franchised firms carry extensive stocks of repair parts. Contact them or name of the nearest service distributor who may have the parts you need.

Birmingham Electric Battery Co.
2230 Second Avenue, South
Birmingham, Alabama 35233

Motor Supply Co.
402-414 N. Central Avenue
Phoenix, Arizona 85004

Pacific Power Equipment Co.
50 Edwards Court
Burlingame, California 94010

Power Equipment Co.
20531 S. Belshaw Ave.
Carson, California 90746

Spitzer Industrial Prod. Co.
43 W. 9th Avenue
Denver, Colorado 80204

Spencer Engine & Magneto, Inc.
1114 W. Cass Street
Tampa, Florida 33606

SEDCO, Inc.
3637 Clearview Parkway N.E.
Atlanta, Georgia 30340

Small Engine Clinic
99128 Aiea Heights Dr.
Aiea, Hawaii 96701

Midwest Engine Warehouse
515 Romans Road
Elmhurst, Illinois 60126

RPW Inc. of Iowa
2100 Broadway
Des Moines, Iowa 50313

Medart Engines & Parts of Kansas
15500 W. 109th St.
Lenexa, Kansas 66215

Kentucky Ignition Co.
737 S. 3rd Street
Louisville, Kentucky 40202

Suhren Engine Co.
8330 Earhart Blvd.
New Orleans, Louisiana 70118

Grayson Co. of Louisiana, Inc.
100 Fannin Street
Shreveport, Louisiana 71101

W. J. Connell Co.
210 Needham Street
Newton Upper Falls, Massachusetts 02164

Auto Electric & Service Corp.
15550 Woodrow Wilson Ave.
Detroit, Michigan 48238

Carl A. Anderson, Inc. of Minnesota
3380 Highway #49
St. Paul, Minnesota 55121

Medart Engines & Parts
3100 Washington Ave.
St. Louis, Missouri 63103

Original Equipment Co., Inc.
905 Second Ave., North
Billings, Montana 59101

RPW, Inc.
7402 "L" Street
Omaha, Nebraska 68127

The Durham Co., Inc.
7 Elkins Road
East Brunswick, New Jersey 08816

Spitzer Electrical Co.
1023 3rd Street N.W.
Albuquerque, New Mexico 87102

Automotive Electric Assoc., Inc.
700 W. 28th Street
Charlotte, North Carolina 28206

Gardner, Inc.
1150 Chesapeake Ave.
Columbus, Ohio 43212

American Electric Ignition Co.
124 N.W. 8th Street
Oklahoma City, Oklahoma 73102

Brown & Wiser
1411 N.W. Flanders
Portland, Oregon 97209

Pitt Auto Electric Co.
5135 Baum Blvd.
Pittsburg, Pennsylvania 15224

R. T. Clapp Co.
2045 Magnolia Ave., N.E.
Knoxville, Tennessee 37917

Automotive Electric Corp.
3250 Millbranch Road
Memphis, Tennessee 38116

Wilson Battery & Electric Co.
618 Jackson St.
Amarillo, Texas 79101

Grayson Company
1234 Motor Street
Dallas, Texas 75207

Wahlberg-McCreary, Inc.
3810 Dacoma Street
Houston, Texas 77018

S. X. Callahan
824 South Laredo
San Antonio, Texas 78207

Frank Edwards Co.
110 South, 300 West
Salt Lake City, Utah 84101

Richmond Battery & Ign. Corp.
959 Myers St.
Richmond, Virginia 23230

Bitco Western, Inc.
1741 First Avenue, South
Seattle, Washington 98134

Automotive Jobbers Supply Co.
125 S. Walnut Street
Spokane, Washington 99204

Wisconsin Magneto, Inc.,
4727 N. Teutonia Ave.
Milwaukee, Wisconsin 53209

CANADA
Auto Elec. Service Company, Ltd.
223 West Second Ave.
Vancouver, British Columbia V5Y 1C7

Auto Elec. Serv. Company, Ltd.
193 Fort Street
Winnepeg, Manitoba R3C 1C8

Auto Elec. Serv. Company, Ltd.
113 Thorncliffe Park Drive
Toronto, Ontario M4H 1M4

Auto Elec. Serv. Company, Ltd.
200 Bates Road
Montreal, Quebec H3S 1A3

CHRYSLER
(FORMERLY WEST BEND)

CHRYSLER OUTBOARD CORPORATION
Hartford, Wisconsin 53027

The engines listed below are known as the "L" series engines. The cylinder head is removable and the piston and connecting rod assembly can be removed without completely disassembling the engine. Cylinder and crankcase are integral.

MODEL	Cyls.	Bore	Stroke	Displ.
61001, '002, '005, '006, '010 & '012	1	2 3/16	1 5/8	6.1
82001, '002, '003, '004, '005, '006, '007, '008, '010, '011, '012, '015, '017, '019 & '024	1	2 17/32	1 5/8	8.2

MAINTENANCE

SPARK PLUG. Recommended spark plug for model 82012 is a Champion L-85 or AC 44F; the recommended spark plug for all other "L" series engines is a Champion L-4 or L-4J or an AC 42FF. Set electrode gap to 0.030 on all models.

CARBURETOR. All models are equipped with a Tillotson series HL carburetor. Refer to Fig. C1 for exploded view of typical carburetor.

Clockwise rotation of both the idle and high speed fuel needles leans the mixture. For initial adjustment, open both needles approximately 1¾ turns. Make final adjustment with engine running at operating temperature. Adjust idle needle for smoothest operation at idle speed, then check acceleration from idle speed to approximately 6000 RPM. Readjust idle fuel needle if engine does not accelerate properly; then, adjust high speed needle with engine under load and at operating speed. Turn the high speed needle clockwise until engine just stops four-cycling (starts to fire on every power stroke). CAUTION: Do not attempt to operate engine with a too lean fuel mixture; improper lubrication and engine seizure may result.

GOVERNOR. All models are non-governed.

MAGNETO AND TIMING. A Wico flywheel type magneto is used on all models. Refer to Fig. C2.

To inspect or service magneto, proceed as follows: Unbolt and remove fan housing and recoil starter assembly as a unit. On engines with model number ending in zero or even number (such as model 82002), turn flywheel retaining nut clockwise to remove; on engines with model number ending in an uneven number, turn nut counter-clockwise to remove. After removing flywheel retaining nut, remove flywheel using special knock-off nut.

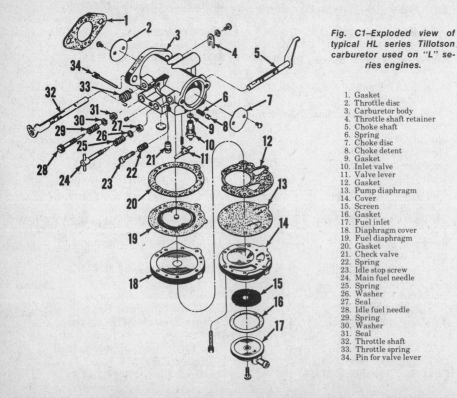

Fig. C1–Exploded view of typical HL series Tillotson carburetor used on "L" series engines.

1. Gasket
2. Throttle disc
3. Carburetor body
4. Throttle shaft retainer
5. Choke shaft
6. Spring
7. Choke disc
8. Choke detent
9. Gasket
10. Inlet valve
11. Valve lever
12. Gasket
13. Pump diaphragm
14. Cover
15. Screen
16. Gasket
17. Fuel inlet
18. Diaphragm cover
19. Fuel diaphragm
20. Gasket
21. Check valve
22. Spring
23. Idle stop screw
24. Main fuel needle
25. Spring
26. Washer
27. Seal
28. Idle fuel needle
29. Spring
30. Washer
31. Seal
32. Throttle shaft
33. Throttle spring
34. Pin for valve lever

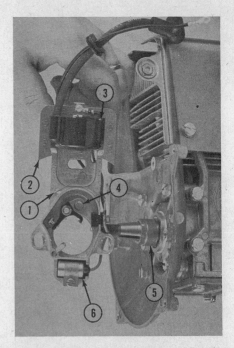

Fig. C2–View of magneto stator plate assembly removed from engine.

1. Breaker cover spring
2. Armature core
3. Ignition coil
4. Breaker point gap
    adjusting screw
5. Breaker cam
6. Condenser

Breaker contact points are accessible after removing flywheel and dust cover from stator plate. Adjust breaker point gap to 0.015 on all models. Condenser capacity is 0.16-0.20 mfd. Timing specifications are as follows:

TIMING CHART

MODEL NUMBER	Stator Position*	Degrees BTDC	Inches BTDC
61001	MR	26°	0.102
61002	MR	26°	0.102
61005	FR	22°	0.070
61006	FR	22°	0.070
61008	FR	22°	0.070
61010	FR	22°	0.070
61012	MR	22°	0.102
82001	MR	26°	0.102
82002	MR	26°	0.102
82003	MR-FA	28°	0.118
82004	FR	22°	0.070
82005	FR	22°	0.070
82006	FR	22°	0.070
82007	MR-FA	28°	0.118
82008	MR	26°	0.102
82010	FR-MR	24°	0.090
82011	FR-MR	24°	0.090
82012	FR	22°	0.070
82015	FR-MR	24°	0.090
82017	MR	24°	0.090
82019	MR	24°	0.090
82021	MR	24°	0.090

*MR=Mid-Range, FR=Full Retard and FA=Full Advance. Mid-range setting of timing is when stator mounting screws are tightened in center of slotted stator mounting holes. Full retarded is when magneto stator is moved all the way to end of slots in direction of flywheel rotation. Full advance is when magneto stator is moved all the way to end of slots in direction opposite flywheel rotation. The specifications FR-MR or MR-FA indicates a stator setting midway between the two positions.

LUBRICATION. Engine is lubricated by mixing oil with fuel. Thoroughly mix ¾-pint of SAE 30 or SAE 40 2-cycle or outboard motor oil with each gallon of regular gasoline.

REPAIRS

TIGHTENING TORQUES. Refer to following table for correct tightening torques. All values are in inch-pounds.

Connecting rod	80-90
Cylinder head:	
All 610 models	90-100
All models except 82012	85-90
82012	120-130
Flywheel	420

Spark Plug—Finger tight plus ½ to ⅝-turn Standard screws:

No. 10-24 thread	30
No. 10-32 thread	35
No. 12-24 thread	45
¼-in., 20 thread	70
5/16-in., 18 thread	160
⅜-in., 16 thread	270

CYLINDER HEAD. Cylinder head is removable on all models and is retained to cylinder with socket head cap screws and plain washers. The cylinder head gasket is available in various thicknesses and care should be taken to select the correct thickness gasket for the engine being serviced. Refer to following table.

ENGINE MODEL No.	Gasket Thickness
61001 & '02	0.032
61005 & '06	0.062
61008 & '10	0.062
61012	0.020
82001 & '02	0.032
82003	0.094
82004, '05 & '06	0.062
82007	0.094
82008, '10 & '11	0.125
82012	0.062
82015	0.125
82017	0.125
82019	0.125
82021	0.125

When reinstalling cylinder head, be sure that gasket, cylinder head and cylinder surfaces are clean and smooth. Install the socket head cap screws with plain washers and tighten screws to the correct torque as given in the following chart:

ENGINE MODEL NO.	Torque Value (in.-lbs.)
All 610 models	90-100
All 820 models except 82012	85-90
82012	120-130

CONNECTING ROD. Piston and connecting rod assembly can be removed after removing cylinder head, crankcase cover and rod cap. Be careful not to lose any of the 28 loose needle rollers when removing connecting rod cap.

The caged needle roller bearing in pin end of connecting rod is not renewable. Renew the connecting rod assembly if any roller in pin end bearing is rough or flat, if pin end rollers can be separated the width of one roller or if

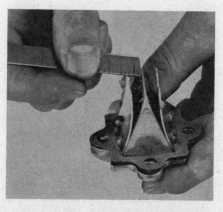

Fig. C-3–Reed stop spacing should be ¼-inch as shown.

crankpin bearing surface is rough or shows signs of wear.

Match marks on connecting rod and cap and piston ring anchor pin should be towards tapered (flywheel) end of crankshaft. When assembling connecting rod to crankshaft, coat crankpin with a light grease such as Lubriplate and use tweezers to place 14 of the rollers between rod and crankpin; then, stick remaining 14 rollers to crankpin and carefully reinstall rod cap with match marks on rod and cap aligned. The parting surface of rod and cap are fractured and if cap is correctly installed, the parting line will be almost invisible and cannot be felt with fingernail. Tighten connecting rod cap screws to a torque of 80-90 inch-pounds.

PISTON, PIN AND RINGS. Piston is equipped with two pinned compression rings. Piston and rings are available in standard size only. Renew piston if scored, ring side clearance is excessive or pin is loose in piston bosses.

The floating type piston pin is retained by a snap ring at each end of pin in piston bosses. Install flat snap rings with square-cut edge away from pin. The piston should be heated on a light bulb prior to removing or installing piston pin; otherwise, pin bosses in piston may be damaged. Install closed end of piston pin towards side of piston with piston ring anchor pin. Piston pin is available in standard size only.

Be sure that piston ring end gaps are aligned with anchor pin in ring grooves. Rings are available in standard size only. Install beveled edge of rings towards top of piston. Rings can be compressed with fingers when installing the piston and connecting rod assembly.

CRANKCASE, CRANKSHAFT, BEARINGS AND SEALS. The crankcase and cylinder are an integral unit of die-cast aluminum with either a cast-in iron cylinder liner or chrome plated cylinder bore. Renew crankcase and cylinder if chrome plating has worn through or if cast iron cylinder bore is worn or out-of-round 0.002 or more.

Crankshaft is supported in two ball bearings. Bearings should be a light press fit on crankshaft and in crankcase and support plate. However, a slip fit in crankcase or support plate is permissible if there is no end play of bearings. Crankshaft must be supported on flat surface inside crankpin throw when pressing bearings onto shaft.

As with all two-cycle engines, sealing of crankcase is very important.

Renew crankshaft seals using a driver that will contact outer edge of seal only. Install seals in crankcase and bearing support plate with lip of seal to inside. Do not scrape gasket material from crankcase or support plate as this may damage the sealing surfaces; soak old gasket material loose with solvent.

REED INLET VALVE. Reeds must seat lightly against reed plate along full length of reed and reed must entirely cover hole in reed plate. Renew reeds if rusted, cracked, broken or warped. Renew the complete reed valve unit if reed plate seats are rough, pitted or worn. Dimension measured from reed plate to reed stop as shown in Fig. C3 should be ¼-inch.

CHRYSLER
(FORMERLY WEST BEND)

CHRYSLER OUTBOARD CORPORATION
Hartford, Wisconsin 53027

These two cycle engines, employing reed type inlet valves, are available with plain type, combination anti-friction and plain type or all anti-friction bearings for the crankshaft. They are also available with vertical or horizontal crankshaft. One casting forms the cylinder, cylinder head and crankcase.

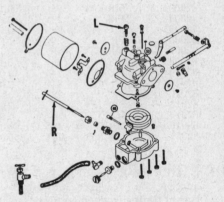

Fig. C4–Components of Tillotson type MD carburetor. Clockwise rotation of idle needle (L) will enrich the mixture.

MODEL	Bore	Stroke	Displ.	Hp @ Rpm
2700 & 2704	1¾	1 9/16	3.76	1.5 @ 3600
2706	1¾	1⅝	3.9	1.5 @ 3600
2723	2	1⅝	5.1	2.3 @ 3600
2725, '26, '27, '28, '29, '30, '31, '32, '33, '34, '35, '36, '38, '40, '42 and '44	2¼	1⅝	6.45	4.0 @ 4500
2752	1¾	1 9/16	3.76	1.5 @ 3600
2756, '562, '563 and '564	1¾	1⅝	3.9	1.6 @ 4000
2760, '61, '612, '62, '63 and '64	2¼	1¾	7.0	5.0 @ 5500
2770, '71, '712, '72, '722, '74, '742 and '75	2	1⅝	5.1	2.8 @ 4000
2777	2	1 9/16	4.9	2.3 @ 3600
2778, '79, '792, '81, '812, '82, '822, '823, '824, '825, '83, '84, '85, '852, '853, '854 and '86	2	1⅝	5.1	2.8 @ 4000
2787, '88, '882 and '883	2	1⅝	5.1	3.0 @ 4500
2790	2¼	1¾	7.0	5.0 @ 5500
58001, '002, '003, '004, '006, '007 and '008	2 1/16	1¾	5.8	4.0 @ 5500
58009, '010	2 1/16	1¾	5.8	5.0 @ 6000
58011, '015	2 1/16	1¾	5.8	3.5 @ 5000
58012, '013	2 1/16	1¾	5.8	6.5 @ 7000
58016, '022	2 1/16	1¾	5.8	4.0 @ 5500
58017, '019, '021, '023, '029 and '031	2 1/16	1¾	5.8	4.0 @ 5000
70001, '002, '006, '007 and '008	2¼	1¾	7.0	5.0 @ 5500
70009, '010	2¼	1¾	7.0	6.0 @ 6000
70012, '013, '017, '019, '021 and '023	2¼	1¾	7.0	7.5 @ 7000

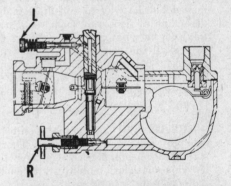

Fig. C5–Section through Tillotson type MT carburetor. Clockwise rotation of idle needle (L) leans the idle mixture.

MAINTENANCE

SPARK PLUG. Refer to table on following page for recommended Champion spark plug and electrode gap.

CARBURETOR. Engines may be equipped with Tillotson MD or MT float fed carburetor or Tillotson H, HL or HP diaphragm type carburetor. On MD carburetor, clockwise rotation of the idle needle (L—Fig. C4) will enrich the idle mixture. On MT, H, HL and HP carburetors, clockwise rotation of the idle needle (L—Fig. C5 or C6) will lean the idle mixture. On all carburetors, clockwise rotation of the main adjustment needle (R—Figs. C4, C5 or C6) will lean the mixture. Normal settings for both idle mixture and main adjustments is ¾-1 turn open for all carburetors.

Correct float setting on MT type is 3/32 inch from flange on bowl cover to nearest face of float when inlet needle is seated; on MD type, farthest face of float (at free end of same) should extend approximately 1/64-3/64 inch beyond body casting when float needle is seated as shown in Fig. C7. On diaphragm type carburetors, a certain amount of fuel leakage may occur

Fig. C6–Flushing diaphragm chamber of diaphragm type carburetor. Clockwise rotation of idle needle (L) leans the idle mixture.

ENGINE MODEL	SPARK PLUG MODEL*	SPARK PLUG GAP	IGNITION TIMING STATOR POSITION (1)	IGNITION TIMING DISTANCE BTDC	REED STOP SETTING	WICO MAGNETO MODEL	ROTATION (DRIVE END)
2700, 2704	J12J	.040	FA	1/8"	1/4"	FW2260	CCW
2706	J12J	.040	FA	1/8"	1/4"	FW2320	CCW
2722, 2723	J12J	.040	MR	3/32"	1/4"	FW2320	CCW
2725	H12J	.040	FR	5/32"	5/16"	FW2466B	CCW
2726	H12J	.040	MR	5/32"	5/16"	FW2471B	CW
2727	H12J	.040	FR	5/32"	5/16"	FW2466B	CCW
2728	H12J	.040	MR	5/32"	5/16"	FW2471B	CW
2729	H12J	.040	FR	5/32"	5/16"	FW2466B	CCW
2730	H12J	.040	MR	5/32"	5/16"	FW2471B	CW
2731	H12J	.040	FR	5/32"	5/16"	FW2466B	CCW
2732	H12J	.040	MR	5/32"	5/16"	FW2471B	CW
2733	H12J	.040	FR	5/32"	5/16"	FW2466B	CCW
2734	H12J	.040	MR	5/32"	5/16"	FW2471B	CW
2735	H12J	.040	FR	5/32"	5/16"	FW2466B	CCW
2736	H12J	.040	MR	5/32"	5/16"	FW2471B	CW
2738	H12J	.040	FR	5/32"	5/16"	FW2471B	CW
2740, 2742	H12J	.040	FR	5/32"	5/16"	FW2471B	CW
2744	H12J	.040	FR	5/32"	5/16"	FW2471B	CW
2752	J12J	.040	FA	1/8"	1/4"	FW2242	CCW
2756	J12J	.040	FA	1/8"	1/4"	FW2317	CCW
27562, 27563	J12J	.040	FA	1/8"	1/4"	FW2466B	CCW
27564	J12J	.040	FA	1/8"	1/4"	FW2605	CCW
2760	H8J	.030	MR	5/32"	3/16"	FW2471B	CW
2761	H8J	.030	MR	5/32"	3/16"	FW2466B	CCW
27612	H8J	.030	MR	5/32"	3/16"	FW2605	CCW
2762	H8J	.030	MR	5/32"	3/16"	FW2471B	CW
2763	H8J	.030	MR	5/32"	3/16"	FW2466B	CCW
2764	H8J	.030	MR	5/32"	3/16"	FW2471B	CW
2770, 2771	J12J	.040	FA	1/4"	1/4"	FW2317	CCW
27712	J12J	.040	FA	1/4"	1/4"	FW2466B	CCW
2772	J12J	.040	MR	7/32"	1/4"	**	CW
27722	J12J	.040	MR	7/32"	1/4"	FW2466B	CCW
2774	J12J	.040	FA	1/4"	1/4"	**	CCW
27742	J12J	.040	FA	1/4"	1/4"	FW2466B	CCW
2775	J12J	.040	FA	1/4"	1/4"	FW2317	CCW
2777	J12J	.040	FA	1/8"	1/4"	FW2260	CCW
2778	J12J	.040	FA	7/32"	1/4"	FW2378	CW
2779	J12J	.040	MR	7/32"	1/4"	FW2317	CCW
27792	J12J	.040	MR	7/32"	1/4"	FW2466B	CCW
2780, 2781	J12J	.040	MR	7/32"	1/4"	FW2317	CCW
27812	H12J	.040	MR	7/32"	1/4"	FW2466B	CCW
2782	J12J	.040	FA	1/4"	1/4"	FW2378	CCW
27822, 27823	H12J	.040	FA	1/4"	1/4"	FW2466B	CCW
27824, 27825	H12J	.040	FA	1/4"	1/4"	FW2605	CCW
2783	J12J	.040	FA	1/4"	1/4"	FW2378	CCW
2784	J12J	.040	FA	7/32"	1/4"	FW2378	CCW
2785	J12J	.040	FA	7/32"	1/4"	FW2378	CW
27852, 27853	H12J	.040	FA	7/32"	1/4"	FW2471B	CW
27854	H12J	.040	FA	7/32"	1/4"	FW2471B	CW
2786	J12J	.040	FA	7/32"	1/4"	FW2378	CW
2787	H8J	.040	MR	7/32"	1/4"	FW2466B	CCW
2788	J12J	.040	MR	7/32"	1/4"	***	CCW
27882	H12J	.040	MR	7/32"	1/4"	FW2466B	CCW
27883	H12J	.040	MR	7/32"	1/4"	FW2605	CCW
2790	H8J	.030	MR	5/32"	3/16"	FW2471B	CW
58001	H8J	.030	MR	5/32"	5/16"	FW2605	CCW
58002	H8J	.030	MR	5/32"	5/16"	FW2639	CW
58003	H8J	.030	MR	5/32"	5/16"	FW2605	CCW
58004, 58006	H8J	.030	MR	5/32"	5/16"	FW2639	CW
58007	H8J	.030	MR	5/32"	3/16"	FW2605	CCW
58008	H8J	.030	MR	5/32"	3/16"	FW2639	CW
58009	H8J	.030	MR	5/32"	1/4"	FW2605	CCW
58010	H8J	.030	MR	5/32"	1/4"	FW2639	CW
58011	H8J	.030	FR	.....	1/4"	FW2605	CCW
58012	H4, HO3	.030	MR	5/32"	1/4"	FW2639	CW
58013	H4, HO3	.030	MR	5/32"	1/4"	FW2605	CCW
58015	H10J	.030	MR	5/32"	1/4"	FW2605	CCW
58016	H8J	.030	MR	5/32"	5/16"	FW2639	CW
58017	H8J	.030	MR	5/32"	5/16"	FW2605	CCW
58019	H-12	.030	FR	5/32"	1/4"	FWB2605B	CCW
58021	H-12	.030	FR	5/32"	1/4"	FWB2605B	CCW
58022	H8J	.030	MR	5/32"	5/16"	FW2639B	CW
58023	H-12	.030	FR	5/32"	1/4"	FWB2605B	CCW
58029	UJ-11G	.030	FR	5/32"	1/4"	FWB2605B	CCW
58031	UJ-11G	.030	FR	5/32"	1/4"	FWB2605B	CCW
70001	H8J	.030	MR	5/32"	3/16"	FW2605	CCW
70002, 70006	H8J	.030	MR	5/32"	3/16"	FW2639	CW
70007	H8J	.030	MR	5/32"	3/16"	FW2605	CCW
70008	H8J	.030	MR	5/32"	3/16"	FW2639	CW
70009	H8J	.030	MR	5/32"	1/4"	FW2605	CCW
70010	H8J	.030	MR	5/32"	1/4"	FW2639	CW
70012	H4, HO3	.030	MR	5/32"	1/4"	FW2639	CW
70013	H4, HO3	.030	MR	5/32"	1/4"	FW2605	CCW
70017	UJ-11G	.030	FR	5/32"	1/4"	FWB2605B	CCW
70019	H-12	.030	FR	5/32"	1/4"	FWB2605B	CCW
70021	UJ-11G	.030	FR	5/32"	1/4"	FWB2605B	CCW
70023	UJ-11G	.030	FR	5/32"	1/4"	FWB2605B	CCW

*Champion.   **FW2317 or FW2471B.   ***FW2466B or FW2471B.   (1) FA—full advance; MR—med.-range; FR—full retard.

through discharge nozzle in a normal carburetor for a short period of time after engine is stopped. Fuel inlet needle and seat should be renewed if carburetor shows a tendency to run rich or if leakage is excessive.

GOVERNOR. Three versions of air vane type speed governors have been used as shown in Figs. C8, C9 and C10. On early engines, the governor spring is contained inside the governor knob (8—Fig. C8). To adjust the governed speed on these installations, loosen set screw (9) and rotate knob (8) to obtain desired operating speed. Clockwise rotation of knob (8) increases the speed.

On later type engines, the air vane (2 —Fig. C9) is connected to the carburetor throttle shaft arm (5) and to the governor spring (4) by a link (3). To adjust governed speed, loosen the two screws which fasten the bracket (6) to the reed plate and move bracket toward or away from carburetor. Moving the bracket away from carburetor increases the speed. NOTE: In order to remove governor link (3) from throttle arm, first remove the air vane hinge pin (1).

On latest engines, the governor mechanism is located inside the fan housing as shown in Fig. C10. To adjust governed speed, move the control lever stop (S) as required. Stop is locked in position by prongs which bite into support plate. If stop is moved in direction shown by arrow in illustration, the speed is increased.

MAGNETO AND TIMING. Breaker contacts are accessible after removing the flywheel. Recommended gap is 0.020. Position of magneto stator plate controls ignition timing. Column four of table (stator position) gives the position stator plate should be set for proper timing. Symbols are: FA (full advance), MR (mid range) and FR (full retard). Position of stator plate at full advance or full retard depends upon direction of crankshaft rotation. For example, on standard rotation engines the flywheel turns clockwise and for

FA (full advance) timing, the stator plate should be turned counter-clockwise as far as the elongated mounting holes will permit. Exact timing (piston travel BTDC) is listed also in table.

LUBRICATION. Engine is lubricated by mixing oil with the fuel. Use ½ pint of SAE 30 or 40 non-detergent or outboard engine oil to each gallon of regular grade gasoline.

REPAIRS

CONNECTING ROD. Piston and connecting rod unit is removed from open (crankcase) end of cylinder after first removing the crankshaft. If connecting rod has an oil hole in the piston pin end, assemble the rod to the piston with the oil hole toward the inlet port of the cylinder. Piston pin should be assembled to piston with closed end of pin toward (nearest) the inlet port. Piston and rod unit should be installed with long tapered side of upper end of same (2—Fig. C17) toward the exhaust port (1) as shown. Crankpin diameter on all models is ¾ inch nominal.

STEEL RODS WITH NEEDLE BEARINGS. To insert the needle rollers, locate the rod about 1/16 inch away

from crankpin. On models with bearing cages and 11 needles, install cage on crankpin and coat cage with grease. Install bearing needles in cage and rotate cage with bearings into upper half of rod, install other half of cage and remaining needles in a similar manner. On models with 28 individual uncaged needle rollers, place a light coat of grease on crankpin, then using blunt tweezers install the twenty-eight needle rollers as shown in Fig. C13. On

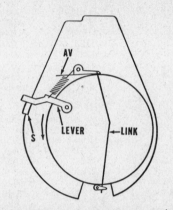

Fig. C10–On latest engines the governed speed is increased by moving the stop (S) in direction indicated by arrow. Air vane is (AV).

Fig. C11–Magneto is correctly timed when stator plate is in the proper location given in table 1.

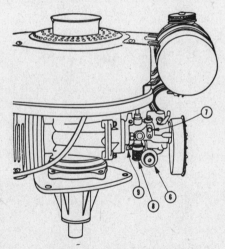

Fig. C8–Governed speed on early production engines is adjusted by knob (8).

Fig. C7–Correct float setting for type MD Tillotson carburetor is when float extends 1/64-3/64-inch beyond body casting as shown.

Fig. C9–Governed speed on later production engines is adjusted by moving bracket (6) which varies tension on spring (4).

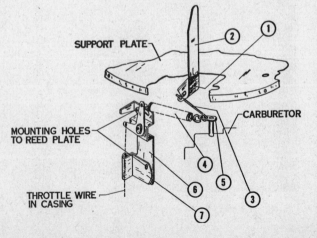

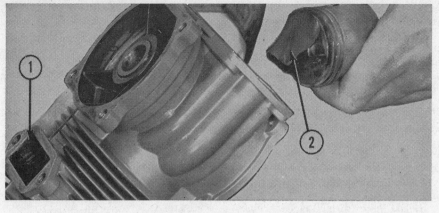

Fig. C12–Tapered surface (2) of piston head should be toward the exhaust port (1).

Fig. C15–Lock the cap retaining screws of aluminum rods by staking.

all steel rods with either type of needle bearing, parting faces of rod and cap are not machined but are fractured to provide the doweling effect of the meshing of the consequent uneven surfaces. It is advisable therefore to wiggle the rod cap back and forth while tightening to make sure that the interstices of the fractured joint are in perfect mesh. When torqued to the recommended tightness of 75-80 inch pounds the parting line is practically invisible (Fig. C14).

Side clearance of rod on crankshaft should be 3/32-inch which is controlled by length of needle rollers. End float of upper end of rod in piston bosses should not exceed 0.015.

Any steel connecting rod which is rusted, pitted or shows evidence of overheating should be renewed.

ALUMINUM RODS WITH PLAIN BEARINGS. Aluminum alloy connecting rods are equipped with cast-in bronze inserts which are non-adjustable and non-renewable. Never file rod or cap to "take up" the bearings. Rec-

ommended diametral clearance of lower bearing is 0.0015-0.0025 inch. Install new rod assembly and/or crankshaft when clearance exceeds 0.0035 inch. Desired side clearance on crankpin is 0.010-0.020. Renew the worn parts when side clearance exceeds 0.040 inch. Piston pin should be a thumb push fit in the non-renewable bushing at top end of rod and a palm push fit in the piston bosses. Rod bearing screws should be torqued to 75-80 inch pounds then locked by staking as shown in Fig. C15.

PISTON, PIN, RINGS & CYLINDER. Pistons are equipped with two 1/16-inch wide compression rings which are pinned to limit their rotation in the grooves. Recommended end gap is 0.003-0.008; wear limit is 0.013. Recommended side clearance is 0.0035-0.005. Reject the piston when a new ring has more than 0.007 side clearance in groove. Beveled edge of rings should be installed toward top end of piston. All gaps should be lined up at the ring anchor pin.

Floating type piston pins are retained by lock rings. Two types of lock rings are used. Wire type rings are used in pistons with rounded lock grooves. In pistons with square-bottom grooves, install flat lock ring with square-cut side of ring away from pin. Pin should be installed with its closed end toward inlet port in cylinder. On some engines, thrust washers are installed at the ends of the piston pin. Pin should have a slightly tighter fit in the piston than in the connecting rod. Oversize pins are not supplied.

Desired clearance of aluminum pistons in engines with steel connecting rods and needle roller bearings is 0.003-0.004 with a wear limit of 0.006 inch. In engines with aluminum rods and plain bearings, desired piston clearance is 0.0025-0.004 with a wear limit of 0.005. Cylinder should be renewed if out of round or taper exceeded 0.002. Oversize pistons and/or rings are not supplied, except for 580 series engines: 0.010 and 0.030 oversize pistons and rings are available only for the 580 series. Rebore or hone cylinder to 2.072-2.073 for 0.010 oversize and to 2.092-2.093 for 0.030 oversize. Also, chrome-faced rings (standard size only)

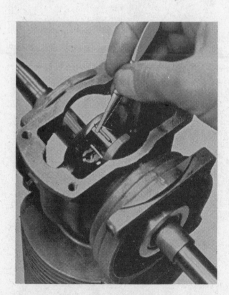

Fig. C13–Inserting needle rollers to upper half of connecting rod.

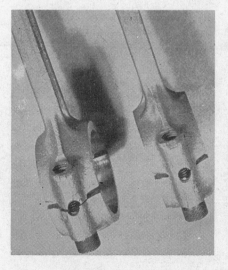

Fig C14–Correct and incorrect connecting rod cap joints. Rod split line is established by deliberate fracturing.

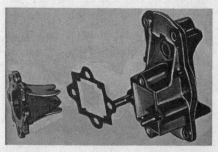

Fig. C16–View of "V" Power Manifold assembly. Additional crankcase stuffing and larger, less restricting reed valve results in horsepower gain.

are available for the 580 series engines with cast iron cylinder bore.

CRANKSHAFT AND SEALS. Desired running clearance of plain type main bearings is 0.001-0.002 for upper or flywheel end; 0.001-0.0025 for lower or pto end with a wear limit of 0.003 for flywheel end; 0.004 for opposite end. Crankshaft end play in plain type bearings is 0.004-0.010 with a wear limit of 0.020. On engines with plain type mains, the upper or flywheel main journal diameter is ¾ inch nominal; the lower or pto journal diameter is ⅞ inch nominal. On engines with anti-friction mains, the upper or fly-

wheel end journal is ¾ inch diameter; the opposite end, 0.781 inch diameter.

All crankcase seals must be maintained in good condition in a two cycle engine because leakage through the seals releases compression and causes loss of power.

It is important therefore to carefully inspect the seals and to exercise extreme care when renewing seals to prevent their being damaged during installation. If a tapered sleeve is not available, use tape to cover any splines, shoulders or threads over which the seal must pass during installation.

REED VALVE UNIT. This remov-

able unit is located between the carburetor and the cylinder block. Reeds should seat lightly against reed plate throughout their entire length with the least possible initial tension. Check seating by blowing and drawing air through ports with mouth.

Refer to TABLE I for recommended reed stop setting for all models except those with the "V" Power Manifold. Setting should be measured at open end of stop to seating surfaces of reed plate. Setting should be ¼-inch for the "V" Power Manifold.

Renew broken, cracked, warped or rusted reeds.

CHRYSLER

(FORMERLY WEST BEND)

CHRYSLER OUTBOARD CORPORATION
Hartford, Wisconsin 53027

These two-cycle engines are known as "L" series engines. All models have a detachable cylinder and a two-piece crankcase. Cylinder has an integral cylinder head and cylinder block. Cylinder head and cylinder block is chrome plated. Crankshaft is supported by two ball bearing mains and connecting rod has a non-renewable needle bearing at piston pin end and renewable loose roller bearings at crankpin end. All engines except models 50052 and 50054 are loop-scav-

enged, utilizing reed valves and flat top pistons. Models 50052 and 50054 are cross-scavenged, utilizing a 3rd port and deflector top piston. All models use a diaphragm type carburetor which allows engine to be operated in any position. Horsepower rating is 4¼ hp at 7000 rpm for loop-scavenged engines and 3⅓ hp at 7000 rpm for cross-scavenged engines.

MODEL	Cyls.	Bore	Stroke	Displ.
50000, '002, '004, '006, '008, '010, '052 & '054	1	2	1-19/32	5.0

MAINTENANCE

SPARK PLUG. Recommended spark plug for all models except 50000 is Champion CJ8. Recommended spark plug for model 50000 is Champion H8J. Set electrode gap to 0.030 for all models. Spark plug torque value for all models except 50052 and 50054 is 22 ft.-lbs. Torque value for models 50052 and 50054 is 15 ft.-lbs.

CARBURETOR. Engines are equipped with a Tillotson series HS diaphragm type carburetor. Refer to Fig. C17 for exploded view of carburetor.

Clockwise rotation of both idle and high speed fuel needles leans the mixture. For initial adjustment, open both needles approximately 1¼ turns. Make final adjustment with engine running at operating temperature. Adjust idle needle for smoothest operation at idle speed, then accelerate engine to about 4000 rpm. If engine tends to accelerate slowly and bog down (too rich), turn idle needle clockwise (lean) as necessary. If engine tends to stall (too lean), turn idle needle counter-clockwise (richer) as necessary. Average needle setting is 1-1/8 turns open. Adjust engine high idle speed as follows: Be

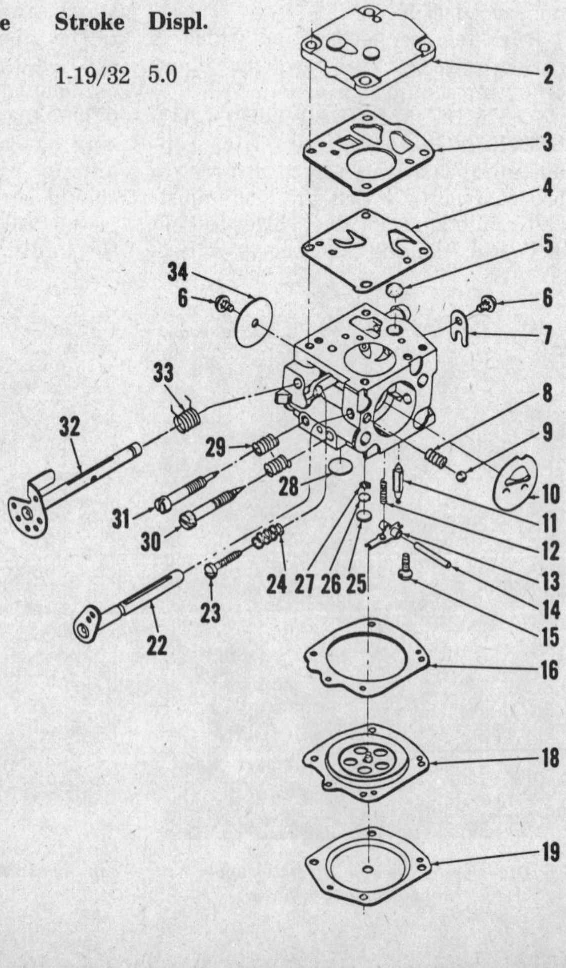

Fig. C17—Exploded view of Tillotson series HS carburetor used on all series 500 engines.

2. Fuel pump cover
3. Gasket
4. Fuel pump diaphragm
5. Inlet screen
7. Throttle shaft clip
8. Friction spring
9. Friction ball
10. Choke shutter
11. Inlet needle
12. Tension spring
13. Inlet control lever
14. Pin
16. Gasket
18. Diaphragm
19. Diaphragm cover
22. Choke shaft and lever
23. Idle speed screw
24. Spring
25. Welch plug (small)
26. Retaining ring
27. Screen
28. Welch plug (large)
29. Spring
30. Main adjusting screw
31. Idle adjusting screw
32. Throttle shaft and lever
33. Spring
34. Throttle shutter

sure idle adjustment is satisfactory, then run engine at 4000 rpm and turn high speed needle clockwise to a point where engine stops four-cycling (engine fires on every power stroke). CAUTION: Do not go any leaner with the high speed needle adjustment as it could result in improper lubrication and engine seizure could result.

If engine idle rpm is too high, turn carburetor stop screw counter-clockwise until desired rpm is obtained.

MAGNETO AND TIMING. A Wico flywheel type magneto is used on all models. Refer to Fig. C18.

To inspect or service magneto, proceed as follows: Unbolt and remove fan housing and recoil starter assembly as a unit. Remove flywheel retaining nut and starter cup, then remove flywheel using special knock-off nut.

Breaker contact points are accessible after removing flywheel and the dust cover from stator plate. Breaker point gap is 0.015 and when adjusting points be sure breaker point cam follower is positioned at index mark on breaker cam. NOTE: Be accurate when setting the breaker contact gap. A gap greater than 0.015 will advance timing; a gap less than 0.015 will retard timing.

If stator plate has been loosened or removed, breaker contact point gap must be reset. When installing stator plate it must be installed in the mid-range position (mounting screws in center of slotted stator mounting holes). With stator installed in mid-range position and breaker contact points set at 0.015 as described above, timing will be 32 degrees BTDC.

LUBRICATION. Engine is lubricated by mixing oil with the fuel. Thoroughly mix ½-pint of SAE 30 or SAE 40 2-cycle or outboard motor oil with each gallon of regular gasoline. Do not use premium gasoline.

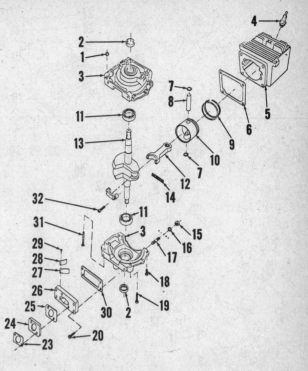

Fig. C19—Exploded view of the loop-scavenged series 500 engine. Carburetor and reed valve assembly may be located either on bottom or side of crankcase. This loop-scavenged engine uses a flat-top piston.

2. Crankcase seals
3. Crankcase halves
4. Spark plug
5. Cylinder
6. Gasket
7. Retaining rings
8. Piston pin
9. Piston rings
10. Piston
11. Ball bearing
12. Connecting rod
13. Crankshaft
14. Crankpin roller set
17. Cylinder stud
23. Carburetor gasket
24. Carburetor adapter
25. Adapter gasket
26. Reed plate
27. Reed valve
28. Reed stop
30. Gasket
32. Connecting rod screw

REPAIRS

CONNECTING ROD. To remove the aluminum alloy connecting rod, remove starter, flywheel, magneto assembly, magneto support plate and cylinder. Separate crankcase halves, remove crankshaft, then separate rod cap from connecting rod and be careful not to lose any of the loose needle rollers. Remove piston pin retaining rings and bump out piston pin.

The caged needle roller bearing in pin end of connecting rod is not renewable. Renew the connecting rod assembly if any roller in pin end is rough or flat, if pin end rollers can be separated the width of one roller, or if crankpin bearing surface is rough or shows signs of wear.

When installing connecting rod to crankshaft, coat crankpin with Lubriplate, or similar grease, then use tweezers to install the 25 rollers. Install connecting rod assembly with match marks toward flywheel end of crankshaft. Tighten connecting rod cap screws to a 70-80 inch-pounds torque.

The parting surface of rod and cap are fractured and if cap is correctly installed, the parting line will be almost invisible and cannot be felt with fingernail.

If piston assembly is installed on connecting rod at this time, install those pistons with deflector top so that longer taper side is toward exhaust side. Pistons with flat top are installed with piston ring anchor pin toward flywheel side.

PISTON, PIN AND RINGS. Pistons are fitted with two 1/16-inch wide compression rings which are pinned to limit rotation in their grooves. Rings are available in standard sizes only. Recommended ring end gap is 0.009-0.012. Recommended side clearance is 0.0025-0.005. Beveled edge of rings should be installed toward top of pistons. All ring gaps must be aligned at the ring anchor pin.

The 0.437 diameter floating type piston pins are retained by lock rings located at each end. Piston pins are available in standard size only. It is recommended that piston be heated on a lightbulb prior to removing or installing piston pin to preclude the possibility of damage to the piston bosses.

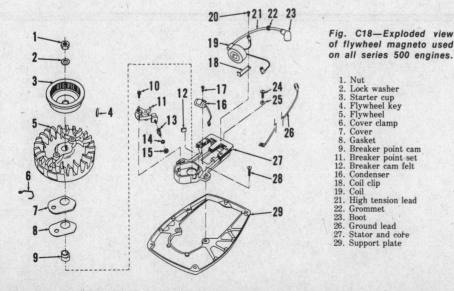

Fig. C18—Exploded view of flywheel magneto used on all series 500 engines.

1. Nut
2. Lock washer
3. Starter cup
4. Flywheel key
5. Flywheel
6. Cover clamp
7. Cover
8. Gasket
9. Breaker point cam
11. Breaker point set
12. Breaker cam felt
16. Condenser
18. Coil clip
19. Coil
21. High tension lead
22. Grommet
23. Boot
26. Ground lead
27. Stator and core
29. Support plate

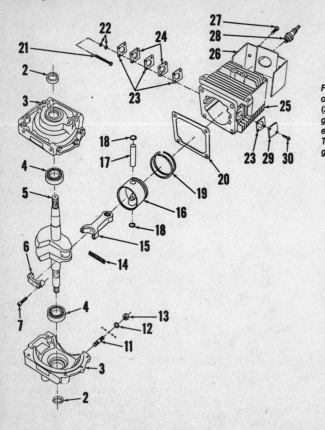

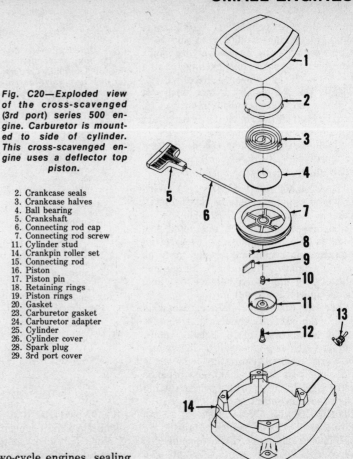

Fig. C20—Exploded view of the cross-scavenged (3rd port) series 500 engine. Carburetor is mounted to side of cylinder. This cross-scavenged engine uses a deflector top piston.

2. Crankcase seals
3. Crankcase halves
4. Ball bearing
5. Crankshaft
6. Connecting rod cap
7. Connecting rod screw
11. Cylinder stud
14. Crankpin roller set
15. Connecting rod
16. Piston
17. Piston pin
18. Retaining rings
19. Piston rings
20. Gasket
23. Carburetor gasket
24. Carburetor adapter
25. Cylinder
26. Cylinder cover
28. Spark plug
29. 3rd port cover

Fig. C21—Exploded view of the starter assembly used on all series 500 engines. Cover (1) for 3rd port engines may be stamped steel instead of the die-cast magnesium.

1. Cover	8. Dog spring
2. Spring keeper	9. Starter dog
3. Rewind spring	10. Brake spring
4. Washer	11. Retainer
5. Handle	12. Shoulder screw
6. Starter rope	13. Ignition switch
7. Pulley	14. Fan housing

CRANKCASE, CRANKSHAFT, BEARINGS AND SEALS. The aluminum die-cast cylinder with integral cylinder head is bolted to a two-piece magnesium die-cast crankcase. Cylinder bore is chrome plated and cylinder should be renewed if chrome plating is worn through, or if cylinder bore is excessively worn or out-of-round.

Crankshaft is supported by two ball type main bearings. Bearings should be a light press fit on crankshaft and in crankcase halves. Crankshaft must be supported on flat surface inside crankpin throw when pressing bearings on crankshaft.

As with all two-cycle engines, sealing of crankcase is very important. Renew crankshaft seals using a driver which will contact outer edge of seal only. Use a seal protector, or tape all threads and keyways, and install seals with lips toward inside.

REED VALVE UNIT. All 500 series engines except models 50052 and 50054 are equipped with a reed valve assembly located between carburetor and crankcase. Reeds must seat lightly against reed plate along full length of reed and reed must completely cover hole in reed plate. Check reed seating by alternately blowing and drawing air through ports with mouth. Dimension from reed plate to reed stop should be ¼-inch.

CHRYSLER CENTRAL SERVICE DISTRIBUTORS

(Arranged Alphabetically by States)

These franchised firms carry extensive stocks of repair parts. Contact them for name of nearest service distributor (dealer) who may have the parts you need.

Birmingham Electric Battery Co.
2230 Second Ave., South
Birmingham, Alabama 35233

Diversified Products
1136 Venice Blvd.
Los Angeles, California 90015

H. G. Makelim Company
219 Shaw Road
So. San Francisco, California 94080

Central Auto Electric Company
12th Avenue & Lincoln Street
Denver, Colorado 80203

Spencer Engine & Magneto, Inc.
1114 W. Cass Street
Tampa, Florida 33606

Sedco, Inc.
3637 Clearview Parkway, N.E.
Atlanta, Georgia 30340

Midwest Engine Warehouse
515 Romans Road
Elmhurst, Illinois 60126

Lally's
118 - 4th St.
Des Moines, Iowa 50308

Medart Engines & Parts of Kansas
15500 W. 109th St.
Lenexa, Kansas 66215

Suhren Engine Co., Inc.
8330 Earhart Blvd.
New Orleans, Louisiana 70118

Yerxa's, Inc.
753 Broadway
South Portland, Maine 04106

Brown's Auto Centre, Inc.
19 Central Street
Worcester, Massachusetts 01608

R. L. Gould & Company
3711 Lexington Ave., N.
St. Paul, Minnesota 55112

Medart Auto Electric Co., Inc.
3100 Washington Avenue
St. Louis, Missouri 63103

Original Equipment, Inc.
905 - 2nd Avenue, North
Billings, Montana 59101

Central Auto Electric Company
808 - 2nd Street, N.W.
Albuquerque, New Mexico 87101

Broadway Ignition Co., Inc.
4747 - 58th Street
Woodside, New York 11377

Hettrich Electric Service
1396 Niagara Street
Buffalo, New York 14213

E. J. Smith & Sons Company
1041 Hawthorne Lane
Charlotte, North Carolina 28201

Gardner, Inc.
1150 Chesapeake Avenue
Columbus, Ohio 43212

Magneto Ignition Company, Inc.
7450 E. 46th Place
Tulsa, Oklahoma 74145

Automotive Products, Inc.
1700 S.E. Grand Avenue
Portland, Oregon 97214

Midco, Inc.
1516 Fairmount Avenue
Philadelphia, Pennsylvania 19130

Pitt Auto Electric Company
5135 Baum Blvd.
Pittsburgh, Pennsylvania 15224

Automotive Electric Corporation
3250 Millbranch Road
Memphis, Tennessee 38116

McCoy Sales & Service
4045 E. Belknap
Fort Worth, Texas 76117

Quick's Service
2220 S. 9th, East
Salt Lake City, Utah 84106

Richmond Battery & Ignition
959 Myers Street
Richmond, Virginia 23230

Cox Engine & Supply Co.
1757 - 1st Avenue South
Seattle, Washington 98134

Wisconsin Magneto, Inc.
4727 N. Teutonia Ave.
Milwaukee, Wisconsin 53209

CANADA

Auto Electric Service Co., Ltd.
223 West Second Ave.
Vancouver, B.C. V5Y 1C7

Auto Electric Service Co., Ltd.
193 Fort Street
Winnipeg, Manitoba R3C 1C8

Auto Electric Service Co., Ltd.
Air-Cooled Engine Division
113 Thorncliffe Park Drive
Toronto, Ontario M4H 1M4

Auto Electric Service Co., Ltd.
200 Bates Road
Montreal, Quebec H3S 1A3

CLINTON

CLINTON ENGINES CORPORATION
Maquoketa, Iowa

CLINTON ENGINE IDENTIFICATION
INFORMATION

In order to obtain the correct service replacement parts when overhauling Clinton engines, it is important that the engine be properly identified as to:

1. Model number
2. Variation number
3. Type letter

A typical nameplate from the model number series engines prior to 1961 is shown in Fig. CL1. In this example, the following information is noted from the nameplate:

1. Model number—**B-760**
2. Variation number—**AOB**
3. Type letter—**B**

In some cases, the model number may be shown as in following example:

D-790-2124

Thus, "D-790" would be the model number of a D-700-2000 series engine in which the digits "2124" would be the variation number.

In late 1961, the identification system for Clinton engines was changed to be acceptable for use with IBM inventory record systems. A typical nameplate from a late production engine is shown in Fig. CL2.

In this example, the following information is noted from the nameplate:

1. Model number—405-0000-000
2. Variation number—070
3. Type letter—D

In addition, the following information may be obtained from the model number on the nameplate:

First digit—identifies type of engine, i.e., 4 means 4-cycle engine and 5 means 2-cycle engine.

Second & third digits—completes basic identification of engine. Odd numbers will be used for vertical shaft engines and even numbers for horizontal shaft engines; i.e., 405 would indicate a 4-cycle vertical shaft engine and 500 would indicate a 2-cycle horizontal shaft engine.

Fourth digit—indicates type of starter as follows:

0—Recoil starter
1—Rope starter
2—Impulse starter
3—Crank starter
4—12-Volt electric starter
5—12-Volt starter-generator
6—110-Volt electric starter
7—12-Volt generator
8—unassigned to date
9—Short block assembly

Fifth digit—indicates bearing type, etc., as follows:

0—Standard bearing
1—Aluminum or bronze sleeve bearing with flange mounting surface and pilot diameter on engine mounting face for mounting equipment concentric to crankshaft center line
2—Ball or roller bearing
3—Ball or roller bearing with flange mounting surface and pilot diameter on engine mounting face for mounting equipment concentric to crankshaft center line
4—Numbers 4 through 9 are unassigned to date

Sixth digit—indicates auxiliary power take-off and speed reducers as follows:

0—Without auxiliary pto or speed reducer
1—Auxiliary power take-off
2—2:1 speed reducer
3—not assigned to date
4—4:1 speed reducer
5—not assigned to date
6—6:1 speed reducer
7—numbers 7 through 9 are assigned to date

Seventh digit—if other than "0" will indicate a major design change.

Eighth, ninth & tenth digits—identifies model variations.

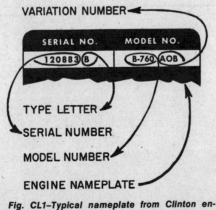

Fig. CL1—Typical nameplate from Clinton engine manufactured prior to late 1961.

Fig. CL2—Typical nameplate from Clinton engine after model identification system was changed in late 1961. First seven digits indicate basic features of engine. Engines with "Mylar" (plastic) nameplate have engine model and serial numbers stamped on the cylinder air deflector next to the nameplate.

CLINTON

CLINTON ENGINES CORPORATION
Maquoketa, Iowa

MODEL NUMBER	Bore	Stroke	Displ.	HP/RPM
E-65 CW & E-65 CCW	2-1/8	1-5/8	5.76	5.2/6500
200, A-200, AVS-200-1000 & VS-200	1-7/8	1-5/8	4.5	1.75/3600
VS-200-1000 & VS-200-2000	1-7/8	1-5/8	4.5	2.0/3600
VS-200-3000	1-7/8	1-5/8	4.5	2.25/3600
VS-200-4000	2-1/8	1-5/8	5.76	2.25/3800
290	1-7/8	1-5/8	4.5	1.6/3600
A-400	2-1/8	1-5/8	5.76	2.5/3600
A-400-1000, AVS-400, AVS-400-1000, BVS-400, CVS-400-1000, VS-400, VS-400-1000, VS-400-2000, VS-400-3000 & VS-400-4000	2-1/8	1-5/8	5.76	2.5/3800
A-460 (Reduction gear)	2-1/8	1-5/8	5.76	2.5/633
490	2-1/8	1-5/8	5.76	2.5/3600
A-490	2-1/8	1-5/8	5.76	2.5/3800
500-0100-000, 501-0000-000	2-1/8	1-5/8	5.76	2.75/3800
501-001-000	2-1/8	1-5/8	5.76	2.75/3800
GK-590	2-1/8	1-5/8	5.76	3.35/6500
502-0308-000, 503-0308-000	2-3/8	1¾	7.75	7.0/6000

Clinton 2-cycle engines are of aluminum alloy die-cast construction with an integral cast-in cast iron cylinder sleeve. Reed type inlet valves are used on all models. Refer to Clinton engine identification information preceding this section.

MAINTENANCE

SPARK PLUG. Champion H-10J or equivalent spark plug is recommended for use in E-65 CW and E-65 CCW models.

Champion H-11 or H-11J or equivalent spark plug is recommended for use in 200, A-200, AVS-200, AVS-200-1000, VS-200, VS-200-1000, VS-200-2000, VS-200-3000 (Types A and B), 290, A-400, A-400-1000 (Type A), AVS-400, AVS-400-1000, BVS-400, VS-400-1000, VS-400-2000, VS-400-3000, VS-400-4000 (Types A and B), 490, and A-490-1000 (Type A) models.

Champion J-12J or equivalent spark plug is recommended for use in VS-200-3000 (Type C), VS-200-4000, A-400-1000 (Types B, C, D, E & F), CVS-400-1000, VS-400-4000 (Types C, D, E & F), A-490-1000 (Types B, C, D, E & F), 500-0100-000, 501-0000-000, and 501-0001-000 models. Engine models 502-0308-000 and 503-0308-000 call for an Autolite A7NX spark plug.

Set electrode gap to 0.030 on all models. Use graphite on threads when installing spark plug and tighten spark plug to a torque of 275-300 inch-pounds.

CARBURETOR. Several different carburetors of both float and diaphragm types have been used on Clinton 2-cycle engines. Refer to the following paragraphs:

CLINTON (WALBRO) "LM" FLOAT CARBURETORS. Clinton (Walbro designed) "LMB" and "LMG" float type carburetors are used. Refer to Fig. CL5 for exploded view of typical model.

For initial adjustment, open both of the fuel adjustment needles approximately 1¼ turns. Make final adjustments with engine running at operating temperature. Move speed control to "fast" position and turn main fuel needle in or out to obtain maximum power under load. If load cannot be applied, turn main fuel needle in or out for smoothest engine operation; then, turn needle out (counter-clockwise) approximately ⅛ to ¼-turn to provide a richer fuel mixture.

Move engine speed control to "slow" or idle position and adjust idle fuel needle and stop screw for best performance and correct idle speed. Check acceleration from slow to fast idle and open idle needle approximately ⅛-turn (counter-clockwise) if necessary for proper acceleration.

Fig. CL5–Exploded view of typical "LMG" series carburetor. "LMV" and "LMB" series are similar.

1. Throttle shaft
2. Choke shaft
3. Spring
4. Throttle disc
5. Spring
6. Carburetor body
7. Idle stop screw
8. Springs
9. Idle fuel needle
10. Spring
11. Choke disc
12. Inlet needle & seat
13. Main nozzle
14. Float
14A. Float pin
15. Gasket
16. Gaskets
17. Float bowl
18. Drain valve
19. Retainer
20. Seal
21. Spring
22. Main fuel needle
23. Lever (optional)

When overhauling "LMB" or "LMG" carburetors, discard main fuel nozzle if necessary to remove same and install a service type nozzle (See Fig. CL6). Do not reinstall old nozzle.

Float setting on "LMB" and "LMG" carburetors should be 5/32-inch clearance between outer rim of carburetor casting and top of free side of float.

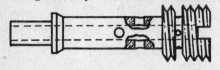

Fig. CL6—When original main fuel nozzle is removed from "LM" series carburetor, it must be discarded and service type nozzle shown must be installed.

Bend tabs on float hinge to adjust float setting and to limit float travel to approximately 3/16-inch at free side of float.

CARTER MODEL "N" FLOAT CARBURETORS. Refer to Fig. CL7 for exploded view of typical Carter model "N" carburetor. The following models have been used:

N-2003-S
N-2029-S
N-2087-S
N-2171-S
N-2457-S

For initial adjustment on models N-2003-S and N-2029-S, open idle fuel mixture needle 1-turn and high speed (load) needle ¾-turn; on models N-2087-S, N-2171-S and N-2457-S, open idle needle 1½ turns and open high speed needle ½-turn. Make final adjustments with engine running at operating temperature. Adjust high speed needle for best performance under load; if load cannot be applied, turn needle in or out to obtain smoothest engine operation and then turn needle out slightly for a richer mixture. Adjust idle needle and idle speed stop screw for proper idle performance.

Float setting on models N-2003-S

and N-2457-S is 13/64-inch clearance between outer edge of casting and free end of float. Float setting on models N-2029-S, N-2087-S and N-2171-S is 11/64-inch clearance between outer edge of casting and free end of float. Adjust by bending lip on float hinge.

On model N-2457-S, low speed jet and high speed fuel nozzle are permanently installed. Do not attempt to remove these parts.

CARTER MODEL "NS" FLOAT CARBURETOR. Refer to Fig. CL8 for exploded view of the Carter NS-3267-S float type carburetor. This carburetor is for engine operation between 3000 and 3800 RPM and no idle fuel mixture adjusting needle is provided. Initial adjustment of the fuel mixture needle is 1-turn open. Adjust needle in or out slightly to provide proper fuel mixture after engine is running and is warm.

Float setting is 13/64-inch clearance between outer edge of bowl cover and top surface of free end of float.

The float needle, pin, and spring are serviced only as a kit with the bowl cover; as the inlet needle seat is an integral part of the bowl cover assembly.

TILLOTSON "HL" DIAPHRAGM CARBURETORS. Refer to Fig. CL9 for exploded view of the Tillotson model "HL" diaphragm type carburetor.

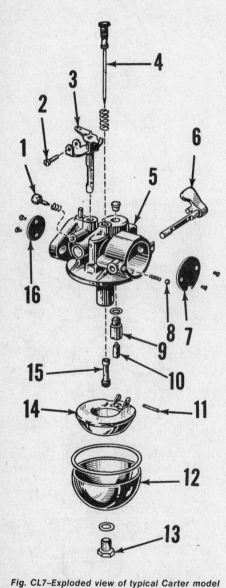

Fig. CL7—Exploded view of typical Carter model "N" carburetor. Design of float and float bowl may vary from that shown.

1. Idle fuel needle	9. Inlet valve seat
2. Idle stop screw	10. Inlet needle
3. Throttle shaft	11. Float pin
4. Main fuel needle	12. Float bowl
5. Carburetor body	13. Retainer
6. Choke shaft	14. Float
7. Choke disc	15. Main nozzle
8. Detent ball	16. Throttle disc

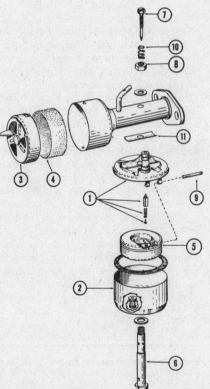

Fig. CL8—Exploded view of float type carburetor used on 501-0000-000 model series engine.

1. Inlet valve & seat	
2. Float bowl	
3. Choke assembly	7. Fuel needle
4. Air cleaner element	8. Nut
5. Float	9. Float pin
6. Main nozzle	10. Spring
	11. Gasket

Fig. CL9—Exploded view of Tillotson "HL" diaphragm type carburetor.

1. Choke disc	11. Gasket
2. Idle stop screw	12. Cover
3. Choke shaft	13. Gasket
4. Throttle shaft	14. Pump diaphragm
5. Main fuel needle	15. Pump body
6. Idle fuel needle	16. Screen
7. Throttle disc	17. Gasket
8. Inlet lever pivot	18. Cover
9. Inlet lever	19. Welch plug
10. Diaphragm	20. Inlet valve & seat

Models HL-13A and HL-44A are used.

Clockwise rotation of both the idle and main fuel needles lean the fuel mixtures. For initial adjustment, open idle needle ¾-turn and open main fuel needle 1 to 1¼ turns. Make final adjustments with engine running at operating temperature. Adjust main fuel needle in or out for smoothest engine performance at high speed; then, open needle slightly for a richer mixture. Adjust idle fuel mixture needle and idle stop screw for proper idle performance. Open idle needle slightly if necessary for proper acceleration from slow to fast speed.

BROWN "CP" DIAPHRAGM CARBURETOR. Refer to Fig. CL10 for exploded view of the Brown model 3-CP carburetor. The fuel must pass through a felt filter and screen, located under plug (3), to enter the diaphragm chamber.

Idle fuel adjustment screw (20) has plain slotted head and main fuel adjustment screw head is knurled or has a "T" head. For initial adjustment, set both the idle and main fuel needles to approximately ½ to ¾-turn open. Make final adjustments with engine running at operating temperature. Adjust main fuel needle for smoothest performance at high speed; then, open needle slightly for richer mixture. Then, adjust idle needle and idle speed

stop screw for proper idle performance. Check engine for acceleration and open the main (high speed) needle slightly further, if necessary, for proper acceleration.

Refer to Fig. CL11 for proper diaphragm lever setting. Always renew the copper sealing gasket if inlet needle seat is removed. **Be sure** to remove old gasket.

BROWN "CS" DIAPHRAGM CARBURETOR. Refer to Fig. CL12 for exploded view of the Brown CS-15 carburetor used on some engine models.

Idle fuel adjustment needle has a slotted screw head; main fuel adjustment needle has a "T" head.

For initial adjustment, open both fuel adjustment needles approximately ¾-

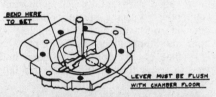

Fig. CL11—Method of checking and setting fuel inlet lever on Brown diaphragm type carburetors.

turn. Make final adjustment with engine running at operating temperature. Adjust main fuel needle for smoothest performance at high speed; then, open needle slightly from this setting for a richer mixture. Adjust idle fuel needle for smoothest idle performance and for proper acceleration.

Refer to Fig. CL11 for proper diaphragm lever setting. Always renew the copper sealing gasket if inlet needle is removed. **Be sure** to remove old gasket.

WALBRO MODEL SDC-34 DIAPHRAGM CARBURETOR. This diaphragm-type carburetor used on model 502-0308-000 engine is shown in Fig. CL13. To make preliminary adjustments, back out idle screw (15—Fig. CL13) clear of throttle stop, then turn back in to just contact stop and add ¾ turn to screw. Open idle mixture needle (20) and high speed mixture needle one full turn each. Make final running adjustments after engine has

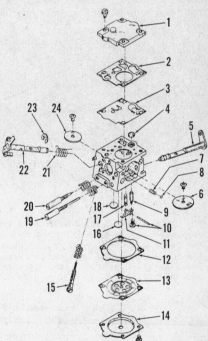

Fig. CL13—Exploded view of typical Walbro SDC diaphragm-type carburetor. Model SDC-34, used on 502-series engines has choke (5) and throttle (22) levers of slightly different configuration from those shown. Also, an additional diaphragm check valve (not shown) is fitted between gasket (2) and pump diaphragm (3).

1. Fuel pump cover	15. Idle speed screw
2. Gasket	& spring
3. Pump diaphragm	16. Welch plug, 5/16
4. Fuel inlet screen	17. Metering lever
5. Choke shaft	spring
6. Choke plate	18. Welch plug, 3/8
7. Choke detent spring	19. High speed needle
8. Choke detent ball	& spring
9. Inlet valve needle	20. Idle mixture needle
10. Lever pin, retainer	& spring
11. Metering lever	21. Throttle return
12. Metering diaphragm	spring
gasket	22. Throttle shaft
13. Metering diaphragm	23. Shaft retainer
14. Diaphragm cover	24. Throttle plate

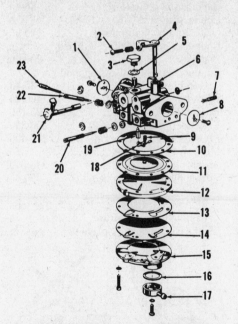

Fig. CL10—Exploded view of Brown CP carburetor.

1. Choke disc	13. Gasket
2. Idle stop screw	14. Diaphragm
3. Filter plug	15. Pump cover
4. Throttle shaft	16. Gasket
5. Gasket	17. Inlet fitting
6. Carburetor body	18. Inlet lever
7. Idle jet	19. Inlet valve
8. Throttle disc	20. Idle fuel needle
9. Inlet lever spring	21. Choke shaft
10. Gasket	22. Main fuel needle
11. Diaphragm	23. Inlet lever pivot
12. Cover	

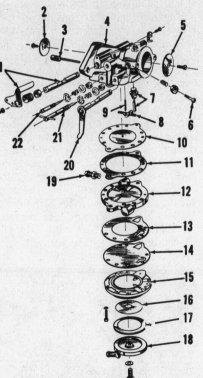

Fig. CL12—Exploded view of Brown CS carburetor.

1. Throttle shaft	12. Cover
2. Throttle disc	13. Gasket
3. Inlet lever pivot	14. Pump diaphragm
4. Carburetor body	15. Pump cover
5. Choke disc	16. Screen
6. Idle stop screw	17. Gasket
7. Inlet needle valve	18. Inlet fitting
& seat	19. Connection
8. Inlet lever	20. Choke shaft
9. Inlet lever spring	21. Main fuel needle
10. Diaphragm	22. Idle fuel needle
11. Gasket	

reached normal operating temperature. It will be noted that on this engine, carburetor is not equipped with an accelerator pump as are many other models of the SDC series. For this reason, some care must be taken when adjusting idle mixture and high speed mixture needles to gain a smooth transition from idle speed to operating speed when throttle is opened sharply. Final adjustments should be made by small fractional changes of mixture settings to gain even, regular acceleration and satisfactory performance. Model 502 engine speed is not controlled by an air vane type governor as is that of model 503, therefore, all control is by throttle operation only, a detail which should be kept in mind during carburetor adjustment.

Refer to Fig. CL14 for adjustment procedure for metering lever. Be sure that metering lever spring is properly seated and that hook on diaphragm and inlet valve needle are correctly engaged.

FUEL PUMP. Some models are equipped with a diaphragm type fuel

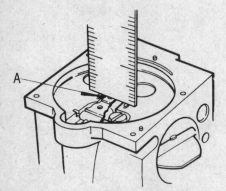

Fig. CL14—View to show adjustment procedure for metering lever of SDC-34 carburetor. Check engagement of inlet valve needle and diaphragm hook to lever and that spring under lever is correctly seated. Metering lever should just touch straight edge (A).

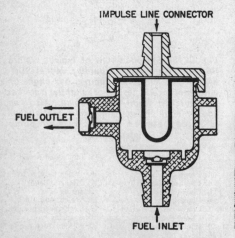

Fig. CL15—Cross-section view of impulse type fuel pump used on some engines. Renew complete pump assembly if inoperative.

pump as shown in the cross-sectional view in Fig. CL15. The pump diaphragm is actuated by pressure pulsations in the engine crankcase transmitted via an impulse tube connected between the fuel pump and crankcase. The pump is designed to lift fuel approximately six inches. Service consists of renewing the complete fuel pump assembly.

GOVERNOR. Except on non-governed karting engines, speed control is maintained by an air-vane type governor. Renew bent or worn governor vane or linkage and be sure that linkage does not bind in any position when moved through full range of travel. On models with speed control lever, adjust lever stop so that maximum speed does not exceed 3600 rpm. On models without speed control, renew or re-tension governor spring to limit maximum speed to 3600 rpm. Be sure that blower housing is clean and free of dents that would cause binding of air vane.

MAGNETO AND TIMING. Ignition timing is 27 degrees BTDC and is non-adjustable. Armature air gap should be 0.007-0.017. Adjust breaker contact gap to 0.018-0.021 on all models.

Magneto may be considered satisfactory if it will fire an 18 mm. spark plug with gap set at 0.156-0.187 (5/32 to 3/16-inch). Refer to Fig. CL16.

LUBRICATION. Use a high-quality outboard motor or two-stroke engine oil, SAE 30 weight. There are no precise API ratings for two-stroke engine oils; consequently, the safest course is to use oils identified by the refiner as designed for two-cycle or outboard motor use. Because of the high level of additives used in four-stroke (automotive) oils, their use should be avoided. NEVER use oils marked ML (light duty), DG (diesel) or SA (light duty). If an improper oil is used to meet an emergency, change to

correct two-stroke oil as soon as possible and discard the improper fuel-oil mix.

Oil to gasoline mixing ratio is determined by type of bearings installed in a particular two-stroke engine. Plain sleeve main and connecting rod bearings require ¾-pint of oil for each gallon of gasoline. Engines equipped with needle bearings call for a mixing ratio of ½-pint of oil per gallon of gasoline. During break-in (first five hours of operation) a 50% increase of oil portion is advisable, especially if engine will be operated at or near maximum load or rpm.

CARBON. Power loss on 2-cycle engines can often be corrected by cleaning the exhaust ports and muffler. To clean the exhaust ports, remove the muffler and turn engine until piston is below ports. Use a dull tool to scrape carbon from the ports; take care not to damage top of piston or cylinder walls.

REPAIRS

NOTE: Graphite should be applied to the threads of all screws which thread into die cast parts.

TIGHTENING TORQUES. Values shown in following tables are in inch-pounds.

Bearing plate to block 75-95
Blower housing 65-70
Carburetor mounting 60-65
Connecting rod (E65, GK590, 502 and 503, aluminum) 70-80
Connecting rod (E65 & GK590, steel) 90-100
Connecting rod (all other models, aluminum) 35-45
Cylinder head (502, 503) 140-160
Engine base 125-150
Flywheel (E65 & GK590) 250-300
Flywheel (all other models) 375-400
Muffler 40-60
Spark plug 275-300
Stator plate to bearing plate 50-60

BEARING PLATE. Because of the pressure and vacuum pulsations in crankcase, bearing plate and gasket

Fig. CL16—Magneto can be considered in satisfactory condition if it will fire an 18 mm. spark plug with electrode gap set at 0.156-0.187.

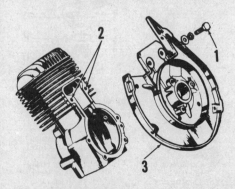

Fig. CL17—If cap screws (1) which thread into holes (2) are too long, they may bottom and damage cylinder walls.

must form an air-tight seal when installed. Make sure gasket surfaces are not cracked, nicked or warped, that oil passages in crankcase, gasket and plate are aligned and that correct number and thickness of thrust washers are used. Also check to be sure the right cap screws are installed when engine is reassembled.

CAUTION: Cap screws (1—Fig. C17) may bottom in threaded holes (2) if incorrect screws are used. When long screws are tightened, damage to cylinder walls can result.

FLYWHEEL. On vertical shaft engines, both a lightweight aluminum flywheel and a cast iron flywheel are available. The lightweight aluminum flywheel should be used only on rotary lawnmower engines where the blade is attached directly to the engine crankshaft. The cast iron flywheel should be used on engines with belt pulley drive, etc.

Some kart engine owners will prefer using the lightweight aluminum flywheel due to the increase in accelerating performance.

CONNECTING ROD. Connecting rod and piston unit can be removed after removing the reed plate and crankshaft.

On E-65 and GK-590 models (karting engines), and on models 502 and 503, needle roller bearings are used at crankpin end of connecting rod. Renew crankshaft and/or connecting rod if bearing surfaces are scored or are rough. When reassembling, place thirteen needle rollers between connecting rod and crankpin. Using a low melting point grease, stick the remaining twelve needle rollers to connecting rod cap and install cap with the embossments (See A—Fig. CL18) on cap and rod properly aligned.

On all other models, an aluminum connecting rod with bronze bearing surfaces is used. Recommended clearances are as follows:

Connecting rod to
crankshaft 0.0026-0.004

Renew rod and/or crankshaft
if clearance exceeds 0.0055
Connecting rod to
piston pin 0.0004-0.0011
Renew rod and/or piston pin
if clearance exceeds 0.002

Reinstall cap to connecting rod with embossments (A—Fig. CL18) aligned and carefully tighten screws to recommended torque value; bend the locking tabs against screw heads as shown in Fig. CL19.

PISTON, PIN AND RINGS. Pistons may be equipped with either two or three compression rings. On three-ring pistons, a locking wire is fitted in a small groove behind each piston ring to prevent ring rotation on the piston. To install the three locking wires, refer to Fig. CL20 and proceed as follows: Hold piston with top up and intake side of piston to right. Install top and bottom locking wires with locking tab (end of wire ring bent outward) to right of locating hole in ring groove and install center locking wire with locking tab to left of locating hole.

Piston and rings are available in oversizes of 0.010 and 0.020 as well as standard size. Piston pin is available in standard size only.

When installing pistons with ring locating pins or locking wires, be sure that end gaps of rings are properly located over the pins or the locking tabs and install piston using a ring compressor. Refer to Fig. CL20.

Be sure to reinstall piston and rod assembly with exhaust side of piston (long sloping side of piston dome)

towards exhaust ports in cylinder.

Check piston, pin and rings against the following specifications:

Specifications for 1-7/8" Pistons:
Ring end gap, desired 0.005-0.013
  Max. allowable...............0.020
Ring side clearance,
  desired 0.0015-0.004
  Max. allowable..............0.006
Piston skirt clearance,
  desired 0.0045-0.0065
  Max. allowable................0.008
Piston pin diameter 0.4294-0.4296
Pin bore in piston........0.4295-0.4298
Piston pin to connecting rod
  clearance, desired......0.0004-0.0011
  Max. allowable.................0.002

Specifications for 2-1/8" Pistons:
Ring end gap, desired
  (2-ring piston) 0.007-0.017
  Max. allowable (2-ring piston) ..0.025
Ring end gap, desired
  (3-ring piston) 0.010-0.015
  Max. allowable (3-ring piston) ..0.017
Ring side clearance, desired
  (2-ring piston) 0.0015-0.004
  Max. allowable (2-ring piston) ..0.006
Ring side clearance, desired
  (3-ring piston) 0.002-0.004
  Max. allowable (3-ring piston) .0.0055
Piston skirt clearance, 2-
  ring piston, desired 0.005-0.007
  Max. allowable................0.008
Piston skirt clearance, 3-
  ring piston, desired 0.0045-0.005
  Max. allowable................0.007
Piston pin diameter 0.4999-0.5001
Pin bore in piston........0.5000-0.5003
Piston pin to rod
  clearance, desired......0.0004-0.0011
  Max. allowable................0.002

Specifications for 2-3/8" Pistons:
Ring end gap desired.......0.007-0.017
  Max. allowable................0.025
Ring side clearance
  desired 0.0015-0.004
  Max. allowable................0.006
Piston skirt clearance
  desired 0.005-0.007
  Max. allowable................0.008
Piston to rod clearance
  desired 0.0004-0.0011
  Max. allowable................0.002

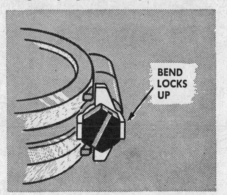

Fig. CL19—Bend connecting rod cap retaining screw locks up as shown.

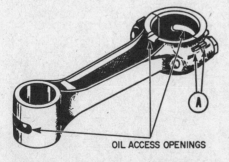

OIL ACCESS OPENINGS

Fig. CL18—Be sure that embossments (A) are aligned when assembling cap to connecting rod.

Fig. CL20—View showing method of installing ring locking wires on 3-ring pistons and placement of rings on two and three-ring pistons. Some two-ring pistons do not have ring locking pins.

CYLINDER AND CRANKCASE. The one-piece aluminum alloy cylinder and crankcase unit is integrally die-cast around a cast iron sleeve (cylinder liner). Cylinder can be honed to 0.010 or 0.020 oversize for oversize piston and rings. Standard cylinder bore sizes are as follows:

1-7/8" bore 1.875-1.876
2-1/8" bore 2.125-2.126
2-3/8" bore 2.375-2.376

CRANKSHAFT. To remove crankshaft, proceed as follows: Remove blower housing and nut retaining flywheel to crankshaft. Thread an impact nut to within 1/8-inch of flywheel, pull

on flywheel and tap impact nut with hammer. After flywheel is removed, remove magneto assembly. Remove the engine base and inlet reed valve plate from crankcase and detach connecting rod from crankshaft. Be careful not to lose the 25 needle rollers on E-65, GK-590, 502 and 503 models. Push connecting rod and piston unit up against top of cylinder. On models with ball bearing main on output end of crankshaft, remove the snap ring retaining ball bearing in crankcase. Remove the magneto stator plate and withdraw crankshaft from engine taking care not to damage connecting rod.

On crankshaft used with needle

roller main or crankpin bearings, renew crankshaft if bearing surface shows signs of wear or is rough or scored. On crankshafts used with plain bushing mains and/or cast-in crankpin bearing, check crankshaft against the following values:

Crankpin diameter 0.7788-0.7795
Main journal diameter,
  flywheel end 0.7495-0.7502
Main journal diameter,
  output end 0.8745-0.8752
  or 0.9995-1.0002
Rod, crankpin end I.D. ...0.7820-0.7827
Main bearing bushing
  I.D., flywheel end 0.7517-0.7525

Fig. CL21—Exploded view of typical vertical shaft 2-stroke engine, Model VS-200 shown. Model 503 differs in type of starter (see Fig. CL102—ACCESSORIES), use of an 8-petal rosette-type reed valve, a detachable cylinder head and has ball and roller bearings to support crankshaft with needle bearing at crankpin.

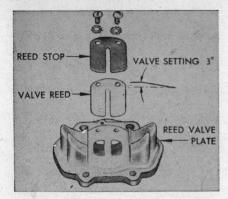

Fig. CL22—Details of two-petal reed inlet valve used on some models. Eight-petal rosette style reed valve is also used—see Fig. CL23.

Main bearing bushing
   I.D., output end 0.8770-0.8780
      or 1.0020-1.0030
Main bearing clearance
   desired 0.0015-0.0030
   Renew bushings and/or shaft
   if..........................0.0055

Renew crankshaft if either main bearing journal or crankpin journal is out-of-round 0.0015 or more.

Main bearing bushings, bushing remover and driver, reamers and reamer alignment plate are available through Clinton parts sources for renewing bushings in crankcase and bearing plate. On vertical crankshaft engines having two bushings in the crankcase, the outer bushing must be removed towards outside of crankcase and the inner bushing towards inside of crankcase. Bushings must be recessed 1/32-inch from inside surface of bearing plate or crankcase except when thrust washer is used between crankcase or plate and thrust surface of crankshaft.

Renew ball bearing type mains if bearing is rough or is worn. Renew needle type main bearings if one or more needles show any defect or if needles can be separated the width of one roller.

When reinstalling crankshaft with bushing or needle roller mains, crankshaft end play should be 0.005-0.020. The gasket used between bearing (stator) plate and crankcase is available in thicknesses of 0.025, 0.030 and 0.035 for adjusting crankshaft end play. It may also be necessary to renew the crankshaft thrust washer.

There is no specification covering end play where ball type main bearing is used. However, crankshaft should turn freely after installation.

CRANKSHAFT OIL SEALS. As on all 2-cycle engines, the crankshaft oil seals must be maintained in good condition to hold crankcase compression on the downward stroke of the piston. It is usually good service procedure, therefore, to renew the seals whenever overhauling an engine. Apply a small amount of gasket sealer to the outer rim of the seal and install with lip towards inside of crankcase. Outer surface of seal should be flush with outer face of crankcase or bearing plate.

REED VALVE. Either a dual reed (Fig. CL21) or eight-petal rosette reed (Fig. CL23) is used.

The 3 degree setting of the dual reed shown in Fig. CL22 is the design of the reed as stamped in the manufacturing process. The 3 degree bend should be towards the reed seating surface. The reed stop should be adjusted to approximately 0.280 from tip of stop to reed seating surface.

Renew reed if any petal is cracked, rusted or does not lay flat against the reed plate. Renew the reed plate if rusted, pitted or shows any signs of wear.

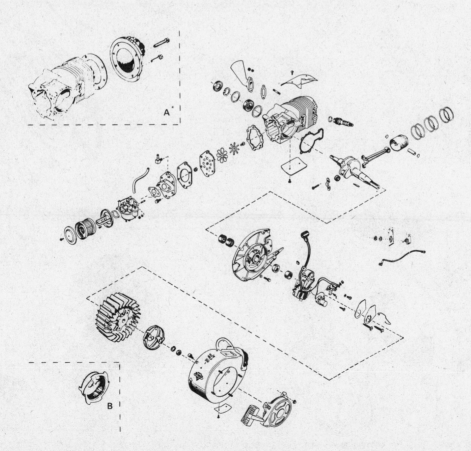

Fig. CL23—Exploded view of E-65 kart engine. Differences from model 502 are minor: Cylinder head is detachable as in inset "A", piston is fitted with two rings instead of three, muffler, starter cup (inset "B") and carburetor are of different design. See Fig. CL13 for carburetor.

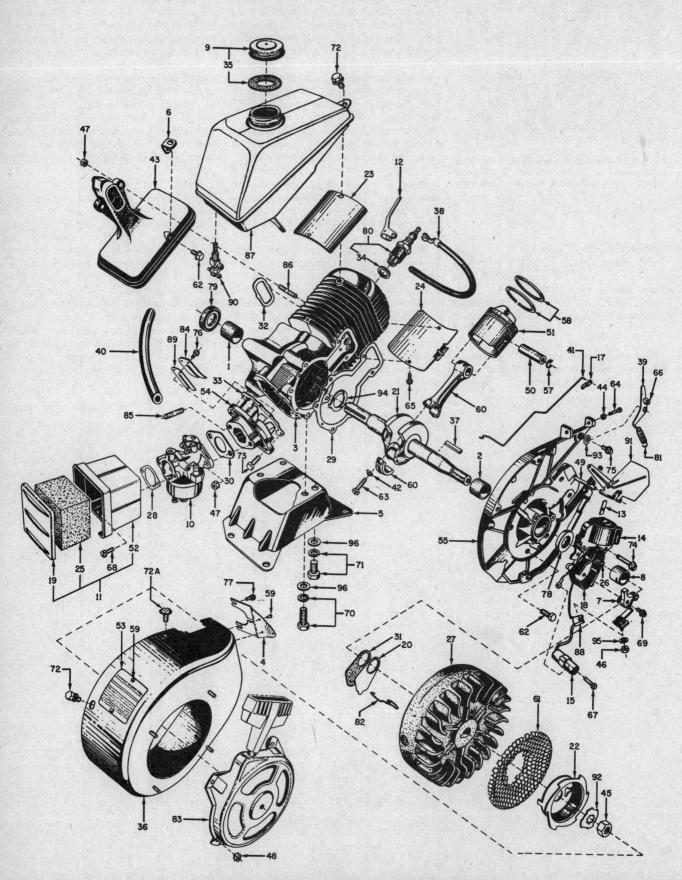

Fig. CL24—Exploded view of typical horizontal crankshaft engine.

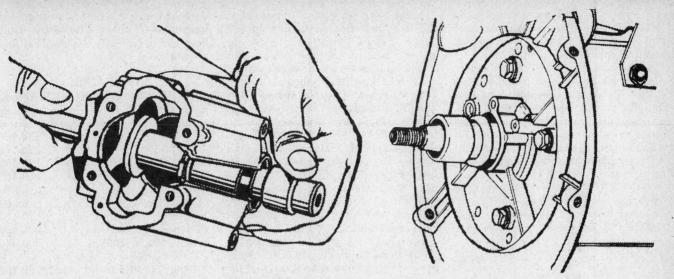

Fig. CL25—Examples of typical use of oil seal loaders for protection of seals during installation of crankshaft. Use ample lubrication.

CLINTON

CLINTON ENGINES CORPORATION
Maquoketa, Iowa

Horizontal Crankshaft Engines

MODEL SERIES	Cyls.	Bore	Stroke	Displ.
300, A-300, 350	1	2	1½	4.72

Vertical Crankshaft Engines

VS-300	1	2	1½	4.72

Refer to model identification information preceding the Clinton service section.

MAINTENANCE

SPARK PLUG. All models use a 14 mm., ⅜-inch reach spark plug. Recommended plug is a Champion J-8. Set electrode gap to 0.025-0.028. When installing, apply graphite to threads and tighten to a torque of 275-300 inch-pounds.

CARBURETOR. Clinton suction type carburetors, Nos. 7100, 7120,

7080-1 and 7080-2; and Carter Model N float type carburetors are used. Refer to appropriate following paragraph:

CLINTON SUCTION TYPE CARBURETORS. Refer to Fig. CL30, Fig. CL31 and Fig. CL32 for exploded views. Carburetor assembly Nos. 7100, 7120 and 7080-1 are no longer available; if necessary to renew complete carburetor, assembly No. 7080-2, along with certain other parts, must be used.

Carburetor is equipped with only one fuel mixture adjustment needle (7—Figs. CL30, CL31 and CL32). Average

adjustment is 3½ turns open. Make final adjustment with engine running at operating temperature and speed with fuel tank approximately ½-full.

CARTER FLOAT TYPE CARBURETORS. Refer to Fig. CL33. Carter Model N-705S is shown; Models N-2019S and N-2147S are similar except for shape of bowl and float.

On Model N-705S carburetor, float should be adjusted so there is 13/64-inch clearance between carburetor casting and free side of float. Initial

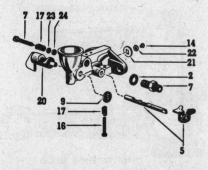

Fig. CL30–View of early production suction lift carburetor. Choke valve (20) or complete carburetor are no longer available. Only one fuel adjustment needle (7) is used.

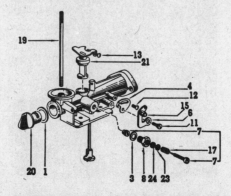

Fig. CL31–View of later production suction lift carburetor. See Fig. CL32 also.

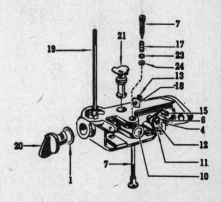

Fig. CL32–View of later production suction lift carburetor. See Fig. CL31 also.

adjustment for both idle and high speed fuel mixture needles is 1½ turns open; make final adjustment with engine running at operating temperature.

On Models N-2019S and N-2147S, float should be adjusted so that there is 11/64-inch clearance between carburetor casting and free side of float. Initial adjustment for both idle and high speed fuel mixture needles is 1½ turns open; make final adjustment with engine running at operating temperature.

GOVERNOR. An air vane type governor is used on all models. Recommended maximum governed speed is 3300 RPM; do not set maximum governed speed above 3600 RPM.

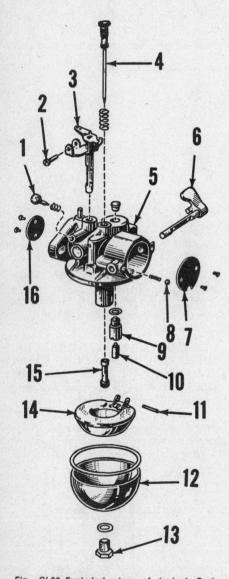

Fig. CL33–Exploded view of typical Carter model "N" carburetor. Design of float and float bowl may vary from that shown.

1. Idle fuel needle
2. Idle stop screw
3. Throttle shaft
4. Main fuel needle
5. Carburetor body
6. Choke shaft
7. Choke disc
8. Detent ball
9. Inlet valve seat
10. Inlet needle
11. Float pin
12. Float bowl
13. Retainer
14. Float
15. Main nozzle
16. Throttle disc

Make sure that governor linkage does not bind when moved through full range of travel and that the blower housing is clean and free of dents that would cause governor air vane to bind.

On models without adjustable speed control, renew governor spring (90—Fig. CL40) and link (46) to obtain correct maximum governed speed.

MAGNETO AND TIMING. Repco flywheel type magnetos are used on all models. Breaker points and condenser are located under flywheel. Magneto can be assumed in satisfactory condition if it will fire an 18 mm. spark plug with electrode gap set to 0.156-0.187 (5/32 to 3/16-inch). See Fig. CL36.

Ignition timing is fixed and nonadjustable at 21 degrees BTDC. Armature air gap should be 0.007-0.017. Condenser capacity is 0.15-0.19 mfd. Adjust breaker point gap to 0.018-0.021.

LUBRICATION. Motor oil of MM or MS grade should be used. Use SAE 30 above 32° F., SAE 10W from −10° F. to 32° F., and SAE 5W below −10° F.

On models equipped with reduction gearing, use SAE 30 oil in gear box.

CRANKCASE BREATHER. Crankcase breather assembly (8—Fig. CL39 or 5—Fig. CL40) should be removed and cleaned if difficulty is experienced with oil loss through hole in

Fig. CL34–Suction lift carburetor adjustments. See text for procedure.

1. Choke
2. Idle speed adjustment
3. Mixture adjustment

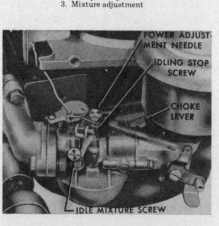

Fig. CL35–Carter model "N" float type carburetor installation.

valve cover or whenever the engine is being overhauled. Be sure that breather is correctly reassembled and reinstalled.

REPAIRS

TIGHTENING TORQUES. Recommended torque values in inch-pounds are as follows:

Base Bolts (A300) 150-160
(300, 350, VS300) 325-375
Bearing plate (A300) 120-150
(300, 350, VS300) 140-160
Carburetor to manifold 35-50
Manifold to block 60-65
End cover or gear box 120-150
Flywheel (A300) 375-400
(300, 350, VS300) 400-450
PTO housing
(300, 350, VS300) 120-150
Spark plug 275-300
Speed reducer mount 110-150

CONNECTING ROD. Rod and piston assembly can be removed from engine after cylinder head and engine base (on horizontal crankshaft models) or crankcase end cover (on vertical crankshaft models) are removed.

Recommended clearances are as follows:

Connecting rod to
crankshaft 0.0018-0.0035
Maximum allowable 0.0045

Fig. CL36–Magneto can be considered in satisfactory condition if it will fire an 18 mm. spark plug with the electrode gap set at 0.156-0.187.

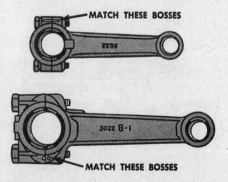

Fig. CL37–When assembling cap to connecting rod, be sure that embossments on rod and cap are aligned as shown.

Connecting rod to

piston pin 0.0004-0.0011

Maximum allowable 0.002

Rod side play 0.005-0.020

Connecting rod is available in standard size only. When reassembling, be sure that embossments on connecting rod and cap are aligned as in Fig. CL37. Oil hole in connecting rod should face flywheel side of engine.

PISTON, PIN AND RINGS. Piston is fitted with two compression rings and one oil control ring. Recommended piston ring end gap is 0.007-0.017; renew if end gap is 0.025 or more. Ring side clearance in groove should be 0.002-0.005; maximum allowable side clearance is 0.006. Rings are available in oversizes of 0.010 and 0.020 as well as standard size.

The piston pin is retained in piston with a snap ring at each end. Piston pin is available in standard size only and should be a "hand push fit" in piston. Piston pin diameter is 0.4999-0.5001; pin bore diameter in piston is 0.5000-0.5003 and pin bore diameter in connecting rod is 0.5005-0.5010.

Piston skirt clearance in cylinder bore should be 0.0045-0.0065. Maximum allowable skirt clearance is 0.008. Piston is available in oversizes of 0.010 and 0.020 as well as standard size.

CYLINDER. Standard cylinder bore diameter is 2.000-2.001. If piston skirt clearance is 0.008 or more with new piston, or ring end gap is 0.025 or more with new rings, renew cylinder and crankcase or hone cylinder for oversize piston and rings. Pistons and rings are available in oversizes of 0.010 and 0.020.

CRANKSHAFT. VS-300 series engines are fitted with needle roller bearings at flywheel end of crankshaft and at lower pto journal; upper pto journal is fitted with a bushing. Main bearings on other engines are plain bushings.

Renew needle roller main bearings if any needle is pitted or has flat spot, or

if needles can be separated the width of one roller. Check crankshaft and bushings against the following values:

Crankshaft main journal dia.,

flywheel end 0.7483-0.7490

Crankshaft main journal dia.,

pto end (VS-300) 0.8745-0.8752

Other models 0.7483-0.7490

Crankpin diameter 0.7483-0.7490

Main bearing clearance 0.0018-0.0035

Maximum allowable 0.005

Crankshaft end play 0.004-0.012

Maximum allowable 0.020

Rod bearing clearance . 0.0018-0.0035

Maximum allowable 0.0045

Recommended maximum allowable crankpin out-of-round condition is 0.001; the crankshaft must be renewed if crankpin out-of-round is 0.0015 or more.

Bushings, where used, are available

for service and must be reamed after installation. Bushing drivers, reamers and reamer alignment plates are available through Clinton parts sources.

When overhauling engine, renew thrust washer (104—Fig. CL40) on horizontal crankshaft engines or thrust washers (134 and 135 or 136—Fig. CL39) on vertical crankshaft engines. For controlling crankshaft end play, the flywheel end thrust washer (134— Fig. CL39 or 104—Fig. CL40) is available in oversizes of 0.005 and 0.010; also, gasket (36—Fig. CL39 or 32—Fig. CL40) is available in thicknesses of 0.005, 0.010, 0.015 and 0.020. The 0.015 thick gasket is standard.

NOTE: Prior to removing crankshaft from vertical crankshaft engines, first remove the PTO housing (51—Fig.

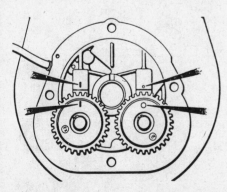

Fig. CL38–Valves are in time when piston is at top dead center and marks on cam gears are aligned as shown. Refer to text for suggested methods of reassembly.

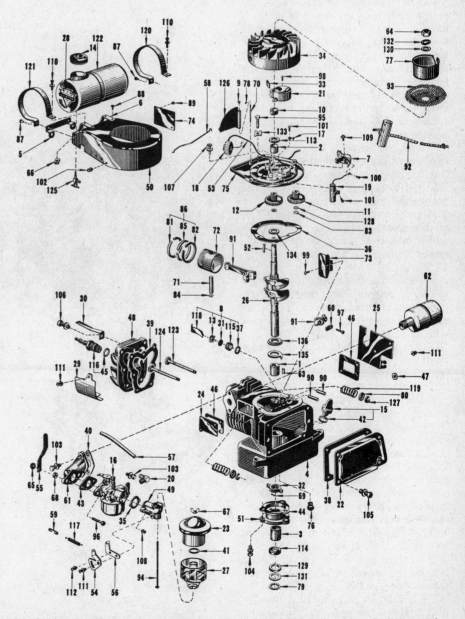

Fig. CL39–Exploded view of model VS-300 engine. Oil pump impeller drive pin (69) must be removed as outlined in text before crankshaft can be removed from crankcase.

CL39) and slide the oil pump impeller (32) from crankshaft. Then, remove the pump impeller drive pin (69) from crankshaft. The crankshaft can then be removed from bearing plate (upper) side of crankcase. Reverse this procedure when re-installing crankshaft. Also, see LUBRICATING SYSTEM paragraph.

CAM GEARS AND BEARING PLATE. Two cam gears are used instead of a conventional camshaft. The gears turn on axle pins that are pressed into the bearing plate. Snap rings (83—Fig. CL39 or 63—Fig. CL40) retain the gears on the axle pins. Wave (spring) washers (128—Fig. CL39 or 99—Fig. CL40) are used between the snap rings and gears to eliminate all end play of cam gears on axle pins. Renew the wave washers if worn or flattened.

Renew the bearing plate and cam axle pins if pins are loose in plate. If axle pins have worked out of plate towards inside of crankcase, but are reasonably tight, press them back into the plate and drill holes through the bearing plate and axle pins so that retaining pins may be installed. Note: Drill holes to size of pins available; retaining pins are not available as a service part.

Valves are properly timed when the cam gears are aligned with marks on the bearing plate as shown in Fig. CL38 and the gears meshed with the crankshaft gear with the crankpin in TDC position. Note the "EX" and "IN" on the gears indicating the exhaust and intake cam gears. Do not reverse gears from position shown in Fig. CL38.

If engine has been completely disassembled, reinstall the bearing plate, cam gears and crankshaft as a unit. Be sure that the two ridges on the thrust washer (134—Fig. CL39 or 104—Fig. CL40) engage tooth slots on the crankshaft gear so that the washer will turn with the crankshaft.

If the bearing plate and cam gear assembly is removed without removing the crankshaft, connecting rod and piston assembly, reinstall as follows: If valves have not been removed, remove cylinder head, push the valves open and hold them in open position with end wrenches placed between the valve heads and the cylinder block. Be sure that the valve tappets (90—Fig. CL39 or 68—Fig. CL40) are in place, turn engine so that piston is at top dead center, align cam gears with marks on bearing plate and, while holding the thrust washer (134—Fig. CL39 or 104 —Fig. CL40) in place against bearing plate, slide the assembly over the crankshaft. The cam gears and crankshaft gear can be meshed by working through the cover plate (22—Fig. CL39) or base plate (1—Fig. CL40) opening. Be sure the thrust washer ridges engage the crankshaft gear before tightening bearing plate to crankcase. Check valve timing after tightening bearing plate and removing the wrenches from between valve heads and cylinder block.

VALVE SYSTEM. Recommended valve tappet gap is 0.007-0.009 for both the intake and exhaust valve. Adjust valve clearance by grinding end of valve stem. A 45 degree bevel should be maintained on ends of valve stems.

Valve face angle should be ground to 45 degrees and valve seat angle between 43½ and 44½ degrees. Recommended seat width is 0.030-0.045; seat should be narrowed by using 30 and 44 degree cutters, tool No. 951-37, when seat width is 0.060 or more. Valve head margin of a new valve is 1/32-inch. When margin is reduced to 1/64-inch by re-grinding and wear, valve should be renewed.

Recommended valve stem to guide clearance is 0.002-0.0045; ream guides to 9/32-inch and install valves with oversize stems if clearance is 0.006 or more.

Install the "C" type valve keepers with sharp edge of keepers towards stem end of valves.

Valves are actuated by pin type tappets. The tappets may be removed and installed through the valve guides if valves are removed or through the crankcase openings if bearing plate and cam gears are removed.

LUBRICATING SYSTEM. Horizontal crankshaft engines are splash lubricated by an oil distributor (27—

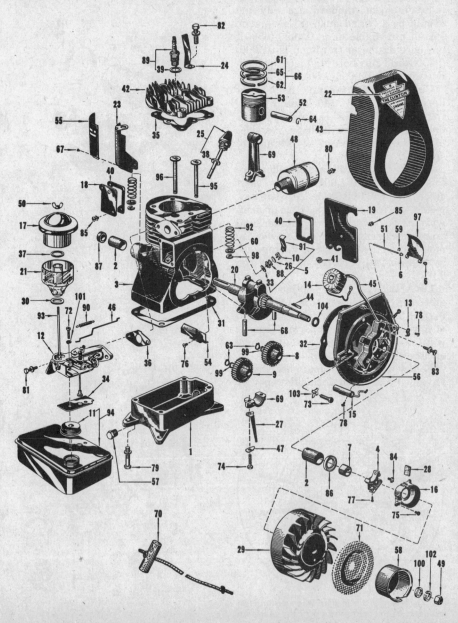

Fig. CL40–Exploded view of model 350 engine. Models 300 and A-300 are similar.

Fig. CL40) attached to the connecting rod cap.

Vertical shaft engines are lubricated by an oil pump. The pump impeller (32 —Fig. CL39) is driven by a pin (69) in the engine crankshaft. Oil is sprayed up into the engine through a brass nozzle (63). Renew the nozzle if it is damaged or has been drilled oversize.

To remove the crankshaft on vertical shaft engines, the PTO housing (51), impeller (32) and impeller drive pin (69) must first be removed from the bottom of the crankcase. Scribe a mark on the PTO housing and the bottom of the crankcase so that the housing may be reinstalled in same position from which it was removed. The oil return hole in the housing must be aligned with the oil return hole in the crankcase.

CLINTON

CLINTON ENGINES CORPORATION
Maquoketa, Iowa

Horizontal Crankshaft Engines

MODEL SERIES	Cyls.	Bore	Stroke	Displ.
500, 650, 700-A, B-700 & C-700	1	2	1⅞	5.89
D-700	1	2⅛	1⅞	6.65
800, A-800, 900, A-1100, B-1100, C-1100 & D-1100	1	2⅜	1⅞	8.3
1200, A-1200 & B-1200	1	2 15/32	2⅛	10.2
494-0000-000 & 494-0101-000	1	2⅜	1⅞	8.3
498-0000-000 & 498-0301-000	1	2 15/32	2⅛	10.2

Vertical Crankshaft Engines

MODEL SERIES	Cyls.	Bore	Stroke	Displ.
VS-700 & VS-750	1	2	1⅞	5.89
VS-800, VS-900, V-1000 & VS-1000	1	2⅜	1⅞	8.3
V-1100 & VS-1100	1	2⅜	2⅛	9.5
V-1200 & VS-1200	1	2 15/32	2⅛	10.2
497-0000-000 & 499-0000-000	1	2 15/32	2⅛	10.2

MAINTENANCE

SPARK PLUG. All models use a 14 mm., ⅜-inch reach spark plug. Recommended plug is a Champion J-8 or equivalent. Set electrode gap to 0.025-0.028. When installing, apply graphite to threads and tighten to a torque of 275-300 inch-pounds.

CARBURETOR. Several different carburetors, both suction lift and float type, have been used on this series of Clinton engines. Refer to the following paragraphs for information on each carburetor model.

Note: The throttle shaft on some carburetors may have several holes in which the throttle link and governor backlash spring (if used) may be installed. On these carburetors, be sure to mark the holes in which spring and linkage were installed so that they may be reinstalled correctly.

CLINTON SUCTION TYPE CARBURETORS. The following Clinton suction type carburetors have been used:

4730-2   4484-2

Refer to Fig. CL45 for exploded view of typical carburetor. Carburetor is equipped with only one fuel adjustment needle (7). Average adjustment is 3½ turns open. Make final adjustment with engine running at operating temperature and with fuel tank approximately ½-full. Adjust for best high speed operation under load.

CLINTON FLOAT CARBURETORS. Several different Clinton LMG and LMV series float type carburetors have been used. To identify a particular carburetor, look for the identification number on the carburetor body as shown in Fig. CL46.

Refer to the exploded view shown in Fig. CL47 for exploded view of typical "LM" series carburetor. When overhauling or cleaning carburetor, do not remove the main fuel nozzle (13) unless necessary. If nozzle is removed, it must be discarded and a service type nozzle (See Fig. CL48) installed.

Choke plate (11—Fig. CL47) should be installed with the "W" or part number to outside. Install throttle plate with the side marked "W" facing towards mounting flange and with the part number towards idle needle side of carburetor bore when plate is in closed position. When installing throttle plate, back idle speed adjustment screw out, turn plate and throttle shaft to closed position and seat plate by gently

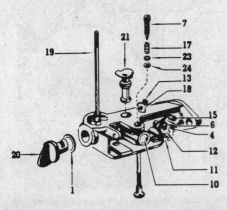

Fig. CL45–Exploded view of suction lift carburetor. Only one fuel mixture adjustment needle (7) is used.

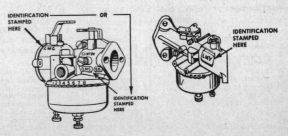

Fig. CL46–View showing locations of identification numbers on "LMB", "LMG" and "LMV" carburetors. Identification number must be used when ordering service parts.

tapping with small screwdriver before tightening plate retaining screws.

If either the float valve or seat is damaged, install a new matched valve and seat assembly (12) and tighten seat to a torque of 40-50 inch-pounds. When carburetor body (6) and float (14) assembly are inverted, there should be 5/32-inch clearance between body casting and free side of float.

Adjust float level by bending the tab that contacts the float valve. When carburetor body and float assembly are returned to normal position, float should not drop more than 3/16-inch at free side of float; adjust by bending tab that contacts the carburetor body.

Reassemble carburetor using new gaskets.

Initial adjustment for both idle needle and high speed is 1¼ turns open. Make final adjustment with engine at operating temperature. If engine does not accelerate properly, open high speed adjustment needle slightly.

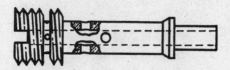

Fig. CL48—When original main fuel nozzle is removed from "LM" series carburetor, it must be discarded and service type nozzle shown must be installed.

CARTER FLOAT TYPE CARBURETORS. Refer to Fig. CL49 for exploded view typical of the Carter "N" series carburetors used on this group of Clinton engines. Some carburetors may differ as to shape of float and bowl.

Refer to the following chart for float setting and for initial adjustment (turns open) of idle and high speed fuel adjustment needles:

Carburetor Model	Float Setting	Initial Adjustment	
		Idle	High Speed
N-705S	13/64 in.	1½	1½
N-707S, SA	13/64 in.	1½	1½
N-2020S	11/64 in.	1½	1½
N-2147S	11/64 in.	1½	1½
N-2236S	11/64 in.	1	2
N-2246S	11/64 in.	1	2
N-2399S	11/64 in.	1½	2
N-2449S	13/64 in.	1½	1½
N-2456S	13/64 in.	1½	1½
N-2459S	11/64 in.	1	1½
N-2466S	11/64 in.	1½	2

Float setting is measured by inverting carburetor casting and float assembly and gaging distance between casting and free side of float. Adjust by bending tab that contacts float valve.

Make final idle and high speed fuel mixture adjustments after engine is at operating temperature.

TILLOTSON FLOAT CARBURETOR. Some early models were equipped with Tillotson "ML" series carburetors. Float setting on ML carburetors is 1 5/64 to 1 3/32-inch from edge of carburetor casting to farthest side of float when carburetor body and float assembly is held in inverted position.

Initial adjustment for idle fuel adjustment needle is 1 turn open; initial adjustment for the high speed needle is 1½ turns open. Make final adjustment with engine running at operating temperature.

ZENITH FLOAT TYPE CARBURETORS. The following Zenith float type

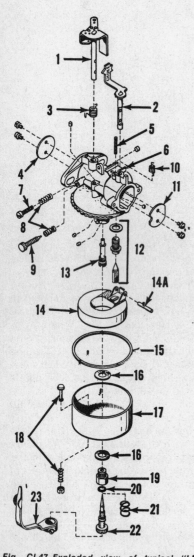

Fig. CL47—Exploded view of typical "LMG" series carburetor. "LMV" and "LMB" series are similar.

1. Throttle shaft	13. Main nozzle
2. Choke shaft	14. Float
3. Spring	14A. Float pin
4. Throttle disc	15. Gasket
5. Spring	16. Gaskets
6. Carburetor body	17. Float bowl
7. Idle stop screw	18. Drain valve
8. Springs	19. Retainer
9. Idle fuel needle	20. Seal
10. Spring	21. Spring
11. Choke disc	22. Main fuel needle
12. Inlet needle & seat	23. Lever (optional)

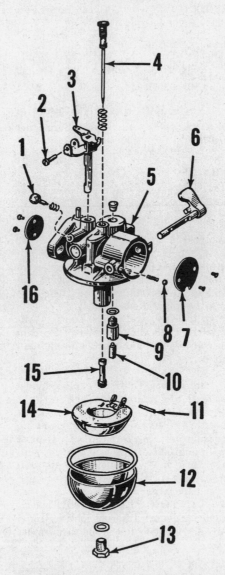

Fig. CL49—Exploded view of typical Carter model "N" carburetor. Design of float and float bowl may vary from that shown.

1. Idle fuel needle	9. Inlet valve seat
2. Idle stop screw	10. Inlet needle
3. Throttle shaft	11. Float pin
4. Main fuel needle	12. Float bowl
5. Carburetor body	13. Retainer
6. Choke shaft	14. Float
7. Choke disc	15. Main nozzle
8. Detent ball	16. Throttle disc

Fig. CL49A—Magneto can be considered in satisfactory condition if it will fire an 18 mm. spark plug with electrode gap set at 0.156-0.187.

carburetors were used on some early model engines:

10390
10658
10665

The 10390 model carburetor has only one fuel mixture adjustment needle.

Set this fuel mixture ¼-turn rich (counter-clockwise) from setting producing maximum high idle speed. On models 10658 and 10665, turning the idle fuel needle clockwise will enrichen the fuel mixture, and turning the main fuel needle clockwise will lean the fuel

mixture. Float setting is non-adjustable on this series of Zenith carburetors.

FUEL PUMP. Some vertical shaft engines are equipped with a diaphragm type fuel pump located on the crankcase cover and operated by pres-

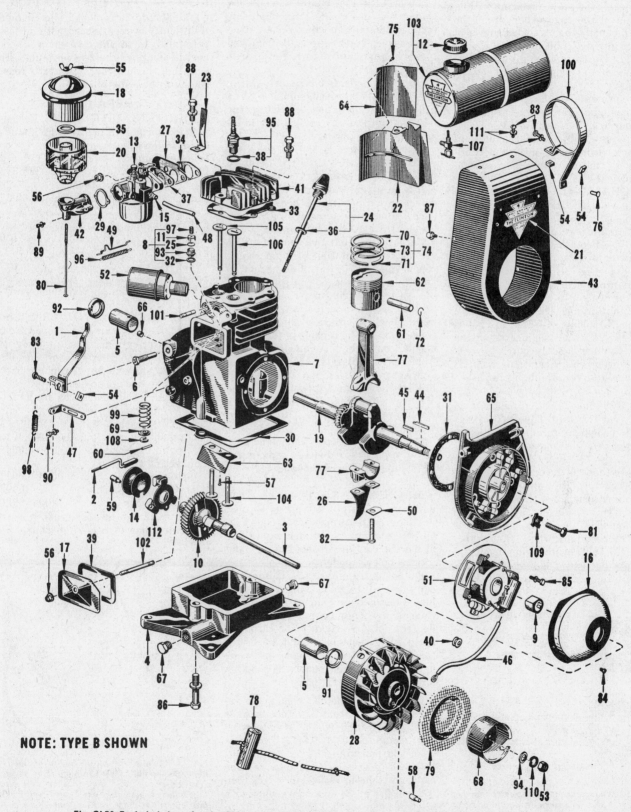

NOTE: TYPE B SHOWN

Fig. CL50–Exploded view of series 700 engine. Early models were equipped with Scintilla magneto (51) as shown.

sure pulsations within the crankcase. Service consists of renewing the diaphragm (79—Fig. CL53).

GOVERNOR. Either a mechanical or an air vane type governor is used. All vertical shaft engines and some horizontal shaft engines use an air vane type governor as shown at (126) in the exploded view of engine in Fig. CL53. Mechanical governors are of the type shown in the exploded views of engines in Figs. CL50 and CL56.

NOTE: The carburetor throttle shaft, governor arm and speed control devices may have several different holes in which springs and linkage can be installed. Before removing carburetor, governor arm, springs, linkage or controls, be sure to mark location of holes in which springs and linkage were installed so that they may be reassembled correctly.

MECHANICAL GOVERNOR. The governor weight unit (112—Fig. CL50 or 126—Fig. CL56) is driven by the cam gear, and is retained to the gear by a pin (59—Fig. CL 50 or 70—Fig. CL 56) driven into the gear. The governor collar (14—Fig. CL 50 or 25—Fig. CL 56) has a notch in the inner flange of the collar which fits around the weight unit retaining pin. The governor shaft (2—Fig. CL 50 or 4—Fig. CL 56) is fitted with a square cross-section weight that contacts the outer flange of the governor collar, and the shaft is supported in a renewable bushing (6—Fig. CL 50 or 55—Fig. CL 56).

It is very important that the travel of the governor and the carburetor throttle be synchronized. With the engine not running, move the governor throttle arm (1—Fig. CL50 or 3—Fig. CL56) so that the governor shaft holds the governor weight unit in fully closed position. At this time, there should be 1/32 to 1/16-inch clearance between the high speed stop on the carburetor throttle arm and the carburetor casting. To obtain this adjustment, increase or decrease the loop in the carburetor to governor link (49—Fig.

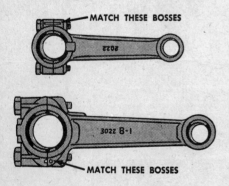

Fig. CL52–When assembling cap to connecting rod, be sure that embossments on rod and cap are aligned as shown.

CL50) on older model engines or loosen the adjustment screw (89—Fig. CL56) on newer model engines and reposition the arm (3) on the adjuster (2) and tighten adjustment screw (89).

Adjust desired maximum speed (do not exceed 3600 RPM) by adjusting tension of governor spring (98—Fig. CL50 or 110—Fig. CL56). CAUTION: Do not use any spring other than correct Clinton part specified for a particular engine as spring must be balanced to governor weight unit for proper speed control.

On most models, a backlash spring (96—Fig. CL50) is used to hold any free play out of governor to carburetor linkage and thereby reduce any tendency for engine to surge.

AIR VANE GOVERNOR. Refer to Fig. CL53. The governor air vane (126) pivots on a renewable pin (69) that is driven into a hole in the bearing plate (72). The vane is connected to the carburetor throttle shaft by link (58).

Check to see that the vane and link are not bent from their original shape; renew vane and/or link if damaged. To maintain proper speed control, the correct governor spring must be used. Be sure to use the correct Clinton part number when ordering the governor spring (113). (The tension of the spring is balanced to the force on the air vane from the air blast off of the engine flywheel). Be sure that vane and linkage move through their full range of travel without binding and take care when servicing engine not to bend the vane or link.

Adjust speed control (tension on governor spring) for desired maximum RPM, but do not exceed 3600 RPM.

MAGNETO AND TIMING. Some early model engines were equipped with Scintilla magnetos (51—Fig. CL50). Condenser, breaker points and armature coil are located under the flywheel on all models.

On Scintilla magnetos, condenser capacity is 0.15 mfd. (minimum). Adjust breaker contact gap to 0.015-0.018. Edge gap should be not less than 5 degrees. Magneto can be rotated on early 700-A models to advance or retard timing; timing is fixed and non-adjustable on other models. Timing for all models is 21° BTDC.

On later magnetos, condenser capacity is 0.15-0.19 mfd. Adjust breaker point gap to 0.018-0.021. Armature air gap should be 0.007-0.017. Timing is fixed and non-adjustable at 21° BTDC.

On all magnetos, magneto can be assumed to be in satisfactory condition if it will fire an 18 mm. spark plug with electrode gap set at 0.156-0.187 (5/32 to 3/16-inch). See Fig. CL49A.

LUBRICATION. Motor oil of MM or MS grade should be used. Use SAE 30 above 32° F., SAE 10W from −10° F. to 32° F., and SAE 5W below −10° F.

On models equipped with reduction gearing, use SAE 30 oil in gear box.

CRANKCASE BREATHER. Crankcase breather assembly (8—Fig. CL50, 10—Fig. CL53 or 14—Fig. CL56) should be removed and cleaned if difficulty is experienced with oil loss through hole in valve cover or whenever the engine is being overhauled. Be sure that the breather is correctly reassembled and reinstalled.

REPAIRS

TIGHTENING TORQUES. Recommended torque values in inch-pounds are as follows:

Adapter flange	120-150
Base bolts	325-375
Carburetor to manifold	35-50
Carburetor (or manifold) to block	60-65
Connecting rod	70-80
Cylinder head	200-220
End cover	120-150
Flywheel	400-450*
Spark plug	275-300
Stator plate	50-60

*350 maximum on 7/16-inch crankshaft.

CONNECTING ROD. Rod and piston assembly can be removed from engine after cylinder head and engine base (on horizontal crankshaft models) or crankcase end cover (on vertical crankshaft models) are removed.

Recommended clearances are as follows:

Connecting rod to crankshaft	0.0018-0.0035
Maximum allowable	0.0045
Connecting rod to piston pin	0.0004-0.0011
Maximum allowable	0.002
Rod side play	0.005-0.020

Connecting rod is available in standard size only. When reassem-

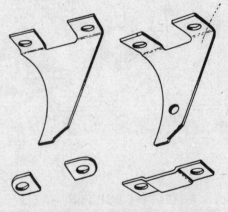

Fig. CL52A–New type oil distributor at right is identified by hole drilled through it as shown. One piece rod lock shown below new type distributor should be used only with new distributor; two-piece rod lock should be used with old type distributor. Refer to text.

bling, be sure that embossments on connecting rod and cap are aligned as shown in Fig. CL52. Oil hole or oil access slot in connecting rod should face flywheel side of engine. On some models, the connecting rod has a "clearance side" which must be towards the camshaft. Be sure that rod locks and oil distributor (on horizontal crankshaft models) clears the camshaft after assembly.

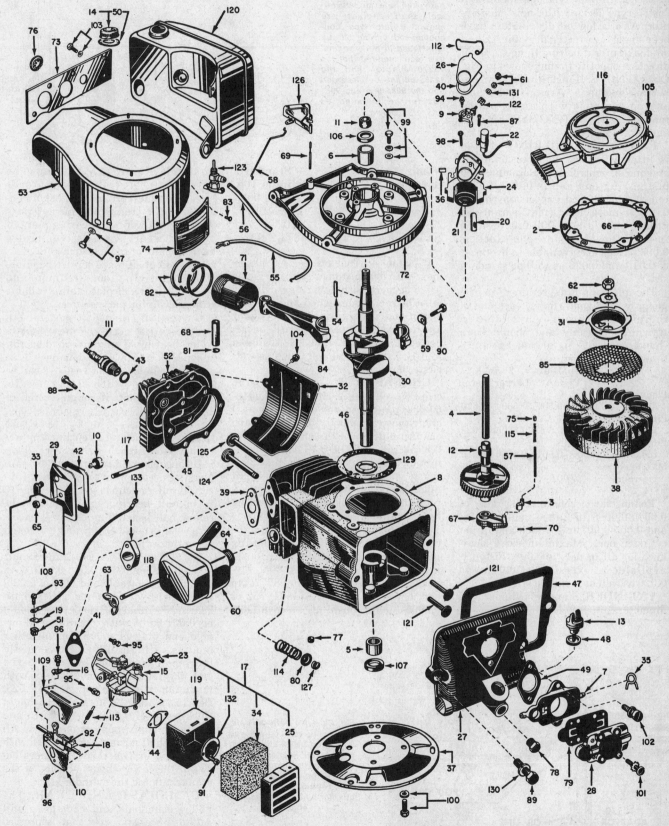

Fig. CL53–Exploded view of model 499-0000-000 vertical shaft engine. Note the fuel pump (items 7, 28 and 79) which attaches to the crankcase cover (27). Engine is lubricated by oil pump (67) although some vertical shaft models are splash lubricated by an oil scoop riveted to the bottom side of camshaft gear.

On horizontal crankshaft engines, refer to Fig. CL52A for view of "old" and "new" rod locks and oil distributor. CAUTION: "Old" type rod locks must be used with "old" type distributor and "new" type locks with "new" distributor. Also, a few oil distributors have been made incorrectly; do not install an oil distributor if bolting flange faces in direction opposite to that shown in Fig. CL52A. NOTE: If installing a new connecting rod in a vertical crankshaft engine equipped with an oil pump, refer to LUBRICATING SYSTEM paragraph.

PISTON, PIN AND RINGS. Piston is fitted with two compression rings and one oil control ring. Recommended piston ring end gap is 0.007-0.017; renew rings if end gap of top ring is 0.025 or more. Ring side clearance in groove should be 0.002-0.005; maximum allowable side clearance is 0.006. Rings are available in oversizes of 0.010 and 0.020 as well as standard size.

The piston pin is retained in the piston with a snap ring at each end of the pin. Piston pin is available in standard size only and should be a "hand push fit" in piston. Specifications are as follows:

	2 in. Dia. Piston	2¼ in. & Larger Piston
Piston pin. dia.	0.4999-0.5001	0.5624-0.5626
Pin bore in piston	0.5000-0.5003	0.5625-0.5628
Pin bore in rod	0.5005-0.5010	0.5630-0.5635
Max. pin to rod clearance	0.002	0.002

Piston skirt clearance should be 0.0045-0.0065 in 2-inch cylinder bore and 0.005-0.007 in 2¼-inch and larger cylinder bore. Maximum skirt clearance for all models is 0.008. Piston is available in oversizes of 0.010 and 0.020 as well as standard size.

CYLINDER. Standard cylinder bore diameters are as follows:

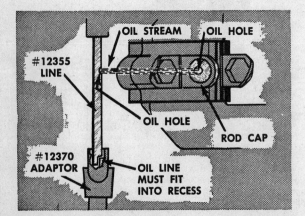

Fig. CL54–On early models, connecting rod bearing was lubricated by oil spray from hole in oil line as shown. Be sure the squared-off end of the oil line fits into the recess in oil pump adapter when reassembling engine.

Fig. CL55–Oil pump adapters and oil lines for early and late model vertical shaft engines are shown. If late type connecting rod without oil cup is installed in early engine, it is recommended that the 12370 adapter and the 12355 oil line be discarded and the 9084 line and 9081 adapter be installed as shown.

Nominal Bore Size	Standard Cylinder Dia.
2 inches	2.000-2.001
2⅛ inches	2.125-2.126
2⅜ inches	2.375-2.376
2-15/32 inches	2.4685-2.4695

If piston skirt clearance is 0.008 or more with new piston or ring end gap is 0.025 or more with new rings, cylinder must be rebored or honed and oversize piston and rings installed or cylinder and crankcase assembly must be renewed. Piston and rings are available in oversizes of 0.010 and 0.020 as well as standard size.

CRANKSHAFT. Connecting rod to crankpin clearance should be 0.0018-0.0035; renew rod and/or crankshaft if clearance exceeds 0.0045. Standard crankpin diameter is either 0.8745-0.8752 or 0.9114-0.9120. Recommended maximum crankpin out-of-round condition is 0.001; crankshaft must be renewed if crankpin out-of-round is 0.0015 or more. Connecting rod is available in standard size only.

Main bearing clearance should be 0.0018-0.0035 on all plain bushing models; renew crankshaft and/or bushings if clearance exceeds 0.005. Flywheel end journal is 0.8745-0.8752; pto end journal is either 0.8745-0.8752 or 0.9995-1.0002. Bushings are available

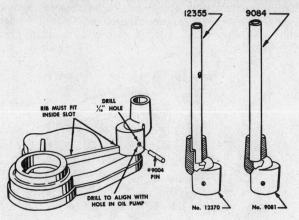

in standard size only and must be reamed after installation for proper size. On some vertical crankshaft engines, upper crankshaft journal rides directly in aluminum bearing plate; if bearing wear is excessive, renew bearing plate or ream bearing out oversize to accept a bronze service bushing. Bushing driving tools, reamers and reamer alignment plates are available through Clinton parts sources.

On vertical crankshaft models with needle roller mains, renew needle roller bearing if any needle has flat spots or is in any way damaged. Also renew needle bearing if needles can be separated the width of one needle. Renew crankshaft if rough, scored or shows signs of wear where contacted by needle rollers. Check upper pto bushing and journal as outlined in preceding paragraph.

On models with tapered roller main bearings, renew bearing cones and cups if roller or cup is scored or rough.

On ball bearing equipped models, renew ball bearing assembly if excessive wear is noted or if bearing is rough when turned.

On 800 and 900 models, crankshaft end play should be 0.008-0.012 with maximum allowable end play of 0.020. On models with tapered roller main bearings, crankshaft end play should be 0.001-0.006 with maximum allowable end play of 0.008. On all other models with plain bushings, needle bearings or ball bearings, crankshaft end play should be 0.008-0.018 with maximum allowable end play of 0.025. Bearing plate gaskets are available in thicknesses of 0.005, 0.010, 0.015 and 0.020 for adjustment of end play. All vertical shaft models are equipped with either one or two thrust washers between the lower thrust surface of the crankshaft and the cylinder block.

CAMSHAFT AND GEAR. The hollow camshaft and cam gear unit rotates on a cam axle that is pressed into the engine crankcase. Camshaft can be removed after removing engine crankshaft and pressing camshaft axle from crankcase. On models with mechanical governor, governor weight unit is attached to cam gear by a pin that is pressed into the gear.

Operating clearance between camshaft axle and camshaft should be 0.001-0.003; renew axle and/or camshaft if clearance exceeds 0.005.

Camshaft end play should be 0.003-0.010; maximum allowable end play is 0.015.

VALVE SYSTEM. Recommended valve tappet gap for both intake and exhaust valves on all models is 0.009-0.011. Adjust clearance by grinding end of valve stem. A 45 degree bevel should be maintained on ends of stems.

Valve face angle is ground to 45 degrees and valve seat angle between 43½ and 44½ degrees. Seat width

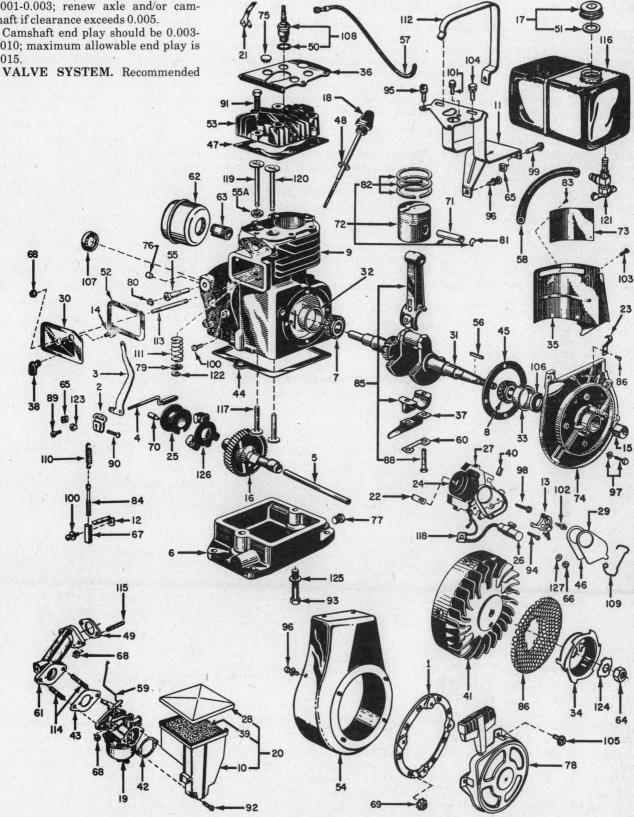

Fig. CL56–Exploded view of model 498-0000-000 engine. Governor weight assembly (126) is retained to camshaft gear by pin (70) that is pressed into the gear.

should be 0.030-0.045, and should be recut using combination tool No. 951-37 which has cutters of 44 and 30 degrees. Do not allow seat width to exceed 0.060.

Valve head margin for a new valve is 1/32-inch. When reduced by regrinding and wear to 1/64-inch, valve should be renewed.

Recommended valve stem to guide clearance is 0.002-0.0045. If clearance is 0.006 or more, guides may be reamed to 0.260 or 0.2812 (9/32-inch) for valves with 0.010 or 1/32-inch oversize stem. Also, valve guide may be knurled and reamed to 0.250 for standard size stem.

Stellite exhaust valves and seats are available; also, stellite exhaust valves with roto-caps are available for service. Install regular exhaust valve in place of intake valve if installing a stellite exhaust valve and seat. Stellite valves are available with standard and 0.010 oversize stems only.

The intake and exhaust valves are actuated by mushroom type tappets that ride directly in unbushed bores in the engine crankcase. Stem diameter of the tappets is 0.2475-0.2485; tappet guide bore diameter is 0.2495-0.2510. Tappets are available in standard size only. If guides are worn excessively, they may be knurled and reamed with same tools as used to knurl and ream valve guides. Tappets may be removed from the engine block after removing the camshaft.

CAUTION: If ends of valve stems or ends of tappet stems have become enlarged or burred, do not force the stems through the bores in block. Remove burrs with emery cloth before attempting to remove valves and tappets.

Valve seat inserts are available for service; also, tools for cutting counterbore and installing the valve seat inserts are available through Clinton parts sources.

LUBRICATING SYSTEM. All horizontal crankshaft engines and some vertical crankshaft engines are splash lubricated; an oil distributor is attached to the connecting rod cap on horizontal crankshaft models and an oil scoop is riveted to the lower side of the cam gear on vertical crankshaft models.

A gear type oil pump, driven by a pin on the lower end of the engine crankshaft, is used on some vertical crankshaft models. On early models equipped with an oil pump, the crankpin bearing was lubricated by oil spraying from a hole in the oil pump tube as shown in Fig. CL54. On later models, the oil pump tube does not have the spray hole and the crankpin bearing is lubricated by oil spray from the top main bearing. If renewing older type connecting rod (with oil cup on cap) using a new type connecting rod (without oil cup), also install a new oil tube adapter and oil tube without the spray hole. Refer to Fig. CL55. Oil pump is available for service as an assembly only.

NOTE: When reassembling engine using early type oil tube with spray hole, be sure the squared-off lower end of the oil tube fits into the recess in the oil tube adapter. Also, if renewing oil pump, adapter and/or oil tube, be sure the correct oil tube and adapter are used. Refer to Fig. CL54 and Fig. CL55.

CLINTON

CLINTON ENGINES CORPORATION
Maquoketa, Iowa

Horizontal Crankshaft Models

MODEL SERIES	Cyls.	Bore	Stroke	Displ.
100	1	2⅜	1⅝	7.2
2100, A-2100	1	2⅜	1⅝	7.2
3100	1	2⅜	1⅞	8.3
4100	1	2⅜	1⅞	8.3
400-0100-000	1	2⅜	1⅝	7.2
402-0100-000	1	2⅜	1⅝	7.2
404-0100-000	1	2⅜	1⅞	8.3
406-0100-000	1	2⅜	1⅞	8.3
408-0100-000	1	2⅜	1⅞	8.3
410-0000-000	1	2½	1⅞	9.2
424-0100-000	1	2⅜	1⅞	8.3
426-0100-000	1	2⅜	1⅞	8.3
492-0000-000	1	2⅜	1⅞	8.3

Vertical Crankshaft Models

MODEL SERIES	Cyls.	Bore	Stroke	Displ.
V-100, VS-100	1	2⅜	1⅝	7.2
VS-2100	1	2⅜	1⅝	7.2
VS-3000	1	2⅜	1⅝	7.2
AFV-3100, AV-3100, AVS-3100, FV-3100, V-3100 & VS-3100	1	2⅜	1⅞	8.3
AVS-4100, VS-4100	1	2⅜	1⅞	8.3
401-0000-000	1	2⅜	1⅝	7.2
403-0000-000	1	2⅜	1⅝	7.2
405-0000-000	1	2⅜	1⅞	8.3
407-0000-000	1	2⅜	1⅞	8.3
409-0000-000	1	2⅜	1⅞	8.3
411-0002-000	1	2⅜	1⅝	7.2
415-0000-000	1	2⅜	1⅞	8.3
417-0000-000	1	2⅜	1⅞	8.3
419-0000-000	1	2½	1⅞	9.2
429-0003-000	1	2½	1⅞	9.2
431-0003-000	1	2½	1⅞	9.2
435-0013-000	1	2⅜	1⅞	8.3
455-0000-000	1	2⅜	1⅞	8.3

MAINTENANCE

SPARK PLUG. All models use a 14 mm., 7/16-inch reach spark plug. Recommended plug is a Champion H-10 or equivalent. Set electrode gap to 0.025-0.028. When installing, apply graphite to threads and tighten to a torque of 275-300 inch-pounds.

CARBURETOR. Clinton (Walbro) float type, Carter float type and Clinton suction type carburetors are used on this group of Clinton engines. Refer to following paragraphs for information on specific type carburetor.

CLINTON (WALBRO) FLOAT CARBURETORS. Several different Clinton (Walbro) LMB, LMG and LMV series carburetors have been used. To identify a carburetor, look for the identification number on the carburetor body as shown in Fig. CL60.

Refer to the exploded view, shown in Fig. CL61, of typical "LM" series carburetor. When overhauling or cleaning carburetor, do not remove the main fuel nozzle (13) unless necessary. If nozzle is removed, it must be discarded and a service type nozzle (See Fig. CL61A) installed.

Choke plate (11—Fig. CL61) should be installed with the "W" or part number to outside. Install throttle plate with the side marked "W" facing towards mounting flange and with the

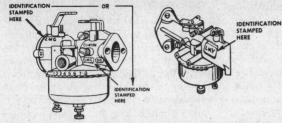

Fig. CL60–Views showing location of identification numbers on "LMB", "LMG" and "LMV" series carburetors. Identification numbers must be used when ordering service parts.

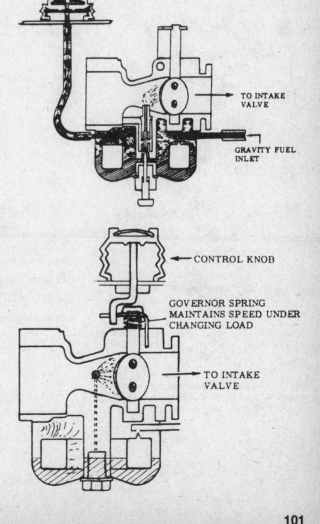

Fig. CL61A–When original main fuel nozzle is removed from "LM" series carburetors, it must be discarded and service type nozzle shown must be installed.

part number towards idle needle side of carburetor bore when plate is in closed position. When installing throttle plate, back idle speed adjustment screw out, turn plate and throttle shaft to closed position and seat plate by gently tapping with small screwdriver before tightening plate retaining screws.

If either the float valve or seat is damaged, install a new matched valve and seat assembly (12) and tighten seat to a torque of 40-50 inch-pounds. When carburetor body (6) and float (14) assembly are inverted, there should be 5/32-inch clearance between body casting and free side of float. Adjust float level by bending the tab that contacts the float valve. When carburetor body and float assembly are returned to normal position, float should not drop more than 3/16-inch at free side of float; adjust by bending tab that contacts the carburetor body. Reassemble carburetor using all new gaskets.

Initial adjustment for both idle

needle and high speed needle is 1¼ turns open. Make final adjustment with engine at operating temperature. If engine does not accelerate properly, Open high speed adjustment needle slightly.

CLINTON "TOUCH 'N' START" CARBURETOR. Refer to Fig. CL61B for cross-sectional view of "Touch 'N' Start" carburetor used on some models. Instead of choke valve (11—Fig. CL61) this carburetor is furnished with a flexible primer bulb which provides a rich charging mixture to carburetor venturi and intake manifold for easier starting. This primer system applies to LMB, LMG and LMV carburetors and service is otherwise identical. Carburetor float

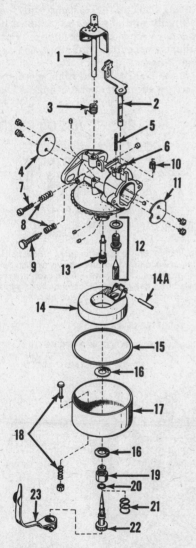

Fig. CL61–Exploded view of typical "LMG" series carburetor. "LMB" and "LMV" series are similar.

1. Throttle shaft
2. Choke shaft
3. Spring
4. Throttle disc
5. Spring
6. Carburetor body
7. Idle stop screw
8. Springs
9. Idle fuel needle
10. Spring
11. Choke disc
12. Inlet needle
13. Main nozzle
14. Float
14A. Float pin
15. Gasket
16. Gaskets
17. Float bowl
18. Drain valve
19. Retainer
20. Seal
21. Spring
22. Main fuel needle
23. Lever (optional)

Fig. CL61B – Cross-section view of "Touch 'N' Start" carburetor and primer bulb. Note absence of choke valve. Refer to text for operation and service.

TO INTAKE VALVE

GRAVITY FUEL INLET

CONTROL KNOB

GOVERNOR SPRING MAINTAINS SPEED UNDER CHANGING LOAD

TO INTAKE VALVE

Fig. CL62–Cross-section of fixed speed carburetor. Note that there is no main nozzle in this carburetor. See text. Fig. CL62A shows governor spring placement.

bowl is vented through primer tube to flexible bulb, and vent is closed when operator's finger depresses primer bulb.

FIXED SPEED CARBURETOR. Fig. CL62 shows a sectional view of constant speed control fitted to some LMB, LMG and LMV style carburetors, for

Fig. CL62A–Top view of fixed speed carburetor showing correct installation of governor link and spring.

four-stroke cycle engine applications only. These carburetors have no main nozzle (13—Fig. CL61) and are without an idle circuit. Engine speed is controlled at 3,000-3,400 RPM (no load) by throttle governor spring. See Fig. CL62A for spring placement. Turn control knob clockwise to stop engine by closing throttle. High speed screw is adjusted to 1¼-1½ turns open. Refer to preceding paragraph, servicing CLINTON (WALBRO) CARBURE-

TORS, for other service details.

CARTER FLOAT TYPE CARBURETORS. Refer to Fig. CL63 for exploded view typical of the Carter "N" series carburetors used. Some carburetors may differ as to shape of float and bowl.

Refer to the following chart for float setting and for initial adjustment (turns open) of idle and high speed fuel needles:

| | —Initial Adjustment— | | |
Carburetor Model	Float Setting	Idle Needle	Main Needle
N-2236S	11/64 in.	1	2
N-2264S	11/64 in.	1	1½
N-2458S	11/64 in.	1	2
N-2459S	11/64 in.	1	1½

Float setting is measured by inverting carburetor casting and float assembly and gaging the distance between casting and free side of float. Adjust by bending tab that contacts float valve.

Make final idle and high speed fuel mixture adjustments after engine is at

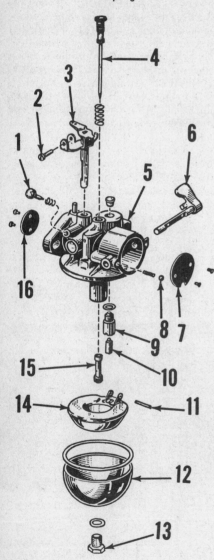

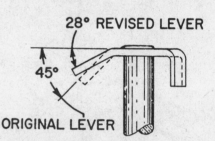

Fig. CL64–Exploded view of Clinton suction lift carburetor. On late production models, idle adjustment screw is threaded directly into carburetor body and does not have the threaded bushing shown. Choke disc (17) and throttle disc (not shown) may be attached with one screw as shown although later models have two holes for attaching screws in each disc and shaft.

1. Choke shaft	12. Springs
2. Idle fuel needle & bushing	13. Spring
7. Main fuel needle	14. Spring
9. Idle stop screw	16. Throttle shaft
10. Screw	17. Choke disc

Fig. CL64A–Choke lever for later production of Clinton suction carburetor shown in Fig. CL64 is modified as shown here to prevent breakage. Early models should have choke lever (1–Fig. CL64) modified as shown.

Fig. CL63–Exploded view of typical Carter model "N" carburetor. Design of float and float bowl may vary from that shown.

1. Idle fuel needle	9. Inlet valve seat
2. Idle stop screw	10. Inlet needle
3. Throttle shaft	11. Float pin
4. Main fuel needle	12. Float bowl
5. Carburetor body	13. Retainer
6. Choke shaft	14. Float
7. Choke disc	15. Main nozzle
8. Detent ball	16. Throttle disc

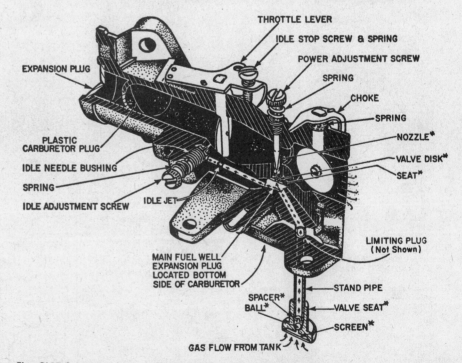

Fig. CL65–Cut-away view of Clinton suction lift carburetor. Refer to text for disassembly procedure.

operating temperature.

CLINTON SUCTION TYPE CARBURETORS. Refer to Fig. CL64 for exploded view and to Fig. CL65 for cutaway view of Clinton suction lift carburetor used on vertical shaft engines. Carburetor used on horizontal shaft engines is similar except that expansion plug and plastic plug shown in the cut-away view are not used.

In Fig. CL66, main fuel needles used in early and late carburetors are shown. Initial adjustment for early (original) type needle is ¾ to one turn open; late (revised) type needle initial adjustment is 1¼ to 1½ turns open.

Early carburetors were equipped with an idle needle bushing. (See Fig. CL64). Initial adjustment for idle needle on these carburetors is 4 to 4¼ turns open. On carburetors not equipped with idle needle bushing (idle needle threaded directly into carburetor body), initial adjustment is 1½ turns open.

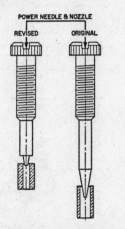

Fig. CL66–View showing early (original) production and late (revised) production main fuel needles for Clinton suction lift carburetors. Original and revised needles are not interchangeable. Needle seats are non-renewable; renew carburetor if seat is split or damaged.

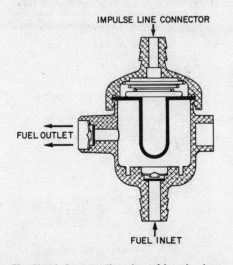

Fig. CL66A–Cross-section view of impulse type fuel pump used on four-stroke cycle engines. Renew complete pump assembly if inoperative.

Make final adjustments with engine warm and running. NOTE: Proper adjustment of high speed needle may result in engine running unevenly with no load applied; engine will not develop full power with high speed needle adjusted for smoothest operation at high speed with no load applied. Fuel tank should be approximately ½ full when making final adjustments.

To remove throttle shaft on carburetors from vertical crankshaft engines, drill through the expansion plug at rear of carburetor body, insert punch in drilled hole and pry plug out. Then remove plastic plug, throttle valve screws, throttle valve and the throttle shaft. When reassembling, use new expansion plug and seal plug with Gasolia sealer (made by Federal Process Co., Cleveland, Ohio) or equivalent sealer. Be sure to expand the plug until it fits tightly.

Test the check valve in the fuel stand pipe by alternately blowing and sucking air through pipe. Stand pipe can be removed by clamping pipe in vise and prying carburetor from pipe. Apply Gasolia or equivalent sealer to stem of new stand pipe and install so that it projects 1.895-1.985 from carburetor body.

To remove the idle needle bushing from early carburetors, remove idle needle and turn bushing out in a counter-clockwise direction using proper size screwdriver. Apply Gasolia or equivalent sealer to outer threads of bushing prior to installation.

To remove idle jet (See Fig. CL65), remove expansion plug from bottom of carburetor, idle needle and, if so equipped, idle needle bushing. Insert a 1/16-inch diameter rod through fuel well and up through idle passage to push jet out into idle fuel reservoir. To install new jet, place mark on the 1/16-inch diameter rod exactly 1¼ inches from end and push new jet into passage until mark on rod is in exact center of fuel well.

Limiting plug (See Fig. CL65) located in fuel passageway from stand pipe should not be removed unless necessary for cleaning purposes. When reinstalling, seal plug with Gasolia or equivalent sealer.

Air leaking into the fuel system will cause improper carburetor operation. If air leak is suspected, apply Gasolia or equivalent sealer to following areas:

1. Stand pipe to carburetor body.
2. Limiting plug to carburetor body.
3. Idle needle bushing threads to carburetor body.
4. Expansion plugs to carburetor body.

FUEL PUMP. Some models are equipped with a diaphragm type fuel pump as shown in the cross-sectional view in Fig. CL66A. The pump diaphragm is actuated by pressure pulsations transmitted via an impulse tube connected between the fuel pump and intake manifold. The pump is designed to lift fuel approximately six inches. Service consists of renewing the complete fuel pump assembly.

GOVERNOR. An air vane type governor is used on all models. The air vane, which is located in the blower housing, is linked to the throttle lever. The governor is actuated by air delivered by the flywheel fan and by governor spring. Any speed within the operating speed range of the engine can be obtained by adjusting tension on the governor spring. Use only the correct Clinton part for replacement of governor spring and do not adjust maximum governed speed above 3600 RPM.

Make sure the governor linkage does not bind when linkage is moved through full range of travel.

MAGNETO AND TIMING. Magneto coil and armature (laminations), breaker points and condenser are located under the engine flywheel. Two different types of breaker point assemblies are used. Early model engines were equipped with shuttle type breaker points as shown in Fig. CL67. The early type breaker points are enclosed in a box which is an integral part of the engine crankcase and are covered by a plate and gasket. Some shuttle type points may also be enclosed in a sealed unit within the breaker box. Do not use oil on felt; lubricate felt and shuttle with a high melting point grease or renew the felt cam wiper.

Later engine models are equipped with rocker type breaker points and the points are enclosed in a breaker box which is attached to the engine crankcase.

Condenser capacity is 0.15-0.19 mfd. Spark timing is fixed and non-adjustable at 21 degrees BTDC. Armature air

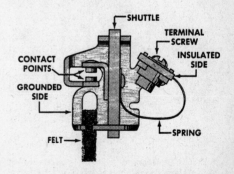

Fig. CL67–Shuttle type breaker points shown are used in early production models.

gap should be 0.007 to 0.017, preferably closer to 0.007. Edge gap for magnetos with shuttle type points is 0.156-0.187; edge gap for magnetos with rocker type points is 0.094-0.250.

Magneto can be considered in satisfactory condition if it will fire an 18 mm. spark plug with electrode gap set at 0.156-0.187. Adjust breaker point gap on all models to 0.018-0.021.

SPARK PUMP. On a limited number of engines, a "Dyna-Spark" ignition system (spark pump or "piezoelectric" ignition system) is used instead of the conventional flywheel type magneto. The system consists of a spark pump (3—Fig. CL68) and a timing switch (1). The spark pump is actuated by an eccentric bearing (2) on the extended end of the engine camshaft and the timing switch is driven by the crankshaft. A spark is generated whenever the cam lever on the spark pump is moved.

As with the conventional magneto, the "Dyna-Spark" ignition system may be considered in satisfactory condition if it will fire an 18 mm. spark plug with electrode gap set at 0.156-0.187 (5/32 to 3/16-inch). See Fig. CL67A. If system is inoperative, inspect wire from spark pump to timing switch and from timing switch to spark plug for shorts or breaks in wire. If wire insulation is frayed allowing the ignition system to short out, the wire can be temporarily repaired with electrician's tape. If inspection does not reveal broken or shorted condition, the complete "Dyna-Spark" unit must be renewed.

CAUTION: Whenever repairing an engine with a "Dyna-Spark" ignition system or removing and reinstalling the "Dyna-Spark" unit, always remove ignition wire from spark plug. The spark pump will generate an ignition spark at a very low engine RPM or whenever the lever on the spark pump is operated.

To remove the "Dyna-Spark" unit, proceed as follows: Disconnect wire from spark plug. Remove engine blower housing and flywheel. Turn engine slowly until eccentric bearing (2) on end of camshaft is in "high lift" position and install a 0.10 spacer between spark pump actuating lever and spark pump frame. Turn engine so that the eccentric bearing is in "low lift" position and remove the spark pump and timing switch from engine. The eccentric bearing may be removed from the camshaft after removing the retaining snap ring.

To install "Dyna-Spark" unit, turn engine so that eccentric bearing is in low lift position and install the spark pump and timing switch on engine. Turn engine so that eccentric bearing is in high lift position and remove the clip (4) or spacer from spark pump. Turn the load screw (6—Fig. CL69) counter-clockwise with slotted tool (7) or needle nose pliers to release tension

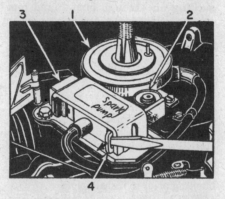

Fig. CL68–After installing spark pump assembly, remove clip (4) with screwdriver as shown. Clip (4) or a 0.10 spacer should be placed between spark pump lever and frame prior to removing the spark pump from engine. Refer to text.

1. Timing switch	3. Spark pump
2. Eccentric bearing	4. Spacer clip

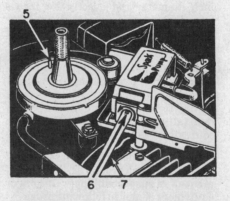

Fig. CL69–Turn load adjusting screw (6) counterclockwise with slotted tool (7) to remove pressure from spark generating cell; spring within spark pump will turn screw back clockwise to apply correct pressure. CAUTION: Never turn load adjusting screw in a clockwise direction. Timing switch is driven by pin (5) which engages engine flywheel.

on the spark generating element. Lever on spark pump should then follow eccentric bearing closely and smoothly as the engine is turned. Be sure that pin (5) properly engages engine flywheel when reinstalling flywheel.

CAUTION: Never turn load screw (6) in a clockwise direction. A coil spring within the spark pump unit will return the load screw to correct tension.

NOTE: If the spark pump has been removed without a 0.10 spacer (or the clip as provided in a new spark pump) installed, refer to Fig. CL70 prior to reinstalling spark pump on engine.

LUBRICATION. Motor oil of MM or MS grade should be used. Use SAE 30 above 32° F., SAE 10W from −10° F. to 32° F., and use SAE 5W oil in temperatures below −10° F.

On models equipped with reduction gearing, use SAE 30 oil in gearbox.

CRANKCASE BREATHER. Crankcase breather assembly located in or behind valve chamber cover should be cleaned if difficulty is experienced with oil loss through breather. Be sure that the breather is correctly reassembled and reinstalled. NOTE:

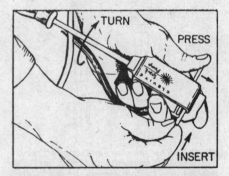

Fig. CL70–If spark pump has been removed without installing clip or spacer (See Fig. CL68), proceed as follows prior to reinstalling pump: Turn load adjusting screw about ½-turn in a counter-clockwise direction and hold screw in this position. Press actuating lever in direction shown and insert a 0.10 thick spacer between inner end of lever and spark pump frame.

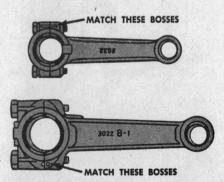

Fig. CL71–When assembling cap to connecting rod, be sure that embossments on rod and cap are aligned as shown.

Fig. CL67A–Magneto can be considered in satisfactory condition if it will fire an 18 mm. spark plug with electrode gap set at 0.156-0.187.

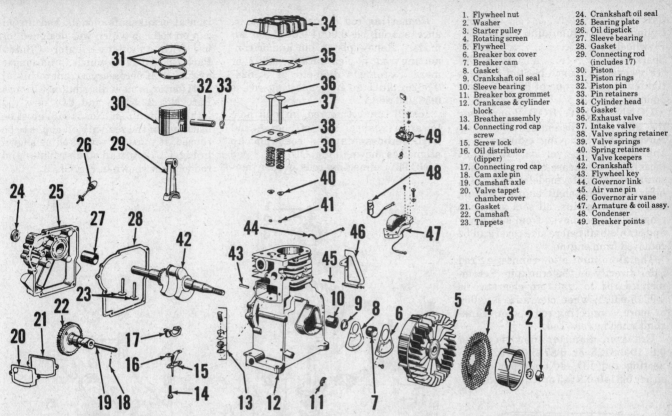

1. Flywheel nut
2. Washer
3. Starter pulley
4. Rotating screen
5. Flywheel
6. Breaker box cover
7. Breaker cam
8. Gasket
9. Crankshaft oil seal
10. Sleeve bearing
11. Breaker box grommet
12. Crankcase & cylinder block
13. Breather assembly
14. Connecting rod cap screw
15. Screw lock
16. Oil distributor (dipper)
17. Connecting rod cap
18. Cam axle pin
19. Camshaft axle
20. Valve tappet chamber cover
21. Gasket
22. Camshaft
23. Tappets
24. Crankshaft oil seal
25. Bearing plate
26. Oil dipstick
27. Sleeve bearing
28. Gasket
29. Connecting rod (includes 17)
30. Piston
31. Piston rings
32. Piston pin
33. Pin retainers
34. Cylinder head
35. Gasket
36. Exhaust valve
37. Intake valve
38. Valve spring retainer
39. Valve springs
40. Spring retainers
41. Valve keepers
42. Crankshaft
43. Flywheel key
44. Governor link
45. Air vane pin
46. Governor air vane
47. Armature & coil assy.
48. Condenser
49. Breaker points

Fig. CL71A–Exploded view of early production horizontal crankshaft model. Camshaft (22) rotates on cam axle (19). Breather assembly (13) is located inside valve chamber. Breaker box is integral part of crankcase and breaker points (49) are accessible after removing flywheel and cover (6). Refer to Fig. CL71B for exploded view of late production horizontal crankshaft model.

Overfilling engine crankcase with lubricating oil or operating engine at speeds over recommended maximum of 3600 RPM will also cause oil loss through crankcase breather.

REPAIRS

TIGHTENING TORQUES. Recommended torque values in inch-pounds are as follows:

Base plate or side cover 75-85
Blower housing 60-70
Carburetor to manifold 35-50
Carburetor (or manifold)
  to block 60-65
Connecting rod 100-125

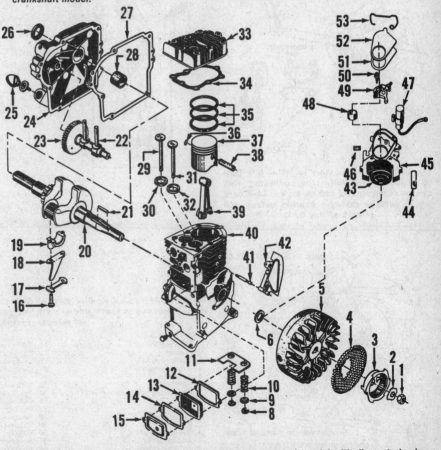

1. Flywheel nut
2. Washer
3. Starter cup
4. Rotating screen
5. Flywheel
6. Crankshaft oil seal
8. Valve keeper
9. Spring retainer
10. Valve springs
11. Spring retainer plate
12. Gasket
13. Breather assembly
14. Gasket
15. Tappet chamber cover
16. Connecting rod cap screws
17. Cap screw lock
18. Oil distributor
19. Connecting rod cap
20. Crankshaft
21. Flywheel key
22. Tappets
23. Camshaft
24. Bearing plate
25. Oil dipstick
26. Crankshaft oil seal
27. Gasket
28. Sleeve bearing
29. Exhaust valve
30. Exhaust valve seat
31. Intake valve
32. Intake valve seat
33. Cylinder head
34. Gasket
35. Piston rings
36. Piston pin retainers
37. Piston
38. Piston pin
39. Connecting rod (includes 19)
40. Crankcase & cylinder block
41. Air vane pin
42. Governor air vane
43. Ignition coil
44. Coil retaining clips
45. Armature & stator assy.
46. Cam wiper felt
47. Condenser
48. Breaker cam
49. Breaker points
50. Screw
51. Gasket
52. Breaker box cover
53. Retainer spring

Fig. CL71B–Exploded view of late production horizontal crankshaft model with die-cast aluminum crankcase and cylinder block assembly. Models with cast iron cylinder block are similar except that valve seat inserts (30 and 32) are not installed at the factory (but may be installed in service).

Cylinder head 225-250
Cylinder head (aluminum) .. 125-150
Flywheel 375-400*
Spark Plug 275-300
*(Flywheel for "Touch-N-Stop" brake is tightened to a torque of 650-700 inch-pounds)

CONNECTING ROD. Connecting rod and piston assembly can be removed after removing cylinder head and engine base (vertical crankshaft models) or crankcase side cover (horizontal crankshaft models). Note: On horizontal crankshaft engines having ball bearing mains, oil seal and snap ring must be removed from side cover and crankshaft before side cover can be removed from engine.

The aluminum alloy connecting rod rides directly on the crankpin. Recommended rod to crankpin clearance is 0.0015-0.003; when clearance is 0.004 or more, connecting rod and/or crankshaft must be renewed.

Crankpin diameter (new) is either 0.8119-0.8125 or 0.8745-0.8752. Connecting rod I.D. at crankpin end is either 0.8140-0.8145 or 0.8770-0.8775.

Connecting rod to piston pin clearance should be 0.0004-0.0011 on all models. Renew piston pin and/or connecting rod if clearance is 0.002 or more. Piston pin diameter is 0.5624-0.5626; pin bore in connecting rod is 0.5630-0.5635.

Install connecting rod with oil hole towards flywheel side of engine and with embossments on rod and cap aligned as shown in Fig. CL71.

NOTE: Connecting rods on early horizontal crankshaft models had an oil cup on rod cap which was designed for use with an oil distributor, Clinton Part No. 31017-1, which is no longer available. If necessary to renew this oil distributor, a new distributor, Clinton Part No. 220-147, and two new rod locks, Clinton Part No. 31018, must be used and, if the rod with oil cup is to be reused, it must be reworked as shown in Fig. CL72. Install oil distributor and rod locks as shown in Fig. CL73.

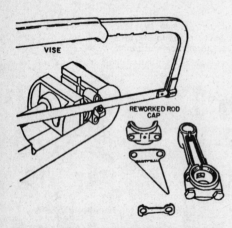

Fig. CL72–When necessary to install late type oil distributor on early type connecting rod, saw oil cup from rod cap as shown. Take care not to damage crankpin bearing surface and smooth off any burrs.

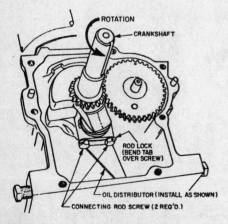

Fig. CL73–View showing correct installation of oil distributor in relation to crankshaft rotation.

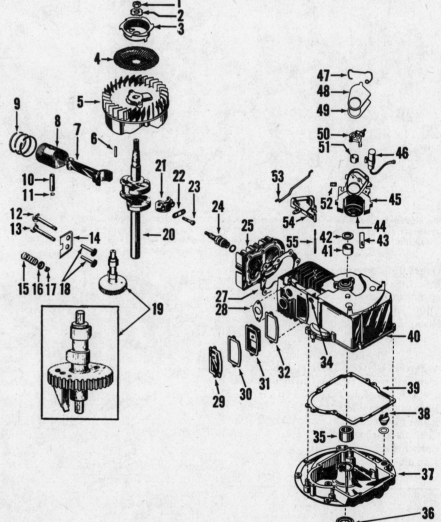

Fig. CL73A–Exploded view of vertical crankshaft model with splash lubrication system; note oil dipper attached to lower side of camshaft gear (inset–19). Refer to Fig. CL76A for exploded view of vertical crankshaft model with oil pump.

1. Flywheel nut
2. Washer
3. Starter cup
4. Rotating screen
5. Flywheel
6. Flywheel key
7. Connecting rod (includes 21)
8. Piston
9. Piston rings
10. Piston pin
11. Pin retainers
12. Intake valve
13. Exhaust valve
14. Spring retainer plate
15. Valve springs
16. Spring retainer
17. Valve keepers
18. Valve tappets
19. Camshaft
20. Crankshaft
21. Connecting rod cap
22. Cap screw lock
23. Connecting rod cap screws
24. Spark plug
25. Cylinder head
27. Gasket
28. Gasket
29. Tappet chamber cover
30. Gasket
31. Breather assembly
32. Gasket
34. Grommet
35. Sleeve bearing
36. Crankshaft oil seal
37. Engine base
38. Oil filler plug
39. Gasket
40. Crankcase & cylinder block
41. Sleeve bearing
42. Crankshaft oil seal
43. Coil retaining clips
44. Ignition coil
45. Armature & coil assembly
46. Condenser
47. Retainer spring
48. Breaker box cover
49. Gasket
50. Breaker points
51. Breaker cam
52. Felt cam wiper
53. Governor link
54. Governor air vane
55. Air vane pin

PISTON, PIN AND RINGS. Recommended piston skirt to cylinder bore clearance for all models is 0.0045-0.0065. Maximum allowable skirt clearance is 0.008. Piston is fitted with two compression rings and one oil ring. Recommended ring side clearance in groove is 0.002-0.005. Maximum allowable side clearance is 0.006. Piston is available in oversizes of 0.010 and 0.020 as well as standard size.

Piston pin should be "hand push fit" in piston. Pin bore in piston is 0.5625-0.5628; pin diameter is 0.5624-0.5626 resulting in a 0.0001 interference to 0.0004 loose fit when both piston and pin are new.

Recommended piston ring end gap is 0.007-0.017; maximum allowable ring end gap is 0.025. Piston rings are available in oversizes of 0.010 and 0.020 as well as standard size. Refer to Fig. CL76 to correct installation of rings on piston.

NOTE: A special chrome "re-ring" set is available for cylinders having up to 0.010 taper and/or out-of-round condition. Complete specifications and installation instructions are packaged with each ring set.

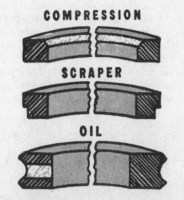

Fig. CL76–Drawing showing proper placement of piston rings. Note bevel at top of ring on inside diameter on top compression ring and notch in lower side of outside diameter of second compression (scraper) ring. Oil ring may be installed with either side up.

CYLINDER AND CRANKCASE. Cylinder and crankcase are an integral unit of either an aluminum alloy diecasting with a cast-in cast iron cylinder liner or a shell casting of cast iron.

Standard cylinder bore diameter for models 419-0000-000, 429-0003-000 and 431-0003-000 is 2.499-2.500; for all other models, standard cylinder bore diameter is 2.3745-2.3755. When piston skirt clearance (with new piston) is 0.008 or more or ring end gap (with new piston ring) is 0.025 or more, cylinder must be rebored or honed to 0.010 or 0.020 oversize or cylinder and crankcase must be renewed.

CRANKSHAFT, MAIN BEARINGS AND SEALS. On models with bushing type main bearings or models where crankshaft rides directly in unbushed bearing bores, recommended crankshaft to bearing clearance is 0.0018-0.0035; renew crankshaft and/or bushing if clearance is 0.005 or more. Refer to Fig. CL77 for proper placement of bushing in crankcase bore. On models where the crankshaft rides directly in the aluminum alloy crankcase, side plate or base plate, the bearing can be renewed by reaming out the bore to accept a service bushing. Necessary reamers, reamer alignment plate and bushing drivers are available through Clinton parts sources. Bushings must be finish reamed after they are installed. Note: Lower bushing in base plate on some late vertical shaft models may have a flange; be sure to check before attempting to remove bushing.

Recommended maximum allowable crankpin out-of-round condition is 0.001; crankshaft must be renewed if

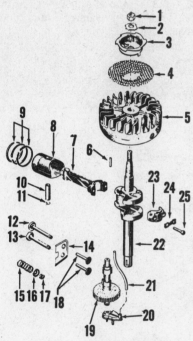

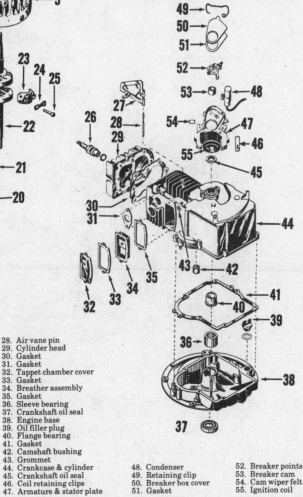

1. Flywheel nut
2. Washer
3. Starter cup
4. Rotating screen
5. Flywheel
6. Flywheel key
7. Connecting rod (includes 23)
8. Piston
9. Piston rings
10. Piston pin
11. Pin retainers
12. Intake valve
13. Exhaust valve
14. Spring retainer plate
15. Valve springs
16. Spring retainers
17. Valve keepers
18. Valve tappets
19. Camshaft
20. Oil pump
21. Oil tube
22. Crankshaft
23. Connecting rod cap
24. Connecting rod cap screw lock
25. Cap screws
26. Spark plug
27. Governor air vane
28. Air vane pin
29. Cylinder head
30. Gasket
31. Gasket
32. Tappet chamber cover
33. Gasket
34. Breather assembly
35. Gasket
36. Sleeve bearing
37. Crankshaft oil seal
38. Engine base
39. Oil filler plug
40. Flange bearing
41. Gasket
42. Camshaft bushing
43. Grommet
44. Crankcase & cylinder
45. Crankshaft oil seal
46. Coil retaining clips
47. Armature & stator plate
48. Condenser
49. Retaining clip
50. Breaker box cover
51. Gasket
52. Breaker points
53. Breaker cam
54. Cam wiper felt
55. Ignition coil

Fig. CL76A–Exploded view of vertical crankshaft model with lubricating oil pump (20). Refer to Fig. CL73A for vertical crankshaft model with splash lubrication.

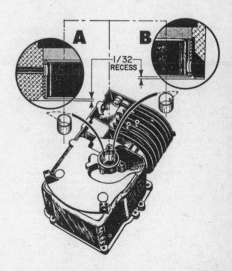

Fig. CL77–When installing crankshaft bushing in crankcase, be sure that oil holes are aligned as shown and that inner edge of bushing is 1/32-inch below thrust face of block.

crankpin out-of-round is 0.0015 or more.

Recommended crankshaft end play on models with bushing type main

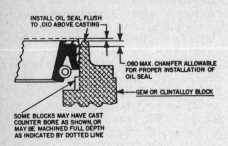

Fig. CL78–Install oil seal in block (crankcase) as shown.

bearings is 0.008-0.018; maximum allowable end play is 0.025. Standard thickness of gasket used between crankcase and side or base plate is 0.015; a 0.010 thick gasket is available for reducing crankshaft end play.

On horizontal crankshaft models with ball bearing type mains (refer to engine identification information section), bearing on pto (side plate) end of crankshaft is retained in the side plate with a snap ring and is also retained on the crankshaft with a snap ring. To remove the side plate, first pry crankshaft seal from side plate and remove the snap ring that retains bearing to

shaft; then, pull side plate and bearing from crankcase and crankshaft. Ball bearing and retaining snap ring can then be removed from the side plate. Renew the ball bearings if excessively loose or if bearing is noisy or rough.

When installing crankshaft seal in crankcase, refer to Fig. CL78 for proper placement of seal.

CAMSHAFT. On early model engines, the camshaft and cam gear unit was hollow and turned on a stationary axle. Later models are equipped with a solid camshaft and gear unit and the camshaft journals ride in bushings or directly in unbushed bores in the crankcase and side plate or base plate.

Clearance between the camshaft and cam axle on early models should be 0.001-0.003; maximum allowable clearance is 0.005. Axle diameter is 0.3740-0.3744 and is a 0.0009 tight to 0.001 loose fit in crankcase and side plate or base.

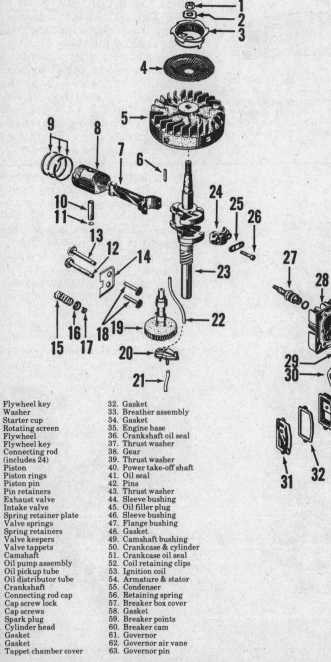

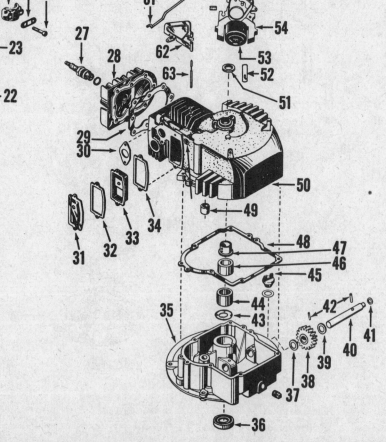

1. Flywheel key
2. Washer
3. Starter cup
4. Rotating screen
5. Flywheel
6. Flywheel key
7. Connecting rod (includes 24)
8. Piston
9. Piston rings
10. Piston pin
11. Pin retainers
12. Exhaust valve
13. Intake valve
14. Spring retainer plate
15. Valve springs
16. Spring retainers
17. Valve keepers
18. Valve tappets
19. Camshaft
20. Oil pump assembly
21. Oil pickup tube
22. Oil distributor tube
23. Crankshaft
24. Connecting rod cap
25. Cap screw lock
26. Cap screws
27. Spark plug
28. Cylinder head
29. Gasket
30. Gasket
31. Tappet chamber cover
32. Gasket
33. Breather assembly
34. Gasket
35. Engine base
36. Crankshaft oil seal
37. Thrust washer
38. Gear
39. Thrust washer
40. Power take-off shaft
41. Oil seal
42. Pins
43. Thrust washer
44. Sleeve bushing
45. Oil filler plug
46. Sleeve bushing
47. Flange bushing
48. Gasket
49. Camshaft bushing
50. Crankcase & cylinder
51. Crankcase oil seal
52. Coil retaining clips
53. Ignition coil
54. Armature & stator
55. Condenser
56. Retaining spring
57. Breaker box cover
58. Gasket
59. Breaker points
60. Breaker cam
61. Governor
62. Governor air vane
63. Governor pin

Fig. CL78A–Exploded view of vertical crankshaft model with auxiliary power take-off; output shaft gear (38) is driven by worm gear on crankshaft. Sleeve bearing (47) is used in upper side of engine base and bearing (44) is installed in lower side.

On models where camshaft turns in bores in crankcase and base or side plate, maximum allowable clearance between camshaft journals and bearing bore is 0.006. Clearance (new) between bore in crankcase and journal (either end) is 0.001-0.003.

Refer to Fig. CL79 for cam gear to crankshaft gear alignment marks.

VALVE SYSTEM. Recommended valve tappet gap for both intake and exhaust valves on all models is 0.009-0.011. Adjust clearance by grinding end of valve stem. A 45 degree bevel should be maintained on ends of stems.

Recommended valve stem to guide clearance is 0.0015-0.0045. If clearance is 0.006 or more, guide may be reamed to 0.260 for valve with 0.010 oversize stem. Also, valve guide may be knurled and reamed to 0.250 for standard size valve stem.

On models with aluminum alloy cylinder block, valves seat on renewable steel inserts; inserts are available in standard size and 0.040 oversize O.D. On models with cast iron cylinder block, valves seat directly in the cylinder block. However, valve seat inserts are available for service and may be installed after cutting counterbore in block. Necessary reamers and installation tool are available through Clinton parts sources. Refer to Clinton Special Service Tool Listing and list of Clinton Central Warehouse Distributors following the Clinton engine repair sections.

Fig. CL79—Valves are correctly timed when marks on camshaft gear and crankshaft gear are in register as shown.

Grind valve face to 45 degrees and valve seat to 44 degrees to provide a 1 degree interference angle. Recommended valve seat width is 0.030-0.045 with maximum allowable width of 0.060 for both intake and exhaust valves.

Use combination cutter No. 951-37 which cuts 44 and 30 degree angles to narrow valve seat width when it exceeds 0.060. Renew valve when head margin is reduced to less than 1/64-inch.

NOTE: Stellite exhaust valves and seat inserts are available as well as the standard hardened steel valves and inserts. Use regular exhaust valve in place of intake valve if installing a stellite exhaust valve and seat. Stellite valves are also available for use with roto-caps.

The intake and exhaust valves are actuated by mushroom type tappets that ride directly in unbushed bores in the engine crankcase. Stem diameter of the tappets is 0.2475-0.2485; tappet guide bore diameter is 0.2495-0.2510. Tappets are available in standard size only. If guides are worn excessively, they may be knurled and reamed back to standard size using same tools as used to knurl and ream valve guides. Tappets can be removed from engine block after removing the camshaft.

CAUTION: If ends of valve stems or ends of tappet stems have become enlarged or burred, do not force the stems through the bores in block. Remove burrs with emery cloth before attempting to remove valves or tappets.

LUBRICATING SYSTEM. All horizontal crankshaft models and some vertical crankshaft engines are splash lubricated. An oil distributor is attached to the connecting rod cap on horizontal crankshaft models and an oil scoop is riveted to the lower side of the camshaft gear on vertical crankshaft models. Note: Refer to CONNECTING ROD paragraph for additional information on the oil distributor use on horizontal crankshaft models.

A gear type oil pump, driven by a pin on the lower end of the engine camshaft, is used on some vertical crankshaft models. When reassembling these engines, be sure the oil tube fits into the recesses in cylinder block and oil pump before installing base plate.

SERVICING CLINTON ACCESSORIES

IMPULSE STARTERS
Early Units
STARTING PROBLEMS. Difficulty in starting engine equipped with impulse type starter may be caused by improper starting procedure or adjustment. The throttle lever must be in the full choke position and left there until engine starts. After impulse starter is fully wound, move handle to start position and push handle down against stop until starter releases. Occasionally there is a hesitation because the engine is on the compression stroke. If engine does not start readily (within 5 releases of the starter), make the following checks:

1. Remove air cleaner and be sure that choke is fully closed when throttle lever is in full choke position. If not, adjust controls so that choke can be fully closed.

2. Check the idle and high speed fuel mixture adjustment needles. (See engine servicing section for recommended initial adjustment for appropriate carburetor.)

3. Check magneto for spark. A magneto in satisfactory condition should fire an 18 mm. spark plug with electrode gap set at 0.156-0.187.

Early Units
OVERHAUL. Prior to disassembling unit, be sure that starter spring is released; turn handle a few turns and then press handle against release button. CAUTION: The impulse starter contains one or two powerful coiled springs. Disassemble the unit with care to avoid dislodging springs from retaining cups; a rapidly uncoiling power spring could cause serious injury. Do not attempt to remove a power spring from the metal cup.

To disassemble the starter, proceed as follows: Remove the four Phillips head screws (3—Fig. CL100) and invert the assembly. Holding the assembly at arms length, lightly tap the legs of the starter frame against work bench to remove bottom cover, power springs and cups, plunger assembly and the large gear. Carefully separate the spring and cup assemblies from the plunger, hold plunger and unscrew ratchet using a ⅜-inch Allen wrench. Remove the snap ring (9) and disassemble plunger unit. Renew all damaged parts or assemblies.

Prior to reassembling unit, coat all internal parts with Lubriplate or similar high melting point grease. Install large gear with beveled edge of teeth to bottom (open) side of starter and engage the lock pawl as shown in Fig. CL100A. Assemble the plunger unit and install it through the large gear so that release button protrudes through top of starter frame. Install power spring and cup assembly with closed side of cup towards large gear and

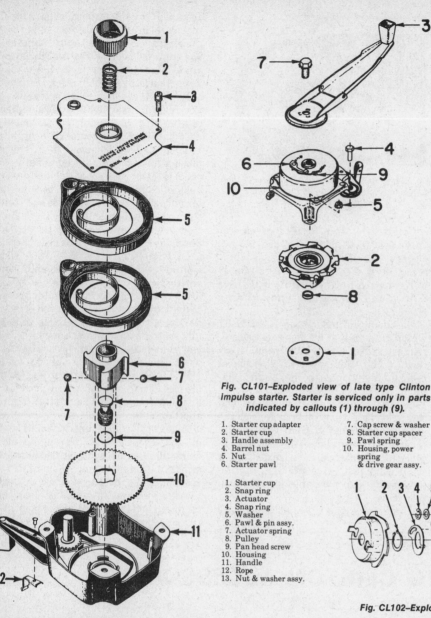

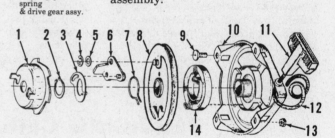

carefully work inner end of spring over the plunger. If two power springs are used, install second spring and cup assembly with closed side of cup towards first spring and cup unit. In some starters, an empty spring cup is used as a spacer; install cup with closed side towards power spring. Install the bottom cover (4—Fig. CL100) and spring (2); then, screw ratchet into plunger bushing. It is not necessary to tighten the ratchet as normal action of the starter will do this.

Late Production Units

Troubleshooting procedure for late type impulse starter unit shown in Fig. CL101 will be similar to that for early unit; refer to STARTING PROBLEMS paragraph for early units.

OVERHAUL. An exploded view of the impulse starter used on current production engines is shown in Fig. CL101.

Service of the late type impulse starter is limited to renewal of handle (3), pawl (6) and/or pawl spring (9). If power spring is broken, or if drive gear that engages starter cup (2) is worn or damaged, a complete new starter assembly must be installed. Starter cup (2) is not included as part of the starter assembly.

Fig. CL101–Exploded view of late type Clinton impulse starter. Starter is serviced only in parts indicated by callouts (1) through (9).

1. Starter cup adapter
2. Starter cup
3. Handle assembly
4. Barrel nut
5. Nut
6. Starter pawl
7. Cap screw & washer
8. Starter cup spacer
9. Pawl spring
10. Housing, power spring & drive gear assy.

1. Starter cup
2. Snap ring
3. Actuator
4. Snap ring
5. Washer
6. Pawl & pin assy.
7. Actuator spring
8. Pulley
9. Pan head screw
10. Housing
11. Handle
12. Rope
13. Nut & washer assy.

Fig. CL102–Exploded view of late production Clinton rewind starter.

Fig. CL100–Exploded view of early type Clinton impulse type starter. Some starters having only one power spring (5) use an empty power spring cup as a spacer.

1. Ratchet
2. Spring
3. Cap screws
4. Cover plate
5. Power spring & cup assy.
6. Plunger hub
7. Steel balls (2)
8. Plunger
9. Snap ring
10. Gear
11. Housing, crank & pinion assy.

1. Flywheel
2. Plate
3. Flywheel nut
4. Spacer
5. Spring
6. Pawl
7. Snap ring
8. Washer
9. Wave washer
10. Pulley
11. Cup
12. Rewind spring
13. Handle
14. Guide
15. Housing
16. Screen
17. Retainer

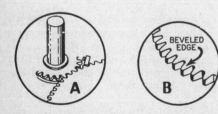

Fig. CL100A–When reinstalling large gear (10–Fig. CL100), be sure beveled edge of gear is towards open side of housing and that lock engages gear as shown.

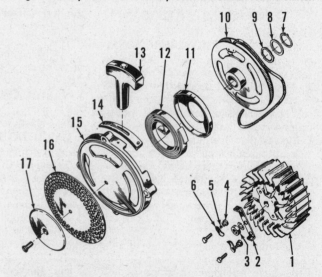

Fig. CL102A–Exploded view of Deluxe Model of Clinton rewind starter of the type used on chain saws and some engines. Starter will operate in either rotation by interchanging springs (5) and inverting pawls (6) and recoil spring (12).

110

REWIND STARTERS

Exploded view of rewind starter currently used on most Clinton engines is shown in Fig. CL102. Other starters used are shown in Figs. CL102A through CL110. Care should be taken when reassembling all starters to be sure the recoil spring is not wound too tightly. The spring should be wound tight enough to rewind the rope, but so the spring will not be fully wound when the rope is pulled out to full length. Coat spring and all internal parts with Lubriplate or equivalent grease when reassembling. Be sure

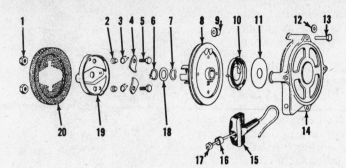

Fig. CL103–Exploded view of an earlier type Clinton rewind starter.

1. Lock nut
2. Pawl spacer
3. Pawl spring
4. Pawl
5. Cap screw
6. Snap ring
7. Wave washer
8. Pulley
9. Rope bushing
10. Rewind spring & cup assy.
11. Washer
12. Lockwasher
13. Barrel nut
14. Housing
15. Handle
16. Retainer
17. Rope
18. Washer
19. Starter cup
20. Rotating screen

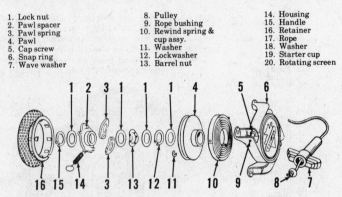

Fig. CL104–Exploded view of an earlier type Clinton rewind starter.

1. Flat washer
2. Drive plate
3. Drive pawls
4. Pulley
5. Rope pulley
6. Housing
7. Handle
8. Rope
9. Roll pin
10. Rewind spring
11. Snap ring
12. Snap ring
13. Wave washer
14. Tension spring
15. Snap ring
16. Starter cup

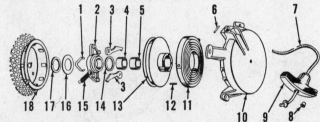

Fig. CL105–Exploded view of an earlier type Clinton rewind starter. Design of housing (10) may vary from that shown. Bushing (5) not used in some starters.

1. Retaining spring
2. Pawl plate
3. Pawls
4. Bushing
5. Bushing
6. Roll pin
7. Rope
8. Washer
9. Handle
10. Housing
11. Rewind spring
12. Roll pin
13. Pulley
14. Spacer
15. Tension spring
16. Washer
17. Snap ring
18. Starter cup

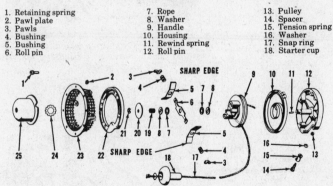

Fig. CL106–Exploded view of Bulldog starter used on some early production engines.

1. Screw & washer assy.
2. Nut & retainer assy.
3. Retainer
4. Spring
5. Friction shoe
6. Brake lever
7. Washer
8. Slotted washer
9. Pulley
10. Rewind spring
11. Centering pin
12. Housing
13. Nut
14. Shoulder screw
15. Roller
16. Washer
17. Rope
18. Handle
19. Spring
20. Washer
21. Snap ring
22. Flange
23. Base
24. Lock washer
25. Pulley (cup)

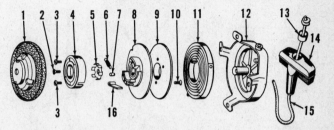

Fig. CL107–Exploded view of Eaton rewind starter used on some early production engines.

1. Starter pulley
2. Screws
3. Screws (2)
4. Retainer
5. Brake
6. Tension spring
7. Spring retainer
8. Hub
9. Plate
10. Screw
11. Rewind spring
12. Housing
13. Cup
14. Handle
15. Rope

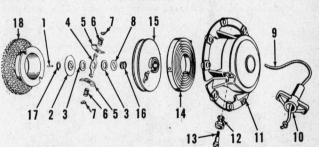

Fig. CL108–Exploded view of a Fairbanks-Morse rewind starter used on early production engines. Refer to Fig. CL109 for a second type of Fairbanks-Morse starter used on other Clinton models.

1. Centering pin
2. Washer
3. Fiber washer
4. Brake lever
5. Friction shoe
6. Spring
7. Retainer
8. Washer
9. Rope
10. Handle
11. Housing
12. Roller
13. Screw
14. Rewind spring
15. Pulley
16. Spring
17. Snap ring
18. Pulley (cup)

Fig. CL109–Exploded view of a Fairbanks-Morse rewind starter used on some Clinton engines. Refer to Fig. CL108 for another type of Fairbanks-Morse starter used.

1. Centering pin
2. Washer
3. Washer
4. Fiber washer
5. Friction shoe
6. Retainer
7. Spring
8. Mounting flange
9. Middle flange
10. Housing
11. Rope
12. Handle
13. Cup
14. Screw
15. Roller
16. Screws
17. Rewind spring
18. Pulley
19. Brake lever
20. Spring
21. Snap ring
22. Pulley (cup)

that spring, pulley and related parts are assembled for correct rotation.

12-VOLT STARTER-GENERATOR

Refer to Figs. CL111 and CL112. Parts and/or service for the starter-generator unit may be obtained at any United Motors (Delco-Remy) Service Station.

12-VOLT STARTER & LIGHTING COIL

Refer to Figs. CL113, CL114, CL115 and CL116. Service and/or parts for the 12-volt starter is available at authorized American Bosch Arma Corp. service stations.

The 12-volt lightning coils are mounted on the magneto armature core as shown in Figs. CL115 and CL116. Wiring diagram when unit is used for lighting circuit only is shown in Fig. CL115. When unit is used to provide a battery charging current, a rectifier must be installed in the circuit to convert the AC current into DC current as shown in Fig. CL116.

Fig. CL113–View of American Bosch 12-volt starter mounted on a late production horizontal crankshaft engine. Square-shaped unit below starter motor is a rectifier to convert AC current from lighting coils on magneto armature core to DC current.

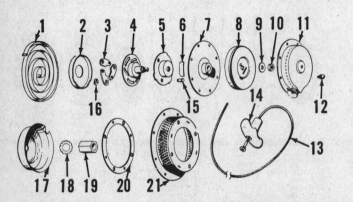

1. Rewind spring
2. Cover
3. Pawls
4. Cam plate & axle
5. Drive plate*
6. Spring*
7. Plate
8. Drum
9. Washer
10. Nut
11. Housing
12. Screws
13. Rope
14. Handle
15. Pin
16. Snap ring
17. Rope pulley
18. Lock washer
19. Driven nut
20. Ring
21. Housing

Fig. CL110–Exploded view of typical Schnacke starter unit used on early production engines. Asterisk indicates part not used on all starters.

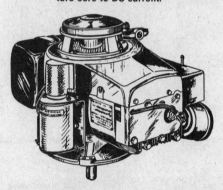

Fig. CL114–View of American Bosch 12-volt starter mounted on a late production vertical crankshaft engine.

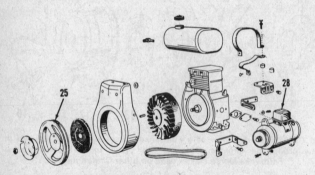

Fig. CL111–The 12-volt starter generator (28) is driven (and drives) by a belt and pulley (25).

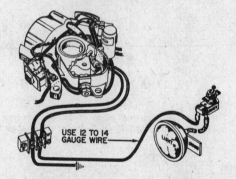

Fig. CL115–View showing wiring circuit from lighting coils when used for lighting purposes only.

Fig. CL112 – Wiring diagram for 12V. D.C. Starter-generator.

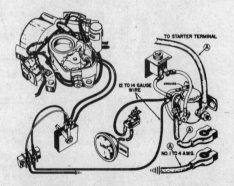

Fig. CL116–View showing wiring circuit from lighting coils; a rectifier is included in circuit to provide DC current for charging a 12-volt battery.

110-VOLT ELECTRIC STARTERS

Exploded views of the two types of 110-volt electric starters are shown in Figs. CL117 and CL118. CAUTION: Always connect starter cord at engine before connecting cord to 110-volt power source.

ELECTRA-START

Electra-Start models have a built-in battery, starter and flywheel mounted alternator. Early models used a wet cell 12-volt battery mounted on mower deck. Late models use a 12-cell nickel-cadmium battery which attaches to crankcase, making the unit fully self-contained. Electra-Start models are equipped with a bulb type fuel primer which pressurizes the carburetor float chamber when bulb is depressed, forcing a small amount of fuel out main nozzle.

Nominal voltage of the nickel-cadmium battery is 15 volts. Charging rate of the flywheel alternator is 0.2-0.25 D.C. Amperes. About 40-125 ampere-seconds are normally required to start the engine and recovery time to full charge should be 3-10 minutes of operation. About 20 minutes running time should be allowed when battery or engine is first put into service.

The alternator output (200-250 milli-amperes) cannot be measured with regular shop equipment. If trouble is encountered, start the engine and operate at rated speed. Disconnect generator lead from red (positive) battery lead and check generator output using one of the following methods:

(1) Connect one lead of a voltmeter or small test light to generator lead and ground the other test lead. Voltmeter should register or test light should glow, indicating charging current.

(2). In the absence of test equipment, momentarily touch the disconnected generator lead to a suitable ground and watch for a spark.

If test equipment or spark indicates charging current the generator should be considered satisfactory. If battery voltage is low, renew the battery.

If a charging current is not indicated, remove the flywheel and renew the generator coil which is mounted on one leg of magneto pole shoe. The halfwave rectifier is built into magneto coil and not renewable separately.

POLYURETHANE AIR CLEANER. Some Clinton models are now equipped with a polyurethane air filter element. After each 10 hours of use, the element should be removed and washed in solvent or kerosene. (Element may be washed in detergent soap and water.) Re-oil the element with 10 weight or 10-30 weight motor oil and wring out to remove excess oil. Insert the element evenly into air cleaner

Fig. CL117–Exploded view of the 110-volt below deck electric starter, which is available on some vertical shaft engines.

1. Engine base
3. Rotor clamp
6. Crankshaft
7. Cover
9. Insulator gasket
10. Insulator gasket
12. Rotor
17. Connector sleeves (3 used)
18. Insulating sleeve
19. Stator

Fig. CL119–Exploded view of polyurethane air cleaner.

1. Gasket	4. Element
2. Body	5. Cover
3. Retainer	6. Screws

NEW TYPE CLUTCH AND GEAR

2nd TYPE CLUTCH AND GEAR

Fig. CL118–Exploded view of the 110-volt electric starter available on some models.

2. Armature	5Z. Earliest clutch assy.	9Y. 2nd clutch gear
3. Bearing	7. Cover	9Z. Earliest clutch gear
4. Brushes	8. Cup	11. Upper housing
5X. Latest clutch assy.	9X. Latest clutch gear	12. Lower housing
5Y. Second clutch assy.		13. Field windings

16. Centering pin
17. Brush mounting plate
24. Spacers
26. Springs
28. Fiber washer

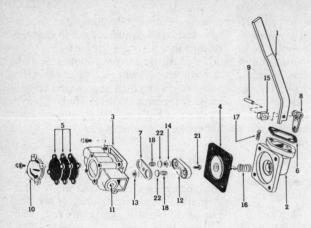

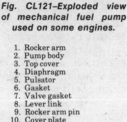

1. Rocker arm
2. Pump body
3. Top cover
4. Diaphragm
5. Pulsator
6. Gasket
7. Valve gasket
8. Lever link
9. Rocker arm pin
10. Cover plate
11. Pipe plug
12. Valve retainer
13. Valve seat
14. Valve seat
15. Rocker spring clip
16. Diaphragm spring
17. Rocker arm spring
18. Valve spring
21. Valve retainer screw
22. Valve (2)

housing and snap cover in place. See Fig. CL119 for exploded view of this type air cleaner.

REMOTE CONTROLS

REMOTE CONTROLS AND GOVERNOR ADJUSTMENT. Several different remote control options are available. Refer to Fig. CL122. Views A through G are for engines with following basic numbers: IBM basic Nos. 494 and 498; old basic Nos. 900, 960, 990, B1260 and B1290. View A shows standard fixed speed for horizontal shaft engine. B, C and F show available remote control options. Typical cable and handle assembly is shown in D. Detail of pivot pin to block is shown in E. View G shows method of securing control wire to lever on some applications.

The remote control allows the engine speed to be regulated by movement of the remote control lever some distance away from the engine. The engine speed will be maintained by the engine governor at any setting of the remote control lever within the prescribed speed range of the engine. Maximum speed should not exceed 3600 RPM.

Adjust the remote control with the engine running by the following procedure:

1. Loosen screw in swivel nut on control lever.
2. Move control lever to high speed position. See view B, Fig. CL122.
3. Move control wire through control casing and swivel nut until maximum desired speed is obtained. (Do not exceed maximum of 3600 RPM.) Lever should remain in high speed position.
4. Tighten screw in swivel nut to hold control wire.
5. Move control lever to slow speed position to be sure engine can slow down to idle speed.

PTO & SPEED REDUCER UNITS

AUXILIARY PTO. Some vertical crankshaft models are equipped with an auxiliary pto as shown in Fig. CL123. Unit is lubricated by oil in engine crankcase. To disassemble unit, drive the pins (6, 7 and 22) partially out of shaft (11), turn shaft half-turn and pull pins. Remove drive gears (2 and 4). Remove output shaft (12) and gear (21) in similar manner.

SPEED REDUCERS. Speed reducers (gear reduction units) with ratios of 2:1, 4:1 and 6:1 are available on a

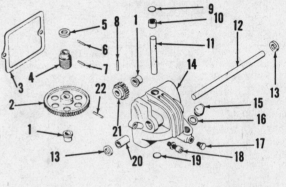

1. Flange bearing
2. Drive gear
3. Gasket
4. Worm gear
5. Thrust washer
6. Pin
7. Pin
8. Pin
9. Expansion plug
10. Needle bearing
11. Worm shaft
12. PTO shaft
13. Oil seal
14. Housing
15. Oil filler cap
16. Gasket
17. Oil drain plug
18. Cap screw
19. Expansion plug
20. Sleeve bearing
21. PTO gear
22. Pin

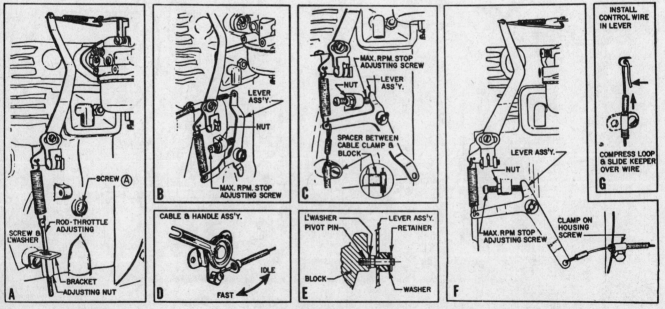

Fig. CL122–Remote control hook-ups for various Clinton engines. Refer to text for engine application and adjustment procedures.

number of horizontal shaft engines.

Refer to Fig. CL124 for exploded view of typical speed reducer for engines of less than 5 horsepower. Unit should be lubricated by filling with SAE 30 oil to the level plug. Oil level should be checked after each 10 hours of operation and changed each 100 hours. Use Fig. CL124 as disassembly and reassembly guide. Unit can be mounted on engine in any of four positions; be sure outer housing is installed so that filler plug is up.

An exploded view of typical speed reducer used on engines of 5 horsepower and larger is shown in Fig. CL125. Units used on early engines support output end of crankshaft in sleeve bearing (1) as shown; late units support output end of crankshaft in a tapered roller bearing. After unit has been drained of oil or after reassembly, initially fill unit with same oil as used in engine. Lubricating oil supply is thereafter maintained from engine crankcase through passage drilled in inner housing (12). Gaskets (4) used between inner housing and engine crankcase or bearing plate are available in thicknesses of 0.010, 0.015 and 0.020. Use proper thickness gasket to maintain specified crankshaft end play. As unit can be mounted on engine in any of four different bolting positions, be sure that outer housing (13) is installed with filler plug to top and oil level and drain plugs down. Note: After engine has been started, oil level will usually be below level of oil level plug.

FLYWHEEL BRAKE

"TOUCH 'N' STOP" BRAKE. Some vertical crankshaft models used on rotary lawnmowers are equipped with a "Touch 'N' Stop" flywheel brake. Actuating the control assembly releases pawl lever (10—Fig. CL126) allowing spring (8) to rotate cam applying brake band (1). To reset, move the cocking lever (11) to release brake band and latch the pawl with brake in released position.

Required service, such as renewal of worn or broken parts or broken springs, should be evident after inspection of unit and reference to Fig. CL126. Tighten flywheel nut (2) to a torque of 600-700 inch-pounds on models so equipped.

Fig. CL124—Exploded view of gear reduction unit used on engines of less than 5 horsepower. Gear ratio may be 2:1, 4:1 or 6:1. Sleeve bearings must be reamed after installation.

1. Sleeve bearing
2. Sleeve bearing
3. Gasket
4. Gasket
5. 2:1 pinion
6. 2:1 gear
7. 4:1 gear
8. 6:1 gear
9. Gear & shaft
10. Gear & shaft
11. Gear & shaft
12. Inner housing
13. Outer housing
14. Key
15. Nut & washer assy.
16. Breather plug
17. Expansion plug
18. Oil level plug
19. Snap ring
20. Screw
21. Screw
22. Oil seal
23. Shaft
24. Thrust washer
25. Thrust washer
26. Flat washer
27. Lockwasher

Fig. CL125—Exploded view of gear reduction unit used on engines larger than 5 horsepower. Gear ratio may be 2:1, 4:1 or 6:1. Sleeve bearing (1) must be finish reamed after installation. Units used on late production engines have tapered roller engine main bearing instead of sleeve bearing (1) shown.

1. Sleeve bearing
2. Flange bearing
3. Gasket
4. Gasket
5. 2:1 pinion
6. 2:1 gear
7. 4:1 gear
8. 6:1 gear
9. Gear & shaft
10. Gear & shaft
11. Gear & shaft
12. Inner housing
13. Outer housing
14. Key
15. Snap.ring
16. Screw & washer
17. Screw & washer
18. Oil seal
19. Shaft

Fig. CL126 – Schematic drawing of "Touch 'N' Stop" brake used on some vertical crankshaft rotary lawnmower engines.

1. Brake band
2. Flywheel nut
3. Flywheel
4. Pin
5. Pivot bolt
6. Screw
7. Cam
8. Spring
9. Spring
10. Pawl lever
11. Cocking lever
12. Flat spring

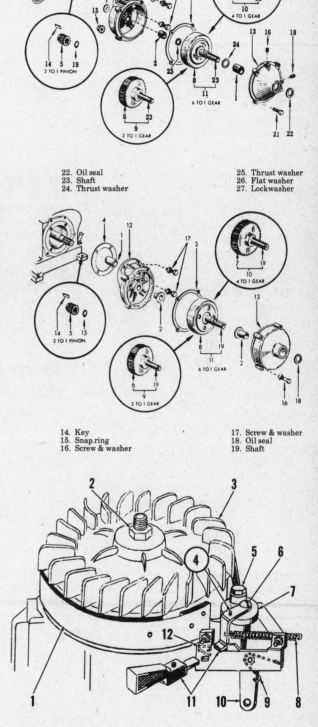

CLINTON SERVICE TOOLS

The following list of special service tools indicates the Clinton part number, tool name and usage by engine groups. Following the tool list are the engine group listing and a cross-reference by engine model number to tool usage group.

Clinton Engine special service tools are available by part number from Clinton Central Warehouse Distributors listed elsewhere in this manual.

Bearing Tools

951-48 REAMER GUIDE. Three bushings included with the following inside diameters: 0.878, 1.0003 and 1.030. Used to line ream bearing in blocks of engine groups II, III, IV, V, VI, VII, VIII, IX, X, XIII, XIV and XV. Used also to ream bearings in bases of engine group VIII.

951-148 GUIDE. A bushing that is used when reaming bearings in bases of engine group XV that have a 1.000 dia. bearing bore.

951-18 and 951-39 BEARING DRIVER. Used to remove and install bearings in two-bearing blocks, or in mounting flanges of engine group II and VIII.

951-29 REAMER. Diameter, 0.8773-0.877. Used to ream bearings in blocks of engine groups II, IV, VI, VII and VIII, and bearing plates of engine groups VII and VIII (using block for guide). Can also be used to ream bearing plates for engine group X if sleeve bearing block of a group VII or VIII engine is available for use as a guide.

951-30 REAMER. Diameter, 0.7518-0.7523. Used to ream bearing in bearing plates of engine groups II, III, IV, V and VI and bearing in blocks of engine group V.

951-44 REAMER. Diameter, 1.0003-1.0008. Used to enlarge bore in bases of engine group XV having a ⅞-inch bore so that a bronze bearing can be installed.

951-59 REAMER. Diameter, 1.0023-1.0028. Used to ream bearing in blocks of engine groups III and X.

951-60 REAMER. Diameter, 0.8144-0.8155. Used to ream bearings in blocks of engine groups XIII, XIV and XV.

951-63 REAMER. Diameter, 0.8758-0.8763. Used to ream bearings in bases of engine groups XIV and XV.

951-143 REAMER. Diameter, 1.1218-1.1220. Used as second step to enlarge 1 inch diameter bore of base in engine group XV so that bronze bearing can be installed. Also see 951-144.

951-144 REAMER. Diameter, 1.1042-1.1062. Used as first step to enlarge 1 inch diameter bore of base in engine group XV so that bronze bearing can be installed. Also see 951-143.

951-146 REAMER. Diameter, 0.9338-0.9340. Used as second step to enlarge bore in aluminum blocks of engines in groups XIV and XV so that bronze bearing can be installed. Also see 951-147.

951-147 REAMER. Diameter, 0.9167-0.9187. Used as first step to enlarge bore in aluminum blocks of engines in groups XIV and XV so that bronze bearing can be installed. Also see 951-146.

Oil Seal Loaders (Installation Sleeves)

For loading (installing) oil seals over shafts, the following oil seal loaders are available:

951-12 ..... for ¾-inch diameter shaft
951-13 .. for 57/64-inch diameter shaft
951-40 .... for 1⅜-inch diameter shaft
951-49 . for 1 3/16-inch diameter shaft
951-55 ..... for ⅞-inch diameter shaft
951-56 ...... for 1 inch diameter shaft
951-57 ..... for ¾-inch diameter shaft
951-47 ..... for ½-inch diameter shaft
951-14 .. for 57/64-inch diameter shaft
951-118 ... for 1¼-inch diameter shaft
951-145 .... for ¾-inch diameter shaft

Oil Seal Pullers and Drivers

951-50 OIL SEAL PULLER. For removing oil seal from flywheel side of engines in groups XIII, XIV and XV.

951-16 OIL SEAL DRIVER. Inside dia., 1.010; outside dia., 1.250; length, 4 inches.

951-17 OIL SEAL DRIVER. Inside dia., 0.885; outside dia., 1.125; length, 4 inches.

951-62 OIL SEAL DRIVER. Inside dia., 0.760; outside dia., 1.000; length, 3 inches.

Valve Tools, 4-Stroke Cycle Engines

951-32 VALVE SPRING COMPRESSOR. For engines in groups V, VI, VII, VIII, IX, X, XIII, XIV and XV. Also see 951-67.

951-67 VALVE SPRING COMPRESSOR. For engines in groups V, VI, VII, VIII, IX, X, XIII, XIV and XV. Also see 951-32.

951-22 VALVE GUIDE REAMER. (0.281 dia.) Used to ream valve guides for installation of valves with oversize (9/32-inch diameter) stems in engine groups VI, VII, VIII, IX and X.

951-43 VALVE GUIDE REAMER. (0.261 dia.) Used to ream valve guides for installation of valves with 0.010 oversize stems in engine groups XIII, XIV and XV.

951-69 VALVE GUIDE REAMER. Used to clean standard size valve guides (0.250 dia.) for engines in groups V, VI, VII, VIII, IX, X, XIII, XIV and XV.

951-58-500 PILOT ASSEMBLY. A kit of valve guide pilots containing one each of the following:

951-137, 0.249 -0.2505 dia.
951-138, 0.2505-0.252 dia.
951-139, 0.2605-0.262 dia.
951-140, 0.2805-0.282 dia.

Used in conjunction with 951-37 Valve Seat Cutter, 951-41 Valve Seat Counterbore Cutter and 951-61 Valve Seat Counterbore Cutter on engines in groups V, VI, VII, VIII, IX, X, XIII, XIV and XV.

951-37 VALVE SEAT CUTTER. Used to recondition valve seats on engines in groups V, VI, VII, VIII, IX, X, XIII, XIV and XV. See also 951-58-500. Set of three new cutting edges are available as Part No. 951-131.

951-136 VALVE LAPPING TOOL. For lapping valves to seats on engines in groups V, VI, VII, VIII, IX, X, XIII, XIV and XV.

951-41 CUTTER. Used to ream valve seat counterbore for installation of 0.040 oversize valve seat insert in engines of groups XIV and XV. Also see 951-58-500.

951-61 CUTTER. Used to cut a counterbore for installation of service valve seat insert in engines of groups V, VI, VII, VIII, IX and X. See also 951-58-500.

951-52 DRIVER. Used to drive valve seat inserts into place on engines in groups V, VI, VII, VIII, IX, X, XIII, XIV and XV.

951-53 ROLLING TOOL. Used to peen or roll metal around outside edge of valve seat insert after installing new insert in engines of groups V, VI, VII, VIII, IX, X, XIII, XIV and XV.

Piston Ring Tools

951-34 COMPRESSOR. Used for compressing piston rings on pistons of 1¾ to 3⅛ inch diameter on engines in groups V, VI, VII, VIII, IX, X, XIII, XIV and XV.

951-150 SLEEVE (1⅞ inch bore)

951-153 SLEEVE (2⅛ inch bore). Used for installing standard size and 0.020 oversize piston assembly in blocks of engines in groups I, II, III and IV.

Flywheel and Crankshaft Tools

IMPACT NUTS. Impact or knock-off nuts are available for removing flywheels as follows:

951-23, for crankshafts having 7/16-inch threads.

951-36, for crankshafts having ⅞-inch threads.

951-66, for crankshafts having ½-inch threads.

951-133 FLYWHEEL PULLER. For use on engines in groups I, II, III, IV, V, VII, VIII, IX, X, XIII, XIV and XV.

951-42 FLYWHEEL HOLDER. All engines. New belt for holder available as Part No. 951-151.

951-45 HAND CRANK. Used for turning engine when adjusting breaker point gap, checking timing, etc., on engines in groups I, II, III, IV, V, VI, VII, VIII, IX, X, XIII, XIV and XV.

951-64 CRANKSHAFT RUNOUT GAGE. All engines; for checking for bent crankshafts.

Camshaft Tools

951-46 CAM AXLE DRIVER. Used to drive cam axle from block in engines of groups VII, VIII, IX and X.

ENGINE GROUPING FOR TOOL USAGE LISTING

GROUP I
E65.

GROUP II
AVS200, AVS200-1000, VS200, VS200-1000, AVS400, VS400, VS400-1000.

GROUP III
VS200-2000, VS200-3000, VS200-4000, AVS400-1000, BVS400, CVS400-1000, VS400-2000, VS400-3000, VS400-4000, 501-0000-000, and 501-0001-000.

GROUP IV
200, A200, A400, A400-1000, GK590, and 500-0000-000.

GROUP V
300, A300, 350.

GROUP VI
VS300.

GROUP VII
650, 700A, B700, C700, D700, D700-1000, D700-2000, D700-3000, 800, A800, 900, 900-1000, 900-2000, 900-3000, 900-4000, A&B1100, C1100, 494-0000-000, 494-0001-000.

GROUP VIII
VS700, VS750, VS800.

GROUP IX
D1100, 1200, 1200-1000, 1200-2000, A1200, B1290-1000, 498-0300-000, 498-0301-000.

GROUP X
VS900, V1000-1000, VS1000, V1100-1000, VS1100, VS1100-1000, V1200-1000, VS1200, 497-0000-000, 499-0000-000.

GROUP XIII
429-003-000, 431-0003-000.

GROUP XIV
100, 100-1000, 100-2000, 2100, A2100, A2100-1000, A2100-2000, 3100, 3100-1000, 3100-2000, 3100-3000, H3100-1000, 4100, 4100-1000, 4100-2000, 400-0000-000, 402-0000-000, 404-0000-000, 406-0000-000, 408-0000-000, 410-0000-000, 424-0000-000, 426-0000-000, 492-0000-000.

GROUP XV
V100-1000, VS100, VS100-1000, VS100-2000, VS100-3000, VS100-4000, VS2100, VS2100-1000, VS2100-2000, VS2100-3000, VS3000, FV3100-1000, AFV3100-1000, AV3100-1000, AVS3100-2000, AVS3100-3000, V3100-1000, V3100-2000, VS3100, VS3100-1000, VS3100-2000, VS3100-3000, AVS4100-1000, AVS4100-2000, VS4100-1000, VS4100-2000, 401-0000-000, 403-0000-000, 405-0000-000, 407-0000-000, 407-0002-000, 409-0000-000, 411-0000-000, 411-0002-000, 415-0000-000, 415-0002-000, 417-0000-000, 419-0000-000, 435-0003-000, 455-0000-000.

ENGINE TO TOOL USAGE GROUP CROSS-REFERENCE

CLINTON CENTRAL WAREHOUSE DISTRIBUTORS

(Arranged Alphabetically by States)
These franchised firms carry extensive stocks of repair parts. Contact them for name and address of nearest service distributor who may have the parts you need.

Auto Electric & Carburetor Co.
2625 Fourth Avenue South
P.O. Box 2246
Birmingham, Alabama 35201

Charlie C. Jones Battery & Electric Co.
2440 West McDowell Road
Post Office Box 6654
Phoenix, Arizona 85005

Lanco
12915 Weber Way
Post Office Box 279
Hawthorne, California 90250

Bee Tee Engine Sales, Inc.
2424 Teagarden Street
San Leandro, California 94577

Central Motive Power
6301 North Broadway
Denver, Colorado 802177

Patten Distributors, Inc.
6840 Stuart Avenue
Jacksonville, Florida 32205

Sedco, Inc.
3637 Clearview Parkway NE
Atlanta, Georgia 30340

Illinois Auto Electric Co.
656 County Line Road
Elmhurst, Illinois 60126

Midwest Engine Warehouse
515 Romans Road
Elmhurst, Illinois 60126

Equipment Service Company
727 North Illinois Street
Indianapolis, Indiana 46204

Lally's, Inc.
1520 Walnut
Des Moines, Iowa 50309

Mid-East Power Equipment Company
185 Lisle Road
Lexington, Kentucky 40501

Yazoo of Louisiana, Inc.
Kerr Lawnmower Center
2615 Airline Highway
Baton Rouge, Louisiana 70805

Springfield Auto Electric Service, Inc.
50 Carew Street
Springfield, Massachusetts 01104

Auto Electric & Service Corp.
15550 Woodrow Wilson
Detroit, Michigan 48238

Engine Parts Supply Company
1220-1224 Harmon Place
Minneapolis, Minnesota 55403

Yazoo Manufacturing Company
3607 Livingston Road
Post Office Box 4207
Jackson, Mississippi 39216

Electrical & Magneto Service Co.
1600 Campbell
Kansas City, Missouri 64108

Medart Engines and Parts
Div. Medart Auto Electric
3100 Washington Avenue
Saint Louis, Missouri 63103

A & I Distributors
Post Office Box 1999
2112 Fourth Avenue North
Billings, Montana 59103

A & I Distributors
807 Second Street South
Great Falls, Montana 59403

R.P.W., Inc.
7404 "L" Street
Omaha, Nebraska 68102

Central Motive Power
808 Second Street NW
Post Office Box 1294
Albuquerque, New Mexico 87103

Durham Company, Inc.
Post Office Box 620
7 Elkins Road
East Brunswick, New Jersey 08816

Cato Distributors
40 Stutson Street
Rochester, New York 14612

E. J. Smith & Sons Company
4000 Golf Acres Drive
Charlotte, North Carolina 28201

V. E. Peterson Company
28101 East Broadway
Walbridge (Toledo), Ohio 43465

Phillips Machinery Company
8833 East Pine
Tulsa, Oklahoma 74115

Brown & Wiser, Inc.
1411 NW Flanders Street
Portland, Oregon 97209

R. K. Mickel Equipment
401-03 Bell Avenue
Altoona, Pennsylvania 16602

McCullough Distributing Co., Inc.
1110 Germantown Avenue
Philadelphia, Pennsylvania 19123

Locke Auto Electric Service, Inc.
231 North Dakota Avenue
Post Office Box 1165
Sioux Falls, South Dakota 57101

RCH Distributors, Inc.
3150 Carrier Street
Box 173
Memphis, Tennessee 38101

Automobile Electric Service
1008 Charlotte Avenue
Nashville, Tennessee 37203

The Motor Mart
2116 Cockrell Avenue
Dallas, Texas 75215

Wes Kern's Repair Service
2423 East Missouri
El Paso, Texas 79901

Yazoo of Texas
1409 Telephone Road
Houston, Texas 77023

A-1 Engine & Mower Co.
437 East 9th - South
Salt Lake City, Utah 84111

Richmond Battery & Ignition Corp.
Post Office Box 25369
Richmond, Virginia 23260

Fremont Electric Company
744 North 44th Street
Seattle, Washington 98103

World Wide Trading Company
Post Office Box 33
850 Heritage Road
De Pere, Wisconsin 54115

CANADA

Loveseth, Ltd.
10180 105th Street
Edmonton, Alberta, Canada

Air Cooled Engine Division
Auto Electric Service Pacific, Ltd.
3451 Wayburne Drive
Burnaby, British Columbia, Canada

Air Cooled Engine Division
Auto Electric Service Western, Ltd.
89 Paramount Road
Winnipeg, Manitoba, Canada

Air Cooled Engine Division
Auto Electric Service Co., Ltd.
113 Thorncliffe Park Drive
Toronto, Ontario, Canada

Air Cooled Engine Division
Autolec Services, Quebec, Ltd.
200 Bates Road, First Floor
Montreal, Quebec, Canada

COX

L. M. COX MANUFACTURING CO., INC.
Cox Center
Santa Ana, Calif. 92702

Series	Bore	Stroke	Displ.	H.P.
140	1.250	1.136	1.4	1
170	1.375	1.136	1.7	1½

MAINTENANCE

SPARK PLUG. Either Champion CJ-8 or AC CS45T spark plug can be used on all models. Recommended tightening torque is 12-14 Ft.-Lbs. Electrode gap should be 0.025.

CARBURETOR. The diaphragm carburetor (Fig. COX 1) is equipped with both idle mixture and main adjustment needles. Initial setting for the main fuel adjustment needle (2) is two turns open from the closed position. Turning the needle (2) in leans the mixture. The main fuel needle should be set for high speed operation under load. The idle mixture screw (1) is normally closed; however, screw can be opened (turned out) slightly to lean the idle fuel mixture. Idle speed is adjusted at screw (4).

MAGNETO AND TIMING. A flywheel type magneto is used as shown in Fig. COX 2. The breaker contact points are enclosed under the flywheel. The armature, coil and condenser are mounted outside the flywheel.

To gain access to the breaker contact points, remove the recoil starter and blower housing. Then, loosen flywheel retaining nut one turn and, while supporting engine with flywheel, tap the nut sharply with a small hammer to unseat the tapered fit between flywheel and shaft. NOTE: End of flywheel nut is shaft for recoil starter. Be careful not to damage nut when removing flywheel. Remove nut, flywheel and breaker box cover. Be careful not to lose the flywheel drive key.

Ignition timing is fixed and not adjustable; however, incorrect breaker point gap will change timing. Ignition breaker point gap at maximum opening should be exactly 0.015. If necessary, the magneto stator plate can be removed after removing the four attaching screws.

LUBRICATION. The engine is lubricated by oil mixed with the fuel. Normal ratio is 1:16 (½ pint oil to 1 gallon of gasoline). For new or rebuilt motors, the first gallon of fuel should have 1 pint of oil mixed with 1 gallon of gasoline. Use regular gasoline and SAE 30 API classification "MS" motor oil. Mix oil and gasoline thoroughly in a separate container.

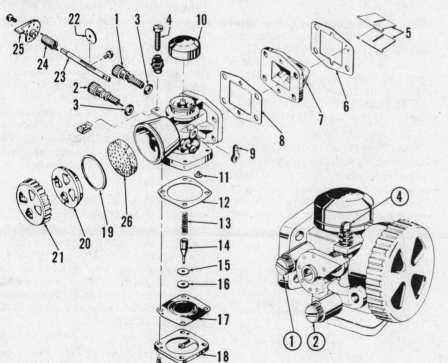

Fig. COX 1–Exploded view of carburetor used. Make certain that pulse chamber cap (10) and reeds (5) are in good condition and correctly installed.

1. Idle mixture screw	10. Pulse chamber cap	18. Cover
2. Main fuel mixture needle	11. Rivet	19. "O" ring
3. "O" rings	12. Gasket	20. Choke disc
4. Idle speed screw	13. Spring	21. Choke cover
5. Reeds	14. Inlet needle	22. Throttle valve
6. Gasket with cut-outs	15. Needle seat	23. Throttle shaft
7. Reed block	16. Seat retainer	24. Return spring
8. Gasket with holes	17. Diaphragm	25. Throttle control
9. Bellcrank		26. Air filter

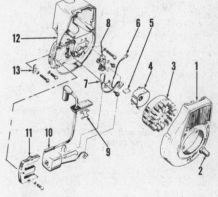

Fig. COX 2–Exploded view of magneto assembly. End of nut (2) is shaft for starter.

1. Blower housing	8. Breaker points
2. Flywheel nut	9. Stop switch
3. Flywheel	10. Coil
4. Cover	11. Coil core
5. Cam oiler felt	12. Magneto stator plate
6. Wire to switch (9)	13. High tension wire retainer
7. Condenser	

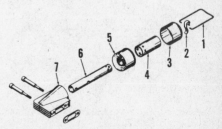

Fig. COX 4–Exploded view of muffler and exhaust collector. Refer to text when assembling.

1. Retainer	
2. Clip	5. Inner cover
3. Outer cover	6. Long baffle tube
4. Short baffle tube	7. Exhaust collector

CARBON. Exhaust ports, muffler and exhaust collector should be cleaned at least every 60 hours of operation. Use a dull non-ferrous tool such as a ¼-inch wooden dowel to clean ports and crank engine several revolutions after cleaning to blow carbon out of cylinder. When assembling, make certain that the two locator pins on collector slide between fins of cylinder. Slot on one end of the long baffle tube of muffler should correctly engage boss in collector. Holes in short baffle tube should be toward exhaust collector.

REPAIRS

CONNECTING ROD. The connecting rod and piston can be with-

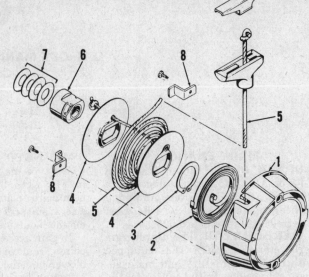

Fig. COX 7—Exploded view of recoil starter. Clutch (6) drives the flywheel nut (2—Fig. COX 2) when rope is pulled.

1. Housing
2. Recoil spring
3. Snap ring
4. Pulley (2 halves)
5. Rope
6. Starter clutch
7. Thrust washers (4 used)
8. Retainers (late models)

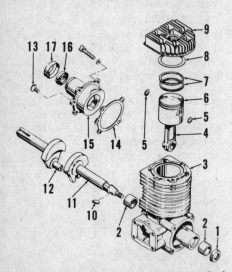

Fig. COX 5—Exploded view of the standard power head assembly. Parts (13, 14, 15 & 16) are different for unit used to drive bicycles. Refer to Fig. COX 6.

1. Seal
2. Bushings
3. Crankcase and cylinder
4. Connecting rod
5. Snap rings
6. Piston
7. Rings
8. Cylinder head gasket
9. Cylinder head
10. Flywheel drive key
11. Crankshaft (flywheel end)
12. Crankshaft (PTO end)
13. Screw
14. Gasket
15. End cover and two main bearings
16. Seal
17. Seal retainer

drawn after removing the cylinder head and the end cover (15—Fig. COX 5) or drive carrier (15—Fig. COX 6).

Connecting rod sintered bronze bushings are integral with connecting rod. Renew connecting rod and/or PTO end of crankshaft if wear is excessive.

When assembling, coat gasket (14—Fig. COX 5 or COX 6) and connecting rod lower bearing bore with SAE 30 oil. Make certain that projection on end of crankshaft (12—Fig. COX 5 or COX 6) enters slot in crankshaft end (11—Fig. COX 5). Gasket (8) should be renewed whenever cylinder head is removed.

PISTON, PIN AND RINGS. Refer to CONNECTING ROD paragraphs for removal procedure. Piston and rings are available in standard size only. When assembling, end gaps in the two rings should be 180 degrees apart. Cylinder head gasket (8—Fig. COX 5)

should be renewed whenever cylinder head is removed.

CRANKSHAFT, BEARINGS AND SEALS. A two-piece crankshaft is used as shown in Fig. COX 5. The flywheel end crankshaft rides in two renewable sintered bronze bushings (2). The PTO end of crankshaft includes the crankpin on all models. On standard engines (Fig. COX 5), the sintered bronze bushings are located in the end cover (15). On bicycle drive units, the PTO end bearings (18 & 22—Fig. COX 6) are of the needle bearing type. Bearing (22) should be lubricated with Lubriplate #630AA or equivalent. On all models, use caution when sliding crankshaft through seals.

The flywheel end of the crankshaft can be removed after removing the flywheel, connecting rod and piston. Hold breaker points open and withdraw crankshaft (11—Fig. COX 5). Bearings (2) and seal (1) can be renewed at this time. When assembling, use caution to prevent damage to seal (1) and breaker points. Gaskets (8 & 14) should be renewed.

INTAKE VALVING. The reed valve assembly (5 & 7—Fig. COX 1) can be removed after removing the carburetor. Check reeds (5) carefully and renew if cracked, distorted or in any other way questionable. Make certain that gasket (6) with cut-outs is installed between reed block (7) and crankcase. Gasket (8) with two small holes should be between carburetor and reed block.

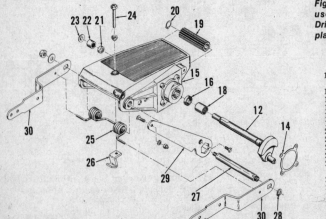

Fig. COX 6—View of parts used with bicycle drive. Drive carrier (15) is used in place of end cover (15—Fig. COX 5).

12. Crankshaft (PTO end)
14. Gasket
15. Drive carrier
16. Seal
18. Needle bearing
19. Drive-roller
20. Snap ring
21. Seal
22. Needle bearing
23. Expansion plug
24. Tension adjusting screw
25. Tension spring
26. Spring hook
27. Pivot shaft
28. Snap ring
29. Lift lever
30. Support straps

SERVICING COX ACCESSORIES

RECOIL STARTER

R&R AND OVERHAUL. The complete recoil starter can be removed after removing the two retaining screws. On early models, a hooked wire should be used to hold the starter assembly (2 thru 7—Fig. COX 7) in housing (1) while removing. Later models are equipped with retainers (8).

To disassemble the removed starter, apply thumb pressure to pulley to prevent pulley from turning. Pull rope free from slot in housing, release thumb pressure slightly and allow spring to slowly unwind. Carefully remove starter assembly from cover. Spring (2) should remain in the housing (1). If spring is to be renewed, remove old spring, hook outer end of spring in housing and wind spring counter-clockwise to the inside. If necessary to disassemble pulley halves (4) from clutch (6), remove snap ring (3) and separate parts.

When reassembling, install new rope (5) through pulley half (engine side) and wind rope around pulley in a counter-clockwise direction. See Fig. COX 7. Carefully install assembled starter in housing, making certain that slot in clutch drive engages inner hook on recoil spring. Pre-load spring by rotating pulley and rope 1 to 1½ turns counter-clockwise and place handle end of rope in slot in housing. Reinstall starter assembly on engine.

CRAFTSMAN

SEARS ROEBUCK & CO.
Chicago, Ill. 60607

The following Craftsman engines were manufactured by the Tecumseh Products Company. The accompanying cross reference chart will assist in identifying an engine for service requirements. Much of the service will be identical to service on similar Tecumseh engines. The Craftsman Service section which follows the cross reference chart includes service which is different than repairing Tecumseh engines.

TWO-STROKE CYCLE MODELS

Craftsman Model Number	Tecumseh Engine Type Number
143.17112	638-07
143.171112	638-07
143.171122	638-01A
143.171272	638-51
200.183112	638-07A
200.183122	638-17A
200.193132	638-07B
200.193142	638-17B
200.193152	650-44
200.193162	650-29A
200.203172	670-39
200.203182	670-32
200.203192	670-18
200.213112	670-39A
200.213122	670-32A
200.503111	1525A
200.583111	1499
200.593121	1525
200.613111	1553

FOUR STROKE CYCLE ENGINES
Vertical Crankshaft

Craftsman Model Number	Service Reference Code	Basic Tecumseh Model Number
143.V20A-1-1-1WA	A	V 20 D

Craftsman Model Number	Service Reference Code	Basic Tecumseh Model Number
143.V25A-5-1-1WA	B	V 25 D
143.V27A-3-1-1WA	B	V 27 D
143.09300	B	LAV 25 B
143.09301	B	LAV 25 B
143.09302	B	LAV 25 B
143.10250	B	LAV 22 B
143.10251	B	LAV 22 B
143.10300	B	LAV 25 B
143.10301	B	LAV 25 B
143.11300	B	LAV 25 B
143.11301	B	LAV 25 B
143.11302	B	LAV 25 B
143.11350	B	LAV 30 B
143.11351	B	LAV 30 B
143.11352	B	LAV 30 B
143.12300	B	LAV 25 B
143.12301	B	LAV 25 B
143.12302	B	LAV 25 B
143.12303	B	LAV 25 B
143.12304	B	LAV 25 B
143.12350	B	LAV 30 B
143.12351	B	LAV 30 B
143.13250	B	LAV 22 B
143.13251	B	LAV 22 B
143.13300	B	LAV 25 B
143.13301	B	LAV 25 B
143.14350	C	LAV 30 B
143.14351	C	LAV 30 B
143.15300	B	LAV 25 B
143.15301	B	LAV 25 B
143.16350	C	LAV 30 B
143.16351	C	LAV 30 B
143.17350	C	LAV 30 B
143.17351	C	LAV 30 B
143.18350	C	LAV 30 B
143.18351	C	LAV 30 B
143.19400	E	LAV 35 B
143.19401	E	LAV 35 B
143.20100	A	V 20 D
143.20400	E	V 35 D

Craftsman Model Number	Service Reference Code	Basic Tecumseh Model Number
143.20401	E	V 35 D
143.20500	K	V 45 B
143.20501	K	V 45 B
143.20502	K	V 45 C
143.20503	K	V 45 C
143.23250	A	HA 22 C
143.23251	A	HA 22 C
143.24250	B	HA 22 C
143.24251	B	HA 22 C
143.25100	B	V 25 D
143.25250	B	HA 22 C
143.25251	B	HA 22 C
143.27100	B	V 27 D
143.27200	A	V 20 D
143.30250	B	LAV 22 B
143.30251	B	LAV 22 B
143.30350	C	LAV 30 B
143.30351	C	LAV 30 B
143.31600	M	V 55 B
143.31601	M	V 55 C
143.36250	A	HA 22 C
143.36251	A	HA 22 C
143.36252	B	H 22 D
143.36253	B	H 22 D
143.36254	B	H 22 H
143.36255	B	H 22 H
143.39250	B	LAV 22 B
143.39251	B	LAV 22 B
143.40250	B	H 22 D
143.40251	B	H 22 D
143.40300	B	LAV 25 B
143.40301	B	LAV 25 B
143.40350	C	LAV 30 B
143.40351	C	LAV 30 B
143.40500	K	V 45 B
143.40501	K	V 45 B
143.40502	K	V 45 C
143.40503	K	V 45 C
143.40600	M	V 55 B
143.41300	B	LAV 25 B
143.41301	B	LAV 25 B
143.41302	B	LAV 25 B

Craftsman Model Number	Service Reference Code	Basic Tecumseh Model Number	Craftsman Model Number	Service Reference Code	Basic Tecumseh Model Number	Craftsman Model Number	Service Reference Code	Basic Tecumseh Model Number
143.41350	C	LAV 30 B	143.56253	A	HA 22 A	143.83251	B	LAV 22 B
143.41351	C	LAV 30 B	143.58250	A	HA 22 C	143.83252	B	LAV 22 B
143.41352	C	LAV 30 B	143.58251	A	HA 22 C	143.84300	B	LAV 25 B
143.42200	B	V 22 H-8	143.59250	B	H 22 D	143.84301	B	LAV 25 B
143.42201	B	V 22 H-8P	143.59251	B	H 22 D	143.84302	B	LAV 25 B
143.42202	B	V 22 H-37	143.60020	A	V 20 G-8	143.86400	E	LAV 35 B
143.42203	B	V 22 H-37P	143.60021	A	V 20 G-8P	143.86401	E	LAV 35 B
143.42204	B	V 22 H-8	143.60025	B	V 25 G-14	143.86402	E	LAV 35 B
143.42205	B	V 22 H-8B	143.60026	B	V 25 G-14P	143.90020	A	H 20 A-15
143.42500	B	V 22 H-8	143.60030	C	V 30 G-8	143.90021	A	H 20 A-15P
143.42501	B	V 25 H-8P	143.60031	C	V 30 G-8P	143.91250	B	H 22 H
143.42700	B	V 25 H-8	143.60040	K	VX 40 A-19	143.91251	B	H 22 H
143.42701	B	V 25 H-8P	143.60125	B	V 25 G-8	143.93000	C	H 30 B-15P
143.43004	C	V 30 H-3P	143.60126	B	V 25 G-8P	143.97250	B	H 22 H
143.43200	C	V 30 H-8	143.60130	C	V 30 G-8	143.97251	B	H 22 H
143.43201	C	V 30 H-29	143.60131	C	V 30 G-8P	143.101010	C	LAV 30 E
143.43202	C	V 30 H-40	143.60140	K	VX 40 A-24	143.101011	C	LAV 30 E
143.43203	C	V 30 H-8P	143.60225	B	V 25 G-8	143.101012	C	LAV 30 E
143.43204	C	V 30 H-29P	143.60226	B	V 25 G-8P	143.101020	C	LAV 30 E
143.43205	C	V 30 H-40P	143.60231	C	V 30 G-4P	143.101021	C	LAV 30 E
143.43250	B	H 22 H	143.60240	K	VX 40 A-19	143.101022	C	LAV 30 E
143.43251	B	H 22 H	143.60325	B	V 25 G-14	143.101030	C	LAV 30 E
143.43300	C	V 30 H-8	143.60326	B	V 25 G-14F	143.101031	C	LAV 30 E
143.43301	C	V 30 H-8P	143.60327	B	V 27 G-16	143.101032	C	LAV 30 E
143.43500	K	V 45 B	143.60328	B	V 27 G-16P	143.102010	C	LAV 30 E
143.43501	K	V 45 B	143.60330	B	V 27 G-2	143.102011	C	LAV 30 E
143.43700	E	V 32 A-28	143.60331	B	V 27 G-2P	143.102012	C	LAV 30 E
143.43701	E	V 32 A-28P	143.60340	K	VX 40 A-19	143.102020	C	LAV 30 E
143.44000	K	V 35 B-28	143.60351	C	LV 30 B	143.102021	C	LAV 30 E
143.44400	E	H 35 D	143.60401	E	LV 35 B	143.102022	C	LAV 30 E
143.44401	E	H 35 D	143.62200	B	V 22 H-8	143.102030	C	LAV 30 E
143.50020	A	V 20 G-8	143.62201	B	V 22 H-8P	143.102031	C	LAV 30 E
143.50021	A	V 20 G-8P	143.62700	B	V 25 H-8	143.102040	C	LAV 30 E
143.50025	B	V 25 G-8	143.62701	B	V 25 H-14	143.102041	C	LAV 30 E
143.50026	B	V 25 G-8P	143.62702	B	V 25 H-3	143.102042	C	LAV 30 E
143.50030	C	V 30 G-14	143.62703	B	V 25 H-8P	143.102050	C	LAV 30 E
143.50031	C	V 30 G-14P	143.62704	B	V 25 H-14P	143.102051	C	LAV 30 E
143.50040	K	V 40 A-4	143.62705	B	V 25 H-3P	143.102060	C	LAV 30 E
143.50045	K	V 40 B-4	143.63200	C	V 30 H-8	143.102061	C	LAV 30 E
143.50125	B	V 25 G-3	143.63201	C	V 30 H-14	143.102062	C	LAV 30 E
143.50126	B	V 25 G-3P	143.63202	C	V 30 H-3	143.102070	C	LV 30 E
143.50130	C	V 30 G-8	143.63203	C	V 30 H-8P	143.102071	C	LV 30 E
143.50131	C	V 30 G-8P	143.63204	C	V 30 H-14P	143.102072	C	LV 30 E
143.50230	C	V 30 G-3	143.63205	C	V 30 H-3P	143.102100	C	LAV 30 E
143.50231	C	V 30 G-3P	143.64000	K	V 40 B-4	143.102101	C	LAV 30 E
143.50250	B	HA 22 A	143.64500	K	V 45 A-4	143.102102	C	LAV 30 E
143.50251	B	HA 22 A	143.65250	B	H 22 H	143.102110	C	LAV 30 E
143.50300	C	H 30 D	143.65251	B	H 22 H	143.102111	C	LAV 30 E
143.50301	C	H 30 D	143.66250	B	H 22 H	143.102112	C	LAV 30 E
143.50400	E	H 35 D	143.66251	B	H 22 H	143.102120	C	LAV 30 E
143.50401	E	H 35 D	143.66500	K	V 45 B	143.102121	C	LAV 30 E
143.50402	E	H 35 H	143.66501	K	V 45 B	143.102130	C	LAV 30 E
143.50403	E	H 35 H	143.67250	B	H 22 H	143.102131	C	LAV 30 E
143.50700	B	V 25 H-8	143.67251	B	H 22 H	143.102132	C	LAV 30 E
143.52200	B	V 22 H-8	143.71250	B	LAV 22 B	143.102140	C	LAV 30 E
143.52201	B	V 22 H-8P	143.71251	B	LAV 22 B	143.102141	C	LAV 30 E
143.52701	B	V 25 H-8P	143.75250	B	LAV 22 B	143.102150	C	LAV 30 E
143.52702	B	V 25 H-8	143.75251	B	LAV 22 B	143.102151	C	LAV 30 E
143.52703	B	V 25 H-8P	143.76250	B	LAV 22 B	143.102152	C	LAV 30 E
143.53001	C	V 30 H-4P	143.76251	B	LAV 22 B	143.102160	B	LAV 25 E
143.53200	C	V 30 H-8	143.76252	B	LAV 22 B	143.102161	B	LAV 25 E
143.53201	C	V 30 H-8P	143.82000	A	H 20 B-15	143.102162	B	LAV 25 E
143.53300	C	V 30 H-8	143.82001	A	H 20 B-15P	143.102170	C	LAV 30 E
143.53301	C	V 30 H-8P	143.82002	A	H 20 B-15	143.102171	C	LAV 30 E
143.54500	K	VX-45 A-24	143.82003	A	H 20 B-15P	143.102172	C	LAV 30 E
143.54502	K	V 45 A-4	143.82004	A	H 20 B-15	143.102190	C	LAV 30 E
143.55250	A	HA 22 A	143.82005	A	H 20 B-15P	143.102191	C	LAV 30 E
143.55251	A	HA 22 A	143.82006	A	H 20 B-15	143.102200	C	LAV 30 E
143.55300	C	H 30 D	143.82007	A	H 20 B-15P	143.102201	C	LAV 30 E
143.56250	A	HA 22 A	143.83000	C	H 30 B-15	143.102202	C	LAV 30 E
143.56251	A	HA 22 A	143.83001	C	H 30 B-15P	143.102210	C	LV 30 E
143.56252	A	HA 22 A	143.83250	B	LAV 22 B	143.102211	C	LV 30 E

Craftsman Model Number	Service Reference Code	Basic Tecumseh Model Number	Craftsman Model Number	Service Reference Code	Basic Tecumseh Model Number	Craftsman Model Number	Service Reference Code	Basic Tecumseh Model Number
143.102212	C	LV 30 E	143.122061	C	LAV 30 L	143.131172	D	LAV 30
143.102220	C	LAV 30 E	143.122071	C	LAV 30 L	143.131182	D	LAV 30
143.102221	C	LAV 30 E	143.122081	C	LAV 30 L	143.133012	D	LAV 30
143.102222	C	LAV 30 E	143.122082	C	LAV 30 L	143.133022	D	LAV 30
143.103010	C	LAV 30 E	143.122091	C	LAV 30 L	143.133032	D	LAV 30
143.103011	C	LAV 30 E	143.122092	C	LAV 30 L	143.133042	D	LV 35
143.103012	C	LAV 30 E	143.122101	B	LAV 25 L	143.133052	D	LAV 30
143.103020	C	LAV 30 E	143.122102	B	LAV 25 L	143.134012	F	LV 35
143.103021	C	LAV 30 E	143.122201	C	LAV 30 L	143.134022	F	LV 35
143.103050	C	LAV 30 E	143.122202	C	LAV 30 L	143.134032	F	LAV 35
143.103051	C	LAV 30 E	143.122211	C	LAV 30 M	143.134042	F	LV 35
143.103052	C	LAV 30 E	143.122212	C	LAV 30 M	143.134052	F	LV 35
143.103060	C	LAV 30 E	143.122221	C	LAV 30 M	143.135012	L	V 50
143.103061	C	LAV 30 E	143.122222	C	LAV 30 M	143.135022	L	V 50
143.104010	E	LAV 35 E	143.122231	C	LAV 30 M	143.135042	L	V 50
143.104011	E	LAV 35 E	143.122232	C	LAV 30 M	143.135052	L	V 50
143.104020	E	LAV 35 E	143.122242	C	LAV 35 M	143.135062	L	V 50
143.104021	E	LAV 35 E	143.122251	C	LV 30 M	143.135072	L	V 50
143.104030	E	LV 35 E	143.122252	C	LV 30 M	143.135082	L	V 50
143.104031	E	LV 35 E	143.122261	C	LAV 30 M	143.135092	L	V 50
143.104040	E	LV 35 E	143.122262	C	LAV 30 M	143.135102	L	V 50
143.104041	E	LV 35 E	143.122271	C	LAV 30 M	143.135112	L	V 50
143.104050	E	LV 35 E	143.122272	C	LAV 30 M	143.136012	M	V 60
143.104051	E	LV 35 E	143.122281	C	LAV 30 M	143.136032	M	V 60
143.104080	E	LAV 35 E	143.122282	C	LAV 30 M	143.136042	M	V 60
143.104081	E	LAV 35 E	143.122291	C	LAVT 30 C	143.136052	M	V 60
143.104090	E	LAV 35 E	143.122311	C	LV 30 N	143.137012	K	V 40
143.104091	E	LAV 35 E	143.122321	C	LAV 30 L	143.137032	K	V 40
143.104100	E	LV 35 E	143.122322	C	LAV 30 L	143.141012	D	LAV 30
143.104101	E	LV 35 E	143.123021	C	LAVR 30 L	143.141022	D	LAV 30
143.104110	E	LV 35 E	143.123022	C	LAVR 30 L	143.141032	D	LAV 30
143.104111	E	LV 35 E	143.123031	C	LAVR 30 L	143.141042	D	LAV 30
143.104120	E	LV 35 E	143.123041	C	LAVR 30 L	143.141052	D	LAV 30
143.104121	E	LV 35 E	143.123051	C	LAVR 30 L	143.141062	D	LAV 30
143.105010	M	V 45 D	143.123052	C	LAVR 30 L	143.141072	D	LAV 30
143.105011	M	V 45 D	143.123071	C	LAVR 30 L	143.141082	D	LAV 30
143.105020	M	V 45 D	143.123091	C	LAVR 30 L	143.141092	D	LAV 25
143.105021	M	V 45 D	143.123092	C	LAVR 30 L	143.141102	D	LAV 30
143.105030	M	V 45 D	143.124011	E	LV 35 L	143.141112	D	LAV 30
143.105031	M	V 45 D	143.124021	E	LAV 35 L	143.141122	D	LAV 30
143.105040	M	V 55 D	143.124031	E	LAV 35 L	143.141132	D	LAV 25
143.105041	M	V 55 D	143.124041	E	LV 35 M	143.141142	D	LAV 30
143.105050	M	V 45 D	143.124051	E	LV 35 N	143.141152	D	LAV 30
143.105051	M	V 45 D	143.124061	E	LAVT 35 C	143.141162	D	LAV 30
143.105060	M	V 45 D	143.124071	E	LV 35 N	143.141172	D	LAV 30
143.105061	M	V 45 D	143.125011	L	VT 45 A	143.141182	D	LAV 30
143.105070	M	V 45 D	143.125021	L	VT 45 C	143.141192	D	LAV 30
143.105071	M	LV 45 D	143.125031	L	VT 45 A	143.141202	D	LAV 30
143.105090	M	V 45 D	143.125041	L	VT 45 C	143.141212	D	LAV 30
143.105091	M	V 45 D	143.125051	L	VT 45 C	143.141222	D	LAV 30
143.105100	M	V 45 D	143.125061	L	VT 45 C	143.141232	D	LAV 30
143.105101	M	V 45 D	143.126011	M	VT 55 A	143.141242	D	LAV 30
143.105110	M	V 55 D	143.126021	M	VT 55 B	143.141252	D	LAV 30
143.105120	M	V 45 D	143.126031	M	VT 55 B	143.141262	D	LAV 30
143.105121	M	V 45 D	143.126041	M	VT 55 C	143.141272	D	LAV 30
143.106010	C	LAV 30 E	143.126051	M	VT 55 C	143.141282	D	LAV 30
143.106011	C	LAV 30 E	143.126061	M	VT 55 C	143.141292	D	LAV 30
143.106012	C	LAV 30 E	143.131022	D	LAV 30	143.141302	D	LAV 30
143.106020	C	LAV 30 E	143.131032	D	LAV 30	143.143012	D	LAV 30
143.106021	C	LAV 30 E	143.131042	D	LAV 30	143.143022	D	LAV 30
143.106030	C	LAV 30 E	143.131052	D	LAV 30	143.143032	D	LAV 30
143.106031	C	LAV 30 E	143.131062	D	LAV 30	143.144012	F	LV 35
143.122011	C	LV 30 L	143.131072	D	LAV 30	143.144022	F	LV 35
143.122012	C	LV 30 L	143.131082	D	LAV 30	143.144032	F	LV 35
143.122021	C	LAV 30 L	143.131092	D	LAV 30	143.144042	F	LV 35
143.122022	C	LAV 30 L	143.131102	D	LAV 30	143.144052	F	LV 35
143.122031	C	LAV 30 L	143.131112	B	LAV 22	143.144062	F	LV 35
143.122032	C	LAV 30 L	143.131122	D	LAV 30	143.144072	F	LV 35
143.122041	C	LAV 30 L	143.131132	D	LAV 30	143.144082	F	LV 35
143.122042	C	LAV 30 L	143.131142	D	LAV 30	143.144092	F	LV 35
143.122051	C	LAV 30 L	143.131152	D	LAV 30	143.144102	F	LV 35
143.122052	C	LAV 30 L	143.131162	D	LAV 30	143.144112	F	LV 35

Craftsman Model Number	Service Reference Code	Basic Tecumseh Model Number	Craftsman Model Number	Service Reference Code	Basic Tecumseh Model Number	Craftsman Model Number	Service Reference Code	Basic Tecumseh Model Number
143.144122	F	LV 35	143.161172	D	LAV 30	143.171312	D	LAV 30
143.144132	F	LV 35	143.161182	D	LAV 30	143.171322	D	LAV 30
143.145012	L	V 50	143.161192	D	LAV 30	143.171332	D	LAV 30
143.145022	L	V 50	143.161202	D	LAV 30	143.173012	D	LAV 30
143.145032	L	V 50	143.161212	D	LAV 30	143.173042	D	LAV 30
143.145042	L	V 50	143.161222	D	LAV 30	143.174012	E	LAV 35
143.145052	L	V 50	143.161232	D	LAV 30	143.174022	E	LAV 35
143.145062	L	V 50	143.161242	D	LAV 30	143.174032	E	LAV 35
143.145072	L	V 50	143.161262	D	LAV 30	143.174042	E	LAV 35
143.146012	M	V 60	143.162022	D	LAV 35	143.174052	E	LAV 35
143.146022	M	V 60	143.162032	D	LAV 35	143.174062	E	LAV 35
143.147012	K	V 40	143.162092	D	LAV 35	143.174072	E	LAV 35
143.147022	K	V 40	142.163012	D	LAV 30	143.174082	E	LAV 35
143.147032	K	V 40	143.163022	D	LAV 30	143.174092	E	LAV 35
143.151012	D	LAV 30	143.163032	D	LAV 30	143.174102	E	LAV 35
143.151022	D	LAV 30	143.163042	D	LAV 30	143.174132	E	LAV 35
143.151032	D	LAV 30	143.163052	D	LAV 30	143.174142	E	LAV 35
143.151042	D	LAV 30	143.163062	D	LAV 30	143.174152	E	LAV 35
143.151052	D	LAV 30	143.164012	E	LAV 35	143.174162	E	LAV 35
143.151072	D	LAV 30	143.164022	E	LAV 35	143.174172	E	LAV 35
143.151082	D	LAV 30	143.164032	E	LAV 35	143.174182	E	LAV 35
143.151092	D	LAV 30	143.164042	E	LAV 35	143.174192	E	LAV 35
143.151102	D	LAV 30	143.164052	E	LAV 35	143.174232	E	LAV 35
143.151103	D	LAV 30	143.164062	E	LAV 35	143.174242	E	LAV 35
143.151104	D	LAV 30	143.164072	E	LAV 35	143.174252	E	LAV 35
143.151105	D	LAV 30	143.174082	E	LAV 35	143.174272	E	LAV 35
143.151142	D	LAV 30	143.164102	E	LAV 35	143.174292	E	LAV 35
143.151152	D	LAV 30	143.164112	E	LAV 35	143.175012	L	V 50
143.151162	D	LAV 30	143.164122	E	LAV 35	143.175022	L	V 50
143.153012	D	LAV 30	143.164132	E	LAV 35	143.175032	L	V 50
143.153022	D	LAV 30	143.164142	E	LAV 35	143.175042	L	V 50
443.153032	D	LAV 30	143.164152	E	LAV 35	143.175052	L	V 50
143.154012	E	LAV 35	143.164162	E	LAV 35	143.175062	L	V 50
143.154022	E	LAV 35	143.164172	E	LAV 35	143.175072	L	V 50
143.154032	E	LAV 35	143.164182	E	LAV 35	143.176012	M	V 60
143.154042	E	LAV 35	143.164202	E	LAV 35	143.176022	M	V 60
143.154052	E	LAV 35	143.165012	L	V 50	143.176032	M	V 60
143.154062	E	LAV 35	143.165022	L	V 50	143.176042	M	V 60
143.154072	E	LAV 35	143.165032	L	V 50	143.176052	M	V 60
143.154082	E	LAV 35	143.165042	L	V 50	143.176062	M	V 60
143.154092	E	LAV 35	143.165052	L	V 50	143.176072	M	V 60
143.154102	E	LAV 35	143.166012	M	V 60	143.176082	M	V 60
143.154112	E	LAV 35	143.166022	M	V 60	143.176092	M	V 60
143.154132	E	LAV 35	143.166032	M	V 60	143.176102	M	V 60
143.154142	E	LAV 35	143.166042	M	V 60	143.177012	K	V 40
143.155012	L	V 50	143.166052	M	V 60	143.177022	K	V 40
143.155022	L	V 50	143.167012	K	V 40	143.177032	K	V 40
143.155032	L	V 50	143.167022	K	V 40	143.177042	K	V 40
143.155042	L	V 50	143.167032	K	V 40	143.177062	K	V 40
143.155052	L	V 50	143.167042	K	V 40	143.177072	K	V 40
143.155062	L	V 50	143.171012	D	LAV 30	143.181042	D	LAV 30
143.156012	M	V 60	143.171022	D	LAV 30	143.181052	D	LAV 30
143.156022	M	V 60	143.171032	D	LAV 30	143.181062	D	LAV 30
143.156032	M	V 60	143.171042	D	LAV 30	143.181082	D	LAV 30
143.157012	K	V 40	143.171052	D	LAV 30	143.181092	D	LAV 30
143.157022	K	V 40	143.171062	D	LAV 30	143.181102	D	LAV 30
143.157032	K	V 40	143.171072	D	LAV 30	143.181112	D	LAV 30
143.161012	D	LAV 30	143.171082	D	LAV 30	143.181122	D	LAV 30
143.161022	D	LAV 30	143.171092	D	LAV 30	143.181132	D	LAV 30
143.161032	D	LAV 30	143.171102	D	LAV 30	143.183042	D	LAV 30
143.161042	D	LAV 30	143.171132	D	LAV 30	143.184012	E	LAV 35
143.161052	D	LAV 30	143.171142	D	LAV 30	143.184052	E	LAV 35
143.161062	D	LAV 30	143.171152	D	LAV 30	143.184082	E	LAV 35
143.161072	D	LAV 30	143.171162	D	LAV 30	143.184092	E	LAV 35
143.161082	D	LAV 30	143.171172	D	LAV 30	143.184102	E	LAV 35
143.161092	D	LAV 30	143.171202	E	LAV 35	143.184112	E	LAV 35
143.161102	D	LAV 30	143.171212	D	LAV 30	143.184122	E	LAV 35
143.161112	D	LAV 30	143.171232	D	LAV 30	143.184132	E	LAV 35
143.161132	D	LAV 30	143.171242	D	LAV 30	143.184142	E	LAV 35
143.161142	D	LAV 30	143.171252	D	LAV 30	143.184152	E	LAV 35
143.161152	D	LAV 30	143.171262	D	LAV 30	143.184162	E	LAV 35
143.161162	D	LAV 30	143.171302	D	LAV 30	143.184172	E	LAV 35

Craftsman Model Number	Service Reference Code	Basic Tecumseh Model Number	Craftsman Model Number	Service Reference Code	Basic Tecumseh Model Number	Craftsman Model Number	Service Reference Code	Basic Tecumseh Model Number
143.184182	E	LAV 35	143.204042	E	LAV 35	143.223012	D	LAV 30
143.184192	E	LAV 35	143.204052	E	LAV 35	143.223022	D	LAV 30
143.184202	E	LAV 35	143.204062	G	ECV 100	143.223032	D	LAV 30
143.184212	E	LAV 35	143.204072	E	LAV 35	143.223042	D	LAV 30
143.184232	G	ECV 100	143.204082	E	LAV 35	143.223052	D	LAV 30
143.184242	G	ECV 100	143.204092	E	LAV 35	143.224012	E	LAV 35
143.184252	G	ECV 100	143.204102	G	ECV 100	143.224022	E	LAV 35
143.184262	E	LAV 35	143.204132	G	ECV 100	143.224032	G	ECV 100
143.184272	E	LAV 35	143.204142	E	LAV 35	143.224062	E	LAV 35
143.184282	E	LAV 35	143.204162	E	LAV 35	143.224092	E	LAV 35
143.184292	E	LAV 35	143.204172	E	LAV 35	143.224102	E	LAV 35
143.184302	E	LAV 35	143.204182	E	LAV 35	143.224112	E	LAV 35
143.184402	E	LAV 35	143.204192	E	LAV 35	143.224122	E	LAV 35
143.185012	L	V 50	143.204202	G	ECV 100	143.224132	E	LAV 35
143.185022	L	V 50	143.205022	L	V 50	143.224142	D	LAV 30
143.185032	L	V 50	143.206012	M	V 60	143.224162	E	LAV 35
143.185042	L	V 50	143.206032	M	V 60	143.224172	E	LAV 35
143.185052	L	V 50	143.207012	H	LAV 40	143.224182	E	LAV 35
143.186012	L	V 60	143.207022	H	LAV 40	143.224192	E	LAV 35
143.186052	M	V 60	143.207032	H	LAV 40	143.224202	E	LAV 35
143.186062	M	V 60	143.207052	H	LAV 40	143.224212	E	LAV 35
143.186082	M	V 60	143.207062	H	ECV 105	143.224222	E	LAV 35
143.186092	M	V 60	143.207072	H	LAV 40	143.224232	G	ECV 100
143.186102	M	V 60	143.207082	H	ECV 105	143.224242	G	ECV 100
143.186112	M	V 60	143.213012	D	LAV 30	143.224252	E	LAV 35
143.186122	M	V 60	143.213022	D	LAV 30	143.224262	E	LAV 35
143.187022	H	LAV 40	143.213042	D	LAV 30	143.224272	E	LAV 35
143.187042	H	LAV 40	143.214012	E	LAV 35	143.224282	E	LAV 35
143.187052	H	LAV 40	143.214022	E	LAV 35	143.224292	G	ECV 100
143.187062	H	LAV 40	143.214032	E	LAV 35	143.224302	G	ECV 100
143.187072	H	LAV 40	143.214042	G	ECV 100	143.224312	E	LAV 35
143.187082	H	LAV 40	143.214052	G	ECV 100	143.224322	E	LAV 35
143.187094	H	LAV 40	143.214062	G	ECV 100	143.224332	E	LAV 35
143.187102	H	ECV 105	143.214072	G	ECV 100	143.224342	E	LAV 35
143.191012	D	LAV 30	143.214082	E	LAV 35	143.224352	G	ECV 100
143.191022	D	LAV 30	143.214092	E	LAV 35	143.224362	G	ECV 100
143.191032	D	LAV 30	143.214102	E	LAV 35	143.224372	E	LAV 35
143.191042	D	LAV 30	143.214112	E	LAV 35	143.224382	E	LAV 35
143.191052	D	LAV 30	143.214122	E	LAV 35	143.224392	E	LAV 35
143.194012	E	LAV 35	143.214132	E	LAV 35	143.224402	E	LAV 35
143.194022	E	LAV 35	143.214192	E	LAV 35	143.224412	E	LAV 35
143.194032	E	LAV 35	143.214202	E	LAV 35	143.224422	E	LAV 35
143.194042	E	LAV 35	143.214212	E	LAV 35	143.225012	J	ECV 120
143.194052	E	LAV 35	143.214222	E	LAV 35	143.225022	J	ECV 120
143.194062	G	ECV 100	143.214232	E	LAV 35	143.225032	L	V 50
143.194072	E	LAV 35	143.214242	E	LAV 35	143.225042	L	V 50
143.194082	E	LAV 35	143.214252	E	LAV 35	143.225052	L	V 50
143.194092	E	LAV 35	143.214262	G	ECV 100	143.225062	J	ECV 120
143.194102	G	ECV 100	143.214272	G	ECV 100	143.225072	J	ECV 120
143.194112	E	LAV 35	143.214282	G	ECV 100	143.225082	L	V 50
143.194122	E	LAV 35	143.214292	E	LAV 35	143.225092	L	V 50
143.194132	E	LAV 35	143.214302	E	LAV 35	143.225102	L	V 50
143.194142	E	LAV 35	143.214312	G	ECV 100	143.226012	M	V 60
143.195012	L	V 50	143.214322	G	ECV 100	143.226032	M	V 60
143.195022	L	V 50	143.214332	E	LAV 35	143.226132	M	V 60
143.196012	M	V 60	143.214342	E	LAV 35	143.226152	M	V 60
143.196022	M	V 60	143.214352	G	ECV 100	143.226162	M	V 60
143.196032	M	V 60	143.216042	M	V 60	143.226182	M	V 60
143.196082	M	V 60	143.216052	M	V 60	143.226222	M	V 60
143.197012	H	LAV 40	143.216062	M	V 60	143.226232	M	V 60
143.197022	H	ECV 105	143.216122	M	V 60	143.226242	M	V 60
143.197032	H	ECV 105	143.216142	M	V 60	143.226262	M	V 60
143.197042	H	LAV 40	143.216182	M	V 60	143.226322	M	V 60
143.197052	H	LAV 40	143.217012	H	ECV 105	143.226332	M	V 60
143.197062	H	LAV 40	143.217022	H	ECV 105	143.227012	I	ECV 110
143.197072	H	LAV 40	143.217032	H	ECV 105	143.227022	I	ECV 110
143.197082	H	ECV 105	143.217042	H	LAV 40	143.227062	I	ECV 110
143.201032	D	LAV 30	143.217052	H	LAV 40	143.227072	I	ECV 110
143.201042	D	LAV 30	143.217062	H	LAV 40	143.233012	D	LAV 30
143.203012	D	LAV 30	143.217072	H	LAV 40	143.233032	D	LAV 30
143.204022	G	ECV 100	143.217092	H	ECV 105	143.233042	D	LAV 30
143.204032	E	LAV 35	143.217102	H	LAV 40	143.234022	E	LAV 35

Craftsman Model Number	Service Reference Code	Basic Tecumseh Model Number	Craftsman Model Number	Service Reference Code	Basic Tecumseh Model Number	Craftsman Model Number	Service Reference Code	Basic Tecumseh Model Number
143.234042	E	LAV 35	143.244052	G	ECV 100	143.254052	E	LAV 35
143.234052	E	LAV 35	143.244062	G	ECV 100	143.254062	G	ECV 100
143.234062	G	ECV 100	143.244072	E	LAV 35	143.254072	E	LAV 35
143.234072	G	ECV 100	143.244082	E	LAV 35	143.254082	E	LAV 35
143.234082	G	ECV 100	143.244092	E	LAV 35	143.254092	E	LAV 35
143.234092	G	ECV 100	143.244102	E	LAV 35	143.254102	E	LAV 35
143.234102	E	LAV 35	143.244112	E	LAV 35	143.254112	E	LAV 35
143.234112	E	LAV 35	143.244122	G	ECV 100	143.254122	E	LAV 35
143.234122	E	LAV 35	143.244132	G	ECV 100	143.254142	G	ECV 100
143.234132	E	LAV 35	143.244142	G	ECV 100	143.254152	G	ECV 100
143.234142	E	LAV 35	143.244202	E	LAV 35	143.254162	G	ECV 100
143.234162	E	LAV 35	143.244212	G	ECV 100	143.254172	G	ECV 100
143.234182	G	ECV 100	143.244222	E	LAV 35	143.254182	G	ECV 100
143.234192	E	LAV 35	143.244232	E	LAV 35	143.254192	G	ECV 100
143.234202	E	LAV 35	143.244242	G	ECV 100	143.254212	E	LAV 35
143.234212	G	ECV 100	143.244252	G	ECV 100	143.254222	E	LAV 35
143.234222	G	ECV 100	143.244262	E	LAV 35	143.254232	G	ECV 100
143.234232	G	ECV 100	143.244272	E	LAV 35	143.254242	G	ECV 100
143.234242	E	LAV 35	143.244282	E	LAV 35	143.254252	G	ECV 100
143.234252	E	LAV 35	143.244292	G	ECV 100	143.254262	G	ECV 100
143.234262	E	LAV 35	143.244302	G	ECV 100	143.254272	G	ECV 100
143.235012	J	ECV 120	143.244312	G	ECV 100	143.254282	G	ECV 100
143.235022	J	ECV 120	143.244322	G	ECV 100	143.254292	G	ECV 100
143.235032	J	LAV 50	143.244332	G	ECV 100	143.254302	E	LAV 35
143.235042	J	ECV 120				143.254312	E	LAV 35
143.235052	J	ECV 120	143.245012	J	LAV 50	143.254322	G	ECV 100
143.235062	L	V 50	143.245042	L	V 50	143.254332	E	LAV 35
143.235072	J	LAV 50	143.245052	J	ECV 120	143.254342	G	ECV 100
			143.245062	J	ECV 120	143.254352	G	ECV 100
143.236012	M	V 60	143.245072	J	ECV 120	143.254362	E	LAV 35
143.236052	M	V 60	143.245082	J	ECV 120	143.254372	G	ECV 100
143.236082	M	V 60	143.245092	J	LAV 50	143.254382	G	ECV 100
143.236102	M	V 60	143.245102	J	ECV 120	143.254392	E	LAV 35
143.236132	M	V 60	143.245112	J	ECV 120	143.254402	G	ECV 100
143.236152	M	V 60	143.245122	J	ECV 120	143.254412	G	ECV 100
143.237012	I	ECV 110	143.245132	J	ECV 120	143.254452	E	LAV 35
143.237022	I	ECV 110	143.245142	J	LAV 50	143.254462	G	ECV 100
143.237032	H	ECV 105	143.245152	J	LAV 50	143.254472	E	LAV 35
143.237042	H	LAV 40	143.245162	J	ECV 120	143.255012	J	LAV 50
143.243012	D	LAV 30	143.245172	J	LAV 50	143.255022	J	LAV 50
143.243022	D	LAV 30	143.245182	J	LAV 50	143.255042	J	LAV 50
143.243042	D	LAV 30	143.245192	J	ECV 120	143.256022	M	V 60
143.243052	D	LAV 30				154.256052	M	V 60
143.243062	D	LAV 30	143.246012	M	V 60	143.256082	M	V 60
143.243072	D	LAV 30	143.246042	M	V 60	143.256092	M	V 60
143.243082	D	LAV 30	143.246352	M	V 60	143.256122	M	V 60
143.244012	E	LAV 35	143.246392	M	V 60	143.257012	H	LAV 40
143.244022	E	LAV 35	143.254012	E	LAV 35	143.257022	H	LAV 40
143.244032	E	LAV 35	143.254022	E	LAV 35	143.257032	H	LAV 40
143.244042	G	ECV 100	143.254032	E	LAV 35	143.257042	H	LAV 40
			143.254042	E	LAV 35			

Horizontal Crankshaft

Craftsman Model Number	Service Reference Code	Basic Tecumseh Model Number
143.501011	B	H 22 K
143.501020	B	H 22 K

Craftsman Model Number	Service Reference Code	Basic Tecumseh Model Number	Craftsman Model Number	Service Reference Code	Basic Tecumseh Model Number	Craftsman Model Number	Service Reference Code	Basic Tecumseh Model Number
143.501041	B	H 22 K	143.531162	B	H 22	143.551012	D	H 30
143.501051	B	H 22 K	143.531172	D	H 30	143.551032	D	H 30
143.501061	B	H 22 K	143.531182	D	H 30	143.551042	B	H 22
143.501071	B	H 22 K	143.534012	F	H 35	143.551052	D	H 30
143.501081	B	H 22 K	143.534022	F	H 35	143.551062	D	H 30
143.501090	B	H 22 K	143.534032	F	H 35	143.551072	D	H 30
143.501091	B	H 22 K	143.534042	F	H 35	143.551082	D	H 25
143.501111	B	H 22 K	143.534052	F	H 35	143.551092	D	H 25
143.501121	B	H 22 K	143.534062	F	H 35	143.551102	D	H 30
143.501131	B	H 22 K	143.534072	F	H 35	143.551152	D	H 30
143.501141	B	H 22 K	143.535012	L	H 50	143.551162	D	H 30
143.501151	B	H 22 K	143.535022	L	H 50	143.551172	B	H 22
143.501161	B	H 22 K	143.535062	L	H 50	143.551192	D	H 30
143.501170	B	H 22 K	143.536012	M	H 60	143.554012	F	H 35
143.501171	B	H 22 K	143.536022	M	H 60	143.554022	F	H 35
143.501181	B	H 22 K	143.536032	M	H 60	143.554032	F	H 35
143.501190	B	H 22 K	143.536042	M	H 60	143.554042	F	H 35
143.501191	B	H 22 K	143.536052	M	H 60	143.554052	F	H 35
143.501201	B	H 22 K	143.536062	M	H 60	143.554072	F	H 35
143.501211	B	H 22 K	143.537012	K	H 40	143.554082	F	H 35
143.501221	B	H 22 K	143.541012	D	H 30	143.555012	L	H 50
143.501231	B	H 22 K	143.541022	B	H 22	143.555022	L	H 50
143.501241	B	H 22 K	143.541032	B	H 22	143.555032	L	H 50
143.501251	B	H 22 K	143.541042	D	H 30	143.555042	L	H 50
143.501261	B	H 22 K	143.541052	D	H 30	143.555052	L	H 50
143.501270	B	H 22 K	143.541062	D	H 30	143.556012	M	H 60
143.501271	B	H 22 K	143.541072	B	H 22	143.556022	M	H 60
143.502011	E	H 35 M	143.541082	B	H 22	143.556032	M	H 60
143.502021	E	HB 35 K	143.541102	B	H 22	143.556042	M	H 60
143.502031	E	HB 35 K	143.541112	D	H 30	143.556052	M	H 60
143.502041	E	H 35 P	143.541122	D	H 30	143.556062	M	H 60
143.504011	E	H 35 K	143.541132	D	H 30	143.556072	M	H 60
143.505010	M	H 55 D	143.541142	D	H 25	143.556082	M	H 60
143.505011	M	H 55 D	143.541152	D	H 30	143.556092	M	H 60
143.506011	C	H 30 P	143.541162	D	H 22	143.556102	M	H 60
143.521011	B	H 22 R	143.541172	D	H 25	143.556112	M	H 60
143.521021	B	H 22 R	143.541182	D	H 25	143.556122	M	H 60
143.521031	B	H 22 R	143.541192	D	H 30	143.556132	M	H 60
143.521051	B	H 22 R	143.541202	D	H 30	143.556142	M	H 60
143.521061	B	H 22 R	143.541212	B	H 22	143.556152	M	H 60
143.521071	B	H 22 R	143.541222	D	H 30	143.556162	M	H 60
143.521081	C	HT 30 A	143.541232	B	H 22	143.556172	M	H 60
143.521091	B	H 22 R	143.541252	B	H 22	143.556182	M	H 60
143.521101	B	H 22 R	143.541262	B	H 22	143.556192	M	H 60
143.521111	B	H 22 R	143.541282	D	H 30	143.556202	M	H 60
143.521121	B	H 22 R	143.541292	D	H 25	143.556212	M	H 60
143.521131	D	HT 30 B	143.541302	D	H 30	143.556222	M	H 60
143.524021	E	HT 35 A	143.544012	F	H 35	143.556232	M	H 60
143.524031	E	HT 35 A	143.544022	F	H 35	143.556242	M	H 60
143.524041	E	H 35 P	143.544032	F	H 35	143.556252	M	H 60
143.524051	E	HT 35 A	143.544042	F	H 35	143.556262	M	H 60
143.524061	F	HT 35 B	143.544052	F	H 35	143.556272	M	H 60
143.524071	F	HT 35 B	143.545012	L	H 50	143.556282	M	H 60
143.524081	F	HT 35 B	143.545022	L	H 50	143.557012	K	H 40
143.525021	L	HT 45 C	143.545032	L	H 50	143.557022	K	H 40
143.526011	L	HT 45 A	143.545042	L	H 50	143.557032	K	H 40
143.526021	M	HT 55 B	143.546012	M	H 60	143.557042	K	H 40
143.526031	M	HT 55 C	143.546022	M	H 60	143.557052	K	H 40
143.531011	D	HT 30 B	143.546032	M	H 60	143.557062	K	H 40
143.531022	D	H 25	143.546042	M	H 60	143.557072	K	H 40
143.531032	B	H 22	143.546052	M	H 60	143.557082	K	H 40
143.531042	B	H 22	143.546062	M	H 60	143.561012	D	H 30
143.531052	D	H 30	143.546072	M	H 60	143.561022	D	H 25
143.531062	B	H 22	143.546082	M	H 60	143.561032	D	H 30
143.531072	D	H 30	143.546092	M	H 60	143.561042	D	H 30
143.531082	D	H 30	143.546102	M	H 60	143.561052	D	H 30
143.531092	B	H 22	143.546112	M	H 60	143.561062	D	H 30
143.531112	B	H 22	143.546122	M	H 60	143.561072	D	H 25
143.531122	D	H 30	143.546142	M	H 60	143.561092	D	H 30
143.531132	D	H 30	143.547012	K	H 40	143.561102	D	H 30
143.531142	B	H 22	143.547022	K	H 40	143.561112	D	H 30
143.531152	D	H 30	143.547032	K	H 40			

Craftsman Model Number	Service Reference Code	Basic Tecumseh Model Number	Craftsman Model Number	Service Reference Code	Basic Tecumseh Model Number	Craftsman Model Number	Service Reference Code	Basic Tecumseh Model Number
143.561122	D	H 22	143.574042	F	H 35	143.586042	M	H 60
143.561132	D	H 30	143.574052	F	H 35	143.586072	M	H 60
143.561142	D	H 22	143.574062	F	H 35	143.586082	M	H 60
143.561152	D	H 22	143.574072	F	H 35	143.586152	M	H 60
143.561162	D	H 25	143.574082	F	H 35	143.586172	M	H 60
143.561172	D	H 30	143.574092	F	H 35	143.586182	M	HH 60
143.561182	D	H 30	143.574102	F	H 35	143.586192	M	H 60
143.561202	D	H 30	143.574112	F	H 35	143.586202	M	HH 60
143.561212	D	H 30	143.575012	L	H 50	143.586212	M	HH 60
143.561222	D	H 30	143.575022	L	H 50	143.586222	M	H 60
143.564012	F	H 35	143.575032	L	H 50	143.586232	M	H 60
143.564022	F	H 35	143.575042	L	H 50	143.586242	M	H 60
143.564032	F	H 35	143.576002	M	H 60	143.586262	M	H 60
143.564042	F	H 35	143.576012	M	HH 60	143.586272	M	H 60
143.564052	F	H 35	143.576022	M	H 60	143.586282	M	H 60
143.564072	F	H 35	143.576032	M	H 60	143.587012	H	HS 40
143.564082	F	H 35	143.576042	M	H 60	143.587022	H	HS 40
143.564092	F	H 35	143.576052	M	H 60	143.587032	H	HS 40
143.564102	F	H 35	143.576062	M	H 60	143.587042	H	HS 40
143.564112	F	H 35	143.576072	M	H 60	143.591012	D	H 25
143.565012	L	H 50	143.576082	M	H 60	143.591022	D	H 30
143.565022	L	H 50	143.576102	M	H 60	143.591032	D	H 30
143.566002	M	H 60	143.576112	M	H 60	143.591042	D	H 30
143.566012	M	H 60	143.576122	M	H 60	143.591052	D	H 30
143.566022	M	H 60	143.576132	M	H 60	143.591062	D	H 30
143.566032	M	H 60	143.576142	M	H 60	143.591072	D	H 30
143.566042	M	H 60	143.576172	M	H 60	143.591082	D	H 25
143.566052	M	H 60	143.576182	M	H 60	143.591092	D	H 30
143.566062	M	H 60	143.576192	M	H 60	143.591102	D	H 30
143.566072	M	H 60	143.576202	M	H 60	143.591112	D	H 25
143.566082	M	H 60	143.576212	M	H 60	143.591122	D	H 30
143.566092	M	H 60	143.576222	M	H 60	143.591132	D	H 25
143.566102	M	H 60	143.576232	M	H 60	143.591142	D	H 30
143.566112	M	H 60	143.576282	M	H 60	143.594012	F	H 35
143.566122	M	H 60	143.576292	M	HH 60	143.594022	F	H 35
143.566132	M	H 60	143.576302	M	HH 60	143.594032	F	H 35
143.566142	M	H 60	143.576312	M	H 60	143.594042	F	H 35
143.566152	M	HH 60	143.576322	M	H 60	143.594052	F	H 35
143.566162	M	H 60	143.576332	M	H 60	143.594060	F	H 35
143.566172	M	H 60	143.577012	K	H 40	143.594072	F	H 35
143.566182	M	H 60	143.577022	K	H 40	143.594082	F	H 35
143.566192	M	H 60	143.577032	K	H 40	143.594092	E	ECH 90
143.566202	M	H 60	143.577042	K	H 40	143.594102	F	H 35
143.566212	M	H 50	143.577072	K	H 40	143.595012	L	H 50
143.566222	M	H 60	143.577082	K	H 40	143.595042	L	H 50
143.566232	M	H 60	143.581002	D	H 30	143.596042	M	H 60
143.566242	M	H 60	143.581022	D	H 25	143.596072	M	H 60
143.566252	M	H 60	143.581032	D	H 30	143.596082	M	H 60
143.567012	K	H 40	143.581042	D	H 25	143.596092	M	H 60
143.567022	K	H 40	143.581052	D	H 30	143.596102	M	HH 60
143.567032	K	H 40	143.581062	D	H 30	143.596112	M	HH 60
143.567042	K	H 40	143.581072	D	H 30	143.596122	M	H 60
143.571002	D	H 30	143.581082	D	H 30	143.597012	H	HS 40
143.571012	D	H 30	143.581092	D	H 30	143.597022	H	HS 40
143.571022	D	H 30	143.581102	D	H 25	143.597032	H	HS 40
143.571032	D	H 30	143.584012	F	H 35	143.601022	D	H 30
143.571042	D	H 30	143.584032	F	H 35	143.601032	D	H 30
143.571052	D	H 30	143.584052	F	H 35	143.601062	D	H 30
143.571062	D	H 25	143.584062	F	H 35	143.604012	F	H 35
143.571072	D	H 30	143.584072	F	H 35	143.604022	E	ECH 90
143.571082	D	H 25	143.584082	F	H 35	143.604032	F	H 35
143.571092	D	H 30	143.584102	F	H 35	143.604042	F	H 35
143.571102	D	H 25	143.584112	F	H 35	143.604052	E	ECH 90
143.571112	D	H 25	143.584122	F	H 35	143.604062	F	H 35
143.571122	D	H 30	143.584132	F	H 35	143.604072	F	H 35
143.571152	B	H 22	143.584142	F	H 35	143.605012	L	H 50
143.571162	D	H 30	143.585012	L	H 50	143.605022	L	H 50
143.571172	D	H 25	143.585032	L	H 50	143.605052	L	H 50
143.571182	D	H 30	143.585042	L	H 50	143.607012	H	HS 40
143.571202	D	H 25	143.586012	M	H 60	143.607022	H	HS 40
143.574022	F	H 35	143.586022	M	H 60	143.607032	H	HS 40
143.574032	F	H 35	143.586032	M	H 60	143.607042	H	HS 40

Craftsman Model Number	Service Reference Code	Basic Tecumseh Model Number	Craftsman Model Number	Service Reference Code	Basic Tecumseh Model Number	Craftsman Model Number	Service Reference Code	Basic Tecumseh Model Number
143.607052	H	HS 40	143.621042	D	H 25	143.641022	D	H 25
143.607062	H	HS 40	143.621052	D	H 30	143.641032	D	H 30
143.611012	D	H 30	143.621062	D	H 30	143.641042	D	H 25
143.611022	D	H 30	143.621082	D	H 25	143.641052	D	H 30
143.611032	D	H 25	143.621092	D	H 25	143.641062	D	H 30
143.611042	D	H 30	143.624012	F	H 35	143.641072	F	H 35
143.611052	D	H 30	143.624022	F	H 35	143.644012	F	H 35
143.611062	D	H 25	143.624032	F	H 35	143.644022	F	H 35
143.611072	D	H 30	143.624042	F	H 35	143.644032	F	H 35
143.611082	D	H 30	143.624092	F	H 35	143.644052	F	H 35
143.611092	D	H 30	143.624102	F	H 35	143.644072	F	H 35
143.611102	D	H 25	143.624112	F	H 35	143.645012	J	HS 50
143.611112	D	H 30	143.625012	L	H 50	143.645022	J	HS 50
143.614012	F	ECH 90	143.625022	L	H 50	143.645032	J	HS 50
143.614022	F	ECH 90	143.625032	L	H 50	143.646112	M	HH 60
143.614032	F	ECH 90	143.625042	L	H 50	143.646192	M	H 60
143.614042	F	H 35	143.625052	L	H 50	143.647012	H	HS 40
143.614052	F	ECH 90	143.625072	L	H 50	143.647022	H	HS 40
143.614062	F	H 35	143.625082	L	H 50	143.647032	H	HS 40
143.614072	F	H 35	143.625092	L	H 50	143.647042	H	HS 40
143.614082	F	H 35	143.625102	L	H 50	143.647052	H	HS 40
143.614092	F	H 35	143.625112	L	H 50	143.647062	H	HS 40
143.614102	F	H 35	143.625122	L	H 50	143.651012	D	H 30
143.614112	F	H 35	143.625132	L	H 50	143.651022	D	H 30
143.614122	F	H 35	143.626022	M	H 60	143.651032	D	H 30
143.614132	F	H 35	143.626042	M	H 60	143.651042	D	H 30
143.614142	F	H 35	143.626132	M	H 60	143.651052	D	H 30
143.614152	F	H 35	143.626162	M	H 60	143.651062	D	H 30
143.614162	F	H 35	143.626182	M	H 60	143.651072	D	H 30
143.615012	F	H 50	143.626202	M	H 60	143.654022	F	H 35
143.615022	L	H 50	143.626222	M	H 60	143.654032	F	H 35
143.615052	L	H 50	143.626232	M	H 60	143.654042	F	H 35
143.615062	L	H 50	143.626242	M	HH 60	143.654052	F	H 35
143.615072	L	H 50	143.626252	M	H 60	143.654062	F	H 35
143.615082	L	H 50	143.626262	M	H 60	143.654072	F	H 35
143.615092	L	H 50	143.626272	M	HH 60	143.654082	F	H 35
143.616022	M	H 60	143.627012	H	HS 40	143.654092	F	H 35
143.616042	M	H 60	143.627032	H	HS 40	143.654102	F	H 35
143.616052	M	HH 60	143.627042	H	HS 40	143.654112	F	H 35
143.616062	M	HH 60	143.631012	D	H 30	143.654122	F	H 35
143.616072	M	H 60	143.631022	D	H 25	143.654132	F	H 35
143.616082	M	H 60	143.631032	D	H 25	143.654142	F	H 35
143.616112	M	H 60	143.631042	D	H 25	143.654152	F	H 35
143.616132	M	HH 60	143.631052	D	H 25	143.654162	F	H 35
143.616142	M	HH 60	143.631062	D	H 25	143.654172	F	H 35
143.617012	H	HS 40	143.631072	D	H 25	143.654192	F	H 35
143.617022	H	HS 40	143.631082	D	H 25	143.654202	F	H 35
143.617032	H	HS 40	143.631092	D	H 30	143.655012	J	HS 50
143.617042	H	HS 40	143.634012	F	H 35	143.656012	M	H 60
143.617062	H	HS 40	143.634022	F	H 35	143.656022	M	H 60
143.617082	H	HS 40	143.634032	F	H 35	143.656032	M	H 60
143.617092	H	HS 40	143.635012	L	H 50	143.656042	M	H 60
143.617112	H	HS 40	143.635022	L	H 50	143.656052	M	H 60
143.617132	H	HS 40	143.635032	J	HS 50	143.656092	M	H 60
143.617152	H	HS 40	143.635042	L	H 50	143.656112	M	HH 60
143.617162	H	HS 40	143.635052	L	H 50	143.656182	M	H 60
143.617182	H	HS 40	143.636052	M	H 60	143.656202	M	H 60
143.621012	D	H 25	143.637012	H	HS 40	143.657012	H	HS 40
143.621022	D	H 25	143.641012	D	H 25	143.657022	H	HS 40
143.621032	D	H 30						

Use the following chart showing the service reference code, bore, stroke and displacement for aid in cross-reference to service information in Tecumseh engine section.

Reference Code	Bore In.	Stroke In.	Displ. Cu. In.
A	2-1/8	1-3/4	6.207
B	2-5/16	1-3/4	7.35
C	2-5/16	1-13/16	7.61
D	2-5/16	1-27/32	7.75
E	2-1/2	1-13/16	8.9
F	2-1/2	1-27/32	9.06
G	2-5/8	1-27/32	10.0
H	2-5/8	1-15/16	10.5
I	2-3/4	1-15/16	11.0
J	2-13/16	1-15/16	12.0
K	2-1/2	2-1/4	11.04
L	2-5/8	2-1/4	12.176
M	2-5/8	2-1/2	13.53

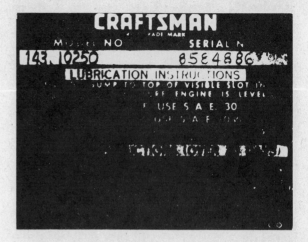

Fig. C1A—View of typical identification plate on Craftsman four stroke cycle engine.

ENGINE IDENTIFICATION

Engines must be identified by the complete model number, including the serial number in order to obtain correct repair parts. These numbers are located on the name plate as shown in Fig. C1A. It is important to transfer identification plate from the original engine to replacement short block assemblies so that unit can be identified when servicing later.

PARTS PROCUREMENT INFORMATION

Parts for Craftsman engines are available from all Sears Retails Stores and Catalog Sales Offices. Be sure to give complete Craftsman model and serial number of engine when ordering parts.

SERVICE NOTES
Four Stroke Models

CARBURETOR. The carburetors used on many Craftsman engines are the same as used on similar Tecumseh engines. Special Craftsman fuel systems are used on some models. The tank mounted suction carburetor is shown in view (A—Fig. C1). The Craftsman float carburetor without speed control shown in view (B) is used without a mechanical or air vane governor. Some engines use a mechanical governor (15, 16 & 17) which controls engine speed by using a throttle valve (7 & 8) located in the intake manifold (6). Refer to the appropriate following paragraphs for servicing Craftsman fuel systems.

FUEL TANK MOUNTED CARBURETOR.

Early Carburetors are equipped with a Bowden wire control as shown in Fig. C2. Later fuel tank mounted carburetors have a manual control knob and a positioning spring as shown in Fig. C3. Other differences are also noted and it is important to identify the type used before servicing. On all tank mounted

carburetors, turn the control valve clockwise to the position shown (Fig. C4), then withdraw the valve. There are no check valves or check balls in the carburetor pick-up tube, but the tube can be removed for more thorough

Fig. C1–Craftsman fuel systems are (A) tank mounted suction carburetor, (B) special float carburetor without governor or (C) the special float carburetor with mechanical governor linkage (15, 16 & 17) hooked up to a throttle (7 & 8) located in the intake manifold (6).

1. Control valve
2. Suction tube
3. Fuel tank
4. Intake manifold
5. Float carburetor
6. Intake manifold
7. Governor throttle shaft
8. Governor throttle plate
9. Return spring
10. Bellcrank
11. Linkage (10 to 12)
12. Governor spring
15. Internal lever
16. External lever
17. Linkage (16 to 7)

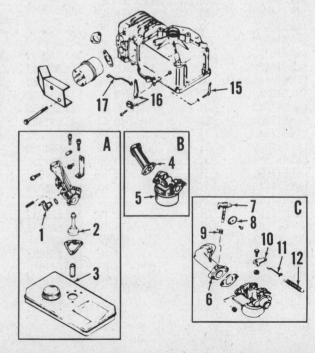

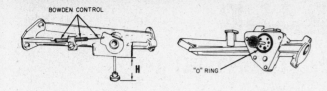

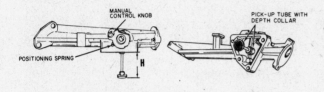

Fig. C2–View of early tank mounted suction carburetor. Notice the Bowden control cable and groove for "O" ring on lower surface. Refer to Fig. C3 for later type.

Fig. C3–View of later tank mounted suction carburetor. The unit is controlled by moving the manual control on carburetor. The lower surface is sealed with a gasket and the "O" ring used on early models is not used. The pick-up tube has a collar to make sure that it is installed at the correct depth.

is important to be sure that float height is correct and that the air filter is installed, is in good condition and clean. Incorrect float height or faulty air cleaner will affect the fuel-air mixture. The fuel pick-up tube (9) should be pressed into bore until collar is against carburetor body. Refer to Fig. C11 for measuring float height with drill bit.

NOTE: Some engines equipped with this carburetor are not equipped with a variable speed governor. These models are equipped with a plain intake manifold as shown (B—Fig. C1). The camshaft timing should be advanced one tooth for engines without governor as shown in Fig. C12.

Camshaft timing marks should be aligned for models with variable speed governor. The governed high speed is adjusted by turning the adjustment screw shown in Fig. C13.

cleaning. To reinstall pick-up tube in early models, it is necessary to remove plug (P—Fig. C5). Insert ⅛-inch drill into passage as shown and press tube into bore until seated against drill bit. Leave drill in place and press strainer (S) onto pick-up tube until height (H—Fig. C2) is 1 27/64-1 7/16 inches. Remove drill bit and install new cap plug. On late carburetors, the tube (T—Fig. C6) has a collar near the top end. Press the tube into bore until the collar is against carburetor body casting; then press the strainer (S) onto tube until distance (H) is 1 15/32 inches. The reservoir tube in the fuel tank should have slotted end toward bottom of tank on all models.

Fuel mixture is not adjustable, but the mixture will be changed by dirty or missing air filter. Be sure that air filter is in good condition and clean.

NOTE: The camshaft timing should be advanced one tooth for engines with this carburetor. Refer to Fig. C12.

CRAFTSMAN FLOAT CARBURETOR.

The carburetor is serviced in manner similar to other float type carburetors. Refer to Fig. C10. The carburetor is equipped with mixture adjustment. It

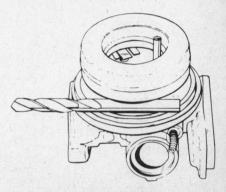

Fig. C11–Float height should be set using a #4 drill bit positioned as shown. Drill size #4 is 0.2090 inch diameter.

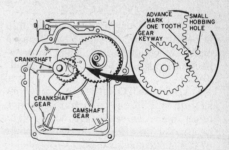

Fig. C12–Camshaft timing marks should be advanced one tooth when engine is not equipped with mechanical governor.

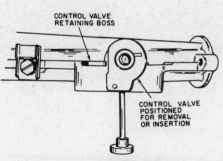

Fig. C4–The control valve must be turned clockwise to the position shown to clear the retaining boss.

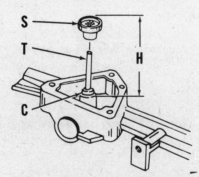

Fig. C6–Tube (T) should be pressed into bore until collar (C) contacts body of late carburetor. Press strainer (S) onto tube until height (H) is correct.

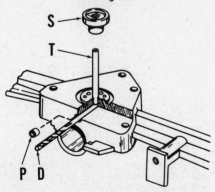

Fig. C5–A ⅛-inch diameter drill bit (D) should be used to gage the correct installed depth of tube (T). New plug (P) should be used when assembling.

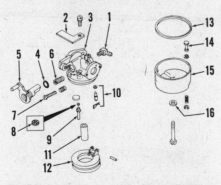

Fig. C10–Exploded view of Craftsman float type carburetor. Refer to text for service instructions.

1. Fuel inlet fitting	9. Fuel pick-up tube
2. Retaining plate	10. Fuel inlet valve
3. Carburetor body	11. Bowl spacer
4. "O" ring	12. Float
5. Control valve	13. Gasket
6. Positioning spring	14. Bowl drain
7. High speed stop	15. Float bowl
8. Screen	15. Gasket

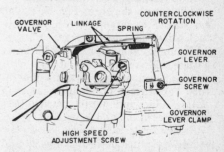

Fig. C13–View of Craftsman float type carburetor installed. The model shown uses mechanical governor controlling the governor throttle valve located in the intake manifold. This system is shown at (C–Fig. C1).

DECO-GRAND
(FORMERLY CONTINENTAL)

DECO-GRAND, INC.
1600 West Maple Road
Troy, Michigan 48084

Horizontal Crankshaft Models

CONTINENTAL MODEL SERIES	Cyls.	Bore	Stroke	Displ.
*AC5, AC6 & AA7	1	2⅛	2	7.1
AU7 & 700	1	2⅛	2	7.1
*AA8, AU8 & 800	1	2¼	2	7.95
AU85 & 900	1	2 5/16	2	8.4
AU10 & 1100	1	2⅝	2	10.82
AU12 & 1200	1	2¾	2	11.87

DECO-GRAND MODEL SERIES	Cyls.	Bore	Stroke	Displ.
DE2	1	2⅛	2	7.1
DE3	1	2 5/16	2	8.4
DE4	1	2⅝	2	10.82
DE5	1	2¾	2	11.87

*Vertical Crankshaft Models

CONTINENTAL MODEL SERIES	Cyls.	Bore	Stroke	Displ.
AV7, AD7, AW7 & 700	1	2⅛	2	7.1
AD8, AW8 & 800	1	2¼	2	7.95
AD85, AW85 & 900	1	2 5/16	2	8.4
1100	1	2⅝	2	10.82

*All vertical crankshaft models and the horizontal models indicated have been discontinued.

MAINTENANCE

SPARK PLUG. Recommended plug is 14 mm., ⅜ inch reach Champion J8 or following equivalent: AC C45, Autolite A7, Prestolite 14 7. Electrode gap is .025.

CARBURETOR. Several different suction and float type carburetors have been used. Refer to following paragraphs for information on each type or model of carburetor used.

AC SUCTION TYPE CARBURETOR. Engine models AC5 and AC6 were equipped with a suction type carburetor as shown in Fig. DG3. The carburetor is equipped with only one fuel adjustment needle (1). For initial adjustment, open the fuel needle 2½ to 3 turns. Make final adjustment with engine running at operating temperature, and with fuel tank approximately ½-full. Adjust fuel needle for smoothest engine operation under full load.

Refer to Fig. DG4 for exploded view of late style fuel metering valve (2) and adjustment needle (7). Fiber washer (1) is not used in some carburetors. Parts shown in Fig. DG4 may be installed in early production carburetors.

BENDIX-STROMBERG FLOAT CARBURETOR. A Bendix-Stromberg float type carburetor was used on some

Fig. DG3–View of AC suction type carburetor used on early engines.

1. Fuel mixture needle
2. Choke
3. Idle stop screw
4. Governor spring

models. Initial adjustment of both the idle and main fuel needles is approximately 1 turn open. Make final adjustments with engine running at operating temperature. With engine running at about 2500 RPM, adjust main fuel needle for smoothest engine

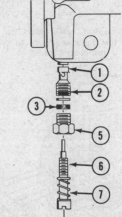

Fig. DG4–Exploded view of fuel mixture needle and related parts from AC suction type carburetor. Sealing washer (1) is not used on all models.

1. Washer
2. Metering valve
3. Washer
5. Nut
6. Needle
7. Spring

operation. Then, adjust idle fuel needle for smoothest idle performance.

CARTER MODEL "N" FLOAT CARBURETOR. Refer to Fig. DG5 for exploded view of typical Carter model "N" float type carburetor. For intitial adjustment, open idle fuel needle about one turn and open main fuel adjustment needle 1½ turns. Make final adjustment with engine running at operating temperature. Adjust main and idle fuel needles alternately until smoothest engine performance is obtained at both operating and idle speeds.

To check float level, invert carburetor casting and float assembly. There should be 11/64-inch clearance between free end of float and outer edge of carburetor casting. Adjust by bending tang on float lever with a small screwdriver.

TILLOTSON "ML" FLOAT CARBURETOR. Series "ML" Tillotson float carburetors have been used on some

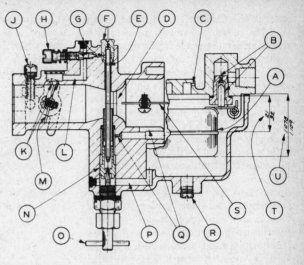

Fig. DG6–Schematic cross-sectional view of Tillotson Model "ML" float type carburetor used on some models.

A. Float
B. Inlet valve & seat
C. Air vent
D. Venturi
F. Idle tube
H. Idle fuel needle
J. Idle speed screw
M. Throttle disc
N. Main fuel nozzle
O. Main fuel needle
R. Bowl drain plug
S. Choke disc
T. Gasoline level
U. Float setting

Fig. DG7–Exploded view of Tillotson model "M" float type carburetor.

1. Carburetor body
2. Plug
3. Choke shaft
4. Choke detent
5. Spring
6. Choke disc
8. Gasket
9. Float
10. Float pin
11. Float cover
12. Gasket
14. Idle fuel needle
15. Spring
16. Idle stop screw
17. Spring
18. Idle tube
19. Inlet valve assy.
20. Gasket
21. Main fuel needle
22. Packing
23. Nut
24. Main nozzle
25. Gasket
26. Throttle shaft
27. Throttle disc
29. Throttle lever
30. Lockwasher

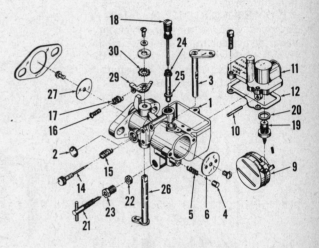

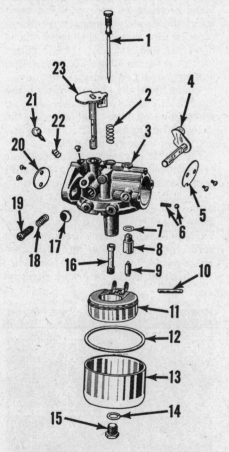

Fig. DG5–Exploded view of model "N" Carter carburetor used on some engines.

1. Main fuel needle	13. Float bowl
2. Spring	14. Sealing washer
3. Carburetor body	15. Retainer
4. Choke shaft	16. Main jet
5. Choke disc	17. Plug
6. Choke detent	18. Spring
7. Sealing washer	19. Idle stop screw
8. Inlet valve seat	20. Throttle disc
9. Inlet valve	21. Idle fuel needle
10. Float pin	22. Spring
11. Float	23. Throttle shaft
12. Gasket	

models. Refer to sectional view in Fig. DG6. For initial adjustment, open the idle fuel needle about 1 turn and open the main fuel needle about 1½ turns. Make final adjustments with engine running at operating temperature. First, with engine running at about half open throttle, adjust main fuel needle for maximum speed and smoothest engine operation. Then, adjust idle fuel needle for smoothest idle performance. Repeat the final adjustments if engine does not accelerate satisfactorily. Check float adjustment as shown in Fig. DG8. Distance (D) should measure 1 5/64-1 3/32 inch. Adjust by bending float lever.

TILLOTSON "MT" FLOAT CARBURETOR. Refer to Fig. DG7 for exploded view of typical Tillotson series "MT" float type carburetor. For initial adjustment, open idle fuel needle (14) about ¾-turn and open main fuel needle (21) about 1 turn. Make final adjustments with engine running at operating temperature. Adjust main fuel needle with engine running at about half open throttle to give maximum speed and smoothest operation. Then, adjust idle fuel needle for

smoothest idle performance.

To check float adjustment, measure float level as shown in Fig. DG8. Distance (D) should measure 1 25/64 to 1 27/64 inch. If not, remove float and bend tang that contacts needle valve to adjust float level.

ZENITH FLOAT CARBURETORS. Refer to Fig. DG9 for exploded view of Zenith model 210 float type carburetor. A Zenith model 10 carburetor used

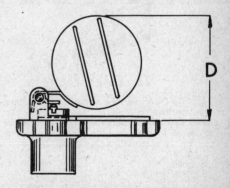

Fig. DG8–To check float level on Tillotson carburetors, invert casting and float assembly and measure distance "D" between gasket surface of casting and farthest side of float. Refer to text for dimension "D".

prior to the model 210 is similar except that the main fuel needle is located in the float bowl in place of the plug (25).

For initial adjustment of the Zenith float carburetors, open the idle fuel needle (2) about two turns and open the main fuel needle (7) about 1 turn. Turning the fuel adjustment needles in richens the idle mixture and leans the high speed (power) fuel mixture. Make final adjustments with engine running at operating temperature. Adjust idle fuel needle for smoothest idle performance; then, adjust main fuel needle for smoothest operation under full load. Check acceleration from idle speed to maximum governed speed and repeat final adjustment procedure if acceleration is unsatisfactory. Float level is non-adjustable.

GOVERNOR. All models are equipped with an air vane type governor or a mechanical governor of the flyball or flyweight type. Refer to the following paragraphs for information on each type of governor used.

Note: A few early production mechanical governors were of the flyweight type; complete information is not available on these units.

AIR VANE (PNEUMATIC) GOVERNORS. Refer to Fig. DG10 for drawing showing typical late production air vane governor. The air vane governor used earlier is similar except that a bellcrank is used in the linkage between the air vane and the carburetor throttle shaft arm on some models.

On models without remote controls, governed speed is adjusted by moving a slide (2) on the bracket (1) to decrease or increase tension on the governor spring (3) and thereby vary engine speed. Some models may be equipped with a remote throttle control which should be adjusted for a maximum governed speed of 3600 RPM. Idle speed on all models is adjusted by the stop screw on the carburetor throttle shaft.

When servicing engines equipped with an air vane governor, be sure that governor linkage is free throughout its range of travel. With the carburetor throttle in closed (idle) position, the air vane must be aligned with the edge of the opening in the blower housing back plate. Bend air vane to align it with edge of hole in back plate or to relieve binding condition. When installing blower housing, pull housing away from air vane while tightening retaining screws to provide maximum clearance for movement of the vane.

MECHANICAL FLYBALL GOVERNOR. Refer to Fig. DG11 for view of the flyball governor unit. Early flyball governor units used six steel balls instead of three as shown. When servicing these early units, it is recommended that three of the steel balls be discarded and a spacer (1) be installed on the governor shaft (3). Install the spacer with protruding hub down. Press or drive the spacer down on the shaft until spacer contacts shoulder on shaft, making sure that slots in the spacer are aligned with three of the grooves in the lower ball race.

Fig. DG12 shows the governor cover (4) removed. The actuating lever (3) contacts the upper flyball race (2).

On engines with carburetor located below the cylinder, linkage from governor to carburetor is as shown in Fig. DG13. To adjust engine governed speed, loosen setscrew retaining governor rod (4) in bellcrank (1) and vary the position of the bellcrank pivot on

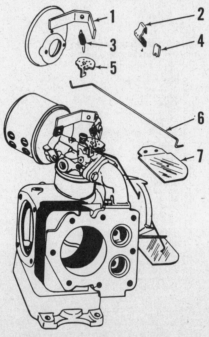

Fig. DG10–Drawing showing typical air vane governor installation.

1. Governor bracket	5. Throttle arm
2. Slide	6. Governor link
3. Governor spring	7. Air vane
4. Clip	

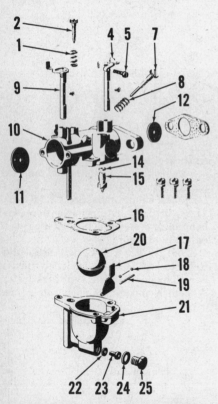

Fig. DG9–Exploded view of typical Zenith float type carburetor used on some models. On some carburetors, main fuel adjustment needle (7) is at location of plug (25) instead of in carburetor body casting.

1. Spring	15. Inlet valve assy.
2. Idle fuel needle	16. Gasket
4. Throttle shaft	17. Float lever
5. Idle stop screw	18. Lead shots
7. Main fuel needle	19. Float pin
8. Spring	20. Float
9. Choke shaft	21. Float bowl
10. Carburetor body	22. Sealing washer
11. Choke disc	23. Main jet
12. Throttle disc	24. Gasket
14. Sealing washer	25. Plug

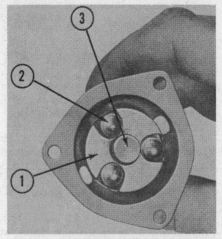

Fig. DG11–Deco-Grand mechanical governor, showing three-ball construction. The old style six-ball type should be converted to the new three-ball type.

1. Spacer
2. Flyballs
3. Governor drive shaft

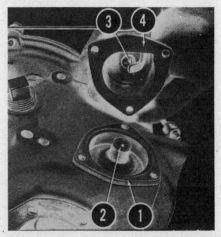

Fig. DG12–View showing mechanical governor cover assembly removed.

1. Governor housing	3. Governor lever
2. Upper ball race	4. Governor cover

the governor rod to change engine governed speed.

On engines with carburetor located on top of the cylinder, engine governed speed can be varied by moving slide (5—Fig. DG15) on the bracket (4) to change tension on the governor spring (6). The link between the governor arm and carburetor throttle shaft can be bent, if necessary, to synchronize throttle and governor travel. Be sure there is no binding tendency throughout range of linkage travel and that the carburetor throttle can move to full open position.

Refer to Fig. DG14 for illustration of governor linkage with remote speed control used on some engines installed in David Bradley garden tractors. The engine governed speed can be changed by varying the position of the control wire housing in the bracket (3). On earlier production units without remote speed control, engine governed speed can be adjusted by varying position of slide (5—Fig. DG15) on bracket (4).

DETEX FLYWEIGHT GOVERNOR. The mechanical governor on late production Detex engines is combined with the Detex ignition unit as shown in the exploded view in Fig. DG17. Refer also to Fig. DG16. Engine governed speed can be varied by remote control cable, if so equipped, or by varying the position of speed control lever (4).

Note: Before disconnecting governor spring (5—Fig. DG16) from governor speed control lever (4) or governor arm (3), mark the holes in lever and arm

Fig. DG13–Deco-Grand AA7 and AA7B governor linkage installation. Desired speed is obtainable by varying the effective length of rod (4) by means of screw at bell-crank end.

1. Bellcrank
2. Bellcrank-to-carburetor rod
3. Carburetor
4. Governor lever-to-bellcrank rod
5. Governor lever
6. Governor cover

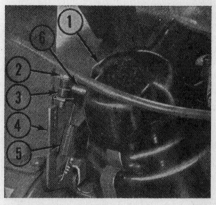

Fig. DG16–View of Detex magneto ignition combined with flyweight type governor. Refer to Fig. DG17.

Fig. DG14–Governor linkage used on later David Bradley installations of some engines.

1. Control lever
2. Governor control
3. Control bracket
4. Throttle stop lever
5. Idle stop screw
6. Governor link rod
7. Governor flange
8. Governor lever
9. Governor spring

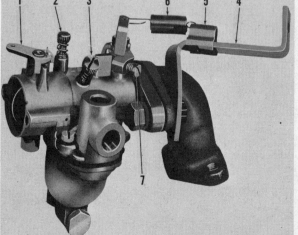

Fig. DG15–Zenith float type carburetor used on some engines.

1. Choke lever
2. Idle mixture adjustment screw
3. Main adjustment screw
4. Bracket
5. Slide
6. Governor spring
7. Idle stop screw

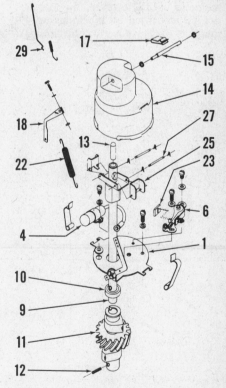

Fig. DG17–Components of Detex ignition system which in this case is combined with the flyweight type speed governor.

1. Base and lever	14. Housing
4. Condenser	15. Governor shaft
6. Breaker points	17. Actuating lever
9. Governor drive shaft & weights	18. Governor lever
	22. Governor spring
10. Seal	23. Cam wiper
11. Camshaft	25. Flyweight
12. Camshaft pin	27. Flyweight pin
13. Governor plunger	29. Gov. to carb. rod

into which the spring is hooked so that the spring may be reinstalled in the correct holes.

To synchronize travel of governor arm and carburetor throttle, proceed as follows: Loosen the clamp screw (2—Fig. DG16) in governor arm (3), and while holding the carburetor throttle in wide open position, turn the governor shaft (6) as far clockwise as possible and retighten the clamp screw. A screwdriver slot is provided in the outer end of the governor shaft to facilitate making this adjustment.

MAGNETO AND TIMING. Early production engines were equipped with Bendix-Scintilla, Phelon (Repco), Watts or Wico magnetos. Late production engines are equipped with Deco-Grand "Detex" ignition which consists of a flywheel type magneto with externally mounted condenser and breaker contact points. Refer to the following paragraphs for service information on each type magneto used.

EARLY PRODUCTION MAGNETOS. Several different flywheel type magnetos were used on early production engines, and service specifications vary as to make and model of the magneto used. However, the magneto can be identified by markings on the magneto and by description. Timing is

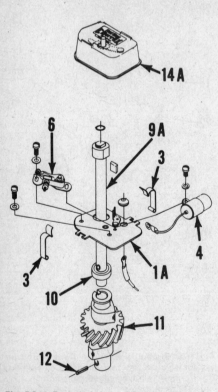

Fig. DG19–Exploded view of Detex ignition unit used with air vane type governor. Breaker cam is located on camshaft axle (9A).

1A. Breaker plate
3. Cover clips
4. Condenser
6. Breaker points
9A. Camshaft axle
10. Seal
11. Camshaft
12. Roll pin
14A. Breaker cover

fixed and non-adjustable on all early production magnetos.

On **Bendix-Scintilla** magnetos, the rotating magnets are a separate unit from the flywheel. To remove the rotating magnets, first remove the magneto mounting flange and the snap ring from engine crankshaft. The rotating magnet can then be pulled from the crankshaft. Breaker point gap should be adjusted to 0.015-0.018. Condenser capacity should be 0.15 mfd. (minimum test value). Magneto edge gap should be at least 5 degrees.

On the **Watts** magneto, armature core and high tension coil are mounted outside of the flywheel and armature core is retained to back plate with two bolts and clamp washers. Armature air gap should be 0.010-0.015. Adjust breaker point gap to 0.015.

On **Wico** magnetos with armature core and high tension coil mounted outside of flywheel (armature core is retained to back plate with four screws), adjust breaker point gap to 0.015. Armature air gap should be 0.009-0.012. Condenser capacity should be 0.16-0.20 mfd.

On **Wico** magnetos with armature core and high tension coil located inside flywheel, adjust breaker point gap to 0.020. Condenser capacity should be 0.16-0.20 mfd.

On **Phelon** (Repco) magnetos, armature and high tension coil are located inside flywheel. Adjust breaker points to 0.018-0.020. Condenser capacity should be 0.15-0.19 mfd.

DETEX IGNITION SYSTEM. Refer to Fig. DG17 for exploded view of Detex ignition unit combined with a flyweight mechanical governor and to Fig. DG19 for exploded view of Detex ignition unit that is used with an air vane type governor. The breaker cam shaft (9—Fig. DG17 or 9A—Fig. DG19) is also the engine camshaft axle and is driven by a pin (12) through the camshaft (11) and axle. As the breaker cam turns at one-half crankshaft speed, an ignition spark is produced every other

engine revolution to ignite the fuel-air mixture for the power stroke.

Timing on engines equipped with Detex ignition is adjustable by rotating the plate to which the breaker plate is attached. Adjust timing to setting that will produce maximum power and smoothest operation for individual engine.

On engines with mechanical governor, the breaker point cover can be removed after first removing the governor spring (5—Fig. DG16) from governor arm (3) and speed control lever (4). Be sure to mark the holes in arm and lever in which the governor spring is hooked before removing spring. Adjust breaker contact gap to 0.020 on all models with Detex ignition.

LOW OIL LEVEL SHUT-OFF. This device, shown in Fig. DG20, includes a float (A) which, when oil level is too low, contacts the ignition-coil-connected stud (B) and grounds the ignition.

LIGHTING COILS. On some engines the flywheel has a double set of magnets and a series of additional coils on the stator plate to provide lighting current. The lighting coils are wound in series, are independent of ignition coil and are used only with Detex ignition. The ignition breaker cam is a long dwell type and a 12 volt capacitor is mounted on the backplate.

Breaker gap is 0.020 as on regular Detex magneto and the testing procedures and values for the condenser are also the same. In servicing the ignition coil, if the lighting generator is of the early type having 6 coils, one of the latter is mounted behind the ignition coil. On these installations the ignition coil primary lead is assembled beneath the lighting coil windings which prohibits removal of the ignition coil. Thus in case of ignition coil failure, the entire generator plate assembly must be replaced.

Later lighting generator is of 5 coil design with the ignition coil mounted on the center lower leg of the lami-

Fig. DG20–Details of Low Oil Level Shut Off used on some later production engines. Unit is mounted in ball (oil reservoir) and cuts off ignition when float (A) drops into contact with coil-connected stud (B).

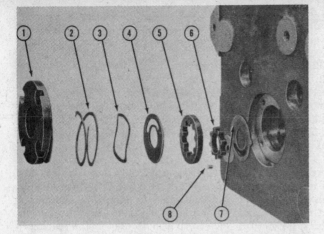

Fig. DG21—Components of oil pump driven off the crankshaft.

nated plate. The ignition coil in these installations may be removed for servicing. Do not, under any circumstances, remove any of the 5 small coils of this assembly.

Early production lighting capacitors had a hard plastic cover and were retained in a clip bracket at each end. Latest capacitor is of paper shell construction and is retained by a spring clip in the center. These capacitors are of electrolytic design and cannot be checked on the standard condenser testers. If a defective capacitor is suspected, it may be checked by a radio repair shop or replaced with a new one.

Assembly procedure for the 5 coil lighting unit is as follows:

1. Locate laminated plate over the oil seal then bring the red and white lead wires under the upper coils to prevent pinching against the cylinder block.
2. Anchor the breaker point lead wire and primary lead of ignition coil to the fibre post on stator plate. This connection must be electrically perfect as looseness can cause a loss of spark strength. Attach spark plug lead to outlet on ignition coil.
3. Feed the 4 lead wires up through the large opening in the back plate. The ignition wire of this group is retained by a clip to the lower flange of the inlet manifold; route the breaker point lead through the grommet of the base plate and connect it to the breaker point post. Leads from the lighting coils, one red and one white, are brought through the grommet on the back plate and connected to the same color leads from the lighting capacitor.
4. The long lead from the lighting capacitor is led through the grommet and connected to the switch plate.

LUBRICATION. Crankcase capacity on all models is one pint. Use SAE 30 oil for summer operation and SAE 10W oil for winter operation. If equipped with reduction gearing, use same weight oil in gearbox as in engine crankcase.

All current production models have a splash lubrication system. Horizontal crankshaft models have an oil dipper on the connecting rod; vertical crankshaft models have a tube inserted in the lower crankshaft throw which picks up oil from a circular oil trough in the engine base.

Early vertical crankshaft models were lubricated by a gear type pump (See Fig. DG21) which delivered oil to an orifice as shown in Fig. DG22.

Early model AA7 horizontal crankshaft engines were lubricated by a pump driven by a cam on the engine crankshaft; however, it is recommended that these engines be converted to splash lubrication. Refer to SERVICE NOTES paragraphs in REPAIRS section.

CRANKCASE BREATHER. On some vertical crankshaft models, the crankcase breather is located in the valve chamber cover. On all other models, the crankcase breather is located in the crankcase just below the cylinder head air baffle.

A flapper type valve is used for the crankcase breather valve on early engines. A ball check valve is used on later engines. If valve appears dirty, remove valve from engine and wash it in solvent.

REPAIRS

TIGHTENING TORQUES. Following are the recommended tightening torques:

Cylinder Head . . . . 250-275 In. Lbs.
(21-23 Ft. Lbs.)
Con. Rod Bolts . . . . 125-150 In. Lbs.
(10-13 Ft. Lbs.)
Con. Rod Screws . . . . . 100-125 In. Lbs.
(8-10 Ft. Lbs.)
Base to Crankcase . . . 325-350 In. Lbs.
(27-29 Ft. Lbs.)
Flywheel Nut . . . . 325-350 In. Lbs.
(27-29 Ft. Lbs.)

Main Bearing Cap . . . 150-175 In. Lbs.
(13-15 Ft. Lbs.)

SERVICING NOTES. When servicing Deco-Grand air cooled engines, the following precautions or procedures should be noted on certain models:

MODEL AA7 OIL PUMP. Deco-Grand recommends that the cam actuated oil pump on early model AA7 engines be discarded and a splash type lubricating system be installed. To install the splash system, install new type connecting rod with oil dipper (3—Fig. DG23). Then, grind or chisel boss from center of engine base and install an oil trough similar to that shown in Fig. DG20.

DISASSEMBLY OF MODEL AV7 ENGINES. On model AV7 vertical crankshaft engines, the crankshaft seal, oil pump gears and oil pump drive key (See Fig. DG21) must be removed from the engine base before the engine base can be removed from the crankshaft and engine crankcase.

CRANKSHAFT REMOVAL, EARLY ENGINES. On early production engines having flywheel end main bearing bushing located in the magneto stator plate, it will be necessary to remove the stator plate before the crankshaft can be removed if the thrust collar on the crankshaft does not have a clearance flat for the camshaft gear.

EARLY TYPE REDUCTION GEAR DRIVE. Early reduction gear drive units were equipped with oilite bushings. Parts are not available for these units; therefore, if necessary to renew any part of a bushing equipped gearbox, it will be necessary to install the later type needle bearing equipped reduction gear drive assembly and engine crankshaft.

VALVE SYSTEM. Valve lash should be 0.014-0.018 for exhaust and 0.012-0.018 for intake. Incorrect valve lash is corrected by grinding end of valve stem. Be sure to grind end of

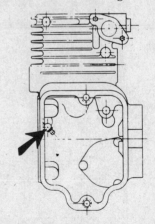

Fig. DG22—Oil orifice on models equipped with oil pump (See Fig. DG21) should clear crankshaft throw by 0.020 with spray directed toward the rear of engine and away from piston.

valve stem flat and square and remove all burrs after grinding. Valve tappet diameter on models with 10.82 cu in. and 11.87 cu. in. displacement should be 0.3110-0.3115 with a tappet bore of 0.3135-0.3150 to provide a clearance of 0.002-0.004. All other models should have a tappet diameter of 0.2820-0.2825 with a tappet bore of 0.2846-0.2854 to provide a clearance of 0.0021-0.0034.

Valve seat inserts are renewable and pressed into a counterbore in cylinder block. Insert should be chilled before installing. Valve seat angle should be 45 degrees.

Valve face angle should be 45 degrees. Intake valve stem diameter should be 0.3105-0.3115 and exhaust valve stem diameter should be 0.3100-0.3105 on models with 10.82 or 11.87 cu. in. displacement. All other models should have 0.2815-0.2825 diameter on intake and exhaust valve stems. Stem-to-guide clearance should be 0.002-0.0045 for intake and 0.003-0.005 for exhaust on models with 10.82 or 11.87 cu. in. displacement. All other models should have 0.0021-0.0039 stem-to-guide clearance for intake and exhaust valves.

CONNECTING ROD. The connecting rod and piston assembly can be removed from above after removing cylinder head and connecting rod cap. On most engines, the aluminum connecting rod rides directly on the crankpin. A heavy-duty forged aluminum connecting rod is available. Some engines may be equipped with a heavy-duty connecting rod having removable bronze bearing inserts.

Crankpin diameter on all models is 0.874-0.875. Desired running clearance between rod and crankpin is 0.004-0.0055. Desired side play of connecting rod on crankpin is 0.020-0.040 for models DE4, DE5, AU10, AU12, 1100 and 1200; desired connecting rod side play for all other models is 0.030-0.050. Connecting rods are available with 0.010, 0.020 and 0.030 undersize crankpin bore as well as in standard size.

If crankpin is worn more than 0.003, or is 0.001 or more out-of-round, renew crankshaft or regrind crankpin for next smaller undersize connecting rod.

Piston pin should have 0.0010-0.0015 clearance in connecting rod. Piston pin is available in 0.010, 0.020 and 0.030 undersize as well as standard size.

Note: On horizontal crankshaft models, be sure that connecting rod is installed with the oil hole in rod up.

PISTON, PIN AND RINGS. On all models, the piston is equipped with two compression rings and one oil control ring. On Model DE5, AU12 and Series 1200 engines, an expander is used under the oil control ring.

Piston ring end gap should be 0.007-0.017 for all model engines. Piston ring side clearance should be as follows:

Cyl. Bore Dia.	Piston Ring Side Clearance	
	Comp. Ring	Oil Ring
2⅛	0.002-0.0035	0.0015-0.003
2¼	0.002-0.0035	0.0015-0.003
2 5/16	0.002-0.004	0.0014-0.0035
2⅝	0.002-0.004	0.0015-0.003
2¾	0.0025-0.0045	0.0015-0.003

Piston pin standard diameter on Models DE4, DE5, AU10, and AU12 and Series 1100 and 1200 engines is 0.4993-0.4995; standard piston pin diameter for all other models is 0.4190-0.4195. On all models pins should be a zero to 0.0005 interference fit in the piston and a 0.0010-0.0015 loose fit in the connecting rod. Pin is available in standard size and in following oversizes: 0.010, 0.020 and 0.030.

Piston skirt to cylinder bore clearance should be 0.005-0.008 on Models DE4, DE5, AU10 and AU12 and Series 1100 and 1200 engines. On all other models, piston to cylinder bore clearance should be 0.008-0.011. On Models DE4, DE5, AU10 and AU12 and Series 1100 and 1200 engines, measure piston clearance at bottom of piston skirt and at right angle to piston pin. On other models, piston to cylinder clearance can be checked as follows: Insert a 0.010 thick, ½-inch wide feeler gage between piston and cylinder bore at right angle to piston pin, and attach a pull scale to the feeler gage. Clearance is correct if 5 to 10 pounds pull is required to withdraw feeler gage.

CYLINDER. Cylinder bore should be honed or rebored to next oversize or renewed if taper of cylinder bore is 0.006 or more, or if out-of-round condition is 0.004 or more. Standard cylinder bore diameters are as follows:

Nominal Cyl. Size	Std. Cylinder Bore
2⅛	2.125-2.127
2¼	2.250-2.252
2 5/16	2.3125-2.3145
2⅝	2.625-2.627
2¾	2.754-2.756

After honing or reboring cylinder, clean the cylinder bore with clean rags and motor oil or with brush and hot, soapy water. Solvents such as gasoline or kerosene will only serve to imbed small abrasive particles in the cylinder wall.

CRANKSHAFT. The flywheel (magneto) end of the crankshaft is supported in either a needle bearing or a sleeve bushing. On some early models, the sleeve bushing is located in the magneto stator plate. On early production engines, the flywheel end main journal diameter was 0.781-0.782 and the sleeve bushing inside diameter was 0.783-0.784 allowing a running clearance of 0.001-0.003. On all later models, flywheel end main journal diameter is 0.7495-0.7500. Bushing inside diameter, on models so equipped, is 0.753-0.754 allowing a running clearance of 0.003-0.0045.

On horizontal crankshaft engines, the crankshaft pto end journal rides in either a sleeve bushing or a ball bearing on direct drive models and in a needle bearing on reduction drive models. Pto end journal diameter is

Fig. DG23–Crankcase cylinder assembly with oil base removed. Note timing mark on crank gear at center face of one tooth and two timing dots on cam gear.

0.8745-0.8750 for bushing equipped models. Bushing inside diameter is 0.8770-0.8774 allowing a running clearance of 0.002-0.0029. Bushing and main bearing cap are cataloged as an integral unit on most models.

On vertical crankshaft engines, lower (pto) crankshaft journal rides in either a ball bearing or a sleeve bushing and needle bearing. Bushing to journal clearance should be the same as for horizontal crankshaft models.

Ball bearing mains, on models so equipped, should be 0.0001-0.0009 interference fit on the crankshaft journal. On models DE4, DE5, AU10, AU12, 1100 and 1200 series engines, the ball bearing is retained in the main bearing cap with a snap ring.

On models so equipped, needle bearing (roller) main bearing clearance can be measured with a dial indicator and should be 0.0005-0.0029.

Crankshaft end play should be 0.012-0.016 on vertical crankshaft engines. On horizontal crankshaft engines, crankshaft end play should be 0.008-0.010 on all models except those where the ball bearing main is retained in the bearing cap with a snap ring; crankshaft end play on these models is controlled by the locked-in bearing. End play can be adjusted by gaskets and shims placed between the crankcase and main bearing cap or, on vertical

Fig. DG24–Exploded view of needle bearing equipped reduction drive assembly.

1. Adapter
2. Gasket
5. Needle bearing
6. Needle bearing
7. Drive gear
8. Thrust washer
9. Thrust washer
10. Cover
11. Gasket
14. Needle bearing
15. Oil seal
16. Oil filler plug
17. Oil level plug

crankshaft models, engine base. Gaskets are available in thicknesses of 1/64 and 1/32 inch; shim thickness is 0.004. Although the end play is controlled by the locked-in ball bearing on some models, shims and/or gaskets are required between the main bearing cap and crankcase to provide clearance between the thrust surface on crankshaft and opposite main bearing.

CAMSHAFT. On models without "Detex" ignition, the hollow camshaft turns on an axle shaft. The camshaft is removed by driving the axle shaft out towards the open side of the crankcase. The axle shaft diameter is 0.3725-0.3735. The camshaft bore inside diameter is 0.3747-0.3767 providing a running clearance of 0.0012-0.0042. The axle shaft has a 0.0005-0.0025 loose fit in the crankcase bore at open side of crankcase and a 0.0005-0.0025 interference fit in closed side of crankcase.

On models with "Detex" ignition, the

camshaft and cam axle shaft are pinned together and the axle turns in unbushed bores in the engine crankcase. Axle shaft diameter is 0.3730-0.3735; bore inside diameter is 0.3747-0.3767 providing a running clearance of 0.0012-0.0037. The camshaft can be removed after removing the pin (12—Fig. DG17 or Fig. DG19) and axle shaft.

REDUCTION GEAR UNIT. Horizontal crankshaft engines are available with a 6:1 ratio gear reduction unit. The standard needle bearing equipped unit is shown in Fig. DG24.

To remove the gear reduction unit from engine crankcase, the cover and drive gear and shaft assembly must first be removed to gain access to two internal mounting bolts.

Gear box should be filled to oil level plug opening with same weight oil as recommended for engine lubrication. Capacity is approximately ⅛-pint.

District Continental Engines
5001 Kennilworth
Hyattsville, Maryland 20781

Vinces Sales & Service
1910 Aliceanna Street
Baltimore, Maryland 21231

Foley, Inc.
200 Summer Street
Worcester, Massachusetts 01608

A. P. Hopkins Company
13931 Oakland Avenue
Detroit, Michigan 48203

Muellers Union "76"
601 East 66th Street
Richfield, Minnesota 55423

Carl A. Anderson
153 East Thompson Avenue
West St. Paul, Minnesota 55118

Biddy Saw Works
120-21st Street, South
Columbus, Mississippi 39701

Medart Engine & Parts Company
3134 Washington Avenue
St. Louis, Missouri 63103

Power Transmission Equipment
15 North 33rd Street
Billings, Montana 59102

Carl A. Anderson
621 South 16th Street
Omaha, Nebraska 68102

Vandusen Aircraft Supplies
500 Industrial Road
Teterboro, New Jersey 07608

Central Auto Electric
808 2nd Street, NW
Albuquerque, New Mexico 87101

Fox Equipment Corporation
2041 Union Road
Buffalo, New York 14224

Engine Service Products
5730 North Tryon Street
Charlotte, North Carolina 28213

Columbus Motor Speedway
1845 Williams Road
Columbus, Ohio 43207

Motor Rebuilders & Parts
2126 Monroe
Toledo, Ohio 43624

Ohio Auto Parts Company
4th & Spring Streets
Columbus, Ohio 43215

Industrial Truck Service
3949 Lakeside Avenue
Cleveland, Ohio 44114

Parts, Inc.
1025 NW 9th Street
Oklahoma City, Oklahoma 73106

Robbins Speed Shop
1111 Lakeview Drive
Lansdale, Pennsylvania 19446

Owen H. Cook, Jr.
3524 Labadie Drive
Fort Worth, Texas 76118

All Small Engine Service
Division Bradshaw Auto Parts Company
359 Pierpont Avenue
Salt Lake City, Utah 84101

Power Systems Development
Box 738
Gloucester, Virginia 23061

West Shore Equipment Company
4695 South 108th Street
Milwaukee, Wisconsin 53228

Manitoba Bearing Works Ltd.
270 St. Mary Avenue
Winnipeg, Manitoba, Canada

Ideal Karts & Parts
1017 Princess Avenue
London 31, Ontario, Canada

Standard Engines
516 Parkdale Avenue North
Box 89, Station "C"
Hamilton, Ontario, Canada

United Continental Engines
8300 Avenue de'l Industrie
Ville d'Anjou
Montreal 437, Quebec, Canada

Model	Bore Inches	Stroke Inches	Displ. Cu. In.
250, 270	2½	1⅝	8.0

The model 250 and 270 engines are used as a power source for centrifugal pumps, diaphragm type pumps, air blowers and generators. The pump, blower or generator must be at least partly disassembled to service some engine components.

MAINTENANCE

SPARK PLUG. Recommended spark plug is a Champion J6J for use on engine powering generator or centrifugal pump; a Champion UJ12 is recommended for use on diaphragm type pump engine. A Champion HO-8A (platinum tip) or UJ-11-G (gold paladium tip) spark plug may be substituted. Electrode gap is 0.025.

CARBURETOR. A Tillotson HS-45A carburetor is used on earlier engines while later models use a Tillotson model HS45C carburetor; refer to exploded view of carburetor in Fig. HL1. Note: As engine speed is controlled by governor plate on rotary inlet valve, there are no governor linkage connections to throttle shaft. Throttle shaft has spring loaded detent to hold shaft in wide open position. Generator engine is not fitted with throttle control knob. Carburetor is accessible after removing air cleaner cover (1—Fig. HL2).

Later model carburetor is fitted with a main nozzle check ball which allows use of larger mesh inlet screen (6—Fig. HL1) and provides easier adjustment of fuel mixture. The check ball assembly will be in the same bore as the small body channel welch plug (22), retaining ring (23) and screen (24), and will replace these parts.

When disassembling, slide diaphragm assembly towards adjustment needle side of carburetor body to disengage diaphragm from fuel inlet control lever. To remove welch plugs, carefully drill through plugs with a small diameter drill and pry plugs out with a pin. Caution should be taken that drill bit just goes through welch plug as deeper drilling may seriously damage carburetor. Note channel screen (24) (early model carburetor) and screen retaining ring (23) which are accessible after removing welch plug (22).

Inlet control metering lever (15) should be flush with metering chamber floor of carburetor body. If not, bend diaphragm end of lever up or down as required so that lever is flush.

Normal adjustment of low speed fuel mixture needle (marked "L" on carburetor body) is ¾-turn open and main mixture adjusting needle (marked "H" on carburetor body) should be opened

one full turn. On pump or blower engine, back idle speed adjusting screw out until carburetor throttle plate will close fully, then slowly turn screw in until it just contacts pin on throttle shaft, then turn screw in an additional 1½ turns.

Start engine and allow to warm up before making final carburetor adjustments. With carburetor throttle shaft in high speed detent position and engine running under load, adjust main (H) fuel needle for smoothest running. Note: On generators, there is no external control for throttle, thus no need to make idle adjustments. Move throttle shaft to idle speed position and

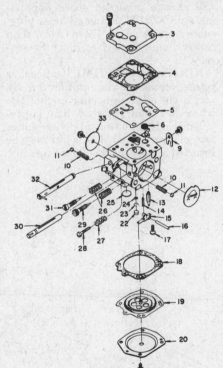

Fig. HL1–Exploded view of Tillotson carburetor used on model 250 and 270.

3. Fuel pump cover
4. Fuel pump gasket
5. Fuel pump diaphragm
6. Inlet screen
9. Throttle shaft clip
10. Shaft detent springs (2)
11. Shaft detent balls
12. Choke shutter
13. Inlet needle
14. Inlet tension spring
15. Inlet control lever
16. Inlet pinion pin
17. Inlet pinion pin retaining screw
18. Diaphragm gasket
19. Metering diaphragm
20. Diaphragm cover
22. Welch plug
23. Retaining ring for (24)
24. Body channel screen
25. Welch plug
26. Adjusting needle springs
27. Idle speed screw spring
28. Idle speed screw
29. Main adjusting needle
30. Choke shaft
31. Idle adjusting needle
32. Throttle shaft
33. Throttle shutter

Fig. HL2–Exploded view of air intake and fuel system. Refer to Fig. HL1 for exploded view of carburetor (24). Control lever and shaft (2) is not used for throttle on generator engine and hole is covered by plug (3).

1. Air filter cover
2. Control shaft assemblies
3. Plug (generator only)
4. Cover retaining nut
5. Nylon washer
6. Air filter element
7. Stud
8. Gasket
9. Spacer
10. Intake manifold
12. Crankcase gasket
13. Air filter mounting plate
17. Fuel tank
18. Fuel filter
19. Fuel filler cap
20. Fitting
21. Fuel line
22. Governor adjusting hole plug
23. Grommet
24. Carburetor assembly

adjust idle fuel needle (L) for smoothest idle. Adjust idle speed stop screw to desired idle speed. If engine will not accelerate from idle speed to full throttle without hesitation, open idle fuel needle an additional ⅛-turn.

GOVERNOR. The governor is a part of the rotary inlet valve; refer to Fig. HL3. As engine speed increases, centrifugal force pivots governor plate on pivot pin (P) against tension of spring (S). The governor plate then closes the opening in rotary valve and thus throttles the engine. Maximum governed engine speed is controlled by tension of governor spring, which is adjusted by turning screw (A).

To check and adjust engine speed, proceed as follows: First, bring engine

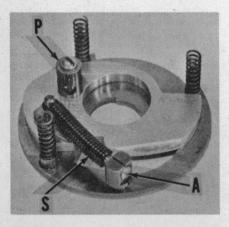

Fig. HL3–View of rotary intake valve and governor assembly. Governor plate pivots on post (P) to close off valve opening in rotary valve plate to govern engine speed. Speed at which plate closes the opening is regulated by tension of governor spring (S) which is adjusted by turning screw (A).

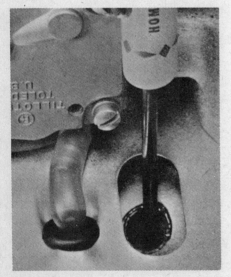

Fig. HL4–Access to governor spring adjusting screw (A–Fig. HL3) is gained by removing air filter cover, rubber plug (22–Fig. HL2) and the brass plug from engine crankcase. Then, turn engine so that screw can be turned with screwdriver as shown.

to normal operating temperature and adjust carburetor for highest speed and best performance obtainable, then check engine speed with tachometer. Refer to the following chart for correct governed speed:

	No Load rpm	Full Load rpm
Generator	3750	3600
Centrifugal Pump	3900-4000	3400-3600
Diaphragm Pump	2800-3000	2800-3000
Blower	3750-3800	3400-3600

If adjustment is necessary, stop engine and remove air filter cover and rubber plug (22–Fig. HL2) from air filter base (13). Remove brass plug from engine crankcase through opening in filter base and turn engine so that adjusting screw (A—Fig. HL3) is accessible. Then, as shown in Fig. HL4, turn adjusting screw clockwise to increase speed or counterclockwise to decrease speed. One turn of the screw will change governed speed approximately 100 RPM. Reinstall brass plug, rubber plug and air filter cover, then recheck engine speed; readjust if necessary.

IGNITION AND TIMING. Breaker points, condenser and ignition coil are accessible after removing engine flywheel (magneto rotor). A hole is provided in magneto back plate and inner face of flywheel so that a pin may be inserted to hold flywheel from turning.

Unscrew flywheel nut and remove flywheel using Homelite puller No. AA-22560, or equivalent.

To adjust breaker point gap, turn engine so that leading edge of breaker cam is about ⅛-inch past breaker point cam follower, then adjust point gap to 0.020.

NOTE: On earlier models, removal of flywheel (magneto rotor) will also require removal of the fan housing (17—Fig. HL8). Fan housing and magneto back plate are integral on later models; removing starter and starter adapter plate will permit access to remove magneto rotor. Also, service crankshafts may have **two keyways** for breaker cam and magneto rotor. The second keyway (painted red) is at 2 o'clock position (when considering cylinder at 12 o'clock position) for use with one-piece fan housing and back plate **only** when breaker points are located **above** crankshaft. On early engines with two-piece fan housing and back plate, breaker points are mounted **below** crankshaft (opposite cylinder). The breaker cam and rotor must be positioned in same keyway. The later one-piece fan housing and back plate may be installed on earlier models by tapping the two drilled stator mounting holes and mounting magneto stator (armature and coil) in original position. When both new crankshaft and fan housing/back plate are used, remount magneto stator in new position, use **red** keyway for installing cam and rotor and mount starter using new

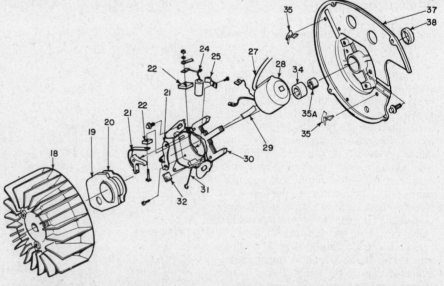

Fig. HL5–Exploded view of model 250 magneto assembly. Model 270 is similar. Magneto components are accessible after removing flywheel; refer to text. A zinc flywheel (magneto rotor) should be used on diaphragm pump engine; other model 250 engines use aluminum flywheel.

18. Flywheel	24. Condenser	34. Breaker cam
19. Breaker box cover	25. Condenser clamp	35. Wire retaining clips
20. Gasket	27. High tension lead	35A. Felt seal
21. Breaker points	28. Ignition coil	37. Back plate
22. Terminal connection	29. Coil wedge	38. Felt seal
	30. Stator & armature assy.	
	31. Breaker box cover spring	
	32. Cam wiper felt	

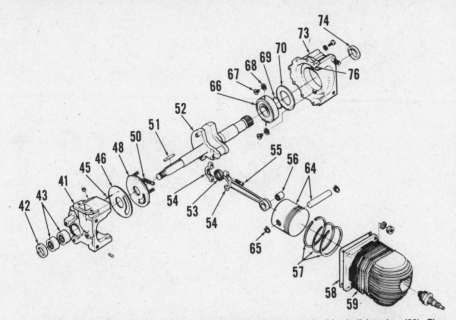

Fig. HL6—Exploded view of engine. Crankshaft end play is controlled by ball bearing (66). Three different crankshafts are used; shaft shown is for diaphragm pump. Crankshaft for generator has tapered end with threaded counterbore for armature retaining bolt. Crankshaft for other applications has externally threaded end.

41. Crankcase half	53. Needle bearing rollers (31)	66. Roller bearing
42. Crankshaft seal	54. Connecting rod & cap	67. Bearing retaining screws
43. Needle roller bearings	55. Socket head screws	68. Bearing retaining washers
45. Dowel pins	56. Needle roller bearing	69. Snap ring
46. Intake valve wear plate	57. Piston rings	70. Bearing gasket
48. Intake valve & governor assy.	58. Gasket	73. Crankcase half
50. Governor spring	59. Cylinder	74. Crankshaft oil seal
51. Cam & flywheel key	64. Piston & piston pin	76. Dowel pin
52. Crankshaft (diaphragm pump)	65. Snap rings	

Fig. HL7—A 10-32 threaded rod or headless screw is used as tool to help in assembling connecting rod to cap. Stick the 31 loose needle rollers to crankpin with beeswax or heavy grease, then carefully position cap so that when assembled, pinned side of piston is towards intake side (upper side) of engine.

adapter plate. New magneto leads, retaining clips and rivets will be required also.

LUBRICATION. Engine on all models is lubricated by mixing oil with regular gasoline. If Homelite® Premium SAE 40 oil is used, fuel:oil ratio should be 32:1. Fuel:oil ratio should be 16:1 if Homelite® 2-Cycle SAE 30 oil or other SAE 30 oil designed for air-cooled two stroke engines is used. Note: A fuel:oil ratio of 32:1 should be used on diaphragm pump models regardless of whether Homelite® Premium SAE 40 or Homelite® 2-Cycle SAE 30 oil is used.

AIR AND FUEL FILTERS. The air cleaner element may be washed by sloshing it around in a container of non-oily solvent. If engine is run continuously, clean air filter daily. After a number of cleanings, filter pores may become permanently clogged, making it necessary to renew element.

The fuel filter is part of the fuel pickup inside fuel tank and can be fished out with wire hook. Under normal operations, the filter element should be changed at one to two month intervals. If engine is run continuously, or fuel is dirty, the filter may need to be changed weekly, or more often if necessary.

CARBON. Carbon should be cleaned from exhaust ports at 100 to 200 hour intervals. Remove muffler, crank piston to top dead center and use a wooden or plastic scraper to remove carbon deposits. Avoid scratching piston or damaging edge of port. Note: For easy access to exhaust port, stand engine on recoil starter end.

REPAIRS

CONNECTING ROD. Connecting rod and piston assembly can be removed after removing cylinder from crankcase. Refer to Fig. HL6. Be careful to remove all of the loose needle rollers when detaching rod from crankpin. Model 250 has 31 bearing rollers in rod bearing while model 270 has 23 rollers.

Renew connecting rod if bent or twisted, or if crankpin bearing surface is scored, burned or excessively worn. The caged needle roller piston pin bearing can be renewed by pressing old bearing out and pressing new bearing in with Homelite tool Nos. 24131-1 (plug) and 24124-1 (sleeve). Press on lettered end of bearing cage only.

Renew crankpin needle rollers as a set if any roller is scored, burned or has flat spots. Stick needle roller set to crankpin with heavy grease or beeswax. Using a 10-32 threaded rod or headless screw, position connecting rod cap so that mating boss on cap and connecting rod will align when pinned

side of piston is on the intake (upper) side of engine; refer to Fig. HL7. Slide connecting rod down over threaded rod or screw, then install socket head screw in opposite side of rod and cap and remove the installation tool. Install remaining socket head screw and tighten both screws to a torque of 32 inch-pounds.

PISTON, PIN AND RINGS. Piston assembly is accessible after removing cylinder assembly from crankcase. Always support piston when removing or installing piston pin. Piston is of aluminum alloy and is fitted with three pinned piston rings.

If piston ring locating pin is worn to half the original thickness, or if there is any visible up and down play of piston pin in piston bosses, renew piston and pin assembly. Inspect piston for cracks or holes in dome and renew if any such defect is noted. Slight scoring of piston is permissible, but if rough surfaces are accompanied by deposit of aluminum on cylinder wall, renew piston.

Always use new piston pin retaining snap rings when reassembling piston to connecting rod. Fit new piston rings in grooves, aligning ring end gaps with locating pin. Be sure locating pin side of piston is away from exhaust side of engine when installing piston and connecting rod assembly.

CYLINDER. Cylinder bore is chrome plated; the plating is light gray in color and does not have the appearance of polished chrome. Renew cylinder if any part of chrome plated bore is worn through; usually, the worn

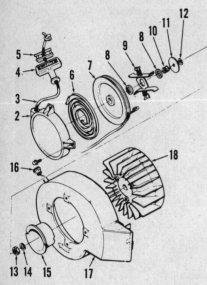

Fig. HL8–Exploded view of Fairbanks-Morse rewind starter. Starter cup (15) has rope notches so that engine can be started with starter assembly removed. Early type fan housing (17) is shown; later fan housing and magneto back plate (37–Fig. HL5) are integral.

2. Cover & bushing assy.
3. Starting cord
4. Starting cord grip
5. Insert
6. Rewind spring
7. Starter pulley
8. Fiber washer
9. Friction shoe assembly
10. Brake spring
11. Brake retaining washer
12. Snap ("E") ring
13. Flywheel nut
14. Lock washer
15. Starter cup
16. Engine stop switch
17. Blower housing
18. Flywheel (magneto rotor)

area is bright as the aluminum is exposed. In some instances, particles from the aluminum piston may be deposited on top of chrome plating. This condition is usually indicated by rough, flaky appearance and deposits can be removed by using a rubber compound buffing wheel on a ¼-inch electric drill. If a screwdriver can be run over the cleaned surface without leaving marks, the cylinder is suitable for further service. If screwdriver scratches surface, renew cylinder.

Lubricate piston, rings and cylinder bore. Compress rings, then slide cylinder down over piston. Tighten cylinder retaining nuts evenly and securely.

CRANKSHAFT, BEARINGS AND SEALS. To remove crankshaft, engine must first be removed from blower, pump or generator. Refer to exploded view of appropriate unit in Fig. HL9, HL10, HL11, HL12 or HL13 for required disassembly. Then refer to Figs. HL5 and HL6 and proceed as follows:

Remove flywheel, magneto assembly and magneto back plate. Remove and discard felt seals (35A & 38—Fig. HL5) from backplate (37). Remove "O" ring oil slinger (not shown) from crankshaft. Remove cylinder, piston and connecting rod assembly, then separate crankcase halves (41 & 73—Fig. HL6).

Fig. HL9–Exploded view of diaphragm pump assembly. Gear teeth on engine crankshaft (1) engage intermediate gear (23). Gearcase cover (4) must be removed from pump so that engine can be separated from cover. When installing diaphragm (44), push rod (38) all the way down before installing upper body (31) to lower body (46) bolts.

1. Engine crankshaft	14. Needle bearing	24. Spacer
4. Gearcase cover	15. Thrust washer	34. Crank
5. Bearing cap	16. Oil filter plug	35. Cap screw
6. Needle bearing	16A. Bearing cap	37. Thrust washers
8. Thrust washer	17. Garlock seals	38. Pump rod assembly
9. Gasket	18. Needle bearing	39. Needle bearings
10. Pump gear	19. Thrust washer	40. Grease fitting
11. Shaft & key assy.	21. Intermediate shaft	41. Washer
12. Key	22. Woodruff key	44. Pump diaphragm
13. Gearcase assembly	23. Intermediate gear	45. Diaphragm cap
		46. Pump body
		48. Wing plug
		49. Gasket
		50. Standpipe
		51. Suction fitting
		52. Pipe nipple
		53. Valve weight
		54. Valve
		55. Valve plate
		56. Discharge fitting

Pull governor weight away from crankshaft, then carefully remove the rotary intake valve and governor assembly (48) to avoid damaging sealing surface of crankshaft. Remove two screws (67) and washers (68) retaining ball bearing (66) in crankcase half (73) and remove shaft and bearing. Tape shaft to prevent scratching sealing surface, then remove snap ring (69) and pull bearing (66) from crankshaft. Remove

intake valve plate (46) from crankcase half (41), pry seal (42) out of bore and press needle roller bearing cages (43) out of crankcase half. Remove seal (74) from opposite half. Note: Remove bearings from crankshaft and flywheel side crankcase half only if renewal is indicated.

Renew crankshaft if it has damaged threads, enlarged keyways, or if run out exceeds 0.003. Inspect drive gear on output end of diaphragm pump engine for wear or other tooth damage. Flywheel end main journal must be free of pits, galling or heavy score marks. If journal is worn or out of round more than 0.001, renew crankshaft. Renew ball bearing at output end if bearing shows perceptible wear or feels rough when rotated. The caged needle roller bearings at flywheel end should be renewed if any roller shows visible flat spot, or if rollers in either cage can be separated more than the width (diameter) of one roller.

When reassembling, soak new bearing gasket (70) in oil, then insert in crankcase half (73). Support crankshaft at throw, then press new ball bearing onto shaft and secure with snap ring (69). Note: Be sure that groove in outer bearing race is towards crankshaft throw. Lubricate seal (74), then using suitable installation tool (Homelite No. 24120-1 or equivalent) press seal into crankcase half with lip of seal inward. Pressing against outer race of bearing (66) only, install crankshaft and bearing assembly into crankcase half (73) and secure with the two screws (67) and washers (68). Note: Use suitable seal protector (Homelite Nos. 24125-1, 24126-1 or 24127-1, or equivalent) to prevent damage to seal.

Using Homelite tool No. 24155-1, press outer needle bearing into crankcase half (41) with stepped end of tool, then press inner bearing into crankcase half with straight end of tool. Note: Press on lettered side of bearing cage only. Install seal (42) with lip in towards needle bearing with straight end of bearing installation tool.

Fit governor and rotary intake valve assembly onto crankshaft so that thrust springs fit into proper bores of crankshaft. Note: Hold governor plate away from crankshaft when installing to prevent scratching seal surface. Lubricate all parts thoroughly and insert intake valve plate (46) in crankcase half (41) so that it is properly positioned on dowel pins and intake opening. Using seal protector (Homelite No. 24121-1 or equivalent), assemble the crankcase half over crankshaft and governor assembly, hold assembly together against thrust spring pressure and install crankcase cap screws. Tighten cap screws to a torque of 80 inch-pounds. Insert new felt seal (38—Fig. HL5) in bore of magneto back plate, place new "O" ring oil slinger on crankshaft and install back plate. Tighten backplate retaining cap screws to a torque of 80 inch-pounds. Complete reassembly by reversing disassembly procedure.

CRANKCASE. Be sure that all passages through crankcase are clean. The

idle passage line which enters crankcase via the intake valve register may be restricted with carbon deposits.

If main bearing bore at output end has a worn appearance, bearing has been turning in bore. If so, crankcase half should be renewed. The mating surfaces of the two-piece crankcase must be free of all nicks and burrs as neither sealing compound nor gaskets are used at this joint. NOTE: Fuel tank bracket mounting screws are secured in engine crankcase with Loctite. When reinstalling bracket, clean the screw threads and threads in crankcase, then apply a drop of Loctite to each screw. Tighten screws to a torque of 120 inch-pounds.

ROTARY INTAKE VALVE. The combination rotary intake valve and governor (see Fig. HL3) should be re-

newed if any of the following conditions are noted: If the sealing faces of valve or governor plate are worn or scored enough to produce a ridge; if spring post is loose or extended to valve seating surface; or, if governor pivot point has started to wear through the surface of valve. Maximum allowable clearance between governor plate and intake valve plate is 0.006. The governor spring and/or governor spring adjusting screw may be renewed separately from the assembly.

Slight scoring of valve face may be corrected by lapping on a lapping plate using a very fine abrasive. Lapping motion should be in the pattern of a figure eight to obtain best results. Slight scoring of the Formica wear plate is permissible. Homelite recommends soaking a new Formica plate in oil for 24 hours prior to installation.

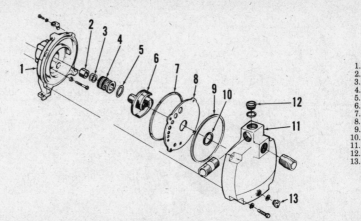

1.	Impeller housing
2.	Spacer
3.	Shims
4.	Seal assy.
5.	Shim
6.	Impeller
7.	Gasket
8.	Wear plate
9.	Gasket
10.	Gasket
11.	End housing
12.	Primer plug
13.	Drain plug

Fig. HL10–Exploded view of centrifugal pump. End housing (11) and impeller (6) must be removed to allow removal of the four cap screws retaining impeller housing (1) to engine. Hold flywheel from turning with pin (see magneto section) to unscrew impeller.

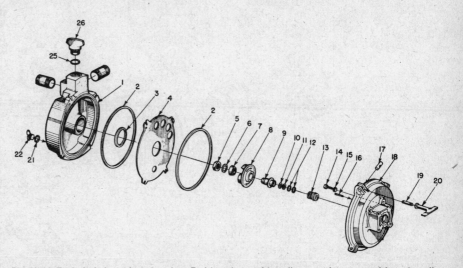

Fig. HL11–Exploded view of trash pump. End housing and impeller must be removed from impeller housing to allow housing to be unbolted from engine. Model 270 uses a spacer in place of washers (12).

1.	End housing	8.	Impeller	15.	Sealing washers
2.	Gasket	9.	Impeller hub	16.	Spiral pin
3.	Gasket	10.	Shim (0.010, as required)	17.	Pivot pin
4.	Wear plate	11.	Shim (0.015, as required)	18.	Impeller housing
5.	Impeller nut	12.	Spacer washers	19.	Studs
6.	Washer	13.	Seal assembly	20.	Wing nuts
7.	Tapered bushing	14.	Screws		

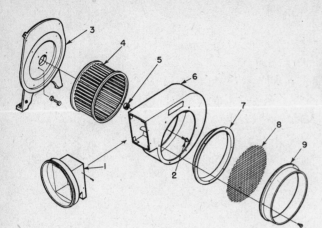

Fig. HL12–Exploded view of blower unit. Remove blower housing and rotor to allow unbolting and removal of blower plate (1) from engine.

1. Blower outlet
2. Slotted head screws
3. Mounting plate
4. Blower rotor
5. Elastic stop nut
6. Blower housing
7. Blower inlet venturi
8. Inlet screen
9. Inlet collar

REWIND STARTER. Refer to Fig. HL8 for exploded view of the Fairbanks-Morse starter used on all applications. In an emergency in case of rewind starter failure, remove starter assembly and wind rope around starter cup (15) to start engine.

Refer to exploded view for proper reassembly of starter unit. Hook end of starter rope in notch of pulley and turn pulley five turns counterclockwise, then let spring wind rope into pulley for proper spring pre-tension.

To remove starter cup, insert lock pin through hole in magneto back plate and hole in flywheel to hold flywheel from turning, then unscrew retaining nut.

DIAPHRAGM PUMP

The diaphragm pump is lubricated by filling gearcase to level of plug (16—Fig. HL9) with SAE 90 gear lubricant and by greasing pump rod upper bearing at fitting (40) once a month with pressure gun.

When installing new diaphragm (44) or assembling upper pump body (31) to lower body (46), the diaphragm must be centered and in fully down position before tightening upper body to lower body bolts.

To remove pump from engine, drain gear lubricant and separate gearcase (13) from gearcase cover (4). Gear teeth are machined on end of engine crank-

shaft to drive intermediate gear (23). Unbolt and remove cover (4) from engine crankcase. When reassembling, use new gasket (9).

CENTRIFUGAL PUMP

Refer to Fig. HL10. To remove pump from engine, remove end housing (11) and wear plate (8) from impeller housing (1), taking care not to damage sealing gaskets. Unscrew impeller (6) from engine crankshaft in counter-clockwise direction by placing wrench on hex end of impeller and striking wrench a sharp blow with hammer. Take care not to lose or damage seals or shims. Impeller housing can now be unbolted from engine.

When reassembling pump, shims (3) are available to maintain minimum clearance between impeller and wear plate (8). When shims are added to decrease clearance, seal shims (5) of the same thickness must be installed to maintain proper tension on seal spring. Before reassembling pump, hold wear plate (without gasket) against impeller housing and turn engine by hand to be sure impeller does not rub against wear plate.

TRASH PUMP

The trash pump (Fig. HL11) impeller (8) is mounted on tapered bushings so that if a solid object lodges in pump to

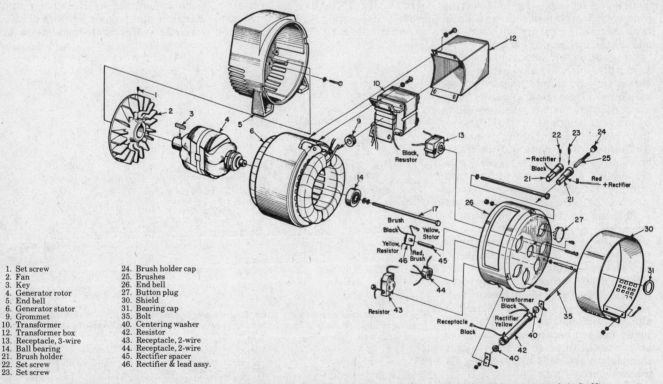

1. Set screw
2. Fan
3. Key
4. Generator rotor
5. End bell
6. Generator stator
9. Grommet
10. Transformer
12. Transformer box
13. Receptacle, 3-wire
14. Ball bearing
21. Brush holder
22. Set screw
23. Set screw

24. Brush holder cap
25. Brushes
26. End bell
27. Button plug
30. Shield
31. Bearing cap
35. Bolt
40. Centering washer
42. Resistor
43. Receptacle, 2-wire
44. Receptacle, 2-wire
45. Rectifier spacer
46. Rectifier & lead assy.

Fig. HL13–Exploded view of generator unit. Through bolt (17) retains generator rotor (4) on tapered end of engine crankshaft. After removing rotor and fan (2) assembly from engine crankshaft, fan housing end bell (5) can be unbolted from engine crankcase.

block the impeller, shaft rotation will not halt immediately.

To remove pump from engine, remove end housing (1) and wear plate (4), then unscrew impeller retaining nut (5) and remove impeller (8), taking care not to damage or lose seal and shims (10, 11 & 12). Unbolt and remove impeller housing (18) from engine.

When reassembling pump, use shims (10 & 11) of total thickness as required to maintain minimum clearance between impeller and wear plate. Shims are placed between shoulder on crankshaft and impeller hub (9). Install seal shims of same total thickness along with spacer washers (12) to maintain seal spring tension. Model 270 is equipped with a spacer in place of washers (12).

GENERATOR

Two generators have been used as shown in exploded views in Figs. HL13 and HL14. Care should be taken in disassembly of the generator that any leads disconnected are identified so they may be reconnected properly. Also, if brushes are to be reinstalled, they should be identified so they can be installed in same location and position from which they were removed. Careful disassembly is necessary to avoid damage to wiring or insulation.

Generator rotor (4) of generator shown in Fig. HL13 is removed from crankshaft after removing retaining cap screw (17) by inserting a pin

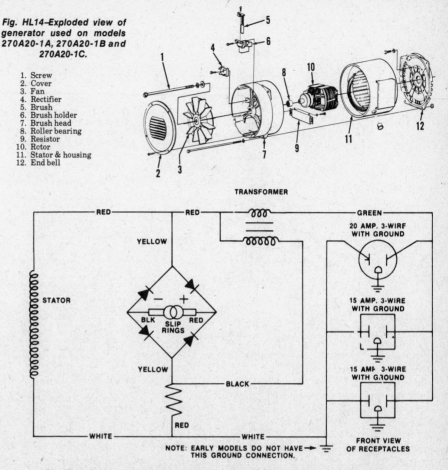

Fig. HL14–Exploded view of generator used on models 270A20-1A, 270A20-1B and 270A20-1C.

1. Screw
2. Cover
3. Fan
4. Rectifier
5. Brush
6. Brush holder
7. Brush head
8. Roller bearing
9. Resistor
10. Rotor
11. Stator & housing
12. End bell

Fig. HL15–Schematic of generator models 270A20-1A, 270A20-1B and 270A20-1C.

(Homelite No. 22271 cut to length of 4-5/16 inches measured from tapered end), tapered end first, and breaking taper fit loose with jackscrew (Homelite tool No. S-394) threaded into end of rotor shaft. Generator end bell (5) can then be removed from engine.

Refer to Fig. HL15 for schematic diagram of models 270A20-1A and 270A20-1B.

Model	Bore Inches	Stroke Inches	Displ. Cu. In.
10	2¾	3⅛	12.62
251	2¾	3⅛	12.62

Model 10 engine is used to power the generator on models 10A35-1L, 10A35-2L or 10HY35-1L. Model 251 engine is used to power generators 251A35 and 251HY35, centrifugal pump 251S3 or trash pump 251TP3. Generator or pump must be partly disassembled to service some engine components. Note: Generators 10A35-1L, 10A35-2L and 10HY35-1L are equipped with Loadamatic which is a registered trademark of Homelite under U.S. Patent Nos. 3,612,892/3,626,197.

MAINTENANCE

SPARK PLUG. Either a Champion J6J, HO-8A or UJ-11-G spark plug may be used. The Champion HO-8A platinum tip or UJ-11-G gold palladium tip plug will provide longer service as well as longer intervals between cleanings. Electrode gap is 0.025.

CARBURETOR. Refer to Fig. HL20. The Tillotson HS carburetor can be removed from engine by removing air intake manifold (4—Fig. HL21) and air cleaner assembly as the two manifold bolts also retain carburetor and reed valve assemblies.

When disassembling carburetor, slide diaphragm assembly towards adjustment needle side of carburetor body to disengage diaphragm from fuel inlet control lever. To remove welch plug (29—Fig. HL20), carefully drill through plug with a small diameter drill and pry plug out with a pin. Caution should be taken that drill bit just

3. Fuel pump cover
4. Fuel pump gasket
5. Fuel pump diaphragm
6. Inlet channel screen
9. Governor spring arm
12. Throttle shaft clip
13. Choke detent spring
14. Choke dentent ball
15. Choke shutter
16. Inlet needle valve
17. Inlet lever spring
18. Inlet control lever
19. Lever pinion pin
20. Pinion pin retaining screw
21. Diaphragm gasket
22. Metering diaphragm
23. Diaphragm cover
25. Nozzle check valve
26. Choke shaft
27. Main adjusting needle
28. Main needle spring
29. Welch plug
30. Idle fuel needle spring
31. Idle adjusting needle
32. Throttle shaft
33. Throttle shutter

Fig. HL22–Adjusting idle speed screw. Throttle rod friction screw is just visible at under side of air intake manifold. Idle speed must not be adjusted to above 2500 RPM.

goes through welch plug as deeper drilling may seriously damage carburetor. Note channel screen (6) and check valve assembly (25) located in bores of carburetor body.

Inlet control metering lever (18) should be flush with metering chamber floor of carburetor body. If not, bend diaphragm end of lever up or down as required so that lever is flush.

Normal adjustment of low speed fuel mixture needle (marked "LO" on air inlet manifold or needle nearest throttle shaft) is one turn open and main mixture adjustment needle

(marked "HI" on air inlet manifold or needle nearest choke shaft) should be opened ¾-turn. On pump engines, back the idle speed adjusting screw (see Fig. HL22) out until carburetor throttle plate will close completely and screw is clear of pin on throttle rod. Slowly turn screw in until it just contacts pin, then turn screw in one additional turn. Generator engines do not have throttle control rod.

Start engine and allow to warm up before making final carburetor adjustments. On generator engines, apply load and readjust main needle so en-

gine runs best, then remove load and adjust idle needle for smoothest operation. Refer to GENERATOR section for idle adjustment on models with Loadamatic.® On pump engines, pump water with throttle control rod pushed all the way in and readjust main mixture needle so engine runs best. Then, lift suction hose out of water, pull throttle rod out and adjust low idle speed for smoothest running. If necessary, readjust idle speed screw to obtain a slow idle speed of 1800-2500 RPM. CAUTION: Do not adjust low idle speed higher than 2500 RPM; higher idle speed will result in damage to governor. Note: The main and idle speed mixture adjustments are interdependent so that changing one needle setting often requires readjustment of other needle.

When reinstalling carburetor, be sure governor link is connected as shown in Fig. HL23.

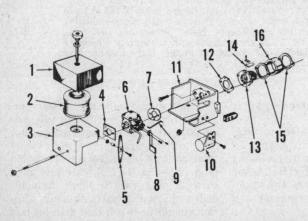

Fig. HL21–Exploded view of induction system. Components (8, 10 and 11) are not used on models with 251 engine.

1. Filter cover
2. Air filter
3. Intake manifold
4. Gasket
5. Bellcrank
6. Carburetor
7. Gasket
8. Throttle arm
9. Link
10. Loadamatic® electromagnet
11. Housing
12. Gasket
13. Reed valve seat
14. Reed valve
15. Gasket
16. Spacer

Fig. HL23–View showing proper installation of governor bellcrank and links. Generator engine not equipped with throttle (idle control) rod is shown.

GOVERNOR. Engine is equipped with a flyweight type governor mounted on engine crankshaft; refer to Fig. HL24 for exploded view showing governor unit. External governor linkage is shown in Fig. HL23.

CAUTION: Never move governor linkage manually, or exert any pressure on lever or linkage to increase engine speed. Working governor linkage manually, even momentarily, may cause damage to governor cup and cam due to friction and burning. Also, on pump engines, do not adjust slow idle speed above 2500 RPM.

Maximum no-load speed for pump engines should be 3800-3900 RPM and for generator engines, should be about 3750 RPM; generator engine speed under load should be 3600 RPM. If necessary to readjust governor, first remove the cover plate (43—Fig. HL24) and slightly loosen governor shaft guide (36) retaining screws. Note that screw hole in guide at carburetor side is slotted; insert screwdriver between side of guide and shoulder machined in housing (45). Pry carburetor side of guide towards cylinder to decrease governed speed or away from cylinder to increase speed. Adjustment provided by total length of slot will change the engine maximum governed speed about 1000 RPM.

If engine governed speed cannot be properly adjusted, check for wear on governor shaft cam and inspect governor spring connected to carburetor throttle shaft.

To renew governor spring (32), cup (31) or back plate (25), first remove starter, magneto rotor (49) and housing (45); the snap ring (34) can then be removed from crankshaft allowing removal of spring cup and back plate.

IGNITION. A breakerless solid state ignition system is used. Refer to Fig. HL24 for exploded view of the magneto (items 49 through 65) and to Figs. HL25 and HL26.

To check the solid state magneto, disconnect spark plug wire and remove spark plug. Insert a bolt or screw in spark plug wire terminal and while holding bolt or screw about ¼-inch away from engine casting, crank engine and check for spark as with conventional magneto. If no spark occurs, refer to following inspection and test procedure:

Visually check for broken or frayed wires which would result in open circuit or short. Be sure stop switch is not permanently grounded. Inspect magneto rotor (49—Fig. HL24), trigger coil (52) and the switch box, condenser and magneto cover assembly (62) for visible damage.

To test magneto components, remove starter assembly, magneto cover and disconnect leads as shown in Fig. HL26, then proceed as follows:

To test ignition coil, refer to test instrument instructions; readings for

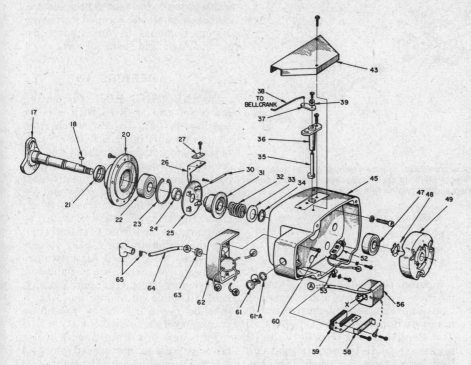

Fig. HL24–Exploded view showing magneto end of crankshaft (17), governor and magneto assemblies. The housing (45) retaining socket head screws can be removed by working through notches in outside of magneto rotor (49) allowing all parts to be removed as a unit after removing governor linkage and disconnecting spark plug wire.

17. Crankshaft, magneto end	30. Weight pivot pin	43. Governor linkage cover	60. Cover retaining screw
18. Woodruff key	31. Governor cup	45. Magneto housing	61. Stop switch
20. Bearing housing	32. Governor spring	47. Bearing	61A. "O" ring
21. Crankshaft seal	33. Spring retainer	48. Loading spring	62. Magneto cover assembly (includes condenser and solid state switchbox)
22. Bearing	34. Snap ring	49. Magneto rotor	
23. Snap ring	35. Governor camshaft	52. Magneto trigger coil	
24. Spacer	36. Camshaft guide	53. Lead clamp	
25. Governor back plate	37. Governor arm	56. Ignition coil	63. Grommet
26. Governor weight arm	38. Bellcrank link	58. Coil spring clip	64. Spark plug wire
27. Governor weight	39. Flat washer	59. Armature core	65. Spark plug terminal

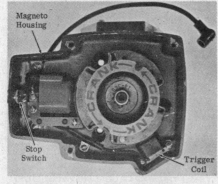

Fig. HL25–View of magneto assembly with rewind starter assembly removed. Armature to magneto rotor air gap and trigger coil to rotor air gap should be adjusted using a 0.0075 thick plastic shim.

Fig. HL26–View showing magneto leads disconnected for testing purposes. Condenser must not touch any other part of the unit. Refer to text for procedure and specifications.

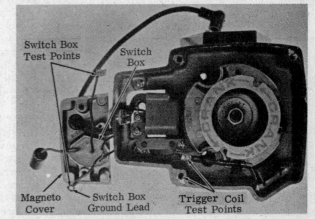

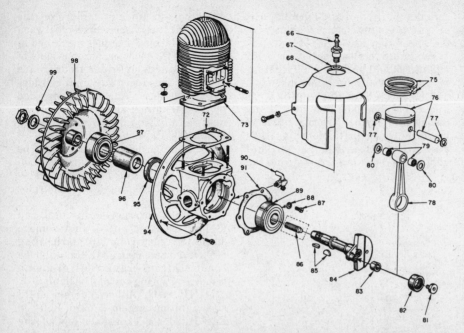

Fig. HL27–Exploded view showing model 251 engine crankcase, cylinder, rod and piston assembly, fan, crankshaft (output end) and related parts. Petcock (90) is to drain crankcase should it become flooded with fuel; do not attempt to start and run engine with petcock open.

66. Spark plug	78. Connecting rod
67. Spark plug gasket	79. Needle bearings
68. Cylinder shield	80. Thrust washers
72. Cylinder gasket	81. Crankpin screw
73. Cylinder	82. Roller bearing
75. Piston rings	83. Inner race
76. Piston & pin assy	84. Crankshaft (output
77. Snap rings	end)

85. Woodruff keys	90. Petcock
86. Stud bolts (251S3	91. Crankcase gasket
pump only)	94. Crankcase
87. Bearing retaining	95. Oil seal
screws	96. Spacer
88. Bearing retaining	97. Bearing
washers	98. Fan
89. Bearing	99. Cork plug

Graham Model 51 and Merc-O-Tronic testers are given below:

Graham Model 51:

Maximum secondary	10,000
Maximum primary	1.7
Coil index	65
Maximum coil test	20
Maximum gap index	65

Merc-O-Tronic

Operating amperage	1.3
Minimum primary resistance	0.6
Maximum primary resistance	0.7
Minimum secondary continuity	50
Maximum secondary continuity	60

If ignition coil does not meet test specifications, renew using correct part number coil. Do not substitute a coil of other specifications with the solid state ignition system. If coil tested ok, check switch box as follows:

With leads and condenser disconnected as shown in Fig. HL26, connect one ohmmeter lead to one switch box test point (flag terminal or ground lead) and other ohmmeter lead to remaining switch box test point. The ohmmeter reading should be either between 5 to 25 ohms or from one megohm to infinity. When ohmmeter test leads are reversed, the opposite reading should be observed. If these ohmmeter readings are not observed, renew magneto cover and switch box assembly. If ignition coil and switch box both test ok, check trigger coil as follows:

Connect ohmmeter positive lead to junction of switch box and trigger coil leads and ohmmeter negative lead to magneto housing (see "Trigger Coil Test Points" in Fig. HL26). It is not necessary to disconnect trigger coil lead from switch box lead. The ohmmeter reading should be 22 to 24 ohms.

To check condenser, stick a pin through the condenser lead to provide a contact point, then test condenser using standard procedure to check series resistance, short and capacitance. Condenser capacitance should be 0.16-0.20 mfd.

If either the switch box or condenser tested faulty, renew the complete condenser, switch box and magneto cover assembly.

LUBRICATION. Engine on all models is lubricated by mixing oil with regular gasoline. If Homelite® Premium SAE 40 chain saw oil is used, fuel:oil ratio should be 32:1. Fuel:oil ratio should be 16:1 if Homelite® 2-Cycle SAE 30 oil or other SAE 30 oil designed for air-cooled two stroke engines is used.

AIR AND FUEL FILTERS. The air cleaner element may be washed in a detergent and water solution or by sloshing it around in a container of non-oily solvent. After a number of cleanings, the filter pores may become permanently clogged, making it necessary to renew element.

The fuel filter is a part of the fuel pick-up inside fuel tank and can be fished from tank filler opening using a wire hook. Under normal operations, the filter element should be changed at intervals of from one to two months. If engine is run continuously or fuel is dirty, filter may need to be changed weekly or at shorter intervals.

CARBON. The carbon should be cleaned from exhaust ports at 100 to 200 hour intervals. Remove muffler, crank piston to top dead center and use a wooden or plastic scraper to remove carbon deposits. Avoid scratching piston or damaging edges of port.

REPAIRS

CONNECTING ROD. Connecting rod lower end is fitted with a roller bearing (82—Fig. HL27) which rides on a renewable inner race (83). To remove piston and connecting rod assembly from crankshaft (84) crankpin, first remove cylinder and the magneto housing and crankshaft rotor end assembly. Place a block of wood between crankshaft throw and crankcase to keep crankshaft from turning, then unscrew crankpin screw (81) (counterclockwise) with ⅜-inch Allen wrench. If renewal of inner race is indicated, remove race from crankpin. Usually, race will slide off of pin; however, it may be necessary to pry race from crankpin with screwdrivers.

To renew crankpin needle roller bearing in the connecting rod, press old bearing out using plug (Homelite tool No. 24120-1), supporting rod on sleeve (Homelite tool No. 24118-1). Install new bearing by supporting rod on sleeve (Homelite tool No. 24124-1) and pressing bearing in with same plug as used to remove old bearing. Shouldered face of sleeve (24124-1) will properly position bearing so that it protrudes equally from each side of rod.

To renew piston pin bearings, support rod on sleeve (Homelite tool No. 24124-1) and press bearings out with plug (24131-1). New bearings are installed separately from opposite ends of bore. Support rod on sleeve (24124-1) and using straight end of plug (24131-1) (end with recessed face), press bearing in (press on lettered side of cage only) until shoulder of plug seats against rod. Turn rod over and press other new bearing into rod in same manner. When properly installed, recessed faces of piston pin thrust washers will clear protruding bearing races and will contact connecting rod.

When reinstalling connecting rod and bearing inner race, thoroughly lubricate all parts and tighten connecting rod cap screw to a torque of 50

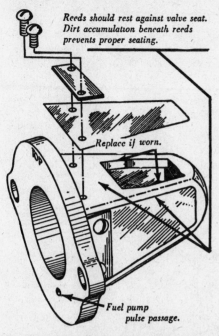

Reeds should rest against valve seat. Dirt accumulation beneath reeds prevents proper seating.

Replace if worn.

Fuel pump pulse passage.

Fig. HL29–View showing reed valve assembly with one valve reed removed. Inspect seat and reeds as noted and be sure fuel pump pulse passage is open.

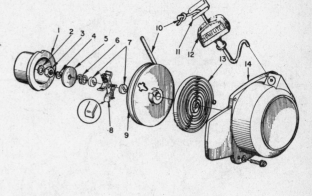

Fig. HL30–Exploded view of rewind starter used on model 251 engine. Starter cup (1) has notches for using emergency starting rope.

1. Starter cup
2. Lock washer
3. Crankshaft nut
4. Snap ring
5. Retaining washer
6. Brake spring
7. Brake washer
8. Friction shoe assembly
9. Starter pulley
10. Starter rope
11. Handle insert
12. Handle
13. Rewind spring
14. Starter cover

ft.-lbs. Note: Locate connecting rod on crankpin so that oil hole in upper end of rod will be towards intake side of engine. Piston should be assembled to connecting rod so that piston ring locating pin will be to same (intake) side of assembly as oil hole in rod.

PISTON, PIN AND RINGS. Piston is accessible after removing cylinder from crankcase. Always support piston while removing or installing piston pin. Piston should be renewed if ring side clearance, measured with new ring installed in top groove, exceeds 0.004. Also, renew piston if piston skirt to cylinder bore clearance exceeds 0.007 when measured with new or unworn cylinder. Inspect piston ring locating pin and renew piston if pin has worn to half of its original thickness. Piston pin should be a snug push-fit-to light press-fit in piston. Piston, pin and rings are available in standard size only. Homelite recommends that piston rings be renewed whenever engine is disassembled for service.

When reassembling piston to connecting rod, insert new snap ring in exhaust side (opposite ring locating pin) side of piston. Lubricate all parts and place piston, exhaust side down, in holding fixture. (Note: A used cylinder sawed in half makes a good holding fixture.) Press pin into upper (intake) side of piston, then insert connecting rod and thrust washers into piston with oil hole in rod up and recessed sides of washers next to piston pin bearings in rod. press pin on through the assembly

and secure with new snap ring. Be sure that piston and rod assembly is installed on crankpin with pinned (intake) side of piston away from exhaust port side of engine.

CYLINDER. Cylinder bore is chrome plated. Inspect cylinder bore for excessive wear and damage to chrome surface of bore. A new cylinder must be installed if chrome is scored, cracked or the base metal underneath exposed.

CRANKSHAFT, BEARINGS AND SEALS. The two-piece crankshaft can be serviced as two separate parts. Refer to following paragraphs for crankshaft service.

CRANKSHAFT, MAGNETO END. To service the shaft, bearings, seal or governor components, proceed as follows: Remove rewind starter as an assembly. Unscrew magneto rotor retaining nut and using suitable puller (Homelite tool No. AA-22560 or equivalent), remove rotor. Disconnect governor linkage and remove governor bellcrank. Using a 3/16-inch Allen wrench, remove the six socket head screws retaining magneto housing to crankcase and remove housing and shaft assembly. Remove the two screws retaining bearing housing (20—Fig. HL24) to magneto housing (45) and separate shaft and bearing assembly from housing (45). Bearing (47) can be renewed at this time. Remove snap ring (34), retainer (33) and governor spring (32) and pry governor back plate (25), with weights, from shaft (17). Remove spacer (24), support bearing

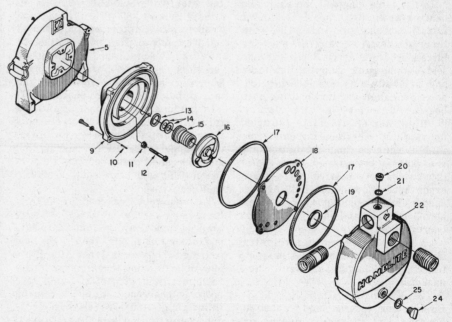

Fig. HL31–Exploded view of model 251S3 pump assembly. Impeller (16) threads onto stud (86–Fig. HL27) threaded into output end of crankshaft. Use shims (14) as required to maintain 0.020-0.030 clearance between impeller and wear plate (18).

5. Engine fan housing
9. Impeller housing
10. Spirol pin
11. Sealing washer
12. Cap screws (to fan housing)
13. Washer
14. Shims (1/32 & 0.010)
15. Seal assembly
16. Impeller
17. Gaskets
18. Wear plate
19. Gasket
20. Primer plug
21. Gasket
22. End housing
24. Drain plug
25. Gasket

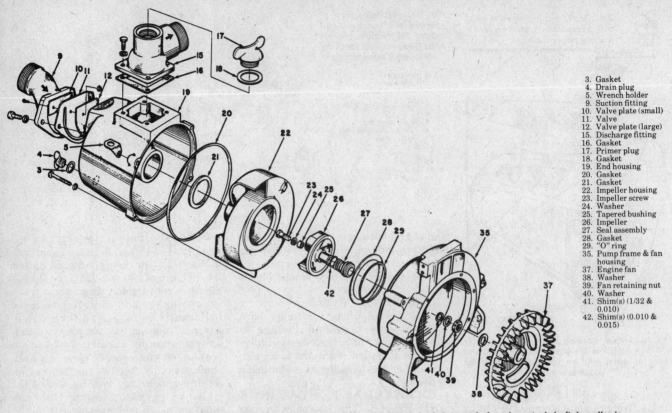

3. Gasket
4. Drain plug
5. Wrench holder
9. Suction fitting
10. Valve plate (small)
11. Valve
12. Valve plate (large)
15. Discharge fitting
16. Gasket
17. Primer plug
18. Gasket
19. End housing
20. Gasket
21. Gasket
22. Impeller housing
23. Impeller screw
24. Washer
25. Tapered bushing
26. Impeller
27. Seal assembly
28. Gasket
29. "O" ring
35. Pump frame & fan housing
37. Engine fan
38. Washer
39. Fan retaining nut
40. Washer
41. Shim(s) (1/32 & 0.010)
42. Shim(s) (0.010 & 0.015)

Fig. HL32—Exploded view of model 251TP3 pump assembly. Impeller screw (23) threads into end of engine crankshaft. Impeller is not solidly connected to engine crankshaft and can slip on tapered bushing (25) and end of crankshaft should a solid object become lodged between impeller and housing.

housing (20) and press shaft from housing. Remove crankshaft seal (21) and snap ring (23), then press bearing (22) from housing.

To assemble magneto end shaft and bearing assembly, proceed as follows: Install new seal (21) in housing with lip of seal towards crankcase side. Lubricate seal and insert shaft through seal and housing. Support flat inner end of shaft and press bearing (22) down over shaft and into housing until bearing inner race is seated against shoulder on shaft. Then, support housing and press bearing outer race into housing so that retaining snap ring (23) can be installed. Place spacer (24) on shaft, then drive or press governor back plate onto shaft against spacer. Install governor cup, spring, spring retainer and snap ring. Attach bearing housing to magneto housing with the two screws, then reinstall shaft, bearing housing and magneto housing to crankcase using new gasket.

CRANKSHAFT, OUTPUT END. First, remove magneto end crankshaft, bearing and magneto housing assembly as described in preceding paragraph. Remove cylinder and piston and connecting rod unit, then proceed as follows:

Remove the crankcase, output crankshaft end and blower rotor (fan) as an assembly from pump or generator; refer to exploded views of pump and generator units shown in this section. Remove fan retaining nut and washer and the two crankshaft bearing retaining screws (87—Fig. HL27) and washers (88). Support magneto (open) end of crankcase, then press crankshaft (84) from fan and crankcase. Remove the three corks (99), if so equipped, from fan, insert jackscrews into the tapped holes and push bearing (97) from fan inner hub. Remove screws and reinstall corks. Corks keep threads clean but are not necessary for operation. Support outer race of bearing (89) and press shaft out of bearing. Remove spacer (96) and crankshaft seal (95) from crankcase.

To reassemble, proceed as follows: Press new seal into crankcase with lip towards inside (away from fan). Support outer hub of fan, then press new bearing (97) onto fan inner hub. Press new inner bearing (89) into crankcase with retaining groove in outer race properly positioned. Support bearing inner race with sleeve, then press crankshaft into bearing. Install bearing retaining screws and washers. Place spacer (96) in position on crankshaft, then carefully press fan onto shaft making sure that keys and keyways are aligned. Install fan retaining washer and nut securely. Complete

reassembly by installing connecting rod and piston, cylinder and magneto end assembly.

CRANKCASE. To renew crankcase, follow procedures as outlined in previous paragraph "CRANKSHAFT, OUTPUT END".

REED INTAKE VALVE. Engine is equipped with a pyramid reed valve assembly shown in Fig. HL21. The reed valve should be inspected whenever carburetor is removed. Refer to Fig. HL29 for inspection points. When installing new reeds on pyramid seat, thoroughly clean all threads and apply Loctite to threads on screws before installing. Be sure reeds are centered before tightening screws.

REWIND STARTER. Refer to Fig. HL30 for exploded view. In an emergency in case of rewind starter failure, engine can be started by removing starter and winding a rope around starter cup (1).

CENTRIFUGAL PUMP
Model 251S3

To remove pump from engine, remove end housing (22—Fig. HL31) taking care not to damage gaskets. Unscrew impeller clockwise by placing wrench on hex portion and striking wrench a sharp blow with hammer. Note: The impeller is mounted on a

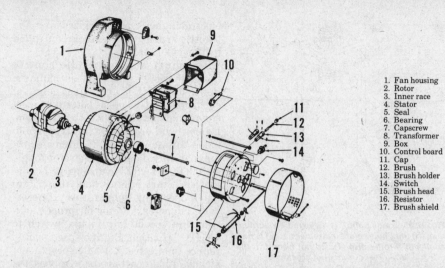

1.	Fan housing
2.	Rotor
3.	Inner race
4.	Stator
5.	Seal
6.	Bearing
7.	Capscrew
8.	Transformer
9.	Box
10.	Control board
11.	Cap
12.	Brush
13.	Brush holder
14.	Switch
15.	Brush head
16.	Resistor
17.	Brush shield

Fig. HL33–Exploded view of model 10A35-IL and 10A35-2L generator. Model 251A35 is similar but Loadamatic® components (10 and 14) are not used. Rotor (2) is retained on tapered end of engine crankshaft by cap screw (7); to remove rotor, remove cap screw, insert armature pin (Homelite part No. 22271 cut to length of 7¾ inches) and thread special jack screw (part No. S-394). Tap the tightened jack screw with hammer to break armature loose from crankshaft.

stud bolt threaded into end of engine crankshaft; the impeller may unscrew off of the stud or stud may be removed with impeller. Take care not to lose the shims (14) or washer (13). After removing impeller, impeller housing can be unbolted and removed from engine fan housing (5).

Before assembling pump, lubricate seal seat and seal head with oil and make sure gaskets are in good condition. Shims (14) are used as required to maintain minimum clearance between

impeller and wear plate (18). When reassembling, place wear plate against impeller housing without a gasket and turn engine by hand to be sure impeller does not rub against wear plate.

TRASH PUMP
Model 251TP3

Refer to Fig. HL32. To remove pump, first remove end housing (19) from pump body and fan housing (35). Remove impeller housing (22) if not re-

moved with end housing. Unscrew impeller retaining cap screw (23) and remove washer (24), tapered bushing (25), impeller and seal assembly. The engine can then be unbolted and removed from housing (35).

Before reassembling pump, make sure gaskets and shaft seal are in good condition, lubricate seal seat and seal head, then proceed as follows: A 0.010 to 0.020 clearance between impeller and impeller housing is maintained by varying number of shims (41) between impeller hub and washer (40). Add shims until impeller just contacts impeller housing when housing is held in position, then remove one 0.015 thick shim. Compressed length of seal assembly (not including seat) should be ⅞ inch, plus or minus 0.010, and is adjusted by adding or removing shims (42) between seal head and impeller. Seal length should be measured after impeller to impeller housing clearance is adjusted. After impeller clearance and seal length are correct, complete reassembly of pump.

GENERATORS
Models 10A35-1L, 10A35-2L, 10HY35-1L, 251A35 and 251HY35-1

Exploded view of model 10A35-1L, 10A35-2L and 251A35 generators is shown in Fig. HL33 and model

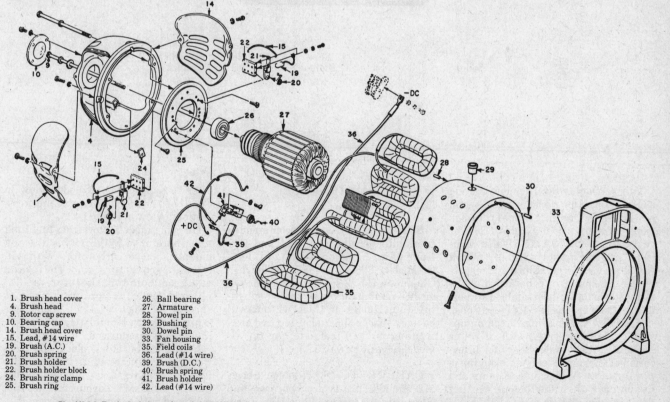

1.	Brush head cover	26.	Ball bearing
4.	Brush head	27.	Armature
9.	Rotor cap screw	28.	Dowel pin
10.	Bearing cap	29.	Bushing
14.	Brush head cover	30.	Dowel pin
15.	Lead, #14 wire	33.	Fan housing
19.	Brush (A.C.)	35.	Field coils
20.	Brush spring	36.	Lead (#14 wire)
21.	Brush holder	39.	Brush (D.C.)
22.	Brush holder block	40.	Brush spring
24.	Brush ring clamp	41.	Brush holder
25.	Brush ring	42.	Lead (#14 wire)

Fig. HL34–Exploded view of model 251HY35-1 generator assembly. Cap screw (9) retains generator rotor (27) to engine crankshaft.

10HY35-1L and 251HY35-1 exploded view is shown in Fig. HL34. Care should be taken in disassembly of the generator that any leads disconnected are identified so that they be reconnected properly. Also, if brushes are to be reinstalled, they should be identified so they can be installed in same location and position from which they were removed. Carefully disassemble to avoid damage to wiring or insulation.

Generator rotor (5—Fig. HL33 or 27 —Fig. HL34) can be removed from engine crankshaft by inserting a pin (Homelite No. 22271 cut to a length of 7¾ inches measured from tapered end) into rotor after removing retaining cap screw (14—Fig. HL33 or 9—Fig. HL34). Then, thread a jackscrew (Homelite No. S-394) into rotor, tighten jackscrew and tap with hammer to loosen taper fit.

Generators 10A35-1L, 10A35-2L and 10HY35-1L are equipped with an automatic idle control (Loadamatic®). An electromagnet is mounted adjacent to the engine's carburetor and acts on the

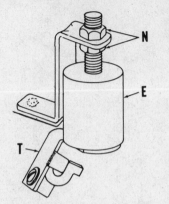

Fig. HL35–Loadamatic® is adjusted by turning nuts (N) until bottom of electromagnet (E) is parallel with throttle arm (T). Do not bend throttle arm or electromagnet bracket.

carburetor throttle arm. When there is no load on the generator, the electromagnet is energized and the engine governor is overridden as the electromagnet pulls the carburetor throttle arm to idle position. The governor resumes control of engine speed when a load is imposed on the generator. The

electromagnet is deenergized and the throttle arm is released to be controlled by the governor.

To adjust automatic idle control (Loadamatic®), proceed as follows: Refer to Fig. HL35 and adjust height of electromagnet to place bottom of electromagnet parallel with throttle arm. Do not bend bracket or throttle arm to make this adjustment. Tighten electromagnet nuts. Position generator toggle switch to "START" to disengage Loadamatic®. Start engine and allow it to reach operating temperature. If necessary, adjust carburetor for proper mixture and speed. Flip toggle switch to "AUTO" position. Engine speed should reduce to idle speed. If idle speed is not steady, adjust carburetor idle mixture. Idle speed should be 2400-2600 rpm and is adjusted by loosening electromagnet. Raising electromagnet will decrease engine speed while lowering electromagnet increases engine speed. Apply a light load to generator and then remove it. Engine speed should increase to governed speed and then return to idle after the load is removed.

Model	Bore Inches	Stroke Inches	Displ. Cu. In.
8	2¾	2⅛	12.62
9	2¾	2⅛	12.62
20	2⅜	1½	6.63
23	2¼	2⅛	8.45
24	2⅝	2⅛	11.50
35	2-7/16	1½	7.0
36	2¼	2⅛	8.45

This section covers Homelite 2-cycle engines used on various pumps and generators. The unit model number (such as pump model number 8S3-1 or generator model 9A115-1) also indicates engine model number (which would be model 8 and model 9 respectively). The pump or generator must be at least partially disassembled to perform certain engine service operations.

CAUTION: Centrifugal type pumps should not be operated without water in pump. Water is necessary for lubrication of the pump seal while engine is running. Cap suction side of pump and fill pump with water before starting engine when pump is assembled.

MAINTENANCE

SPARK PLUG. Recommended spark plug for all except 36S2 and 8S3-1 pumps is Champion HO-8A or UJ-11-G. Models 36S2 and 8S3-1 require a Champion UJ-22 spark plug. Model J6 or J6J Champion plugs can be substituted for HO-8A or UJ-11-G; but will be more susceptible to fouling and electrode erosion. Electrode gap for all models should be 0.025.

CARBURETORS. Tillotson Series MD and MT float type carburetors and Homelite carburetors have been used;

refer to appropriate exploded view in Fig. HL40 or Fig. HL41, or to the cross-sectional view in Fig. HL43.

On some models, flow from fuel tank to carburetor is by gravity with tank mounted above carburetor. With Tillotson carburetors and fuel tank mounted below carburetor, a diaphragm type fuel pump is used as shown in Fig. HL42. On models equipped with Homelite carburetor, fuel tank is pressurized.

On all carburetors, clockwise rotation of fuel mixture adjustment needles leans the mixture. NOTE: Later models with MT carburetor are not equipped with a throttle disc or shaft.

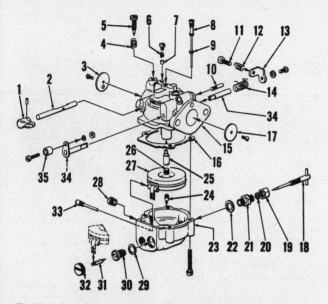

Fig. HL40–Exploded view of typical Tillotson Series MD carburetor as used on some Homelite pump models.

1. Choke lever	13. Throttle stop lever	25. Main nozzle
2. Choke shaft	14. Throttle return spring	26. Main nozzle plug
3. Choke disc	15. Carburetor body	27. Float
4. Spring	16. Gasket	28. Bowl drain plug
5. Idle fuel screw	17. Throttle disc	29. Gasket
6. Spring	18. Main fuel needle	30. Inlet valve seat
7. Choke friction pin	19. Packing nut	31. Inlet valve needle
8. By-pass tube	20. Packing	32. Plug
9. Gasket	21. Packing gland	33. Float pin
10. Throttle stop pin	22. Gasket	34. Throttle shaft
11. Idle speed screw	23. Fuel bowl	35. Roller
12. Spring	24. Fuel bowl plug	

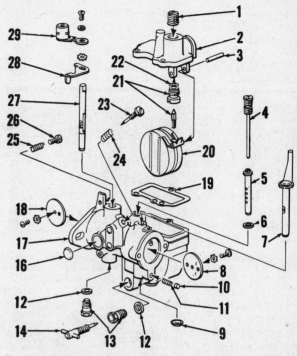

Fig. HL41–Exploded view of typical Series MT Tillotson float type carburetor as used on some Homelite pump and generator models.

1. Pipe plug	11. Spring	21. Inlet valve assy.
2. Float bowl cover	12. Gasket	22. Gasket
3. Float pin	13. Packing nut	23. Idle fuel needle
4. By-pass tube	14. Main fuel needle	24. Spring
5. Main nozzle	16. Expansion plug	25. Spring
6. Gasket	17. Carburetor body	26. Idle stop screw
7. Choke shaft	18. Throttle disc	27. Throttle shaft
8. Choke disc	19. Gasket	28. Throttle stop lever
9. Expansion plug	20. Float	29. Throttle lever
10. Choke friction pin		

Normal idle needle (5—Fig. HL40) setting for Tillotson MD carburetors is ¼-turn open; main (high speed) needle (18) setting is 1¼-1½ turns open. Float setting with fuel bowl assembly held in upside down position should be 1/32-inch from the lowest point of float at free end, to rim of fuel bowl.

Normal idle needle (23—Fig. HL41) setting for Tillotson MT carburetors is ¾-turn open; main (high speed) needle (14) setting is 1-turn open. Float setting, with the float bowl cover assembly (2) inverted, should be 1-13/32-inch as measured from the top of the float (20) to the gasket surface of the float bowl cover.

Normal mixture adjustment needle (32—Figs. HL43 and HL44) setting for the Homelite carburetor is 1½ turns open. Carburetor operates by pressurizing the fuel tank and loss of tank pressure will prevent carburetor from operating properly.

GOVERNOR. All are equipped with rotary type inlet valves. The governor is a centrifugal type and is an integral part of the rotary inlet valve as indicated in Fig. HL45. On models so equipped, Formica wear plate (15—Fig. HL50) is pinned to the engine crankcase with opening in wear plate in register with intake opening in crankcase. On all models, the inlet opening in the valve plate (IV—Fig. HL45) is controlled by the combination

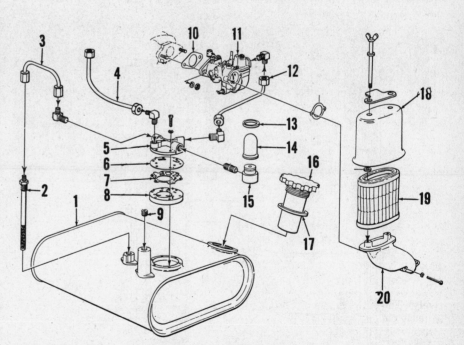

Fig. HL42–Exploded view of fuel system on models using Tillotson float type carburetor. Exploded view of carburetor is shown in Fig. HL41. Actuating primer bulb (14) will pump fuel into carburetor float bowl.

1. Fuel tank	6. Pump diaphragm	11. Carburetor assy.	16. Filler cap
2. Fuel filter	7. Gasket	12. Fuel line	17. Gasket
3. Pump suction line	8. Diaphragm cover	13. Ring	18. Air cleaner cover
4. Pump pulse line	9. Pipe plug	14. Priming bulb	19. Element
5. Pump body	10. Gasket	15. Adapter	20. Adapter

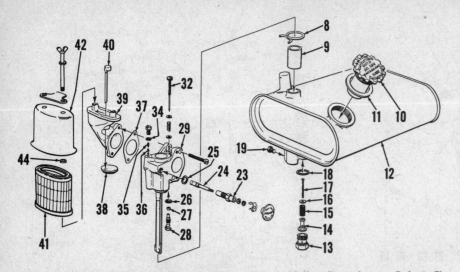

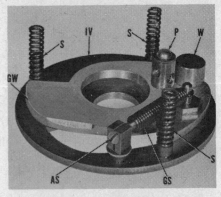

Fig. HL43–Exploded view of fuel system on models equipped with Homelite carburetor. Refer to Fig. HL44 for cross-sectional views of carburetor assembly. Fuel tank is pressurized to force fuel upward into carburetor.

8. Hose clamps	16. Washer	27. Sleeve	37. Gasket
9. Adapter hose	17. Screw	28. Jet	38. Carburetor cover
10. Fuel cap	18. Gasket	29. Carburetor body	39. Adapter
11. Gasket	19. Drain plug	32. Fuel needle	40. Vent tube
12. Fuel tank	23. Plunger tube	34. Gasket	41. Filter element
13. Filter plug	24. Primer plunger	35. Spring	42. Air filter cover
14. Filter adapter	25. Gasket	36. Priming valve	44. Washer
15. Screen	26. Gasket		

Fig. HL45–View of late production rotary inlet valve and governor assembly. Early production units did not have adjusting screw (AS) and engine governed speed was non-adjustable.

AS. Adjusting screw	IV. Intake valve plate
GS. Governor spring	P. Pivot post
GW. Governor weight & plate assy.	S. Springs
	W. Weight

shutter and governor weight (GW) which when the engine is stationary, is held in the open position by spring (GS). When engine speed exceeds the designed limit, centrifugal force acting on the weight overcomes the opposing spring pressure and partially covers the manifold opening and thus throttles the engine. As the throttled engine slows down, centrifugal force diminishes and the spring again uncovers the opening to restore engine speed.

GOVERNOR ADJUSTMENT. On later production engines equipped with adjustable governor (Fig. HL45) or on earlier engines in which adjustable governor has been installed, engine governed speed may be adjusted as follows:

First, bring engine to normal operating temperature and adjust carburetor for highest speed and best performance obtainable. Then, on model 35 engine, remove drain petcock (DP—Fig. HL46) on muffler side of front-half crankcase; on models 8, 9 and 9-A, disconnect pulse line (L—Fig. HL47) (above drain petcock) and unscrew the 90° elbow (E); or, on model 20 engine, remove slotted head brass plug (P—Fig. HL48) in front half of crankcase.

Turn adjusting screw (AS—Fig. HL45) clockwise to increase no-load speed, or counterclockwise to decrease no-load speed as required. One turn of the adjusting screw will change engine no-load governed speed approximately 100 RPM. Accurately adjust generator engine no-load speed to 3750 RPM.

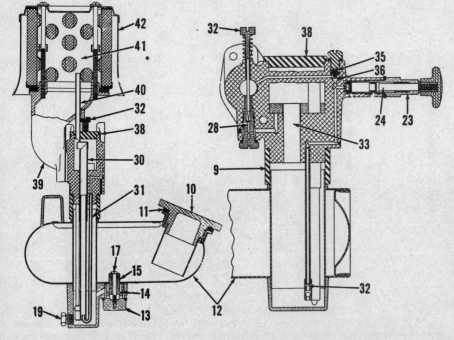

Fig. HL44–Cross-sectional view of Homelite carburetor. Refer to Fig. HL43 for additional legend and exploded view of complete fuel system.

3. Priming tube and foot valve	31. Pressure tube
30. Feed tube	33. Overflow tube

Fig. HL46–Governor adjusting screw (see Fig. HL45) is accessible on model 35 engines after removing drain petcock (DP).

Fig. HL47–On engine models 8 and 9, governor adjusting screw (see Fig. HL45) is accessible after removing pulse line (L) and elbow (E).

Fig. HL48–On engine model 20, governor adjusting screw (see Fig. HL45) is accessible after removing slotted head plug (P).

Recommended no-load engine governed RPM for the various pump applications is as follows:

Pump Model	No-Load RPM
20S1½-1A	3900-4000
20DP-3	2850-2950
35S2-1	2850-2950
8S3-1, 9S3-1	2850-2950
8S3-1P, 9S3-1P	4200-4300*
36S2	2650-2750
All other pumps	3800-3900

*3850 RPM at 60 psi pump pressure

IGNITION & TIMING. Breaker point gap on all models should be 0.020. Gap should be measured when breaker arm rub block is ⅛-inch past breaking edge of cam.

Breaker spring tension should be 14-21 oz. as measured at center of breaker

shoe. Ignition timing is fixed and non-adjustable. The cam must be installed with arrow facing out. Refer to Fig. HL49 and HL49A for typical magneto assembly.

Condenser capacity ....0.34 mfds
Coil primary .... 0.95 ohms
Coil secondary ..... 5500-6000 ohms

NOTE: Later model 9 engines are equipped with a starter plate (1—Fig. HL49) which has countersunk screw holes and is retained by flathead screws in compliance with OSHA regulations. Model 8, 35, 36, and early model 9 engines may be fitted with Kit A-51497 which contains the starter plate and screws needed to comply with OSHA regulations.

LUBRICATION. Engine on all models is lubricated by mixing oil with regular gasoline. If Homelite® Premium SAE 40 oil is used, fuel:oil ratio should be 32:1. Fuel:oil ratio should be 16:1 if Homelite® 2-Cycle SAE 30 oil or other SAE 30 oil designed for air-cooled two stroke engines is used. Note: A fuel:oil ratio of 32:1 should be used on diaphragm pump models regardless of whether Homelite® Premium SAE 40 or Homelite® 2-Cycle SAE 30 oil is used.

CLEANING CARBON. Carbon deposits should be cleaned from the exhaust ports and muffler at regular intervals. When scraping carbon be careful not to damage the finely chamfered edges of the exhaust ports.

REPAIRS

CONNECTING ROD. On model 20 engines, the connecting rod lower bearing is of the needle roller type and rod cap is detachable from rod. The rod and piston assembly can be removed from the engine after removing the cylinder assembly. Be careful to avoid loss of the 31 individual needle rollers in the crankcase. Crankpin diameter is 0.6937-0.6940. Renew connecting rod if surfaces of rod and cap which form the outer race for the needle rollers are rough, scored or worn. If any one

needle roller is worn or if rollers can be separated more than the width of one needle, reject the bearing. This applies also to the needle roller caged bearing assembly or assemblies mounted in the upper end of the connecting rod. Homelite recommends the renewal of the crankpin (lower) connecting rod bearing at each overhaul.

Inspect crankpin and if it is scored or is out-of-round or tapered more than 0.001, install a new crankshaft.

Refer to PISTONS for correct reassembly of rod to piston. When reassembling rod to crankshaft always renew the Allen type retaining cap screws and align mating marks on rod and cap.

On models 36S2, 23S2, some 8S3-1, 8S3-1P and 8S3-1R and all 9S3-1, 9S3-1P and 9S3-1R (Refer to 42—Fig. HL52), the connecting rod lower bearing is of the double track ball bearing type. To remove the connecting rod, it is necessary to remove the cylinder, timer bracket and the connecting rod retaining Allen head screw (43); then, with the use of special pullers, remove the connecting rod and bearings. Renew bearing if it feels lumpy when rotated or has perceptible wear.

On models 24S3, 24S3-1P and some 8S3-1, 8S3-1P and 8S3-1R, the lower

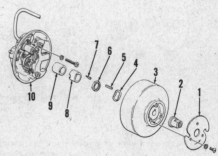

Fig. HL49–To remove magneto rotor (3), unscrew retaining nut (2) against plate (1) which acts as puller. Some models do not have magneto cam retaining nut (6). Notch in inner end of cam (8) must fit over pin in spacer (9). See "NOTE" in text.

1. Starter plate	5. Rotor key
2. Rotor nut	6. Breaker cam nut
3. Magneto rotor (flywheel)	7. Breaker cam key
4. Wave washer	8. Breaker cam
	9. Cam spacer
	10. Magneto assembly

Fig. HL49A–Exploded view of typical magneto assembly (see 10–Fig. HL49).

11. Back plate	17. Breaker point arm
12. Grommet	18. Ignition coil
13. Ground (switch) lead	19. Coil wedges
14. Condenser	20. Spark plug wire
15. Breaker point base	21. Terminal
16. Cam wiper felt	22. Spark plug boot

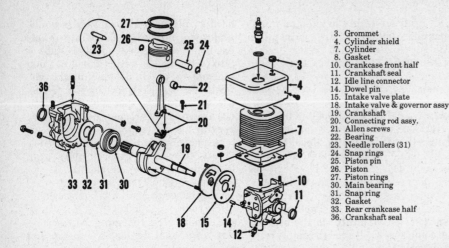

Fig. HL50—Exploded view of engine used on model 20DP3. Other model 20 engines are similar in construction.

3. Grommet
4. Cylinder shield
7. Cylinder
8. Gasket
10. Crankcase front half
11. Crankshaft seal
12. Idle line connector
14. Dowel pin
15. Intake valve plate
18. Intake valve & governor assy.
19. Crankshaft
20. Connecting rod assy.
21. Allen screws
22. Bearing
23. Needle rollers (31)
24. Snap rings
25. Piston pin
26. Piston
27. Piston rings
30. Main bearing
31. Snap ring
32. Gasket
33. Rear crankcase half
36. Crankshaft seal

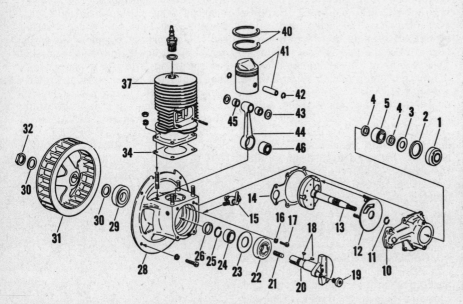

Fig. HL51—Exploded view of engine used on model 36S2 pump; engine used on 23S2 pump is of similar construction.

1. Bearing
2. Seal retaining ring
3. Seal
4. Spacers
5. Bearing
10. Timer bracket
11. Snap ring
12. Intake valve & governor assy.
13. Intake valve shaft

15. Drain petcock
16. Lockwasher
17. Main bearing retaining screw
18. Woodruff keys
19. Crankpin screw
20. Crankshaft
21. Pump drive stud
22. Main bearing

23. Gasket
24. Spacer
25. Snap ring
26. Spacer
28. Crankcase
29. Fan bearing
30. Washer
31. Fan
32. Fan nut

34. Gasket
37. Cylinder
40. Piston rings
41. Piston & pin
42. Snap rings
43. Washers
44. Connecting rod
45. Needle bearings
46. Crankpin bearing

end of the connecting rod is equipped with 25 needle rollers (52—Fig. HL52). As the lower end of the rod doesn't have a removable rod cap, removal of the cylinder, timer bracket and Allen head connecting rod bearing retainer is necessary before removing the connecting rod and piston assembly. Install large washer (54) with tapered side of hole toward pump and small washer (51) with tapered side toward inlet valve. Race (53) should be heated to 180° F. to aid in assembling to crankpin.

PISTON RINGS, PISTONS AND PINS. On all models, the piston assembly is accessible after removing the cylinder assembly from crankcase. Always support the piston when removing or installing the piston pin. All models are equipped with an aluminum alloy piston.

Piston ring end gap should be 0.105 to 0.115 on piston with ring locating pin and 0.008 to 0.020 on models with unpinned rings. Side clearance of piston ring in groove should be 0.0025-

0.004. Clearance between piston skirt and cylinder bore, measured at right angle to piston pin, should be 0.002-0.005 on models with 2¼ inch bore and 0.004-0.007 on other models.

On all models, reject the pin and the piston if there is any visible up and down play of pin in the piston bosses. Neither the piston nor the pin are available separately.

Install new needle roller bearing assemblies to upper end of connecting rod if any of the rollers have slight flat spots or are pitted. Do likewise if rollers can be separated more than the thickness of one roller.

Inspect piston for cracks and for holes in dome of same and reject if any are found. Slight scoring of piston walls is permissible, but if rough surfaces are accompanied by a deposit of aluminum on cylinder walls, reject the piston. Refer to CYLINDER for methods of removing such deposits.

If piston ring locating pins in piston grooves are worn to half their normal thickness, reject the piston.

When piston and rings unit is assembled to connecting rod, the side of the piston which has the piston ring locating pins should be on the intake (away from exhaust side) side of the cylinder. Always use new piston pin retaining snap rings when reassembling piston to connecting rod. All wearing parts of the engine are supplied as replacements in standard size only.

CYLINDER. Cylinder bore is chrome plated. Inspect chrome bore for excessive wear and damage to chrome surface of bore. A new cylinder must be installed if chrome is scored, cracked or the base metal underneath exposed.

CRANKSHAFT, BEARINGS AND SEALS. If shaft has damaged threads or enlarged keyways or if run out exceeds 0.003, reject the shaft. Journals for roller type bearings must be free of pits, galling or heavy score marks. If they are out of round or worn more than 0.001 reject the shaft.

If any needle roller shows wear or any visible flat spot, or if rollers can be separated more than the width (or diameter) of one roller, reject all of the rollers. If annular ball bearing feels "lumpy" when rotated, or has perceptible wear, reject the bearing.

Suitable pullers, pushers and mandrels (available from Homelite) should be used in removing and installing main and connecting rod bearings.

Crankshaft seals must be maintained in first class condition because crankcase compression leakage through seals causes a loss of power.

Centrifugal pumps must be disassembled to remove crankshaft from

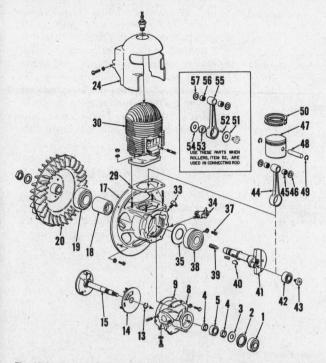

1. Bearing
2. Retaining ring
3. Seal
4. Spacers
5. Ball bearing
8. Timer bracket
9. Gasket
13. Snap ring
14. Intake valve & governor assy.
15. Intake valve shaft
17. Crankcase
18. Spacer
19. Fan bearing
20. Fan
24. Cylinder shield
30. Cylinder
33. Pulse line connection
34. Drain petcock
35. Gasket
37. Retaining screw
38. Main bearing
39. Pump drive stud
40. Woodruff keys
41. Crankshaft
42. Ball bearing
43. Crankpin screw
44. Connecting rod
45. Needle bearings
46. Washers
47. Piston
48. Piston pin
49. Snap rings
50. Piston rings
51. Washer
52. Needle rollers (25)
53. Inner race
54. Washer
55. Connecting rod
56. Needle bearings
57. Washers

Fig. HL52–Exploded view of engine used on 8S3 series pumps. Some engines are equipped with needle roller crankpin bearings (see inset) while others have a double-row ball bearing (42) in crankpin end of connecting rod.

spring posts are loose or extend to valve seating surface; if the governor pivot point has started to wear through the surface of the valve.

Slight scoring of valve may be corrected by lapping on a lapping plate using very fine abrasive. Lapping motion should be in the pattern of a figure eight to obtain best results. Slight scoring of the Formica wear plate is permissible. Homelite recommends soaking a new wear plate in oil for 24 hours prior to installation.

DIAPHRAGM PUMP

The diaphragm pump is lubricated by filling gearcase to level of plug (25—Fig. HL53) with SAE 90 gear lubricant and by greasing pump rod upper bearing once a month with pressure gun through fitting in upper end of rod.

When installing new diaphragm or assembling upper pump body to lower body, the diaphragm must be centered and in fully down position before tightening upper body to lower body bolts as shown in Fig. HL55.

crankcase; refer to CENTRIFUGAL PUMPS paragraph.

CRANKCASE. Be sure that all passages through the crankcase are clean. This is especially true of the idle passage line (in the front half crankcase) which enters the crankcase via the intake valve register. This passage is sometimes restricted by carbon deposits which can be cleaned with a piece of wire. The same holds true of the passage for the fuel tank pressure line (on models with pressurized fuel tank) or the actuator line on pump equipped engines.

If main bearing bores are worn, indicating that the bearing has been turning in the crankcase, the bearing and/or the crankcase should be rejected. On models so constructed, the mating surfaces of two-piece crankcase (Fig. HL50) must be free of all nicks and burrs as neither sealing compound nor gaskets are used at this joint.

Always use new bearing seals when reassembling engine.

ROTARY VALVE. The combination rotary type inlet valve and governor (Fig. HL45) should be rejected if any of the following conditions are encountered during inspection:

The sealing faces of valve are scored or worn enough to produce a ridge; if

Fig. HL53–Exploded view of drive gear case for diaphragm type pump; refer to Fig. HL54 for exploded view of the pump assembly. Pinion machined on rear end of engine crankshaft engages the intermediate gear (16); pinion on shaft (18) drives crank gear (12). Guard A-51135 is available to cover pump rod and crank.

3. Gear case cover	12. Pump crank gear	18. Intermediate shaft	24. Gear case
4. Bearing caps	13. Key	19. Retainer screws	25. Filler plug
5. Needle bearings	14. Pump crank shaft	20. Thrust washer	26. Seals
6. Thrust washers	15. Spacer	21. Needle bearing	27. Bearing cap
7. Retainer screws	16. Intermediate gear	22. Thrust washer	29. Pump crank
8. Gasket	17. Woodruff key	23. Needle bearing	30. Pump upper body
9. Crankshaft seal			

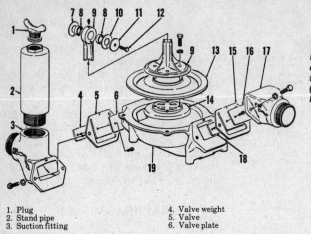

1. Plug
2. Stand pipe
3. Suction fitting
4. Valve weight
5. Valve
6. Valve plate

Fig. HL54–Exploded view of diaphragm type pump assembly. Pump upper body is (30–Fig. HL53). Refer to Fig. HL55 for pump assembly information.

7. Thrust washer
8. Needle bearings
9. Pump rod
10. Thrust washer
11. Washer
12. Cap screw
13. Pump diaphragm
14. Diaphragm cap
15. Valve
16. Valve plate
17. Discharge fitting
18. Valve weight
19. Pump lower body

peller and discard shim or shims as required from between impeller and crankshaft so that rubbing condition is eliminated. Install assembled impeller housing, then install pump end plate (4) with new gasket (8) and one or two new gaskets (7) as required so that end plate holds impeller housing securely against pump body. Note: End plate should rock slightly before being tightened.

TRASH PUMP

Trash pump used on the models in this section is the same as the pump shown in Fig. HL32. Refer to TRASH PUMP in model 251 section for overhaul of trash pump.

To remove pump from engine, drain gear lubricant and separate gearcase (24—Fig. HL53) from gearcase cover (3). Gear teeth are machined on end of engine crankshaft to drive intermediate gear (16). Unbolt and remove cover (3) from engine crankcase. When reassembling, use new gasket (8).

CENTRIFUGAL PUMP

Refer to exploded view of early type centrifugal pump in Fig. HL56; for later type pumps, refer to Fig. HL31 and HL32 in preceding Homelite section on model 251 engine. The pump must be disassembled and the impeller unscrewed from stud (21—Fig. HL51 or 39—Fig. HL52) in end of engine crankshaft so that the crankcase can be unbolted from pump body and crankshaft be removed from crankcase. Shims are used between impeller and end of crankshaft to maintain minimum clearance between impeller and wear plate (10—Fig. HL56); two shims are normally used. Remove shims if impeller rubs against wear plate when reassembling engine.

If necessary to renew pump seals, proceed as follows: Apply a thin coat of shellac to plain side of ceramic ring (15) and press new washer (16) against ring. Then, apply a thin coat of shellac on washer and press the washer and ceramic ring, washer side in, against and into recess of pump body. Slide seal (14) over hub of impeller with hy-car side of seal towards impeller. Thread impeller onto stud that is screwed into end of crankshaft.

Place the assembled impeller housing (9, 10 and 12) over impeller and in proper engagement with pin (18), press against housing and turn engine. If impeller rubs, remove im-

Fig. HL55–View showing proper installation of pump diaphragm. Refer to Figs. HL53 and HL54 for exploded views of pump gear box and pump assembly.

PUMP ROD

UPPER PUMP BODY

LOWER PUMP BODY

DIAPHRAGM

DIAPHRAGM MUST BE CENTERED AND IN FULL DOWN POSITION BEFORE INSTALLING BOLTS

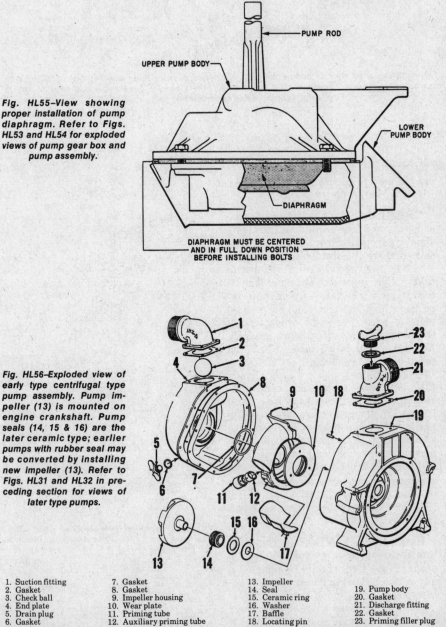

Fig. HL56–Exploded view of early type centrifugal type pump assembly. Pump impeller (13) is mounted on engine crankshaft. Pump seals (14, 15 & 16) are the later ceramic type; earlier pumps with rubber seal may be converted by installing new impeller (13). Refer to Figs. HL31 and HL32 in preceding section for views of later type pumps.

1. Suction fitting
2. Gasket
3. Check ball
4. End plate
5. Drain plug
6. Gasket
7. Gasket
8. Gasket
9. Impeller housing
10. Wear plate
11. Priming tube
12. Auxiliary priming tube
13. Impeller
14. Seal
15. Ceramic ring
16. Washer
17. Baffle
18. Locating pin
19. Pump body
20. Gasket
21. Discharge fitting
22. Gasket
23. Priming filler plug

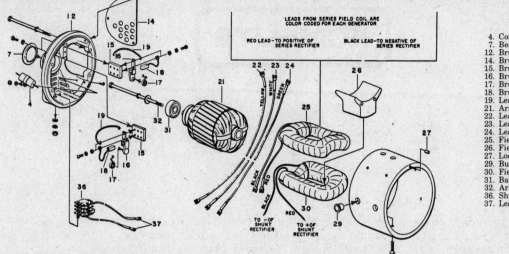

4. Condenser
7. Bearing cap
12. Brush head
14. Brush head cover
15. Brush holder block
16. Brush holder
17. Brush spring
18. Brush
19. Lead (#14 wire)
21. Armature
22. Lead 20" #10 wire
23. Lead, 16" #10 wire
24. Lead, 24" #14 wire
25. Field series coil
26. Field pole
27. Locating pin
29. Bushing
30. Field shunt coil
31. Ball bearing
32. Armature bolt
36. Shunt rectifier
37. Leads, 8" #20 wire

Fig. HL57–Exploded view showing construction of model 9A115-1 and 9A115/230-1 generator units. It will be necessary to remove armature (21) from engine crankshaft to service crankshaft seal, bearing and crankcase.

GENERATORS

Generator unit models 9HY-1, 9HY-1A, 9HY-1B and 9HY-1C are similar to the model 251HY 35-1 generator unit shown in Fig. HL34 in preceding section on Homelite model 251 engine. Voltamatic generators 9A34-1, 9A34-1A, 9A115-1A and 9A115/230-1A are similar to generator shown in Fig. HL13 in 250/270 section. Note: Voltamatic is a registered Homelite trademark identifying a method of voltage regulation protected by U.S. Patent No. 3,428,883.

For exploded view showing construction of generator models 9A115-1 and 9A115/230-1, refer to Fig. HL57. Identify each generator lead as it is disconnected so that the unit may be reassembled with leads properly connected. To remove armature (21) from engine crankshaft, remove the through bolt (32), then pull armature with pin (Homelite tool No. 22271 cut to proper length) and jackscrew (Homelite tool No. S-394) threaded into outer end of armature shaft.

Refer to Figs. HL58 and HL59 for schematic of generator models 9HY-1A, 9HY-1B and 9HY-1C. Refer to Fig. HL140 for schematic of generator model 9A34-1 and to Fig. HL141 for schematic of model 9A34-1A.

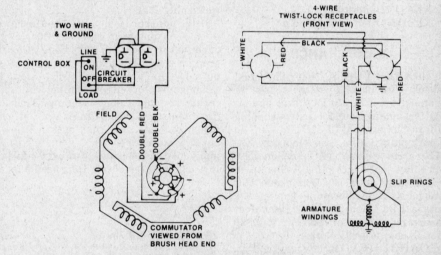

Fig. HL58–Schematic of 9HY-1C generator. Refer to Fig. HL59 for schematic variations for generators 9HY-1A and 9HY-1B.

Fig. HL59–Receptacles on generator 9HY-1A (A) and 9HY-1B (B) are wired as shown. Remainder of generator is wired as shown for 9HY-1C in Fig. HL58.

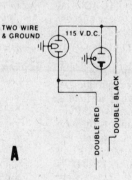

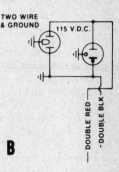

Model	Bore Inches	Stroke Inches	Displ. Cu. In.	Reed Type
XL-12	1¾	1⅜	3.3	Flat
Super XL	1-13/16	1⅜	3.55	Pyramid

This section covers service of Homelite model XL-12 and Super XL engines that are used in the following Homelite tools and equipment.

XL Brushcutter
XL100 Circular Saw
XL120 Circular Saw
XLA115 Generator
XLS1½-1 Centrifugal Pump

MAINTENANCE

SPARK PLUG. A Champion TJ-8J spark plug or equivalent is used in generator, XL-100 saw and brushcutter application; for extended plug life, a Champion UTJ-11P platinum tip spark plug may be used. On model XL-120 circular saw, use Champion CJ-6 or equivalent spark plug. A Champion CJ-8 spark plug is recommended for model XL100A. For pump application, use a Champion TJ-6J or equivalent spark plug. Set electrode gap to 0.025 for all engine applications.

CARBURETOR. Refer to Fig. HL60 for exploded view of Tillotson HS diaphragm type carburetor with integral fuel pump used on XL-12 and Super XL engines. Carburetor is accessible after removing air box cover (Fig. HL61). NOTE: If early type cover gasket becomes damaged when air box cover is removed, install new gasket as follows: Carefully remove old gasket from air box and be sure that surface is free of all dirt, oil, etc. Apply "3M" or Homelite No. 22788 cement to new gasket and carefully place gasket, adhesive side down, on lip around air box chamber. On later engines, gasket is bonded to filter element; install new filter element if either gasket or filter is damaged.

When disassembling carburetor, slide the diaphragm assembly towards adjustment needle side of carburetor body to disengage diaphragm from fuel inlet control lever. To remove welch plugs, carefully drill through large plug (27—Fig. HL60) with a ⅛-inch drill or through small plug (24) with a 1/16-inch drill and pry plugs out with a

pin inserted through the drilled hole. Caution should be taken that the drill just goes through the welch plug as deeper drilling may seriously damage the carburetor. Note channel screen (26) and screen retaining ring (25) which are accessible after removing welch plug (24).

Inlet control lever (17) should be flush with metering chamber floor of carburetor body. If not, bend diaphragm end of lever up or down as required so that the lever is flush.

On generator engine, make initial carburetor adjustment as follows: Turn fuel adjustment needle in gently until it just contacts seat, then back needle out 1¼ turns. For final adjustment, apply load to generator to allow engine to warm up, then slowly turn needle in

until engine speed starts to drop. Correct final setting is ⅛-turn open from this point.

On brushcutter, turn idle speed stop screw in until it just contacts throttle lever tab, then turn screw in ¾-turn further. Turn idle and main fuel adjustment needles in gently until they just contact seats, then back each needle out ⅝-turn. With engine warm and running, adjust idle fuel needle so that engine runs smoothly, then adjust idle stop screw so that engine runs at 2600 RPM, or just below clutch engagement speed. Check engine acceleration and open idle fuel needle slightly if engine will not accelerate properly. Adjust main fuel needle under load so engine will neither slow down or smoke excessively.

Fig. HL60–Exploded view of typical Tillotson series HS carburetor used on XL-12 and Super XL engines. Carburetor used on generator engine does not have idle fuel mixture adjustment needle (30). On some models, idle speed adjustment screw (34) is located in air box casting and is adjustable without removing cover (8–Fig. HL61).

3. Throttle disc
6. Pump cover
7. Gasket
8. Pump diaphragm
9. Inlet screen
10. Throttle shaft clip
11. Choke shaft & lever
12. Detent spring
13. Choke detent ball
14. Choke disc
15. Inlet needle
16. Spring
17. Diaphragm lever
18. Lever pin
19. Pin retaining screw
20. Gasket
21. Diaphragm
22. Diaphragm cover
24. Welch plug
25. Retaining ring
26. Channel screen
27. Welch plug
28. Springs
29. Main fuel needle
30. Idle fuel needle
31. Throttle shaft & lever
32. Throttle spring
33. Idle speed screw spring
34. Idle speed adjustment screw

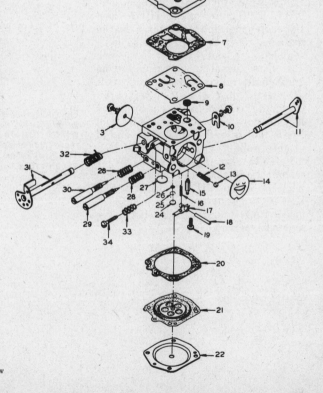

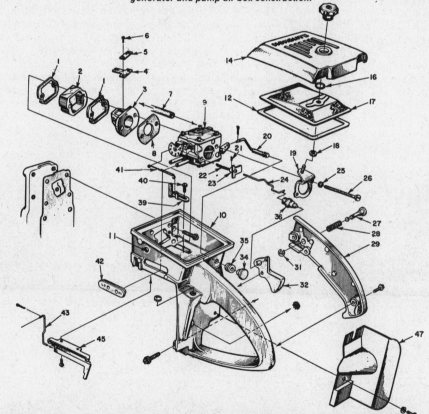

1. Gaskets
2. Spacer
3. Fuel line
4. Carburetor assembly
5. Cotter pin
6. Choke rod
8. Air filter cover
10. Retaining ring
11. Air filter element
12. Gasket
13. Gasket
14. Mounting bracket
15. Throttle rod
16. Throttle rod boot
19. Throttle lock pin
20. Spring
21. Handle cover
23. Retaining ring
24. Throttle trigger
25. Spring
26. Idle speed screw (external)
28. Grommet
29. Choke button
30. Plug
31. Air box housing
32. Headless screw
33. Plug
34. Adjusting needle grommet
35. Reed valve
36. Reed back-up
37. Reed stop

Fig. HL61–Exploded view of handle and air box assembly used on early XL100 saw; model XL120 handle and air box assembly is shown in Fig. HL61A. Late model XL-100 has air vane governor similar to that shown in Fig. HL61A. Refer to Figs. HL62 and HL63 for differences in brushcutter, generator and pump air box construction.

Fig. HL61A–Exploded view of model XL-120 air box and handle. Late model XL-100 is similar except that a flat reed intake valve is used as shown in Fig. HL61. Note the Super XL engine pyramid reed valve assembly (items 1 through 6). Tension of governor spring is adjusted by loosening screw (40) and moving speed adjusting plate (39); refer to text.

1. Gaskets	11. Plug	23. Throttle rod collar	35. Grommet
2. Spacer	12. Cover gasket	24. Throttle rod	36. Choke rod boot
3. Reed valve seat	14. Air box cover	25. Lock washers	39. Speed adjusting plate
4. Valve reeds	16. Snap ring	26. Carburetor mounting screws	40. Plate retaining screw
5. Reed plates	17. Filter element	27. Throttle lock pin	41. Governor spring
6. Reed screws	18. Stud gasket	28. Lock spring	42. Adjusting needle grommet
7. Fuel line	19. Bracket & stud	29. Handle cover	43. Governor link
8. Gasket	20. Choke rod	31. Snap ring	45. Governor air vane
9. Carburetor	21. Set screw	32. Throttle trigger	47. Muffler shield
10. Handle & air box	22. Throttle rod spring	34. Choke rod button	

On pump engine, set idle stop screw so that it does not interfere with full travel of throttle stop lever. Open idle fuel adjustment needle one turn and leave needle at this setting; all adjustment should be made with main needle. Open main fuel adjustment needle one turn for initial adjustment, be sure pump is filled with water and start engine. Pump water until engine is at full operating temperature, then turn main fuel needle in slowly until engine begins to lose speed under load. Correct final adjustment is $\frac{1}{8}$-turn open from this point.

On circular saw, turn idle speed stop screw in until it just contacts throttle stop lever plus $\frac{3}{4}$-turn additional. Open both the idle fuel needle and the main fuel needle one turn each. With engine warm and running, adjust idle speed stop screw so that engine runs at just below clutch engagement speed, or about 2600 RPM. Check engine acceleration and open idle fuel needle slightly if engine does not accelerate properly on initial adjustment. Adjust main fuel needle with engine under load so that engine runs at highest practicable speed obtainable without excessive smoke.

GOVERNOR. The early XL100 Circular Saw engine is nongoverned.

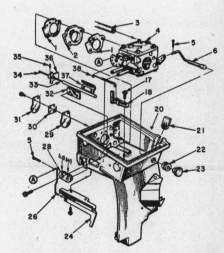

Fig. HL62–Exploded view of air box assembly used on brushcutter; pump air box is similar except that throttle control parts (items 32 through 37) are not used. Air filter cover and element as shown in Fig. HL61 are used.

1. Gaskets	26. Governor link
2. Spacer	28. Adjustment needle grommet
3. Fuel line	
4. Carburetor assy.	29. Reed valve
5. Cotter pins	30. Reed back-up
6. Choke rod	31. Reed stop
17. Screws (2)	32. Clamp spacer
18. Adjusting plate	33. Throttle cable casing
20. Air box	34. Throttle cable
21. Felt plug	35. Set screw
22. Grommet	36. Collar
23. Choke button	37. Clamp
24. Governor air vane	38. Governor spring

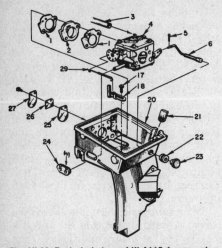

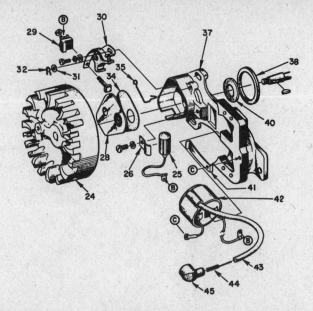

Fig. HL64–Exploded view of the flywheel type magneto. Connect condenser and low tension leads as indicated by letters "B" and "C".

24. Flywheel
25. Condenser
26. Condenser clamp
28. Breaker box cover
29. Terminal block
30. Breaker point set
31. Washer
32. Pivot post clip
34. Gasket
37. Plate and armature assy.
38. Gasket
40. Felt seal
41. Coil retaining clip
42. Ignition coil assy.
43. High tension wire
44. Connector spring
45. Spark plug boot

1. Gaskets
2. Spacer
3. Fuel line
4. Carburetor assy.
5. Cotter pin
6. Choke rod
17. Screws (2)
18. Adjustment plate
20. Air box
21. Felt plug
22. Grommet
23. Choke button
24. Adjustment needle grommet
25. Reed valve
26. Reed back-up
27. Reed stop
29. Throttle opening spring

Refer to appropriate following paragraph for information on other units which are equipped with governors.

CIRCULAR SAW GOVERNOR. Refer to exploded view of air box and handle assembly in Fig. HL61A. To adjust governed speed, loosen screw (40) and move slotted speed adjusting plate (39) to obtain desired maximum speed, then tighten screw. Maximum governed no-load speed should be 5000 rpm.

BRUSHCUTTER GOVERNOR. The engine used in Brushcutter application is equipped with an air-vane type governor; refer to Fig. HL62. Air vane (24) is connected to throttle shaft through link (26) and is balanced by tension of spring (38). When throttle trigger (62 —Fig. HL71) is fully depressed, collar (36—Fig. HL62) on remote control cable moves away from throttle shaft lever allowing governor to control engine speed.

To adjust governor using vibrating reed or electronic tachometer, proceed as follows: With engine warm and running and throttle trigger released, adjust position of collar on remote control cable so that engine slow idle speed is 2500 rpm, or just below clutch engagement speed. Then when throttle trigger

1. Plug
2. Gasket
3. Felt washer
4. Plug
5. Fuel tank
7. Fuel cap
8. Gasket
9. Valve
10. Nut
11. Flat washer
12. Compression spring
13. Wick washer
14. Gasket
15. Fuel pick-up wick
16. Fuel pick-up stud
17. Fuel tank cover
18. Fuel line
19. Round head screws (16)
20. Fuel line elbow
21. Cylinder
22. Crankcase
23. Seal
24. Needle bearing
26. Thrust bearing race
27. Needle thrust bearing
28. Flywheel key
29. Crankshaft
30. Connecting rod
31. Needle bearing
32. Rod cap screws
33. Crankpin rollers (28)
34. Piston & pin assy.
35. Snap rings (only one used on late models)
36. Piston rings
37. Gasket
40. Manifold
41. Spark plug
42. Spark plug gasket

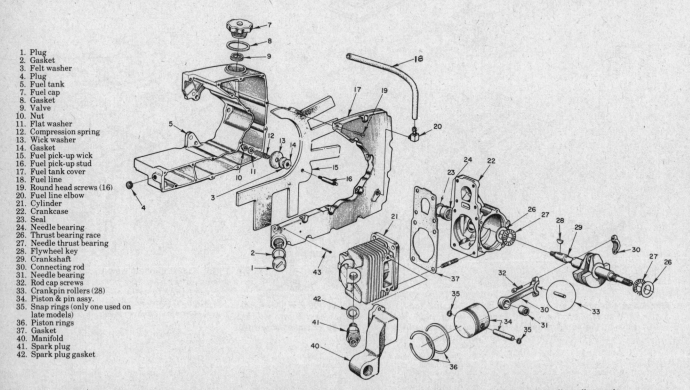

Fig. HL65–Exploded view of early XL-12 engine assembly. Later models are similar. Crankcase side cover, needle roller main bearing and the crankshaft seal are a part of the circular saw, pump, generator or brushcutter assembly as shown in Fig. HL68, HL69, HL70, or HL71. Saw, pump, generator or brushcutter must be disassembled to gain access to crankshaft; refer to appropriate unit paragraph.

is fully depressed, collar should move away from throttle shaft lever and engine no-load speed should be 6300 rpm. To adjust maximum governed no-load speed, loosen screw (17—Fig. HL62) and move speed adjusting plate (18) as required to obtain no-load speed of 6300 rpm. When adjusting maximum no-load speed, be sure throttle trigger is fully depressed and that collar (36) clears carburetor throttle shaft lever.

If carburetor or linkage has been removed, be sure that governor link is reconnected at hole "A" in carburetor throttle shaft lever as indicated in Fig. HL62. Governor spring (38) is connected to third hole away from hole "A" (two open holes between link and spring). Be sure that governor linkage moves smoothly throughout range of travel.

PUMP GOVERNOR. On pump applications, engine is equipped with air-vane type governor as shown in Fig. HL62; however, no control linkage is used (items 32 through 37).

With engine running under no load (CAUTION: Be sure pump housing is filled with water), engine speed should be 6400 to 6600 rpm. If not, loosen screw (17) and move speed adjusting plate (18) as necessary so that engine governed speed is 6500 rpm.

If carburetor has been removed or linkage has been disconnected, be sure that governor link (26) is reconnected in hole "A" in carburetor throttle shaft lever. On pump applications, the governor spring should be connected to hole next to hole "A" in throttle shaft lever. Be sure that idle speed screw on carburetor is backed out so that it will not interfere with full movements of throttle shaft lever and that governor linkage moves smoothly throughout range of travel.

GENERATOR GOVERNOR. Engine speed on generator applications is controlled by a mechanical flyweight type governor located within the generator unit; refer to exploded view of generator in Fig. HL70. Slotted end of extension shaft (1) fits over pinned end of carburetor throttle shaft. Centrifugal force of governor weights (64) acting through arms (63) actuate governor cup (40), cam (16) and connecting linkage against force of governor spring (39). The spring (29—Fig. HL63) in air box is adjusted to full tension and is used as a throttle opening spring and to keep slack out of linkage.

To adjust governed speed with tachometer or frequency meter, proceed as follows: To use an RPM indicator, remove receptacle housing (52—Fig. HL70) to gain access to end of generator shaft. With engine at operating temperature, governed no-load speed

Fig. HL66–When installing reed valve, reed back-up and reed stop, be sure reed is centered between two points indicated by black arrows.

should be approximately 3750 rpm, or a reading of 63 cycles per second should be indicated on frequency meter. If engine speed or cycles per second is not as specified, loosen the two screws clamping governor shaft guide (10) to bearing housing (13) and move guide towards engine to increase speed, or towards generator to decrease speed. Note: Only one mounting hole of governor shaft guide is slotted and guide pivots on opposite screw. Tighten screws when proper speed is obtained.

If carburetor has been removed, reconnect throttle opening spring as indicated in Fig. HL63. If plate (18) has been removed, reinstall screws loosely, push plate to apply as much spring tension as possible (to end of slot) and tighten screws. Servicing of the mechanical governor unit requires disassembly of the generator unit; refer to exploded view in Fig. HL70, and to GENERATOR paragraph.

MAGNETO. A Wico flywheel type magneto with external armature and ignition coil is used. Breaker points and condenser are located behind flywheel.

Armature core and stator plate are riveted together and are serviced only as a unit. Stator plate fits firmly on shoulder of crankcase; hence, armature air gap is non-adjustable.

Magneto stator plate has slotted mounting holes, and should be rotated as far clockwise as possible before tightening mounting screws to obtain correct ignition timing of 30 degrees BTDC. Set breaker point gap to 0.015. Condenser capacitance should test 0.16-0.20 mfd. CAUTION: Be careful when installing breaker points not to bend tension spring any more than necessary; if spring is bent excessively, spring tension may be reduced causing improper breaker point operation.

LUBRICATION. The engine on all models is lubricated by mixing oil with regular gasoline. Fuel:oil ratio should be 32:1 when Homelite® SAE 40 Premium Motor Oil is mixed with fuel. Fuel:oil ratio should be 16:1 if Homelite® SAE 30 2-Cycle oil or another good grade of oil designed for air cooled two stroke engines is used.

Lubricate generator by removing receptacle cover (52—Fig. HL70) from end of generator and applying 4 or 5 drops of oil to the felt washer (47) after each 200 hours of operation.

Gear case of circular saw must be filled to proper level with SAE 90 gear oil (Homelite part no. 55291-C) as follows: Remove saw blade and working through opening in retractable blade guard (49—Fig. HL68), remove drain plug (1). Remove filler plug (9) and with base plate of saw level, pour oil into filler plug opening until it starts to run out drain plug. Reinstall plugs and blade. Oil in gear case should be changed after each 100 hours of operation.

To lubricate brushcutter, proceed as follows: Each 10 hours of operation, squirt a few drops of SAE-30 oil into hole marked "OIL" on underside of

Fig. HL67–Exploded view of recoil starter used on later models. Early models are similar.

1. Starter housing
2. Rope handle
3. Bushing
4. Rewind spring
5. Washer
6. Spring lock
7. Rope pulley
8. Washer
9. Screw
10. Nut
11. Lock washer
12. Washer
13. Screen
14. Lock nut
15. Stud
16. Pawl
17. Washer
18. Spring
19. Flywheel

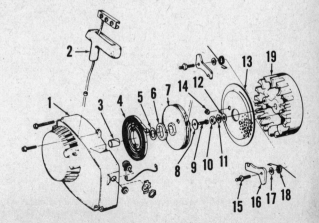

upper head casting. Remove driveshaft each 50 hours of operation, clean the shaft and lubricate it full length with a good grade of wheel bearing grease. Lower gear head should be repacked with a good grade of wheel bearing grease after each 50 hours of operation. Note: Do not wash lower head and bearing housing in solvent as this will wash lubricant from the sealed ball bearings, causing premature bearing failure.

Pump is lubricated by water in pump. CAUTION: Do not start pump engine without filling pump with water.

CARBON. Muffler, manifold and cylinder exhaust ports should be cleaned periodically to prevent loss of power through carbon build up. Remove muffler and scrape free of carbon; a bent wire can be inserted through hole in housing pump and generator mufflers to clean outer shell. With muffler or manifold removed, turn engine so that piston is at top dead center and carefully remove carbon from exhaust ports with a wooden scraper. Be careful not to damage chamfered edges of exhaust ports or to scratch piston. Do not run engine with muffler removed.

REPAIRS

CONNECTING ROD. Connecting rod and piston assembly can be removed after removing cylinder from crankcase. Refer to Fig. HL65. Be careful to remove all needle rollers when detaching rod from crankpin. Early models have 28 loose needle rollers while later models have 31 needle rollers.

Renew connecting rod if bent or twisted, or if crankpin bearing surface is scored, burned or excessively worn. The caged needle roller piston pin bearing can be renewed by pressing old bearing out and pressing new bearing in with Homelite tool No. 23756. Press on lettered end of bearing cage only.

It is recommended that the crankpin needle rollers be renewed as a set whenever engine is disassembled for service. On early models with 28 needle rollers, stick 14 needle rollers in the rod and remaining 14 needle rollers in rod cap with light grease or beeswax. On late models with 31 needle rollers, stick 16 rollers in rod and 15 rollers in rod cap. Assemble rod to cap with match marks aligned, and with open end of piston pin towards flywheel side of engine. Wiggle the rod as cap retaining screws are being tightened to align the fractured mating surfaces of rod and cap.

PISTON, PIN AND RINGS. The piston is fitted with two pinned compression rings. Renew piston if scored, cracked or excessively worn, or if ring side clearance in top ring groove exceeds 0.0035.

Recommended piston ring end gap is 0.070-0.080; maximum allowable ring end gap is 0.085. Desired ring side clearance in groove is 0.002-0.003.

Piston, pin and rings are available in standard size only. Piston and pin are available in a matched set, and are not available separately.

Piston pin has one open and one closed end and may be retained in piston with snap rings or a Spirol pin. A wire retaining ring is used on exhaust side of piston on some models and should not be removed.

To remove piston pin on all models, remove the snap ring at intake side of piston. On piston with Spirol pin at exhaust side, drive pin from piston and rod with slotted driver (Homelite tool No. A-23949). On all other models, insert a 3/16-inch pin through snap ring at exhaust side and drive piston pin out.

When reassembling, be sure closed end of piston pin is to exhaust side of piston (away from piston ring locating pin). Install Truarc snap ring with sharp edge out.

CRANKSHAFT. The crankshaft is supported in two caged needle roller bearings and crankshaft end play is controlled by a roller bearing and hardened steel thrust washer at each end of the shaft. Refer to Fig. HL65. On generator, crankshaft end play is taken up by a loading spring (12—Fig. HL70).

To remove crankshaft, it will be necessary to disassemble the circular saw drive case, pump, generator or brushcutter upper drive housing. Refer to Figs. HL68 through HL71 and appropriate accompanying paragraphs.

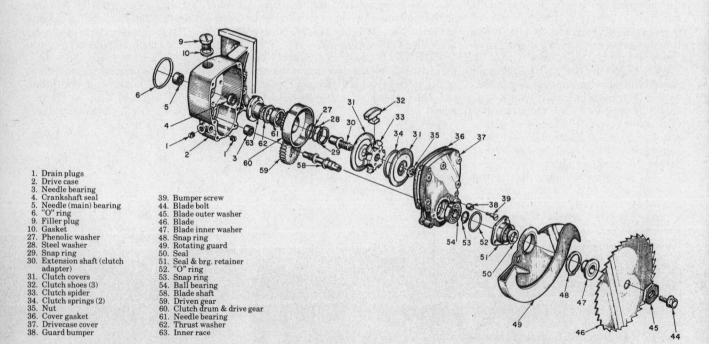

1. Drain plugs
2. Drive case
3. Needle bearing
4. Crankshaft seal
5. Needle (main) bearing
6. "O" ring
9. Filler plug
10. Gasket
27. Phenolic washer
28. Steel washer
29. Snap ring
30. Extension shaft (clutch adapter)
31. Clutch covers
32. Clutch shoes (3)
33. Clutch spider
34. Clutch springs (2)
35. Nut
36. Cover gasket
37. Drivecase cover
38. Guard bumper
39. Bumper screw
44. Blade bolt
45. Blade outer washer
46. Blade
47. Blade inner washer
48. Snap ring
49. Rotating guard
50. Seal
51. Seal & brg. retainer
52. "O" ring
53. Snap ring
54. Ball bearing
58. Blade shaft
59. Driven gear
60. Clutch drum & drive gear
61. Needle bearing
62. Thrust washer
63. Inner race

Fig. HL68–Exploded view of circular saw drive case assembly. Drive case (2) carries crankshaft needle roller bearing (5) and crankshaft seal (4). "O" ring (6) seals drive case to engine crankcase.

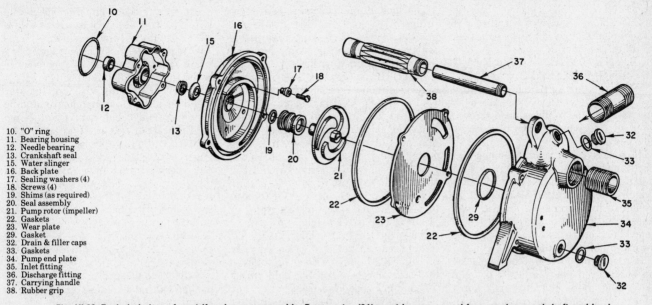

10. "O" ring
11. Bearing housing
12. Needle bearing
13. Crankshaft seal
15. Water slinger
16. Back plate
17. Sealing washers (4)
18. Screws (4)
19. Shims (as required)
20. Seal assembly
21. Pump rotor (impeller)
22. Gaskets
23. Wear plate
29. Gasket
32. Drain & filler caps
33. Gaskets
34. Pump end plate
35. Inlet fitting
36. Discharge fitting
37. Carrying handle
38. Rubber grip

Fig. HL69—Exploded view of centrifugal pump assembly. Pump rotor (21) must be unscrewed from engine crankshaft and back plate (16) be removed to allow removal of bearing housing (11) and engine crankshaft. Bearing housing retains crankshaft needle roller bearing (12) and crankshaft seal (13).

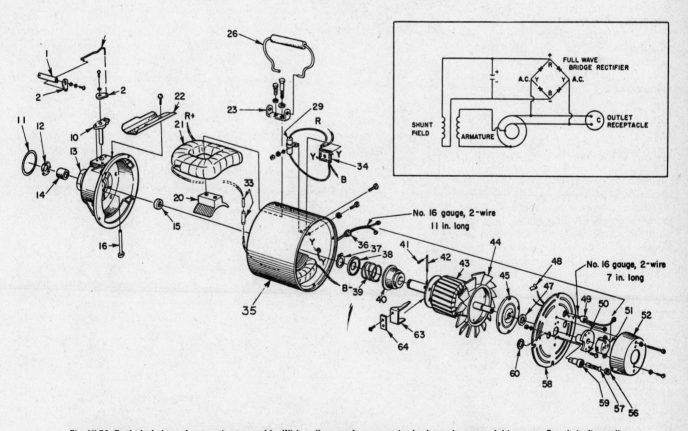

Fig. HL70—Exploded view of generator assembly. Wiring diagram for generator is shown in upper right corner. Crankshaft needle roller (main) bearing (14) and crankshaft seal (15) are carried in bearing housing (13). Armature (43) must be unscrewed from engine crankshaft to allow removal of bearing housing and crankshaft.

1. Throttle shaft extension
2. Linkage arms
6. Governor link
10. Governor shaft guide
11. "O" ring
12. Loading spring
13. Bearing housing
14. Needle bearing
15. Crankshaft seal
16. Governor cam & shaft
20. Generator field pole

21. Generator field coil
22. Linkage guard
23. Handle bracket
26. Carrying handle
29. Capacitor
33. Connector
34. Rectifier
35. Generator yoke (frame)
36. Insulating bushing
37. Snap ring
38. Centering washer

39. Governor spring
40. Governor cup
41. Cotter pins (4)
42. Pivot pins (2)
43. Generator armature
44. Fan
45. Collector ring
47. Felt washer
48. Brush holder clip
49. Insulating bushing

50. Flanged Oilite bushing
51. Outlet receptacle
52. Receptacle housing
56. Brush holder cap
57. Brush
58. Brush head
59. Brush holder
60. Holder retaining ring
63. Governor arms (2)
64. Governor weights (2)

CYLINDER. The cylinder bore is chrome plated. Renew the cylinder if chrome plating is worn away exposing the softer base metal.

CRANKCASE, BEARING HOUSING AND SEALS. CAUTION: Do not lose bearing housing-to-crankcase screws. New screws of same length must be installed in place of old screws. Refer to parts book if correct screw length is unknown.

The needle roller main bearings and crankshaft seals in crankcase and bearing housing can be renewed using Homelite tool Nos. 23757 and 23758. Press bearings and seals from crankcase or bearing housing with large stepped end of tool No. 23757, pressing towards outside of either case.

To install new needle bearings, use the shouldered short end of tool No. 23757 and press bearings into bores from inner side of either case. Press on lettered end of bearing cage only.

To install new seals, first lubricate the seal and place seal on long end of tool No. 23758 so that lip of seal will be towards needle bearing as it is pressed into place.

To install crankshaft, lubricate thrust bearings (27—Fig. HL65) and place on shaft as shown. Place a hardened steel thrust washer to the outside of each thrust bearing. Insert crankshaft into crankcase being careful not to damage seal in crankcase. Place a seal protector sleeve (Homelite tool No. 23759) on crankshaft and large "O" ring or gasket on shoulder of bearing housing. Note: On early production, crankcase was sealed to drivecase with an "O" ring; however, use of "O" ring has been discontinued and a gasket, rather than an "O" ring, should be used on all models. Lubricate seal protector sleeve, seal and needle bearing and assemble bearing housing to crankshaft and crankcase. Use **NEW** bearing housing retaining screws. Clean the screw threads and apply Loctite to threads before installing screws. Be sure the screws are correct length; screw length is critical. Tighten the screws alternately and remove seal protector sleeve from crankshaft. Reassemble circular saw drive case, pump, generator or brush cutter upper drive housing as outlined in appropriate paragraph.

FLAT REED INTAKE VALVE. The reed valve is attached to the carburetor air box as shown in Fig. HL66, and is accessible after removing air box from crankcase.

Check the reed seating surface on air box to be sure it is free of nicks, chips or burrs. Renew valve reed if rusted, pitted or cracked, or if it does not seat flatly against its seat.

The reed stop is curved so that measurement of reed lift distance is not practical. However, be sure that reed is centered over opening in air box and reed stop is aligned with reed.

NOTE: If air box has been removed to service reed valve (35—Fig. HL61 or 4—Fig. HL61A), inspect gasket between air box and crankcase. If gasket is damaged and cylinder is not being removed for other purposes, it is suggested that the exposed part of the old gasket be carefully removed and the new gasket be cut to fit between the air box and crankcase. Also, refer to note in CARBURETOR paragraph in MAINTENANCE section.

REWIND STARTER. To disassemble starter, refer to exploded view in Fig. HL67 and proceed as follows: Pull starter rope out fully, hold pulley (11) and pry rope knot from pulley. Let pulley rewind slowly. Hold pulley while removing screw (14) and washer (13). Turn pulley counterclockwise until disengaged from spring, then carefully lift pulley off starter post.

Turn open side of housing down and rap housing sharply against top of work bench to remove spring. CAUTION: Be careful not to dislodge spring when removing pulley as spring could cause injury if it should recoil rapidly.

Install new spring with loop in outer end over pin in blower housing and be sure spring is coiled in direction shown in Fig. HL67. Install pulley (11), turning pulley clockwise until it engages spring and secure with washer and screw. Insert new rope through handle and hole in blower housing. Knot both ends of the rope and harden the knots with heat or cement. Turn pulley clockwise eight turns and slide knot in rope into slot and keyhole in pulley. Let starter pulley rewind slowly.

Starter pawl spring outer ends are hooked behind air vanes on flywheel in line with starter pawls when pawls are resting against flywheel nut. Pull starter rope slowly when installing blower housing so that starter cup will engage pawls.

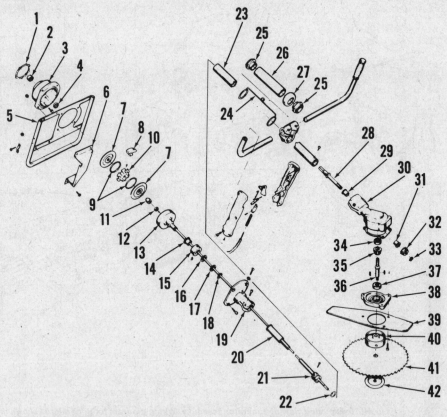

Fig. HL71–Exploded view of early type brushcutter assembly. Refer to Fig. HL72 for later brushcutter.

1. Gasket	12. Nut	22. "O" ring
2. Needle roller bearing	13. Driveshaft & clutch	23. Tube
3. Bearing housing	drum	24. Hanger
4. Seal	14. Flanged bearing	25. Collar
5. Frame assy.	15. Collar	26. Hanger tube
6. Exhaust deflector	16. Thrust washer	27. Bumper
7. Clutch cover	17. Spacer	28. Gear shaft
8. Clutch shoe	18. Snap ring	29. Bearing
9. Clutch spring	19. Upper head	30. Lower head
10. Clutch hub	20. Shaft casing	31. Bearing
11. Spacer	21. Split bushing	32. Bevel gear

33. Snap ring
34. Ball bearing
35. Bevel gear
36. Blade shaft
37. Ball bearing
38. Bearing retainer
39. Blade guard
40. Spindle head
41. Blade
42. Nut

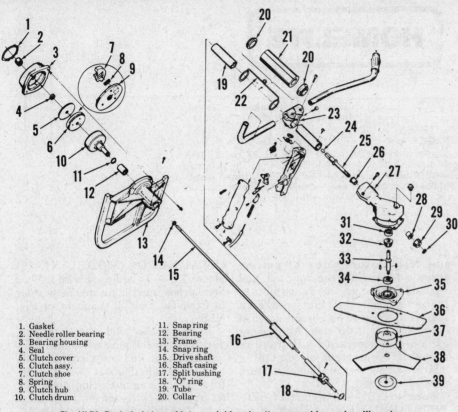

Fig. HL72–Exploded view of late model brushcutter assembly used on XL series.

1. Gasket	11. Snap ring	21. Hanger tube	26. Bearing	31. Ball bearing	36. Blade guard
2. Needle roller bearing	12. Bearing	22. Hanger	27. Lower head	32. Bevel gear	37. Spindle head
3. Bearing housing	13. Frame	23. Handle clamp	28. Bearing	33. Blade shaft	38. Blade
4. Seal	14. Snap ring	24. Bumper	29. Bevel gear	34. Ball bearing	39. Nut
5. Clutch cover	15. Drive shaft	25. Gear shaft	30. Snap ring	35. Bearing retainer	
6. Clutch assy.	16. Shaft casing				
7. Clutch shoe	17. Split bushing				
8. Spring	18. "O" ring				
9. Clutch hub	19. Tube				
10. Clutch drum	20. Collar				

CIRCULAR SAW DRIVECASE

Refer to exploded view of circular saw drivecase assembly in Fig. HL68. To gain access to engine crankshaft, the unit must be disassembled as follows:

Drain all lubricating oil from gearbox. Hold hex blade washer (45), unscrew cap screw (44) and remove washer and saw blade. Remove blower housing and starter assembly. Using No. 6 Truarc pliers, remove snap ring (48). Remove bumper screw (39) and bumper (38), disconnect guard return spring and remove rotating guard (49). Remove upper saw guard (not shown) and the bearing retainer (51). Remove snap ring (53) from shaft (58) and remove screws retaining cover (37) to drive case (2). Using Homelite bearing puller, tool No. A-23778, remove ball bearing (54) and cover from shaft.

While holding flywheel with Homelite tool #A-23761, remove nut (35), clutch cover (31) and unscrew clutch rotor using Homelite tool No. A-23696. Remove extension shaft (30) from crankshaft with a socket head screw (Allen) wrench. Remove snap ring (29) and pull clutch drum (60) from flanged bushing (63). Withdraw driven gear

(59) and shaft (58); clamp flat outer end of shaft in smooth jawed vise, if necessary to remove gear from shaft, and unscrew gear.

The drive case can now be removed from engine crankcase. Need and procedure for further disassembly should be obvious from inspection of parts. Reassemble unit by reversing disassembly procedure. Refer to LUBRICATION paragraph for refilling unit with oil.

CENTRIFUGAL PUMP

Refer to exploded view of pump in Fig. HL69. Remove pump end plate (34) and wear plate (23). While holding flywheel, unscrew the pump impeller (21). Remove seal (20), back plate (16), shims (19) and water slinger (15). Bearing plate (11), which carries crankshaft needle roller bearing (12) and seal (13) can then be removed.

When reassembling unit, use all new seals and gaskets. Shims (19) are available in thicknesses of 0.010 and 0.015; install shims to provide minimum clearance between impeller (21) and wear plate (23) without causing impeller to rub against the plate.

Refill pump assembly with water before attempting to start engine. Water in pump is necessary to lubricate pump seal (20).

GENERATOR

Refer to exploded view of the generator unit in Fig. HL70. To gain access to the engine governor unit or engine crankshaft, proceed as follows:

Remove two outside screws holding receptacle cover (52) to brush head (58) and move receptacle assembly aside. Remove brush holder caps (56) and brushes, taking particular care to note position and location of brushes so that they may be reinstalled in same position and location. Remove brush head (58), bearing (50) and felt washer (47). Remove screws retaining collector ring (45) and remove collector ring from fan. Remove fan (44), from armature (43) taking care not to lose the Woodruff key (not shown). Unbolt generator yoke (35) from bearing housing (13) and slide yoke from armature. Using a strap wrench, unscrew the armature from engine crankshaft while holding engine flywheel. Procedure and need for further disassembly is obvious from inspection of unit. After reassembly check adjustment of governor as outlined in GOVERNOR paragraph.

BRUSHCUTTER

To gain access to crankshaft bearing housing (3—Fig. HL71 or HL72), or engine crankshaft, proceed as follows:

On early models, unbolt upper head (26—Fig. HL71) from bearing housing and remove brushcutter unit and frame (5). While holding engine flywheel, remove nut (12), spacer (11) and outer clutch cover; then unscrew clutch hub (10) from engine crankshaft. Remove inner clutch cover. Bearing housing can now be removed from engine crankcase. Note: Some early models have a flexible driveshaft instead of the rigid driveshaft shown in Fig. HL71. To remove nut (42) from blade shaft, insert a ¼ inch steel rod in hole in spindle head (40) to hold shaft from turning.

On later models, unscrew capscrews securing frame (13—Fig. HL72) to bearing housing (3) and separate brushcutting unit from engine. Remove snap ring (11) and clutch drum (10). Rotate clutch hub in counterclockwise direction to remove clutch assembly. Bearing housing can now be removed from engine as previously outlined. To remove nut (39) from blade shaft, insert a ¼ inch steel rod in hole in spindle head (27) to prevent shaft from turning.

Model	Bore Inches	Stroke Inches	Displ. Cu. In.
XL-88, XL-98, XL-98A, XLS2-1, XLS2-1A	2 1/16	1½	5.0

This section covers service of the model XL-88, XL-98 and XL-98A Multi-Purpose saw and XLS2-1 and XLS2-1A pump. The saw may be equipped with either an abrasive wheel or carbide tipped wheel. Caution should be taken that abrasive wheels installed on this unit are rated for spindle speeds of 5000 rpm or higher.

MAINTENANCE

SPARK PLUG. A Champion model CJ-6 spark plug is used. For heavy duty operation, a Champion HO-8A platinum tip or UJ-11-G gold palladium tip spark plug can be used, though it will be necessary to pull the plug wire further out of the retaining clip in air box. Set electrode gap to 0.025 on all models.

CARBURETOR. All models are equipped with a Tillotson model HS diaphragm carburetor. Refer to Figs. HL75 and HL76 for exploded views of carburetor. Carburetor used on model XL-98A (See Fig. HL76) has a fixed main jet (19) and a governor valve (6) which is designed to maintain a governed speed of about 5000 rpm. Neither main jet nor governor valve is adjustable. Carburetor on model XLS2-1A does not have adjustable idle or high speed mixture screws.

Initial carburetor adjustment on saw models is one turn open for idle mixture and high speed mixture screw, if so equipped. Adjust idle mixture screw and idle speed screw to obtain smooth idle with engine warm and running at 2400-2600 rpm which should be just below clutch engagement speed. Adjust high speed mixture screw, on models so equipped, to obtain optimum engine performance at cutting speed with saw under normal load. Do not adjust mixture screws too lean as engine damage may result.

To adjust carburetor on XLS2-1 pump models, turn idle and high speed mixture screws until they are 1½ turns open. Start engine and allow to run until warm. Adjust high speed mixture screw for highest pumping speed obtainable then turn high speed mixture screw ⅛ turn counterclockwise. Note: Governor is designed to limit maximum no-load speed to 6400 rpm. Ad-

just idle mixture screw by pulling throttle button all the way out and turn idle mixture screw to obtain highest and smoothest idle speed. Turn idle speed screw to obtain idle speed of approximately 3000 rpm. Adjustment of one mixture screw will require checking adjustment of remaining mixture screw as operation of mixture needles is related.

Refer to Tillotson section of SERVICE FUNDAMENTALS section for service and overhaul of carburetor.

MAGNETO. (MODEL XL-88) Model XL-88 is equipped with a Wico breakerless solid state magneto; refer to exploded view of magneto in Fig. HL80.

To check the solid state magneto, disconnect spark plug wire, turn ignition switch on and crank engine while holding terminal about ¼-inch away from ground (engine casting) and check for spark as with conventional magneto. If no spark occurs, refer to the following inspection and test procedure:

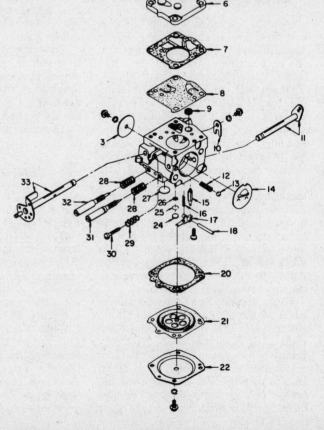

Fig. HL75–Exploded view of Tillotson series HS carburetor used on all models except XL-98A. Model XLS2-1A does not have mixture needles (29 & 30).

3. Throttle plate
6. Diaphragm cover
7. Gasket
8. Fuel pump diaphragm
9. Filter screen
10. Throttle shaft clip
11. Choke shaft
12. Detent spring
13. Choke detent ball
14. Choke plate
15. Inlet valve needle
16. Inlet lever spring
17. Inlet control lever
18. Lever hinge pin
19. Pin retainer screw
20. Diaphragm gasket
21. Metering diaphragm
22. Diaphragm cover
24. Welch plug-3/16
25. Retainer ring
26. Channel screen
27. Welch plug-11/32
28. Mixture needle springs (2)
29. Main fuel needle
30. Idle fuel needle
31. Throttle shaft
32. Throttle spring
33. Idle speed screw spring
34. Idle sreed screw

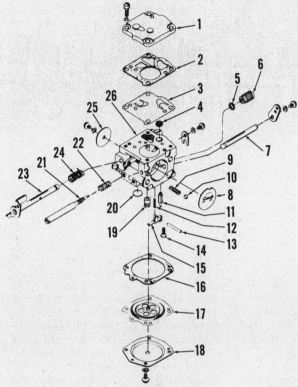

Fig. HL76–Exploded view of Tillotson model HS carburetor used on model XL-98A. Note governor valve (6). There is no high speed mixture needle on this carburetor.

1. Diaphragm cover
2. Gasket
3. Fuel pump diaphragm
4. Filter screen
5. Gasket
6. Governor valve
7. Choke shaft
8. Choke plate
9. Spring
10. Choke detent ball
11. Inlet valve needle
12. Inlet lever spring
13. Lever pin
14. Screw
15. Inlet control lever
16. Diaphragm gasket
17. Metering diaphragm
18. Diaphragm cover
19. Main jet
20. Welch plug
21. Idle mixture screw
22. Spring
23. Throttle shaft
24. Spring
25. Throttle plate
26. Body

Secondary continuity:

Minimum 50
Maximum 60

Renew the ignition coil if found faulty and again check for spark. If no spark then occurs or if ignition coil checked OK, proceed as follows:

Remove the flywheel and again check for broken or frayed wires. If no defect is noted, remove the screw attaching condenser to magneto back plate and be sure condenser is not touching back plate or other ground. Push a pin through the condenser lead and using condenser tester, check for short, series resistance and capacitance; condenser capacitance should be 0.16-0.20 mfd. If condenser is faulty, renew the switch box and condenser assembly (26). If condenser tested OK, proceed as follows:

Disconnect coil primary at insulating sleeve (39) and disconnect

Visually inspect rotor (flywheel) for damage. Check for broken or frayed wires.

To test the ignition coil, disconnect the wires at insulating sleeve (39) and test coil according to tester procedure. Specifications for testing with either Graham Model 51 or Merc-O-Tronic tester are as follows:

Graham Model 51:

Maximum secondary 10,000
Maximum primary 1.7
Coil index 65
Minimum coil test 20
Maximum gap index 65

Merc-O-Tronic

Operating amperage 1.3
Primary resistance:

Minimum 0.6
Maximum 0.7

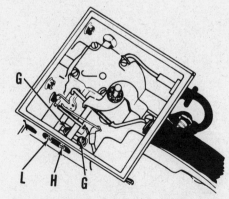

Fig. HL77–Drawing showing locations of idle (L) and high speed (H) mixture screws and governor plate screws (G) on model XL-88. Models XL-98, XLS2-1 and XLS2-1A are similar.

Fig. HL78–Exploded view of model XL-88 air box and handle assembly. Models XL-98, XLS2-1 and XLS2-1A are similar. Governed speed is adjusted by loosening screw (43) and moving slotted speed adjusting plate (42). Reed retainer (2) should be installed in engine intake port, then install reed seat (4) with reeds (3).

1. Gasket
2. Reed retainer
3. Valve reeds
4. Reed seat
5. Gaskets
6. Gaskets
7. Spacer
8. Fuel line
9. Carburetor
12. Cotter pin
13. Choke rod
14. Return spring
15. Throttle rod
16. Boot
17. Filter element
19. Air filter cover
22. Air deflector
23. Throttle lock pin
24. Throttle lock spring
25. Handle cover
26. Nylon bushing
27. Snap ring
28. Grommet
29. Throttle trigger
30. Choke button
31. Handle & air box
32. Plug
33. Plug
35. Bushing
36. Collar
37. Coupling
38. Air vane & shaft
39. Set screws
40. Grommet
42. Speed adjusting plate
43. Adjusting plate screw
44. Governor spring
45. Governor arm & shaft
46. Carburetor link

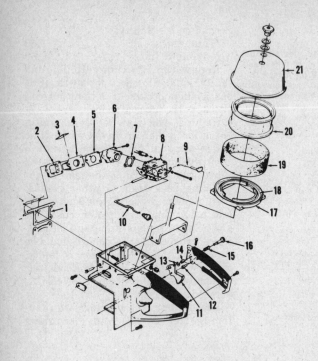

Fig. HL79–Exploded view of air box assembly used on model XL-98A.

1. Gasket
2. Reed retainer
3. Reed petal
4. Reed seat
5. Gasket
6. Intake manifold
7. Gasket
8. Carburetor
9. Choke button
10. Throttle rod
11. Throttle trigger
12. Pin
13. Snap ring
14. Nylon bushing
15. Lock spring
16. Throttle lock
17. Air cleaner base
18. Gasket
19. Filter element
20. Filter mount
21. Filter cover

Connect one ohmmeter lead to connector between switch box and trigger coil and other ohmmeter lead to back plate (ground). Reading should be either between 0 to 85 ohms or between 85 to 150 ohms. Reverse the leads; second reading on ohmmeter should be opposite first reading. That is, if first reading was in specified range of 0-85 ohms, second reading should be within range of 85-150 ohms. Then, connect the ohmmeter leads to unused terminal of trigger coil and to magneto back plate. Ohmmeter reading should then be 20 to 26 ohms. If trigger coil does not test within specifications, renew the magneto back plate and trigger coil assembly.

When reassembling magneto, check back plate and remove any sharp edges, especially where wires may contact the back plate. Be sure all leads are in place as shown in Fig. HL81. Be sure the back plate is clean and check all screws for tightness. If there is any doubt about the strength of the rotor (flywheel) magnets, install a new flywheel; be sure to remove "keeper" plates from new flywheel before installing it.

(MODELS XL-98, XL-98A). Models XL-98 and XL-98A are equipped with the capacitor discharge ignition system shown in Fig. HL82. Refer to CAPACITOR DISCHARGE IGNITION SYSTEM section of this manual for explanation of ignition system operation.

The capacitor discharge magneto is operating satisfactorily if spark will jump a ⅜-inch gap when engine is turned at cranking speed. If magneto fails to produce spark, service consists of locating and renewing inoperative unit; no maintenance is necessary.

To check magneto with volt-ohmmeter, proceed as follows: Remove starter housing and disconnect wire

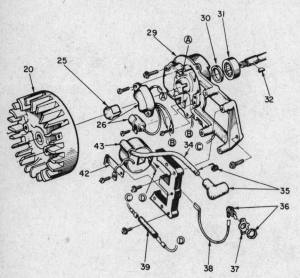

Fig. HL80–Exploded view of the solid state (breakerless) magneto used on model XL-88. Trigger switch and condenser (26) are available as assembly only. The trigger coil is molded into back plate (29).

20. Flywheel (rotor)
25. Dust cap
26. Trigger switch & condenser
29. Back plate & trigger coil
30. Crankshaft seal
31. Roller bearing
32. Woodruff key
34. Spark plug wire
35. Spark plug terminal
36. Magneto grounding switch
37. "ON-OFF" plate
38. Ground lead
39. Insulating sleeve
42. Coil retaining clip
43. Ignition coil

switch box ground lead from back plate (See Fig. HL81). Remove the screw attaching condenser to back plate and be sure condenser is insulated from any ground. Be sure the switch box ground lead and ignition coil lead are not touching anything and connect leads of an ohmmeter to the two leads. Meter should read either between 1 megohm and infinity or between 5 and 25 ohms; with ohmmeter leads reversed, reading should be opposite that of preceding test. That is, if first reading obtained was 5-25 ohms, second reading should be 1 megohm to infinity. If ohmmeter readings are not as specified, renew the switch box and condenser assembly. If switch box tested OK, test trigger coil as follows:

Fig. HL81–Drawing showing points for ohmmeter test lead connections for checking solid state magneto trigger coil, condenser and switch box. Refer to text for procedure and specifications.

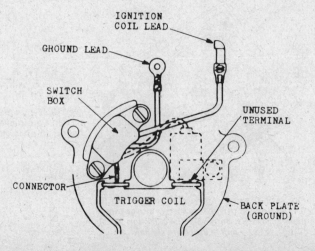

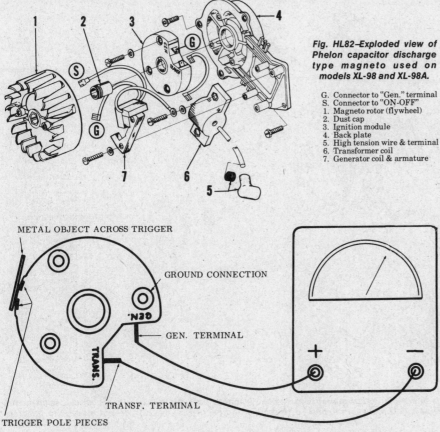

Fig. HL82–Exploded view of Phelon capacitor discharge type magneto used on models XL-98 and XL-98A.

G. Connector to "Gen." terminal
S. Connector to "ON-OFF"
1. Magneto rotor (flywheel)
2. Dust cap
3. Ignition module
4. Back plate
5. High tension wire & terminal
6. Transformer coil
7. Generator coil & armature

METAL OBJECT ACROSS TRIGGER

GROUND CONNECTION

GEN. TERMINAL

TRANSF. TERMINAL

TRIGGER POLE PIECES

Fig. HL83–Drawing showing volt-ohmmeter connections to ignition module (3–Fig. HL82) for checking module. It should be noted that this is not a conclusive test and module should be renewed in event of spark failure when other magneto components test OK.

continuity through generator. Reverse leads from ohmmeter; ohmmeter should then show no continuity (infinite resistance) through generator. Renew generator if continuity is noted with ohmmeter leads connected in both directions. A further check can be made using voltmeter if continuity checked correctly. Remove spark plug and reinstall rotor leaving wire (G) from generator disconnected. Connect positive (red) lead from voltmeter to wire (G) from generator and negative (black) lead of voltmeter to magneto back plate; wires must be routed so that starter can be reinstalled. A firm pull on starter rope should spin engine at about 500 RPM and voltmeter should show minimum reading of 4 volts. If both generator and transformer coil tested OK, a faulty ignition module (3) should be suspected.

A partial check of ignition module can be made using ohmmeter. With ohmmeter set to R X 1000 scale, connect positive (red) lead of ohmmeter to module terminal marked "Gen." and negative ohmmeter lead to module ground connection (see Fig. HL83). An instant deflection of ohmmeter needle should be noted; if not, reverse ohmmeter leads and observe needle. If no deflection of needle is noted with ohmmeter leads connected in either direction, module is faulty and should be renewed. If needle deflection is observed, select R X 1 (direct reading) scale of ohmmeter and connect positive

from ignition switch. Check to be sure there is no continuity through switch when in "ON" position to be sure a grounded switch is not cause of trouble and inspect wiring to be sure it is not shorted. CAUTION: Be sure that storage capacitor is discharged before touching connections; flip ignition switch to "OFF" position or ground switch lead (S).

Resistance through secondary (high tension) winding of transformer coil should be 2400 to 2900 ohms and resistance through primary winding should be 0.2-0.4 ohms. Connect ohmmeter leads between high tension (spark plug) wire and ground, then between input terminal and ground. If transformer coil does not test within specifications, renew coil and recheck for spark at cranking speed. If magneto still does not produce spark, check generator as follows:

Remove rotor (flywheel) and disconnect lead from generator to generator (G) terminal on module (3) and switch lead (S) at ignition switch. Connect negative lead of ohmmeter to ground wire from generator and the positive lead of ohmmeter to generator (G) wire. The ohmmeter should register showing

Fig. HL84–Exploded view of conventional flywheel type magneto used on models XLS2-1 and XLS2-1A. Coil clip retaining screw location is shown by letter "B". Condenser lead and ignition coil primary lead are attached to terminal block (28) at "D".

23. Rotor (flywheel)
25. Breaker point set
26. Clip
27. Washer
28. Terminal block
29. Breaker box cover
30. Gasket
31. Felt retainer
32. Cover spring clip
34. Back plate
35. Crankshaft seal
36. Roller bearing
37. Rotor key
38. Coil core (armature)
42. Clamp
43. Condenser
45. Ignition coil
46. Coil retaining clip
48. Ground lead
49. Ignition switch
50. "ON-OFF" plate
51. Spark plug terminal
52. Spark-plug wire

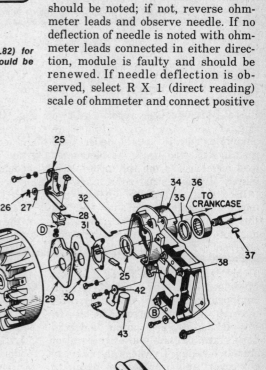

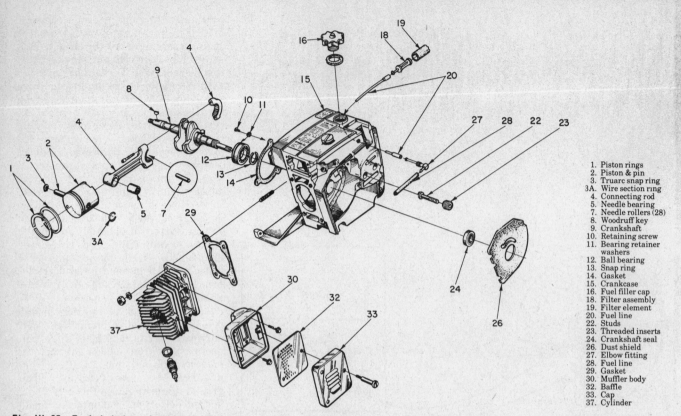

Fig. HL-85—Exploded view of model XL-88 engine assembly; other models are similar. Magneto back plate (28—Fig. HL80) carries magneto end of crankshaft. Model XL-88 saw arm stud retainers (23) must be unscrewed to remove the captive studs (22); do not attempt to unscrew the studs.

1. Piston rings
2. Piston & pin
3. Truarc snap ring
3A. Wire section ring
4. Connecting rod
5. Needle bearing
7. Needle rollers (28)
8. Woodruff key
9. Crankshaft
10. Retaining screw
11. Bearing retainer washers
12. Ball bearing
13. Snap ring
14. Gasket
15. Crankcase
16. Fuel filler cap
18. Filter assembly
19. Filter element
20. Fuel line
22. Studs
23. Threaded inserts
24. Crankshaft seal
26. Dust shield
27. Elbow fitting
28. Fuel line
29. Gasket
30. Muffler body
32. Baffle
33. Cap
37. Cylinder

(red) lead to module terminal marked "Gen." and place negative (black) lead against terminal marked "Trans." Place a screwdriver across the two trigger poles (see Fig. HL83); the ohmmeter needle should deflect and remain deflected until the ohmmeter lead is released from the module terminal. If the desired results are obtained with ohmmeter checks, the module is probably OK; however, as this is not a complete check and other magneto components and wiring check OK, renew module if no ignition spark can yet be obtained.

(MODELS XLS2-1, XLS2-1A). Models XLS2-1 and XLS2-1A are equipped with a conventional flywheel magneto ignition system as shown in Fig. HL84. Breaker points and condenser are accessible after removal of starter housing, flywheel and breaker box cover. Adjust breaker point gap to 0.015. Condenser capacity should test 0.18-0.22 mfd. Ignition timing is fixed at 30° BTDC. After reinstalling flywheel, check armature air gap which should be 0.005-0.007. To adjust air gap, turn flywheel so that magnets are below legs of armature core and place plastic shim (Homelite part No. 23987) between armature and magnets. Loosen then tighten armature retaining screws and remove shim.

GOVERNOR. An air vane type governor is used on models XL-88, XL-98, XLS2-1 and XLS2-1A as shown in Fig. HL78. Governed speed is adjusted by loosening screws (43—Fig. HL78) and moving plate (42). Maximum governed speed should be 5000 rpm for models XL-88 and XL-98 and 6400 rpm for models XLS2-1 and XLS2-1A.

Model XL-98A is equipped with a governor valve (6—Fig. HL76) located in the carburetor. At the desired governed speed, the governor valve will open and allow additional fuel into the engine. This excessively rich fuel mixture will prevent engine overspeeding. Governed speed should be 5000 rpm and is not adjustable. If valve (6) does not function properly, it must be renewed as a unit.

LUBRICATION. Engine on all models is lubricated by mixing oil with regular gasoline. If Homelite® Premium SAE 40 chain saw oil is used, fuel:oil ratio should be 32:1. Fuel:oil ratio should be 16:1 if Homelite® 2-Cycle SAE 30 oil or other SAE 30 oil designed for air-cooled two stroke engines is used.

CARBON. Muffler and cylinder exhaust ports should be cleaned periodically to prevent loss of power due to carbon build up. Remove muffler cover and baffle plate and scrape muffler free of carbon. With muffler cover removed, turn engine so that piston is at top dead center and carefully remove carbon from exhaust ports with wooden scraper. Be careful not to damage the edges of exhaust ports or to scratch piston. Do not attempt to run engine with muffler baffle plate or cover removed.

REPAIRS

CONNECTING ROD. Connecting rod and piston assembly can be removed after removing cylinder from crankcase. Be careful to remove all of the 28 loose needle rollers when detaching rod from crankpin.

Renew connecting rod if bent or twisted, or if crankpin bearing surface is scored, burned or excessively worn. The caged needle roller piston pin bearing can be renewed by pressing old bearing out and pressing new bearing in with Homelite tool No. 23955. Press on lettered end of bearing cage only.

It is recommended that the crankpin needle rollers be renewed as a set whenever engine is disassembled for service. Stick 14 needle rollers in rod and the remaining 14 needle rollers in rod cap with light grease or beeswax. Assemble rod to cap with match marks aligned and with open end of piston pin towards flywheel side of engine. Wiggle the rod as cap retaining screws are being tightened to align the fractured surfaces.

PISTON, PIN AND RINGS. The piston is fitted with two pinned compression rings. Renew piston if scored, cracked or excessively worn, or if ring side clearance in top ring groove exceeds 0.0035.

Recommended piston ring end gap is 0.070-0.080; maximum allowable ring end gap is 0.085. Desired ring side clearance in groove is 0.002-0.003.

Piston, pin and rings are available in standard size only. Piston and pin are available as a matched set and are not available separately.

Piston pin on models XL-88 and XL-98 is retained in piston by a wire type snap ring on exhaust side and by a Truarc snap ring on opposite end. Disassemble piston and rod by removing the Truarc snap ring and pushing pin out with a 3/16-inch diameter pin. Piston pin on models XL-98A, XLS2-1 and XLS2-1A is retained by Truarc snap rings at each end.

When reassembling piston to connecting rod, be sure closed end of pin is towards exhaust port. Install piston pin retaining Truarc snap rings with sharp side out. Rotate snap ring to be sure it is secure in retaining groove, then turn gap toward closed end of piston.

CRANKSHAFT. Flywheel end of crankshaft is supported in a roller bearing in magneto back plate and drive end is supported in a ball bearing located in crankcase. End play is controlled by the ball bearing.

Renew the crankshaft if the flywheel end main bearing or crankpin bearing surface or sealing surfaces are scored, burned or excessively worn. Renew the ball bearing if excessively loose or rough. Also, reject crankshaft if flywheel keyway is beat out or if threads are badly damaged.

CYLINDER. The cylinder bore is chrome plated. Renew cylinder if chrome plating is worn away exposing the softer base metal.

Fig. HL86–Installing shoes and springs on clutch spider plate.

To remove cylinder, first remove the blower (fan) housing, carburetor and air box (handle) assemblies and remove the screw retaining magneto back plate to flywheel side of cylinder. The cylinder can then be unbolted from crankcase and removed from the piston.

CRANKCASE, MAGNETO BACK PLATE AND SEALS. To remove the magneto back plate, first remove the blower (fan) housing and flywheel. Loosen the cylinder retaining stud nuts on flywheel side of engine to reduce clamping effect on back plate boss, then unbolt and remove the back plate assembly from crankcase.

To remove crankshaft from crankcase, first remove the cylinder, connecting rod and piston assembly and the magneto backplate as previously outlined. Remove drive clutch assembly and dust shield (26—Fig. HL85) on saws and pump assembly (Fig. HL89) on models XLS2-1 and XLS2-1A. Then, remove the two ball bearing retaining screws (10) from inside of crankcase and remove crankshaft and ball bearing assembly from crankcase. Remove snap ring (13) and press crankshaft from bearing if necessary.

REED VALVES. The pyramid type reed valve seat is made of "Delrin"

plastic and reeds are located by pins molded on seat. The reeds are held in place by a molded retainer that also serves as a gasket between reed seat and crankcase. Reeds are 0.004 thick.

When installing reed valve assembly, it is important that reed retainer be installed in crankcase first, then install reed seat with reeds in place. Oil can be used to stick reeds to seat. Also, special type shoulder retaining screws must be used.

CLUTCH. All models except models XLS2-1 and XLS2-1A are equipped with a centrifugal clutch. To remove the clutch assembly, first remove the blade and arm assembly (see Fig. HL87 or HL88). The clutch bearing inner race (27) unscrews counterclockwise (left-hand threads). Remove inner race with impact wrench, or if impact wrench is not available, use a ¾-inch socket wrench and strike wrench handle a sharp blow to loosen threads.

Remove clutch drum, pulley and bearing assembly and remove thrust washer (30). Then, unscrew clutch spider plate (31) using a spanner wrench (Homelite tool No. A-23934 or equivalent) in counterclockwise direction. Remove clutch cover (34).

Inspect clutch drum and pulley for excessive wear or scoring. Inspect all

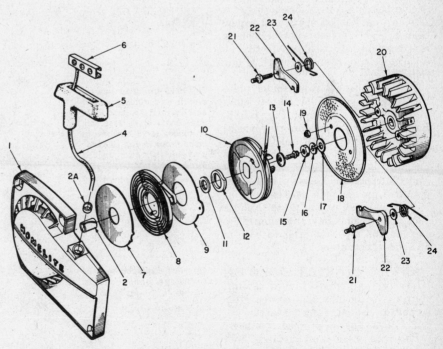

Fig. HL87–Exploded view of typical rewind starter assembly and engine flywheel.

1. Starter housing	8. Rewind spring	14. Cap screw	20. Flywheel (magneto rotor)
2. Bushing	9. Outer spring shield	15. Flywheel nut	21. Shoulder studs
2A. Rope bushing	10. Pulley & cup assy.	16. Lock washer	22. Starter pawls
3. Starter rope	11. Bushing	17. Flat washer	23. Washers
4. Starter rope	12. Spring lock	18. Rotating screen	24. Pawl springs
5. Hand grip	13. Washer	19. Self-locking nuts	
6. Insert			
7. Inner spring shield			

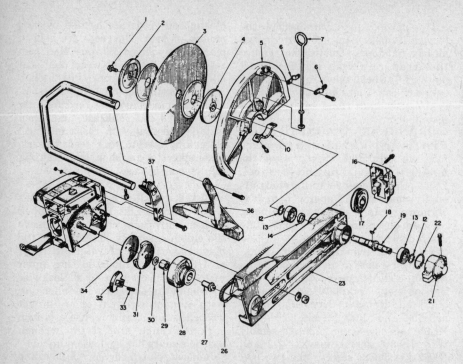

Fig. HL88–Exploded view of drive arm and cutting wheel assembly used on model XL-88. Cutting wheel or saw blade can be mounted on either side of arm. Shaft guard (21) is used to cover opposite end of shaft. Belt can be renewed after removing arm from engine and the cap (16) from end of arm.

1. Cap screw	12. Snap ring	21. Shaft guard	30. Thrust washer
2. Outer blade washer	13. Ball bearing	22. Snap ring	31. Spider plate
3. Cutting wheel	14. Spacer	23. Arm	32. Clutch shoes
4. Inner washer	16. Arm cap	26. Drive belt	33. Clutch springs
5. Guard	17. Driven pulley	27. Clutch bearing race	34. Clutch cover
6. Clamps	18. Woodruff key	28. Clutch drum & pulley	36. Saw support
7. Eye or hook bolt	19. Blade shaft	29. Needle bearing	37. Handle bar bracket
10. Guard clamp			

pulley as the rapidly uncoiling spring could cause injury.

Check all starter parts for wear or other damage and renew as necessary. Rope bushing (2A) in housing should be renewed if rope notch is worn in bushing. When reassembling starter, lubricate starter post lightly and install spring without lubrication. Refer to exploded view in Fig. HL87 for reassembly guide. Pre-wind the spring 2 to 4 turns.

BLADE SHAFT, BEARINGS AND PULLEY

Refer to exploded view of unit in Fig. HL88 or HL89. To renew the blade drive mechanism, proceed as follows:

On model XL-88, unbolt and remove the arm assembly from engine. Remove shaft guard (21—Fig. HL88), blade or cutting wheel (3) and blade guard (5). Remove arm cap (16) and drive belt (26). Remove the large internal snap ring (22) from arm and external snap ring (12) from shaft at opposite side of arm. Support the arm and press shaft and outer bearing out towards outside of arm. Remove the driven sheave from arm. Press bearing from inner side of arm. Remove snap ring retaining outer bearing to shaft, then press shaft from bearing.

To disassemble blade drive on models XL-98 and XL-98A, remove

needle bearing rollers for scoring, excessive wear or flat spots, and renew bearing if such defect is noted. Bearing is excessively worn if rollers can be separated more than the width of one roller.

Pry clutch shoes from spider plate with screwdriver. To install new shoes and/or springs, refer to Fig. HL86. Reinstall clutch by reversing removal procedure. Lubricate needle roller bearing in clutch drum with a small amount of Homelite® ALL-TEMP Multi-Purpose Grease or a high temperature grease such as Texaco Unitemp #500 or Humble (Esso) Nebula EP1. Note: The bearing should be cleaned and repacked after each 45 to 50 hours of operation.

REWIND STARTER. Refer to Fig. HL87 for exploded view of rewind starter. To disassemble starter after removing housing and starter assembly from engine, proceed as follows:

Pull rope out a short distance, hold rope and pry retainer (6) from hand grip. Untie knot in end of rope, then allow pulley to rewind slowly. Remove hex head screw (14) and remove rope pulley. CAUTION: Be careful not to dislodge spring (8) while removing

Fig. HL89–Exploded view of clutch and cutting wheel assembly used on model XL-98A. Blade shaft assembly on model XL-98 is shown in inset. Refer to Fig. HL88 for parts identification except for: 8. Spacer; 9. Bearings & shaft.

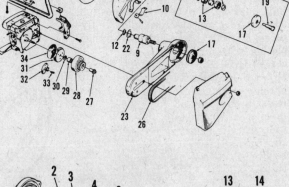

Fig. HL90–Exploded view of centrifugal pump used on models XLS2-1 and XLS2-1A.

1. Impeller housing
2. Seal washer
3. Washer
4. Shims
6. Seal
7. Impeller
8. Gasket
9. Wear plate
10. Gasket
11. Gasket
12. End housing
13. Fill plug
14. Discharge fitting
15. Inlet fitting
16. Drain plug

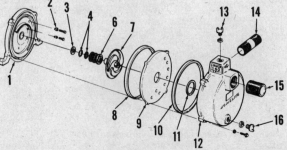

blade arm from engine and detach drive cover and components (1 thru 8—Fig. HL89) as well as clamp (10). Remove driven pulley (17) and drive belt (26). Note that pulley on model XL-98 is retained by a nut while blade shaft (19) holds pulley (17) in position and shaft must be removed with pulley. Remove snap rings and press bearings out of blade arm.

To reassemble, reverse disassembly procedure. Place belt over drive pulley on engine, then mount arm to engine crankcase. A wrench with tapered handle (Homelite tool No. A-24085) can be inserted between arm and crankcase to help tension the drive belt. Be sure belt is tight enough to drive blade or wheel under full cutting load without slippage, then tighten arm retaining nuts.

CENTRIFUGAL PUMP

Refer to Fig. HL90 for an exploded view of centrifugal pump used on models XLS2-1 and XLS2-1A. Disassembly of pump is evident after referring to Fig. HL90 and inspection of unit. Pump impeller (7) is threaded on engine crankshaft with left hand threads.

Use new gaskets and seals to reassemble pump. Assemble components (1 thru 7) and place a straight edge across face of impeller housing (1). Measure distance between impeller (7) and straight edge. Install shims (4) to obtain desired clearance of 0.015-0.025 in. Shims are available in thicknesses of 0.010 and 0.015 in.

Refill pump with water before attempting to start engine. Water is necessary in pump to lubricate pump seal (6).

Model	Bore Inches	Stroke Inches	Displ. Cu. In.
EZ-10, Chipper	1.4375	1.3	2.1

MAINTENANCE

SPARK PLUG. A Champion DJ-6J spark plug with tapered seat is used; no gasket is required. Adjust electrode gap to 0.025.

CARBURETOR. A Walbro model HDC diaphragm type carburetor is used on all models. Refer to Fig. HL91 for exploded view of carburetor.

For initial carburetor adjustment, back idle speed adjusting screw out until throttle valve will completely close, then turn screw back in until it contacts idle stop plus ½ turn additional. Turn both fuel adjusting needles in until lightly seated, then back main fuel needle (located to left and marked "HI" on grommet when viewing adjustment needle side of throttle handle) out about one turn and back idle ("LO") needle out about ¾-turn. Start engine, readjust idle speed and fuel needles so that engine idles at just below clutch engagement speed. With engine running at full throttle under load, readjust main fuel needle to obtain optimum performance at high speed. Do not adjust main fuel needle too lean as engine may be damaged.

MAGNETO. Refer to exploded view of magneto in Fig. HL94. Breaker points and condenser are accessible after removing starter assembly, mag-neto rotor (flywheel) and breaker box cover.

Condenser capacity should test approximately 0.2 mfds. Adjust breaker points to 0.015. After reinstalling magneto rotor (flywheel), check magneto armature core to rotor air gap. Air gap should be 0.008-0.012 and can be adjusted using plastic shim stock available as Homelite part No. 24306.

CARBON. Carbon deposits should be removed from muffler and exhaust ports at regular intervals. When scraping carbon, be careful not to damage chamfered edges of exhaust ports or scratch piston. A wooden scraper should be used. Turn engine so that piston is at top dead center so that carbon will not fall into cylinder. Do not attempt to run engine with muffler removed.

LUBRICATION. Engine on all models is lubricated by mixing oil with regular gasoline. If Homelite® Premium SAE 40 chain saw oil is used, fuel:oil ratio should be 32:1. Fuel:oil ratio should be 16:1 if Homelite® 2-Cycle SAE 30 oil or other SAE 30 oil designed for air-cooled two stroke engines is used.

The clutch needle roller bearing should be cleaned and relubricated after each 100 hours of use. A high temperature grease such as Homelite® ALL-TEMP Multi-Purpose Grease should be used.

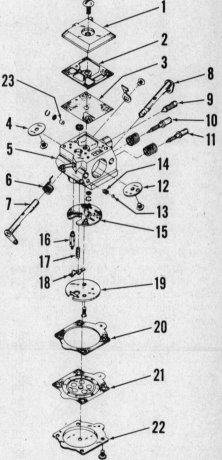

Fig. HL91–Exploded view of Walbro model HDC carburetor.

1. Pump cover
2. Gasket
3. Fuel pump diaphragm & valves
4. Throttle plate
5. Body
6. Return spring
7. Throttle shaft
8. Choke shaft
9. Idle speed screw
10. Idle mixture screw
11. High speed mixture screw
12. Choke plate
13. Choke friction ball
14. Spring
15. Gasket
16. Fuel inlet valve
17. Spring
18. Diaphragm lever
19. Circuit plate
20. Gasket
21. Metering diaphragm
22. Cover
23. Limiting jet

SPECIAL SERVICE TOOLS. Special service tools which may be required are listed as follows:

Tool No.   Description & Model Usage
24299—Anvil, crankshaft installation.
24300—Sleeve, crankshaft bearing.
24294—Plug, needle bearing assembly.
24292—Plug, seal removal.
24298—Plug, bearing and seal.
24320—#3 Pozidriv screwdriver bit.
A24290—Bracket, rotor remover.
A-24060—Wrench, clutch spanner.
A-24309—Jackscrew, crankshaft and bearing.
23136-1—Body for A-24309.
24295—Bearing collar for A-24309.
24291—Sleeve, drivecase seal.
24297—Sleeve, crankcase seal.

CYLINDER. The cylinder can be unbolted and removed from crankcase after removing starter housing and throttle handle. Be careful not to let piston strike crankcase as cylinder is removed.

The cylinder bore is chrome plated and cylinder should be renewed if the chrome plating has worn through exposing the softer base metal. Also inspect for cracks and damage to compression release valve bore.

Fig. HL92–Exploded view of handle assembly and related assemblies.

1. Air filter
2. Carburetor
3. Throttle rod
4. Oil line
5. Spacer
6. Gasket
7. Reed valve seat
8. Reed retainer
9. Reed petals
10. Spring post
11. Spring
12. Choke rod
13. Throttle stop
14. Spring
15. Trigger
16. Bushing
17. Spring
18. Throttle latch
19. Air filter bracket

Fig. HL93–Before tightening screws retaining air filter bracket (19–Fig. HL92) in throttle handle, place air filter element on bracket stud and align filter with edges of air box.

Fig. HL94–Exploded view of ignition assembly. Felt seal (3) is cemented to breaker box cover (4).

1. Nut
2. Flywheel
3. Felt seal
4. Box cover
5. Condenser
6. Breaker points
7. Breaker box
8. Ignition coil
9. Felt seal
10. Fuel tank

REPAIRS

TIGHTENING TORQUES. Recommended minimum tightening torques are listed in the following table; all values are in inch-pounds. To find maximum torque value, add 20 percent to given value.

6/32 Compression release clamp ... 20
6/32 Compression release post
nut 20
6/32 Breaker box 20
6/32 Breaker point adjustable
arm 20
6/32 Condenser 20
8/32 Air filter bracket 25
8/32 Connecting rod 55
8/32 Throttle handle cover 35
8/32 Rewind spring cover 35
8/32 Intake manifold (reed
spacer) 20
8/32 Coil assembly 20
8/32 Fuel tank 35
10/32 Main bearing retainer
screws 50
10/32 Muffler body 50
10/32 Starter housing 50
10/32 Carburetor 20

Fig. HL95–Exploded view of typical engine assembly.

1. Fuel tank
2. Oil tank
3. Cylinder
4. Compression release valve
5. Gasket
6. Piston rings
7. Piston
8. Piston pin
9. Pin retainer
10. Needle bearing
11. Connecting rod
12. Capscrew
13. Bearing rollers (28)
14. Connecting rod cap
15. Seal
16. Crankcase
17. "O" ring
18. Drivecase
19. Roller bearing
20. Crankshaft
21. Screw
22. Bearing retainer
23. Ball bearing
24. Snap ring

Fig. HL96–Installing piston and connecting rod assembly using locally made tool to hold rod cap In position. Tool can be made from flat strip of metal. Using grease, stick 14 rollers in cap and 14 rollers in rod; make sure that match marks on rod and cap are aligned.

Fig. HL97–Roller type main bearing used at flywheel end of crankshaft is marked on one side, "PRESS OTHER SIDE". Be sure to observe this precaution when installing bearing in crankcase.

PISTON, PIN AND RINGS. Model EZ-10 and Chipper piston has one Head land type ring. Piston ring should be renewed if ring end gap exceeds 0.016 inch; desired ring end gap is 0.006-0.016 inch. The base side of the ring has a cut-out at the end gap to fit the ring locating pin in piston ring groove.

Piston pin is retained by snap rings at both ends of piston pin. Open end of snap ring should be towards closed end of piston.

Assemble piston to connecting rod so that piston ring locating pin is towards intake side of cylinder (away from exhaust port).

CONNECTING ROD. Connecting rod and piston assembly can be detached from crankshaft after removing cylinder; refer to Fig. HL95. Be careful to remove all of the 28 loose needle bearing rollers.

Renew connecting rod if bent, twisted or if crankpin bearing surface shows visible wear or is scored. The needle roller bearing for piston pin should be renewed if any roller shows flat spot or if worn so that any two rollers can be separated the width equal to thickness of one roller and if rod is otherwise serviceable. Press on lettered side of bearing cage only when removing and installing bearing.

The crankpin needle rollers should be renewed at each overhaul. To install

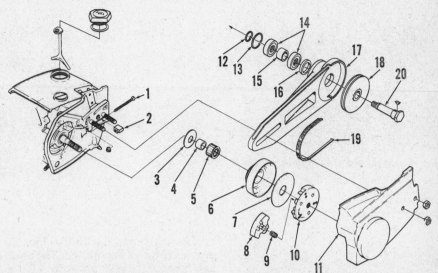

Fig. HL98–Exploded view of clutch and wheel arm assemblies.

1. Belt tension screw	6. Clutch drum	11. Side cover	16. Spacer
2. Arm locating block	7. Thrust washer	12. Snap ring	17. Wheel arm
3. Thrust washer	8. Clutch shoe	13. Snap ring	18. Driven pulley
4. Inner race	9. Spring	14. Ball bearing	19. Belt
5. Needle bearing	10. Clutch hub	15. Spacer	20. Shaft

connecting rod, refer to Fig. HL96. Stick 14 rollers in cap with grease. Support rod cap in crankcase, then place rod over crankpin and to cap with match marks aligned and install new retaining cap screws.

CRANKSHAFT, BEARINGS AND SEALS. Crankshaft is supported by a roller bearing (19—Fig. HL95) mounted in crankcase bore and by a ball bearing (23) mounted in drivecase (18).

To remove crankshaft, first remove blade arm, clutch assembly, starter housing, magneto rotor, throttle handle, cylinder, piston and connecting rod assembly and the fuel/oil tank assembly. Remove retaining screws and separate drivecase and crankshaft from crankcase. Note: Use "Pozidriv" screwdriver bit only when removing drivecase to fuel tank cover screw (25). Remove the two main bearing retaining screws (21) and special washers (22), then push crankshaft and ball bearing (23) from drivecase. Remove snap ring (24) and press crankshaft from ball bearing.

When reassembling, be sure groove in outer race of ball bearing is towards crankpin and that retaining snap ring is seated in groove on crankshaft. Install new seals (15) with lip of seal inward. Using protector sleeve to prevent damage to seal, press the crankshaft and ball bearing into drivecase and install new retaining screws and washers. Assemble crankcase to crankshaft and drivecase using new "O" ring (17) and protector sleeve to prevent damage to crankcase seal. Be sure bar studs are in place before installing fuel tank.

COMPRESSION RELEASE. When throttle lock is pushed in, a lever connected to throttle lock lifts away from compression release valve (4—Fig. HL95). When engine is cranked, compression forces valve open and compression is partly relieved through port in cylinder. Squeezing throttle trigger after engine is running releases throttle lock, allowing spring (11—Fig. HL92) to snap lever against release valve, closing the valve.

Service of compression release valve usually consists of cleaning valve seat and port in cylinder as carbon may gradually fill the port.

When overhauling engine, cylinder should be inspected for any damage to compression release port.

PYRAMID REED VALVE. A "Delrin" plastic pyramid type reed intake valve seat and four reeds are used.

Fig. HL99–Although clutch shown above is not used on model EZ or Chipper, easy method of clutch spring and shoe installation is shown.

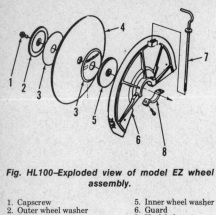

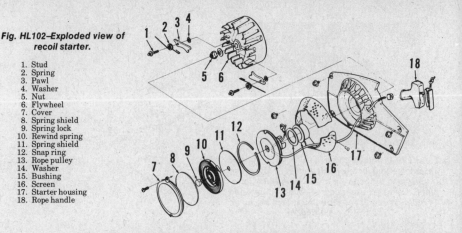

1. Stud
2. Spring
3. Pawl
4. Washer
5. Nut
6. Flywheel
7. Cover
8. Spring shield
9. Spring lock
10. Rewind spring
11. Spring shield
12. Snap ring
13. Rope pulley
14. Washer
15. Bushing
16. Screen
17. Starter housing
18. Rope handle

Fig. HL100—Exploded view of model EZ wheel assembly.

1. Capscrew
2. Outer wheel washer
3. Spacer
4. Wheel
5. Inner wheel washer
6. Guard
7. Hook bolt
8. Clamp

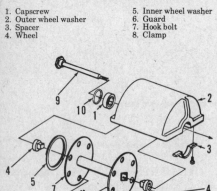

Fig. HL101—Exploded view of cutting assembly on Chipper.

1. Bearing
2. Guard
3. Clamp
4. Insert
5. Retainer
6. Cutters
7. Hub
8. Cutter pin
9. Shaft
10. Snap ring

Reeds are retained on pins projecting from the reed seat by a moulded retainer. Inspect reed seat, retainer and reeds for any distortion, excessive wear or other damage.

To reinstall, use a drop of oil to stick each reed to the plastic seat, then push reed retainer down over the seat and reeds. Then install the assembly in crankcase; never install retainer, then attempt to install reed seat and reeds.

CLUTCH. Refer to Fig. HL98 for exploded view of the shoe type clutch. The clutch hub (10) is threaded to crankshaft; turn clutch hub in clockwise direction to remove from crankshaft.

If clutch slips with engine running at high speed under load, check clutch shoes for excessive wear. If clutch will not release (cutting unit is driven at normal idle speed), check for broken or weak clutch springs.

Refer to Fig. HL99 for easy method of installing clutch shoes and springs on clutch hub.

CUTTING WHEEL AND CHIPPER. Model EZ-10 is equipped with an abrasive wheel (4—Fig. HL100) for cutting while Chipper

models are equipped with the chipping device shown in Fig. HL101. The abrasive wheel or chipper is attached to the drive assembly shown in Fig. HL98.

To disassemble drive mechanism, remove wheel or chipper assembly from arm (17—Fig. HL98). Remove side cover (11) and belt (19). Separate arm assembly from engine. Remove snap rings (12 and 13), shaft (20) and driven pulley (18). Inspect components (14, 15 and 16) and remove if necessary. Bearings (14) are a press fit in arm.

Belt tension is adjusted by turning adjusting screw (1) with side cover (11) retaining nuts loosened to allow arm (17) to move. Belt tension should be adjusted so that belt is tight enough to prevent slippage under load.

REWIND STARTER. Exploded view of rewind starter is shown in Fig. HL102. Starter can be removed as a complete unit by removing housing retaining screws. To disassemble starter, hold cover (7) while removing retaining screws, then allow cover to turn slowly until spring tension is released. Remainder of disassembly is evident from inspection of unit and with reference to exploded view.

Refer to Fig. HL103 to correctly install starter dogs on flywheel. Rewind spring is wound in clockwise direction in cover (7—Fig. HL102). When installing a new starter rope, knot rope ends as shown in Fig. HL104, pull the knots tight and coat with Duxseal (Homelite part No. 24352). Before installing cover (7—Fig. HL103) retaining screws, turn cover to pull rope handle against starter housing, then continue turning cover three turns to properly tension the rewind spring.

Fig. HL103—View showing proper installation of pawl springs.

Fig. HL104—When installing new starter rope, knot ends as shown. Seal rope holes in pulley and coat knots with Duxseal (Homelite part No. 24382)

HOMELITE CAPACITOR DISCHARGE (CD) IGNITION SYSTEM

OPERATING PRINCIPLES

The Homelite capacitor discharge ignition system used in the Multi-Purpose Saw models XL98 and XL98A generates alternating current which is rectified into direct current. The current is stored as electrical energy in a capacitor (condenser) and is discharged on timing signal into the transformer (coil) that steps up the voltage to fire the spark plug. Instead of using breaker points as in a conventional magneto, ignition timing is done by magnetically triggered solid state switch components. Refer to Fig. HL150 for schematic diagram of capacitor discharge ignition system. Ignition system components are as follows:

1. **SPARK PLUG**— A conventional Champion spark plug with a 0.025 inch firing gap.

2. **FLYWHEEL (ROTOR)**—The CD flywheel is slightly different from breaker ignition flywheels in that it has two pole pieces to trigger the solid state components. One pole piece triggers the switch for normal starting and operating ignition timing and the second pole piece is a safety device to prevent the engine from running backwards. The flywheel magnet passes the generator coil and core to generate electrical current.

3. **GENERATOR**—The generator is an alternator type similar to that used in a battery charging circuit. The generator coil module is a permanently sealed unit mounted on a core. The module generates electrical current to charge the capacitor.

4. **CAPACITOR**—The capacitor stores electrical energy which is discharged into the transformer on signal from the switch module.

5. **TRANSFORMER**—The transformer increases the voltage discharged from the capacitor to a voltage high enough to fire the spark plug. The transformer is mounted on the generator core and can be renewed separately.

6. **TIMING SWITCH MODULE**—The timing switch module, which is mounted on the backplate under the flywheel, consists of two magnetic devices which will trigger the silicon controlled rectifier (SCR) switch contained in the module. One magnetic device will trigger the switch for retarded timing at cranking speed and the second will trigger the switch for advanced timing when the engine is running. The advance triggering device is located 16 degrees ahead of the retard device. At cranking speed, the advance triggering device will not generate enough electricity to trigger the SCR switch, but the retard device is stronger and will trigger the SCR switch at cranking speed, thus allowing the electrical energy stored in the capacitor to be discharged into the transformer and fire the spark plug. When the engine is running, the increased speed at which the pole piece in the flywheel passes the advanced triggering device generates enough electrical energy to trigger

the SCR switch, thus the capacitor is discharged into the transformer 16 degrees sooner than at cranking speed. When the pole piece passes the retard device, a triggering current is also created, but the capacitor has already been discharged and no ignition spark will occur. Should the engine be turned backwards far enough to charge the capacitor, a second "safety" pole piece in the flywheel will trigger the SCR switch and the spark plug will be fired when the engine exhaust port is open. Thus, when the engine is turned backwards, a "poof" may be heard from the exhaust but a power stroke will not be created.

TESTING THE CD IGNITION SYSTEM

Models XL-98 And XL-98A

Procedure and specifications for checking the capacitor discharge ignition system with a Graham or Merc-O-Tronic tester were not available at time of publication, but a number of tests to indicate condition of the ignition system components can be made using a volt-ohmmeter, preferably a Triplett or Monarch. To make the volt-ohmmeter tests, refer to Figs. HL151 through HL152 and proceed as follows:

Turn the ignition switch to "ON" position, disconnect lead terminal from spark plug and insert a screw into the terminal. Hold terminal insulating boot to position the screw head ¼-inch from engine ground and observe for spark while pulling the starter rope. If a

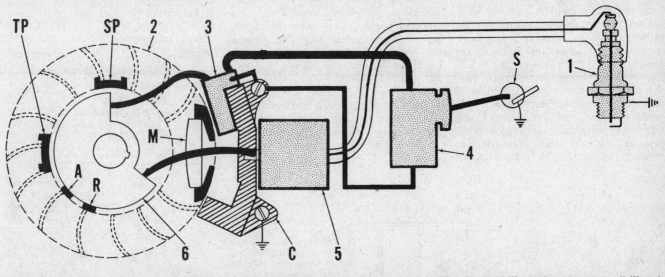

Fig. HL150—Schematic diagram of CD ignition system. Electrical energy created by magnet (M) in flywheel (2) passing generator coil (3) and core (C) is stored in the capacitor (4) until SCR switch in timing module (6) is turned on by timing pole piece (TP) passing magnetic triggering device (A or R) in module. The capacitor will then discharge the stored electrical energy into the transformer (5) which builds up the voltage to fire the spark plug (1). SCR switch is actuated by retard magnetic triggering device (R) at cranking speeds and by advance triggering device (A) when engine is running. Safety pole piece (SP) will cause spark plug to be fired on exhaust stroke if engine is turned backwards. "ON-OFF" switch (S) is used to stop engine by grounding the capacitor.

spark is observed, the magneto can be considered OK; if no spark is observed, proceed as follows:

CAUTION: Discharge capacitor by switching ignition to "OFF" position or by touching the switch lead to ground if disconnected from switch.

Remove fan housing and flywheel and thoroughly inspect to see that all wires are properly connected and there are no broken or loose connections. If all wires are secure and in place, make the following tests: NOTE: Except where rotor is required to be in place during the generator coil test, components may be tested on or off the unit.

Select Rx1 scale of ohmmeter and connect one lead of ohmmeter to timing switch module marked "TRANS." and the other lead to terminal marked "GEN." as shown in Fig. HL151. Strike the pole pieces with a screwdriver as shown; the ohmmeter needle should show a deflection and remain deflected until the leads are disconnected. If no deflection is noted, reverse the leads and again strike pole pieces with screwdriver. If no needle deflection is noted with ohmmeter leads connected in either manner, renew the switch module.

To check capacitor, select Rx1000 scale of ohmmeter and disconnect ignition switch lead or turn switch to "ON" position. Connect negative (black) lead of ohmmeter to capacitor terminal used for generator coil lead connection and the positive (red) lead to capacitor ground lead terminal. An instant deflection of needle should occur; if not, reverse ohmmeter leads. If no deflection of ohmmeter needle occurs with leads connected in either direction, renew the capacitor.

Again using Rx1000 scale of ohmmeter, test transformer by connecting either lead of ohmmeter to transformer high voltage lead and other ohmmeter lead to transformer ground; the resulting reading should be between 2400 and 2900 ohms. If proper reading is obtained, disconnect leads, select Rx1 scale of ohmmeter and connect one ohmmeter lead to transformer input terminal and other lead to transformer ground; reading should be between 0.2

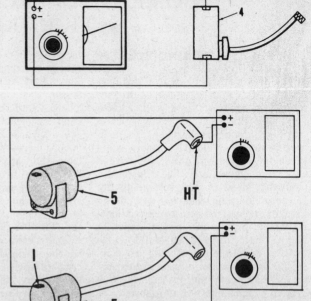

Fig. HL152—View showing ohmmeter connections for checking capacitor; refer to text for procedure.

Fig. HL153—High tension coil of transformer should have between 2400 and 2900 ohms resistance; make ohmmeter connections as shown in top view. Resistance of input coil should be between 0.2 and 0.25 ohms with leads connected as shown in bottom view.

and 0.24 ohms. If either reading is not between desired readings, renew transformer.

The generator coil (square coil mounted on core) can be checked for continuity as follows: With flywheel removed, disconnect lead from terminal marked "GEN." on switch module. Select Rx1 scale of ohmmeter and connect one lead of ohmmeter to ground and other lead to the lead disconnected from switch module; then, reverse the leads. The ohmmeter should show continuity (by deflection of needle) with the leads connected in one direction, but not in the opposite. If the continuity is not observed in either direction, or if the needle deflects showing continuity in both directions, renew the generator coil. The generator coil can be tested for output by using the voltmeter as follows: Refer to Fig. HL155. Remove spark plug, disconnect lead from ignition switch and bring lead out through switch hole in throttle handle. Disconnect ground lead from capacitor. Select lowest "DC" scale on voltmeter. Connect positive (red) lead of voltmeter to switch wire

and the negative (black) lead to engine ground. Spin engine by pulling firmly on starter rope. A minimum of 4 volts should be observed on voltmeter.

It is possible for some capacitor discharge ignition system components to be faulty, but not be detected by the volt-ohmmeter tests. If after testing, a faulty component is not located, renew the components one at a time until the trouble is located. The components should be renewed in the following order:

1. Capacitor
2. Generator coil and core
3. Transformer
4. Timing switch module

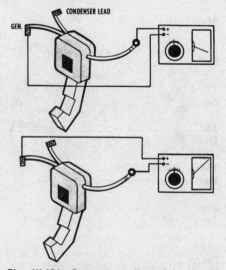

Fig. HL154—Generator coil module should show continuity in one direction only; reversing the leads should cause opposite reading to be observed.

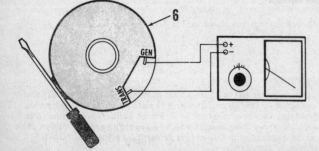

Fig. HL151—Checking the timing switch module using an ohmmeter; refer to text for procedure.

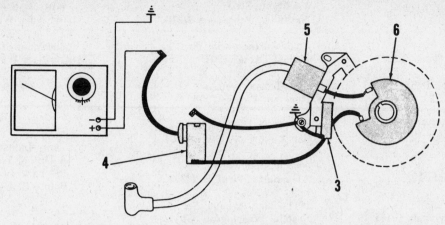

Fig. HL155—Testing output of generator with voltmeter; refer to text for procedure; minimum output should be 4 volts.

HOMELITE AUTHORIZED FACTORY BRANCHES

(Arranged Alphabetically by States)

When communicating with any of the establishments listed below, insert the name "Homelite" before the listed address, except those in Canada and Europe.

211 M. Street
Fresno, California 93721

1200 Monterey Pass Road
Monterey Park, California 91754

2234 Auburn Blvd.
Sacramento, California 95821

727 Airport Blvd.
So. San Francisco, California 94080

1300 S. Cherokee Street
Denver, Colorado 80223

164 E. Service Road
Hartford, Connecticut 06101

6965 Phillips Hwy. (U.S. No. 1 South)
Jacksonville, Florida 32216

4820 South Atlanta Rd.
Smyrna, Georgia 30080

3820 W. North Avenue
Stone Park, Illinois 60161

1818 W. 16th Street
Indianapolis, Indiana 46202

3209 Old Minden Rd.
Bossier City, Louisiana 71010

2414 Aisquith St.
Baltimore, Maryland 21218

124 Second Avenue
Needham Heights, Mass. 02194

30425 Stephenson Highway
Madison Heights, Michigan 48071

3781-28th St. S.W.
Grandville, Michigan 49418

1646 Terrace Drive
Roseville, Minnesota 55113

12088 Sante Fe Drive
Lenexa, Kansas 66215

5733 Manchester Avenue
St. Louis, Missouri 63110

1433 So. 13th Street
Omaha, Nebraska 68103

1006 St. George Avenue
Avenel, New Jersey 07001

39 River Road
North Arlington, New Jersey 07032

1910 Broadway, N.E.
Albuquerque, New Mexico 87125

2180 Walden Avenue
Buffalo, New York 14225

658 New Loudon Road
Latham, New York 12110

Rte. 1, Boston Post Road
Port Chester, New York 10573

2518 Erie Boulevard, East
Syracuse, New York 13224

4205 Golf Acres Drive
Charlotte, North Carolina 28208

7806 Anthony Wayne Avenue
Cincinnati, Ohio 45216

4821 Briar Road
Cleveland, Ohio 44135

11101 SW Greenburg Road
Portland, Oregon 97223

126 Frankstown Ave.
Altoona, Pennsylvania 16602

176 Lincoln Highway
Malvern, Pennsylvania 19355

5025 Longshore Avenue
Philadelphia, Pennsylvania 19135

4200 Ohio River Blvd.
Pittsburgh, Pennsylvania 15202

1324 No. Hollywood
Memphis, Tennessee 38108

405 Maple Street
Nashville, Tennessee 37210

1225 No. Industrial Blvd.
Dallas, Texas 75207

2412 Texas Avenue
Houston, Texas 77003

113 North Highway 91
Salt Lake City, Utah 84104

4605 Eisenhower St.
Alexandria, Virginia 22304

1911—22nd Avenue, So.
Seattle, Washington 98144

E. 3927 Trent Avenue
Spokane, Washington 99220

5128 MacCorkle Ave., S.E.
Charleston, West Virginia 25304

9010 W. Schlinger Ave.
W. Allis, Wisconsin 53214

556 Main St.
DePere, Wisconsin 54115

CANADA

Terry Industries,
A Div. of Textron Canada Ltd.
180 Labrosse Avenue
Pointe Claire, Quebec

EUROPE

Homelite, A Div. of Textron Inc.
Biesbosch 79A
Amstelveen, Holland

HONDA
HONDA MOTOR COMPANY, LTD.
Tokyo, Japan
U. S. Distributor is:
AMERICAN HONDA MOTOR CO., INC.
100 W. Alondra Blvd.
Gardena, California 90247

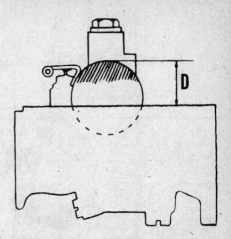

MODEL	Cyls.	Bore	Stroke	Displ.
G-20	1	58 mm.	50 mm.	132 cc.
		2 9/32 in.	1 31/32 in.	8.05 cu. in.
G-30	1	66 mm.	50 mm.	170 cc.
		2 19/32 in.	1 31/32 in.	10.37 cu. in.

MAINTENANCE

SPARK PLUG. Recommended spark plug is NKG type B-6H. Set electrode gap to 0.6-0.7 mm. (0.024-0.028 in.).

CARBURETOR. A Keihin float type carburetor is used. Refer to Fig. HN1-1 for exploded view of carburetor and to Fig. HN1-2 for cross-sectional view.

Carburetor is equipped with idle fuel (pilot screw) adjustment needle only; main fuel mixture is controlled by size of main jet (30—Fig. HN1-1) installed in carburetor. For most conditions, a #75 main jet is recommended for G-20 engines and a #85 main jet for G-30 engines. For high altitude operation (over 3300 ft.), use a smaller number size main jet. For cold weather operation, use a larger number size jet.

Adjusting the idle fuel (pilot screw) needle affects high idle no load operation of engine as well as low idle speed operation. For initial adjustment, open pilot screw ⅞-turn. With engine warm and running, adjust pilot screw for maximum engine no load performance from low idle speed to high idle speed. Adjust idle speed stop screw for desired slow idle speed.

To check for proper float level, refer to Fig. HN1-3; measure distance (D) from bottom side of float to gasket surface of float body when holding float so that float lever just contacts needle valve tip. Float level is correct if distance (D) is 17.5 mm. (11/16-inch). Note that needle valve is spring loaded and any pressure such as weight of float resting against needle valve may result in incorrect measurement of float level.

GOVERNOR. A mechanical flyweight type governor is used. Governor weights (13—Fig. HN1-8) are mounted in camshaft gear. Engine governed speed is adjusted by turning control knob to increase or decrease governor spring tension. Length of rod connecting carburetor throttle shaft lever to governor arm should be so that throttle is held in wide open position when engine is not running. Bend loop in rod to increase or decrease rod length as necessary.

For overhaul of governor unit, refer to CAMSHAFT paragraph and to Fig. HN1-8.

MAGNETO. Refer to Fig. HN1-4 for exploded view of the flywheel type magneto ignition system. Magneto can be considered in satisfactory condition if ignition spark will jump a 6 mm. (¼-inch) gap at 500 engine RPM, or a 7 mm. (9/32-inch) gap at 3000 engine RPM. Breaker points and condenser are serviced as a complete assembly only.

To adjust engine timing, turn engine so that both the intake and exhaust valves are closed and the "F" mark on flywheel is aligned with mating joint between oil pan and upper crankcase on camshaft side of engine. Then, carefully remove flywheel to avoid turning

Fig. HN1-3–When carburetor body and float valve assembly are inverted, distance from body to bottom of float should be 17.5 mm. (11/16-inch) when measured as shown. Bend float lever if measurement is not correct.

Fig. HN1-1–Exploded view of the Keihin float type carburetor used on Honda industrial engines. Refer to Fig. HN1-2 for cross-sectional view of carburetor, and to Fig. HN1-3 for view showing method of checking float level adjustment.

1. Choke shaft
2. Throttle stop lever
3. Throttle return spring
4. Throttle shaft
5. Throttle disc
6. "O" ring
7. Carburetor body
8. Plug
9. Gasket
10. Spring
11. Idle air (pilot) screw
12. Clip
13. Throttle shaft lever
14. Idle (slow) jet
15. Spring
16. Idle stop screw
17. Choke friction ball & spring
18. Air jets
19. Choke disc
20. Gasket
21. Inlet valve seat
22. Inlet valve
23. Float
24. Float pin
25. Overflow tube
26. Drain valve
27. Spring
28. Float bowl
29. Gasket
30. Main jet
31. Main jet holder
32. Main nozzle

Fig. HN1-2–Cross-sectional view of the Keihin float type carburetor; refer to Fig. HN1-1 for exploded view and to Fig. HN1-3 for checking float level.

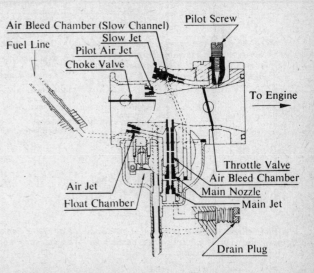

Air Bleed Chamber (Slow Channel)
Fuel Line
Slow Jet
Pilot Air Jet
Choke Valve
Pilot Screw
To Engine
Air Jet
Float Chamber
Throttle Valve
Air Bleed Chamber
Main Nozzle
Main Jet
Drain Plug

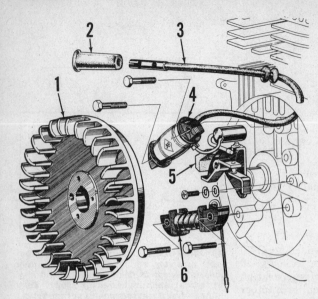

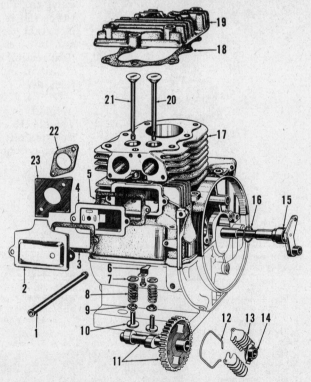

Fig. HN1-4—Exploded view of the flywheel type magneto ignition system. Condenser and breaker point assembly (5) are serviced as a unit only. The lighting coil (6) is optional equipment.

1. Flywheel
2. Spark plug boot
3. High tension wire
4. Ignition coil
5. Condenser & breaker point assy.
6. Lighting coil (optional)

Fig. HN1-7—Drawing showing tightening sequence for the four short cylinder head cap screws. Long cap screws (A) also retain fuel tank.

crankshaft and adjust breaker points so they are just starting to open (breaker arm just touches crankshaft). Breaker point gap should be 0.3-0.4 mm. (0.012-0.016 inch) when engine is properly timed.

LUBRICATION. Crankcase capacity is 1¼ pints. Recommended motor oil is API classification DG or MS, with later API codes, use SC or SD. Use SAE 30 oil for normal or warm temperatures; use SAE 20 oil when engine is operating in extremely cold temperatures.

On engines equipped with speed reduction unit, use same weight oil as used in engine crankcase. Reduction case capacity is ¼-pint.

REPAIRS

CYLINDER HEAD. When installing cylinder head, insert the four short cap screws with flat washers and tighten to a torque of 3.8-4.1 kg.-m. (28-30 Ft.-Lbs.) following the numbered sequence shown in Fig. HN1-7. When installing the fuel tank, tighten the three long cap screws (A) to a torque of 2.2-2.5 kg.-m. (16-18 Ft.-Lbs.).

PISTON, PIN AND RINGS. The piston is accessible for service after splitting oil pan from cylinder and upper crankcase assembly and re-

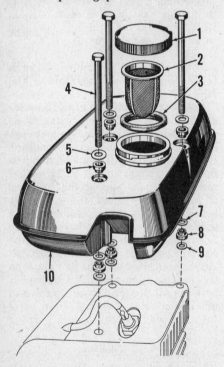

Fig. HN1-5—Three of the cylinder head bolts (4) also retain fuel tank assembly (10) to engine. Note placement of washers (5), insulators (6 & 8) and insulator washers (7 & 9).

1. Fuel cap
2. Filler screen
3. Gasket
4. Cylinder head cap screws
5. Flat washers
6. Insulators
7. Insulator washers
8. Insulators
9. Insulator washers
10. Fuel tank

1. Breather tube
2. Tappet cover
3. Gasket
4. Breather assembly
5. Gasket
6. Oil separator
7. Valve spring seats
8. Valve springs
9. Spring retainers
10. Valve lifters (tappets)
11. Camshaft
12. Governor weight center
13. Governor weights
14. Governor slider (sleeve)
15. Camshaft holder
16. "O" ring
17. Cylinder & upper crankcase
18. Cylinder head gasket
19. Cylinder head
20. Exhaust valve
21. Intake valve
22. Gasket
23. Carburetor insulator

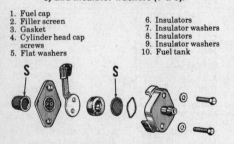

Fig. HN1-6—Exploded view of fuel shut-off cock. Note screens (S) which may need occasional cleaning.

Fig. HN1-8—Exploded view of cylinder and upper crankcase assembly. Hollow camshaft (11) turns on camshaft holder (15). Governor weight plates (13) are carried by camshaft gear and pivot on weight center (12).

moving the crankshaft, connecting rod and piston assembly (1—Fig. HN1-9). Piston pin is retained by a snap ring in piston at each end of pin. Piston pin should be a hand push fit in piston and connecting rod (Zero to 0.012 mm.) (0.0005 inch). Piston pin diameter, new, is 17.994-18.000 mm. (0.7084-0.7087 inch); renew if worn to 17.95 mm. (0.7067 inch).

Desired piston ring end gap for all rings is 0.2-0.4 mm. (0.008-0.016 inch); maximum allowable ring end gap is 1.5 mm. (0.059 inch). Ring side clearance in groove should be 0.02-0.06 mm. (0.0008-0.0024 inch) for top ring and 0.01-0.05 mm. (0.0004-0.002 inch) for second ring and oil control ring. Maximum allowable side clearance is 0.15 mm. (0.006 inch) for all rings.

Clearance between cylinder wall and piston, measured at piston skirt and at right angle to piston pin, should be 0.07-0.1 mm. (0.0028-0.0039 inch); maximum allowable clearance is 0.25 mm. (0.0098 inch). Standard cylinder bore is 58.00-58.01 mm. (2.2835-2.2839 inch) for model G-20, and 66.00-66.01 mm. (2.5984-2.5988 inch) for model G-30 engine. Piston and rings are available in oversizes of 0.25, 0.50 and 0.75 mm. (approximately 0.010, 0.020 and 0.030 inch) as well as standard size. Install chrome faced compression ring in top ring groove and install all rings with manufacturer's mark up.

CRANKSHAFT ASSEMBLY.
Refer to Fig. HN1-9 for assembled view

(1) and exploded view (items 2 through 20) of the built-up crankshaft assembly. Crankshaft is assembled by pressing right crankshaft (10) and left crankshaft (20) onto crankpin (8). Disassembly should not be attempted unless shop is equipped with special disassembly tools and alignment gages. Unit is serviced as a complete assembly (1) to renew units extensively worn or where disassembly tools and gages are not available.

Crankpin bearing clearance (connecting rod radial play) should be 0.004-0.036 mm. (0.00016-0.0014 inch); maximum wear limit is 0.1 mm. (0.0039 inch). Side play of connecting rod on crankpin should be 0.1-0.35 mm. (0.0039-0.0138 inch); maximum allowable side (axial) play is 0.85 mm. (0.0335 inch). Crankpin bearing wear and connecting rod side play can be checked by measuring connecting rod small end "shake" or side movement; maximum allowable shake is 3.0 mm. (0.118 inch).

When reinstalling crankshaft assembly, be sure piston ring end gaps are placed 120 degrees apart and lubricate the cylinder bore, piston, rings and bearings. Align the "O" marks on crankshaft gear and camshaft gear and be sure bearing on left crankshaft is fitted on the bearing set ring (15) in upper crankcase. Note: Place oil seals on crankshaft before installing the assembly in upper crankcase. Apply liquid gasket to crankcase and oil pan

mating surfaces when installing oil pan.

CAMSHAFT AND TAPPETS.
After removing the crankshaft assembly, remove camshaft holder (15—Fig. HN1-8) and withdraw camshaft (11) and governor weight assembly from upper crankcase (17). Tappets (10) can then be removed from bores in crankcase. Remove governor weight center (12), weights (13) and sleeve (slider) (14) if necessary.

Desired clearance between camshaft holder and camshaft is 0.016-0.061 mm. (0.0006-0.0024 inch); maximum allowable clearance is 0.1 mm. (0.0039 inch). Camshaft holder diameter is 10.966-10.984 mm. (0.4317-0.4324 inch) at inner end and 11.000-11.027 mm. (0.4331-0.4342 inch) at outer (large) end; minimum allowable diameter is 10.92 mm. (0.4299 inch) at inner end and 10.954 mm. (0.4313 inch) at outer end.

Desired camshaft end play is 0.1-0.5 mm. (0.0039-0.0197 inch); maximum allowable end play is 1.0 mm. (0.039 inch). Maximum cam lobe diameter (new) is 29.32-29.40 mm. (1.1543-1.1575 inch); minimum allowable cam lobe diameter is 29.0 mm. (1.1417 inch).

VALVE SYSTEM.
Valves are removable after removing cylinder head and tappet cover. Valve face and seat angle for both valves is 45°. Desired seat width is 0.7-1.0 mm. (0.028-0.039 inch); narrow seat using a 75 degree cutter if seat width exceeds 2.0 mm. (0.078 inch). Obtain desired valve (tappet) clearance of 0.06 mm. (0.0024 inch) by grinding ends of valve stems. To check valve clearance, turn engine so that both valves are closed and "T" mark on flywheel is aligned with mating joint between oil pan and upper crankcase on camshaft side of engine.

Intake valve stem diameter, new, is 6.965-6.980 mm. (0.2742-0.2748 inch); renew valve if stem diameter is less than 6.92 mm. (0.2724 inch). Desired intake valve stem to guide clearance is 0.02-0.05 mm. (0.0008-0.002 inch); maximum allowable clearance is 0.12 mm. (0.0047 inch).

Exhaust valve stem diameter, new, is 6.940-6.973 mm. (0.2732-0.2745 inch); renew valve if stem diameter is less than 6.90 mm. (0.2716 inch). Desired exhaust valve stem to guide clearance is 0.045-0.075 mm. (0.0018-0.003 inch); maximum allowable clearance is 0.15 mm. (0.0059 inch).

Valve spring free length is 27 mm. (1.063 inches); renew springs if free length is less than 25 mm. (0.985 inch). Valve springs should exert a force of 5.98-6.62 kg. (13.2-14.6 lbs.) when

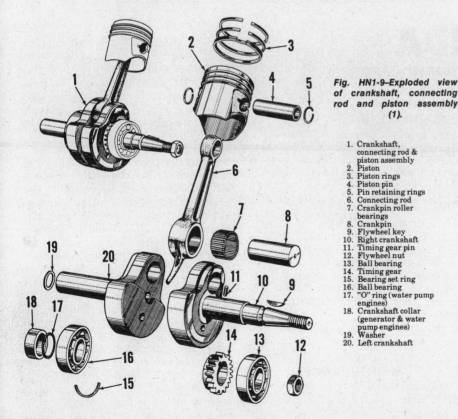

Fig. HN1-9—Exploded view of crankshaft, connecting rod and piston assembly (1).

1. Crankshaft, connecting rod & piston assembly
2. Piston
3. Piston rings
4. Piston pin
5. Pin retaining rings
6. Connecting rod
7. Crankpin roller bearings
8. Crankpin
9. Flywheel key
10. Right crankshaft
11. Timing gear pin
12. Flywheel nut
13. Ball bearing
14. Timing gear
15. Bearing set ring
16. Ball bearing
17. "O" ring (water pump engines)
18. Crankshaft collar (generator & water pump engines)
19. Washer
20. Left crankshaft

compressed to a length of 22 mm. (0.866-inch), or a force of 12.45-13.75 kg. (27.5-30.4 lbs.) when compressed to a length of 16.5 mm. (0.650 inch).

REWIND STARTER. Refer to Fig. HN1-10 for exploded view of the rewind starter assembly used on some models. Starter can be disassembled as follows: Pull rope out slightly and untie knot at handle end while holding the rope pulley (6) from turning. Remove handle from rope and allow spring to unwind slowly. Remove cap screw (1), friction plate (2), spring (3) and friction disc (5). Remove ratchets (4) from pulley and remove pulley and spring from housing. Reassemble by reversing disassembly procedure and check action of starter before reinstalling.

Fig. HN1-11–Exploded view of optional reduction unit.

1. Oil filler cap
2. Oil dipstick
3. "O" ring
4. Drain plug
5. Gasket
6. Oil seal
7. Cover
8. Gasket
9. Key
10. Thrust washer
11. Drive sprocket
12. Ball bearing
13. Driven sprocket
14. Drive chain
15. Reduction case
16. Hollow dowels
18. Ball bearing
19. Gasket
20. Key

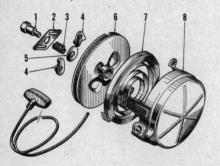

Fig. HN1-10–Exploded view of rewind starter assembly. Starter cup (attached to engine crankshaft) is not shown.

1. Special bolt
2. Friction plate
3. Friction spring
4. Ratchets
5. Washer
6. Rope pulley
7. Rewind spring
8. Housing

REDUCTION DRIVE. Refer to exploded view of optional reduction drive unit in Fig. HN1-11. To disassemble unit, remove cover (7) and pull drive sprocket (11), driven sprocket (13) and chain (14) as a unit. Remove reduction case (15) from engine. Reassemble by reversing disassembly procedure. Refer to LUBRICATION paragraph for proper oil to refill unit.

HONDA

HONDA MOTOR COMPANY , LTD.
Tokyo, Japan
U. S. Distributor is:
AMERICAN HONDA MOTOR CO., INC.
100 W. Alondra Blvd.
Gardena, California 90247

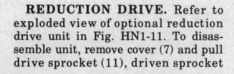

MODEL	Cyls.	Bore	Stroke	Displ.	H.P.
G25	1	46mm	35.6mm	59cc	1.8
		1-13/16 in	1-13/32 in	3.61 cu in	
G28	1	49mm	35.6mm	67cc	2.0 @ 5000 rpm or
		1-15/16 in	1-13/32 in	4.09 cu in	2.8 @ 6000 rpm

These engines are equipped with an automatic clutch and output shaft reduction system—see Fig. HN2-11. When crankshaft of Model G25 turns at 5000 rpm, output shaft turns at 2400 rpm. 5000 engine rpm of Model G28 turns pto shaft at 2500 rpm.

E600 portable generator units are powered by Model G25 engine. Refer to GENERATOR section for service. Model G28 engine is classified as a general purpose engine and in addition to its use in Model E900 generator, also serves as power unit for Model F28 power tiller which is convertible to a snow blower.

Services to both engines are the same except as specified.

MAINTENANCE

SPARK PLUG. For Model G25, NGK spark plug type C-6H is used. C-6HB is recommended for Model G28. Plug electrode gap is set to 0.6-0.7mm (0.024-0.028 inch).

CARBURETOR. A Keihin float type carburetor is used on Model G25. Refer to Fig. HN2-1 for cross-sectional view. Idle fuel mixture is adjusted by turning needle (8). Initial setting is ¾-1 turn open for the idle mixture needle. Main fuel mixture is controlled by size of main jet (4). Standard main jet size is #70; however, a smaller main jet size (number) may provide better operation at high altitudes. Turn idle speed stop screw (S—Fig. HN2-2) until idle speed is approximately 1500 rpm. With engine idling, the clutch should be disengaged and output shaft should not be turning.

To check for proper float level, refer to Fig. HN2-3. Measure distance (H) from bottom side of float to carburetor body when holding float so that float lever just contacts needle valve tip. Float level is correct if height (H) is 16-17mm (⅝ to 21/32-inch). NOTE: Needle valve is spring loaded and any pressure such as weight of float resting against

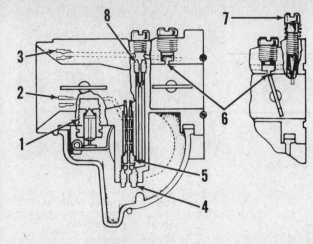

idle to operating speed setting.

Fig. HN2-1–Cross-sectional view of carburetor used on G25 engines. Fuel inlet needle valve (1) is provided with a spring inside needle.

1. Fuel inlet needle valve
2. Air jet
3. Pilot air jet
4. Main jet
5. Main nozzle
6. Bypass
7. Idle mixture needle
8. Pilot jet

Main jet (11) is fixed, providing proper fuel to air ratio when engine operates under load. Standard main jet size is No. 68, with substitute sizes ranging from No. 60 to 72 to meet operational requirements at higher or lower elevations.

Float valve setting of this carburetor calls for use of a template gage which straddles float when carburetor body is inverted. Correct space between float and flange of carburetor body is 2mm (0.080 inch) which is approximate diameter of 5/64-inch drill which might be used for lack of another gage. Because float needle valve contains a small plunger which is loaded by a very light action spring, contact with float arm must be very slight or a small clearance (0.01mm or 0.0004 inch) allowed between tip of valve and float arm to insure correct fuel level.

needle valve may result in incorrect measurement of float level.

Model G28 is furnished with a carburetor of style shown in Fig. HN2-4. Initial setting of idle mixture adjustment screw (20—Fig. HN2-4) is ¾ to 1¼ turns open. With engine running, mixture screw is adjusted alternately with throttle stop (idle speed) screw (26) to provide smooth idle at 1200-1500 rpm or so that automatic clutch is disengaged and output shaft is not turning. Mixture adjustment screw (20) of this carburetor also serves as an air bleed at no-load rated rpm, and

final adjustment should be a balance between idle speed and open throttle to rated rpm (no load on output shaft) with no surge or hestitation as throttle/governor knob is changed from

In most applications, this engine uses a manual choke as shown in Fig. HN2-4 which is controlled by the operator. Generator, Model E900 is fitted with an automatic choke as shown in Fig. HN2-4A. This choke operates by expansion and contraction of U-shaped bi-metallic strip (1) and may be checked for proper performance by reference to the following:

AIR TEMPERATURE	CHOKE VALVE POSITION
0°C/32°F.	Fully closed
10°C/50°F.	1/8 Open
20°C/69°F.	1/4 Open
*80°C/176°F.	Wide open

*Air temperature raised by heat radiated from running engine.

Correct choke opening for a given

Fig. HN2-2–The idle speed stop screw (S) and fuel bowl drain (D) are accessible through holes in cover as shown.

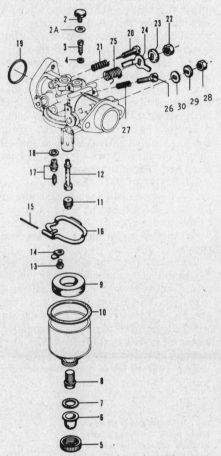

Fig. HN2-4–Exploded view of carburetor used on model G28 engine. Refer to text for service.

2. Cap plug	16. Float arm
2A. Flat washer	17. Float valve assembly
3. Throttle shaft guide screw	18. Gasket
4. Lock washer	19. "O"-ring
5. Sediment bulb retainer	20. Idle mixture screw
6. Sediment bulb	21. Spring
7. Gasket	22. Throttle shaft nut
8. Float bowl retainer	23. Lock washer
9. Float	24. Throttle lever
10. Float bowl gasket	25. Throttle shaft spring
11. Main jet	26. Idle speed screw
12. Main nozzle	27. Spring
13. Pin set plate screw	28. Choke shaft nut
14. Pin set plate	29. Lock washer
15. Float pin	30. Spacer

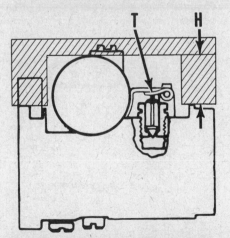

Fig. HN2-3–Float height (H) should be set as described in text by bending tang (T).

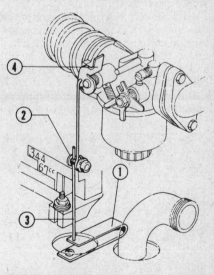

Fig. HN2-4A–Thermostatic controlled automatic choke used on G28 engine when fitted to model E900 generator. Note that bi-metallic strip is mounted below engine deck and near heat source for stable temperatures. See text.

1. Bi-metallic sensor
2. Adjusting clamp
3. Control rod
4. Choke lever

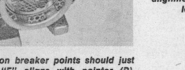

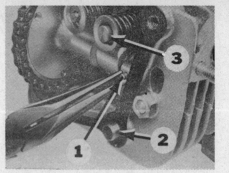

Fig. HN2-5–Drawing of speed control system. Arrows show direction of movement to increase engine speed.

1. Governor weights
2. Speed control knob
3. Governor spring
4. Governor lever and shaft
5. Link rod
6. Carburetor

Fig. HN2-8–Camshaft center shaft is retained in head by dowel pin (1). After center shaft is pulled from opposite end, camshaft and sprocket can be removed.

1. Shaft retainer dowel
2. Hollow dowel
3. Valve rotator (Exh only)

temperature is adjusted by releasing rod clamp (2) so that rod length can be changed to set choke valve to proper position. Take care not to bend or distort bi-metallic control strip. If engine is sluggish, stalls or lacks power, especially during warm-up, operation of automatic choke should be checked.

GOVERNOR. A mechanical flyweight type governor is used. Governor weights (1—Fig. HN2-5) are mounted on the clutch center (Fig. HN2-12) at end of crankshaft. Engine governed speed is adjusted by turning control knob (2—Fig. HN2-5) to increase or decrease governor spring tension. Length of rod (5) should be so that throttle valve is wide open when engine is not running and the speed control knob (2) is set at the high speed position. If rod length is incorrect, bend loop (L) in rod as necessary. If rod length is incorrect, engine speed may vary excessively (hunt).

IGNITION. The ignition system is the energy transfer type with the low tension coil and breaker points located under the flywheel. High tension coil and condenser are mounted on engine below fuel tank.

Breaker point gap should be approximately 0.3-0.4mm (0.012-0.016 inch);

however, gap should be adjusted to provide correct ignition timing. To adjust ignition timing, remove the recoil starter and cooling shroud from side of engine. Remove starter pulley and screens from flywheel and turn flywheel in normal direction of rotation (counter-clockwise as viewed from flywheel end) until "F" mark on flywheel is aligned with pointer on crankcase as shown in Fig. HN2-7. Breaker points should just open when "F" mark aligns with pointer. If points open too soon, decrease the breaker point gap. Breaker point gap can be adjusted through holes in flywheel, but flywheel must be removed to remove points.

LUBRICATION. Engines use a splash lubrication system with a dipper on connecting rod. The camshaft, valves and rocker arms are lubricated by oil picked up by the cam chain and tension roller.

Crankcase capacity is approximately 1½ pints. Oil level should be maintained between marks on the oil level dipstick. The filler plug (dip stick) should NOT be screwed into crankcase when checking oil level. Recommended motor oil is API classification MS, or if newer API code is used, SC or SD.

SAE 10W/30 oil is recommended for

all season use, however, if single viscosity oils are used, SAE 30 is called for in temperatures over 15°C (59°F), SAE 10W is required below 0°C (32°F) and SAE 20W should be used in mid-range temperatures (32°F to 59°F). Engine oil should be checked for level every 20 hours operation and changed after every 100 hours.

VALVE CLEARANCE. The valves are actuated by a chain driven camshaft located in the cylinder head and rocker arms (cam followers). Valve clearance should be set when engine is cold and piston is at TDC on compression stroke. The flywheel has a mark "T" indicating top dead center when aligned with crankcase mark (P—Fig. HN2-7). Clearance should be 0.05mm (0.002 inch) for both valves.

REPAIRS
VALVES AND CYLINDER HEAD. Remove the cylinder head cover (with rocker arms). Remove dowel pin (1—Fig HN2-8), withdraw the camshaft center shaft from opposite end of head and remove camshaft. Remove the four stud nuts and one screw then lift off the cylinder head. Cylinder head gasket surfaces must be perfectly flat.

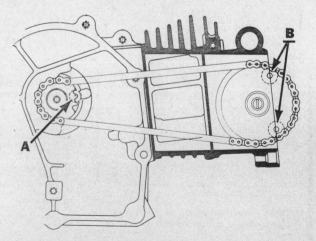

Fig. HN2-9–Valve timing. Align mark on crankshaft sprocket (A) with crankcase cutout and two holes (B) of camshaft sprocket on gasket surface of cylinder head as shown. "T" mark on flywheel should be in alignment with timing rib on left crankcase.

Fig. HN2-7–Ignition breaker points should just open as mark "F" aligns with pointer (P). Piston is at TDC when mark (T) is aligned with pointer.

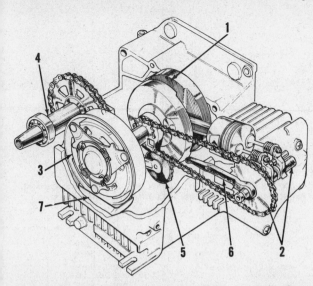

Fig. HN2-11–View of engine showing layout of parts. The automatic clutch (3) disengages at idle speed.

1. Crankshaft
2. Camshaft
3. Clutch
4. Output shaft
5. Chain tension roller
6. Oil guide
7. Oil separator

Six hollow dowels are used on these engines for alignment of cylinder, cylinder head and cylinder head cover. Two of these dowels are installed between cylinder and crankcase over diagonally opposite stud bolts. Two more are fitted at joint between cylinder and cylinder head, and two are also used to line up cylinder head cover. During assembly, be sure that these dowels are fitted into correct bolt holes and that assembly gaskets are correctly placed.

When assembling, hollow dowels should be installed around two of the studs between the cylinder and cylinder head. Tighten the four cylinder head retaining nuts diagonally to 70-78 inch-pounds torque. Make certain that all are tightened evenly. Turn the flywheel until the "T" mark is aligned with mark (P—Fig. HN2-7) on crankcase and install camshaft with holes in sprocket parallel to gasket surface as shown in Fig. HN2-9.When the camshaft center shaft is installed, make

certain that oil guide is correctly positioned between cylinder head and camshaft sprocket. Align hole in center shaft and install dowel pin (1—Fig. HN2-8). Valve clearance must be adjusted after assembling, and after head bolts are tightened to specified torque value. Important: Do not tighten cylinder head after adjusting valve tappet clearance. Cylinder head cover is also tightened to 70-78 inch-pounds torque.

PISTON, RINGS AND CYLINDER. To remove the cylinder, first remove the cylinder head as in the previous paragraphs, then withdraw the cylinder. Rings should be installed with marked side toward closed end of

piston. Arrow on top of piston should point down. Piston and rings are available in standard size only for model G25 engine. For model G28, oversizes of 0.25, 0.50 and 0.75mm (0.010, 0.020 and 0.030 inch) are available with corresponding oversizes in renewal cylinders.

If cylinder bore is out-of-round or tapers more than 0.05mm (0.002 inch) cylinder should be renewed. Piston ring side clearance is 0.02-0.06mm (0.0008-0.0024 inch) for top compression ring. Side clearance for second and oil control rings is 0.01-0.05mm (0.0004-0.002 inch). Service limit of side clearance for all rings is 0.15mm (0.006 inch).

Assembly details. Stagger piston ring end gaps equally in ring grooves. Manufacturer's marks are imprinted on top side of ring. Install with these marks toward top of piston. Top compression ring is chromed and easily identifiable. Second compression ring and oil ring are parkerized. Arrow mark on head of piston should point down. Piston pin retaining snap rings should be installed with open part of snap ring NOT aligned with cut-out in piston. Hollow dowels are installed between cylinder and crankcase on two of the studs.

CRANKSHAFT AND CONNECTING ROD. The crankshaft and connecting rod are available only as an assembly and should not be disassembled. Removal is accomplished after

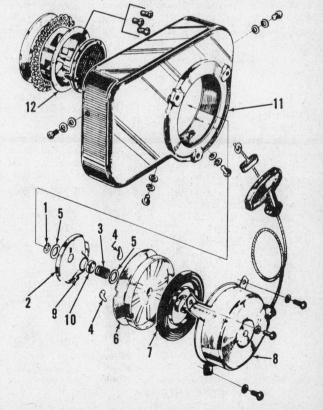

Fig. HN2-14–Exploded view of starter assembly. Refer also to Fig. HN2-15.

1. Snap ring
2. Friction plate
3. Friction spring
4. Ratchet pawls
5. Washers
6. Pulley
7. Rewind spring
8. Housing
9. Set spring
10. Spring cup
11. Cooling shroud
12. Starter cup

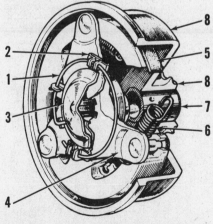

Fig. HN2-12–Cross-sectional view of clutch and governor weights. Assembly is mounted on end of crankshaft.

1. Weight retainer ring
2. Governor weights
3. Governor slider
4. Drive plate
5. Clutch shoes (weights)
6. Springs
7. Bushing
8. Clutch drum and sprocket

removing the clutch and reduction assembly, cylinder, piston, flywheel and separating the crankcase halves.

When assembling, make certain that crankcase halves are clean and free from nicks and burrs.

CLUTCH AND REDUCTION UNIT. The automatic clutch (3—Fig. HN2-11) is located on the crankshaft and drives the output shaft (4) via a chain reduction drive. The clutch should be disengaged when engine is idling. The clutch and reduction unit can be removed after removing the crankcase side cover. Refer to Fig. HN2-12 for cross-sectional view of the clutch assembly. Clutch shown in Fig. HN2-12 is that installed in model G25 engine. Clutch used in model G28 is similar except that only two shoes are fitted to clutch drum.

REWIND STARTER. Refer to Figs. HN2-14 and HN2-15 for views of rewind starter used. Starter can be disassembled as follows: Pull rope out slightly and untie knot at handle end while holding the rope pulley (6) from turning, remove handle from rope and allow spring to unwind slowly. Remove snap ring (1), washer, friction plate (2), springs (3 & 9), cup (10), and washer. Remove ratchets (4) from pulley and remove pulley and spring from housing. Reassemble by reversing disassembly procedure and check action of starter before reinstalling on engine.

GENERATOR

Generator wiring diagram for model E600 is shown in Fig. HN2-20. The exciter coil (8) is located under the

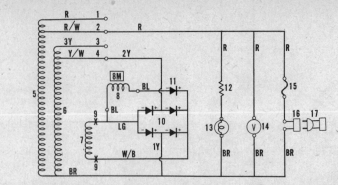

Fig HN2-20—Wiring diagram for E600, 60 hertz generator. Magnet (8M) is in engine flywheel. Terminals (1 & 3) are used for 50 hertz units, together with different drive pulleys.

BL. Blue	1,2,3 & 4. Terminals	10. Bridge rectifier (4 diodes)
BR. Brown	5. AC generator coil	11. External exciter diode
LG. Light green	6. Internal exciter coil (stator)	12. Resistor
R. Red	7. Armature (field) coil	13. Pilot light
R/W. Red/White stripe	8. External exciter coil	14. Voltmeter
W/B. White/Blue stripe	(engine)	15. Fuse
Y. Yellow	8M. Magnet in flywheel	16. Connector
Y/W. Yellow/White stripe	9. Brushes	17. Load

engine flywheel and uses the permanent magnet (8M) in the flywheel to generate the initial exciter current. This initial exciter current is changed to DC by diode (11) then routed to the rotating field (7) of the armature through brushes (9) and slip rings. The current through field (7) causes the armature to become a rotating electromagnet. As the armature (electromagnet) turns AC current is generated in stator windings (5 & 6). Current generated in winding (6) is routed through the full wave rectifier (10) and is then used to energize the armature field (7). The AC current generated in winding (5) is connected to the output connection (16).

On all 60 HZ (cycle) generators, the generator armature should turn 1,800 RPM when the engine output shaft is operating at 2,440 RPM. On all 50 HZ generators, the generator armature should be rotating at 1,500 RPM when engine output shaft is turning 2,440 RPM. The generator drive belt should have 3/8 to 7/16-inch belt flex between the pulleys. To tighten the drive belt, loosen the engine clamp bolt (Fig. HN2-21) and turn the adjust bolt (Fig. HN2-22). Make certain that clamp bolt (Fig. HN2-21) is retightened after belt tension is adjusted.

To remove the engine, loosen the engine clamp bolt and adjusting bolt (Fig. HN2-21 & HN2-22), remove the generator drive belt, disconnect wires from engine to generator, then slide engine out toward direction of muffler. Make certain that the two blue wires from engine are connected to the two blue wires from generator when assembling.

The pilot light on panel is 24 volt, 2 Watt. The fuse is 5 Amp.

TEST AND REPAIR. To check the engine exciter coil (8—Fig. HN2-20), disconnect the two blue wires shown in Fig. HN2-23. Coil (under engine flywheel) should have approximately 4 ohms resistance without engine running. With engine operating at max-

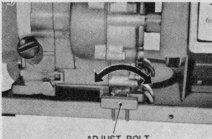

ADJUST BOLT

Fig. HN2-22—Belt tension is adjusted by turning the adjust bolt.

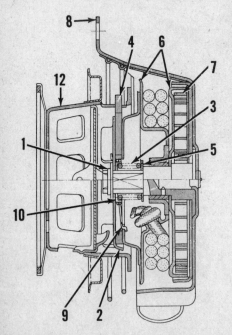

Fig. HN2-15—Cross-sectional view of starter. Refer to Fig. HN2-14 for legend.

ENGINE CLAMP BOLT

Fig. HN2-21—View showing the engine clamp bolt. Turning in direction of arrow loosens clamp.

Fig. HN2-23—Refer to text for checking the external (on engine) exciter coil.

Fig. HN2-24—View of terminals connected for 60 hertz operation. Refer to text for testing.

imum governed speed, voltage should be at least 20 Volts (AC). If incorrect, remove engine flywheel and renew the exciter coil.

To check the condition of stator windings on 60 hertz generator units, disconnect Yellow/White and Red/White wires from terminals (2 & 4—Fig. HN2-24). Resistance between the Yellow/White wire and point (BR) between the two lower diodes should be 0.85 ohms (for 120 Volt) or 1.40 ohms (for 220 Volt). Resistance between Red/White wire and point (BR)

should be 1.3 ohms (for 120 volt models) or 4.5 ohms (for 220 volt models). A short circuit is indicated if resistance is too low; an open circuit or poor connection if resistance is too high.

To check the condition of stator windings of 50 hertz generator units, disconnect Yellow wire from terminal (3) and Red wire from terminal (1). Resistance between Yellow wire and point (BR) should be 1.06 ohms (120 Volt models), 1.73 ohms (for 220 Volt models) or 1.88 ohms (for 240 Volt models). Resistance between Red wire and point (BR) should be 1.7 ohms (for 120 Volt models), 5.9 ohms (for 220 Volt models) or 7.2 ohms (for 240 Volt models).

To check condition of diode (11—Fig. HN2-25), disconnect (and insulate) both blue wires (Fig. HN2-23). Check resistance between ends of diode (11—Fig. HN2-25) with ohmmeter, then reverse the ohmmeter leads. Diode should have infinite resistance with one connection and little resistance with ohmmeter leads reversed. If resistance is the same (either high or low) in both directions, diode may be faulty. Very low resistance in both directions

Fig. HN2-25—View showing location of the diodes. Refer to text for testing.

can also be caused by short in the connecting wires.

To check condition of diodes (10—Fig. HN2-25) on 60 hertz units, disconnect Red wire from terminal (2—Fig. HN2-24), Yellow wire from terminal (4), Brown wire from point behind (BR) and both wires from brushes. With ends of wires insulated, each diode (10—Fig. HN2-25) can be checked with ohmmeter. Diodes should have infinite resistance in one direction and low resistance with ohmmeter leads reversed.

HONDA

HONDA MOTOR COMPANY, LTD.
Tokyo, Japan

U.S. Distributor is:
AMERICAN HONDA MOTOR CO., INC.
100 W. Alondra Blvd.
Gardena, California 90247

| MODEL | Cyls. | GENERATOR | | Displ. | OUTPUT | |
		Bore	Stroke		DC	AC
EI-300	1	42mm	40mm	55.4cc	12-13V	100V
		1.65 in.	1.57 in.	3.38 cu. in.	5.4 Amps	250W @ 50Hz
EII-300	1	42mm	40mm	55.4cc	12-13V	100V
		1.65 in.	1.57 in.	3.38 cu. in.	8.0 Amps	300W @ 60Hz
EIII-300	1	42mm	40mm	55.4cc	12-13V	120V
		1.65 in.	1.57 in.	3.38 cu. in.	8.0 Amps	300W @ 60Hz
EIV-300	1	42mm	40mm	55.4cc	12-13V	220V
		1.65 in.	1.57 in.	3.38 cu. in.	5.4 Amps	250W @ 50Hz
EV-300	1	42mm	40mm	55.4cc	12-13V	220V
		1.65 in.	1.57 in.	3.38 cu. in.	8.0 Amps	300W @ 60Hz
E300	1	42mm	40mm	55.4cc	12V	120-240V
		1.65 in.	1.57 in.	3.38 cu. in.	8.0 Amps	250-300VA @ 50-60Hz
ED250	1	42mm	40mm	55.4cc	6/12/24V	....
		1.65 in.	1.57 in.	3.38 cu. in.	10/16.5/10.4 Amps	
ER400	1	42mm	40mm	55.4cc	12-14V	115V
		1.65 in.	1.57 in.	3.38 cu. in.	*8.0 Amps	300 W @ 60Hz

*For use as 12V battery charger only.

MAINTENANCE

SPARK PLUG. Recommended plug for all models is NGK type CM-6. Plug gap should be set to 0.4mm (0.016 inch).

CARBURETOR. The float type carburetor shown in Fig. HN3-1 is used. The idle mixture needle (1—Fig. HN3-2) should be set to provide smooth running at idle speed. Initial setting is

⅞-turn open. Final setting may be 1⅜ turns open (± ¼-turn). Idle speed is adjusted by turning stop screw (2).

To remove carburetor, the fan cover and governor must be removed. Refer to the GOVERNOR section for removal. Refer to Fig. HN3-1 for exploded view of the carburetor. When reinstalling, gasket should be installed between a cylinder and insulator. "O" ring (13) should be installed between insulator and carburetor.

Float level is 14.5mm (0.570 inch) measured with carburetor inverted from bottom of float to surface of body flange. Some engines may be equipped with manual choke, and model ER400 has an automatic choke of type shown in Fig. HN3-3. "U"-shaped bi-metallic strip acts as a thermostat to control choke valve opening. At 20°C (68°F) open end of "U" should be 8mm (0.315 inch). Adjustment is not recommended, however, if automatic choke does not function properly, opening or closing of loop in choke rod may restore performance so that choke will operate.

GOVERNOR. A mechanical, flyweight governor is used for all models. See Fig. HN3-4A for later type. The flyweights (14—Fig. HN3-4) and slider (16) are mounted on cooling fan. As engine speed increases, the weights push slider out against lever (17). Governor rod (10) is attached to throttle lever on carburetor and governor lever (19).

To adjust the governor, loosen screw (20), pull lever (19) out toward arrow (A), push lever (17) toward governor weights (arrow B), then tighten screw (20). Make certain that end of governor spring is in correct hole in lever (21). Hole (A—insert Fig. HN3-4) is for 60 hertz operation; hole (B) is for 50 hertz.

Set the speed control at idle position, then turn adjuster (22) in spring (18) so that lever (L—Fig. HN3-2) is against idle stop screw (2).

Maximum engine speed should be adjusted to 3400-3600 RPM for types EI-300 and EIV-300 (50 hertz). Maximum engine speed should be 4000-4300 RPM for types EII-300, EIII-300 and EV-300 (60 hertz). Speed is adjusted by

turning screw (HS– Fig. HN3-5).

IGNITION. A magneto type ignition system is used. The low tension coil is located in the generator stator and is not serviced separately. The high tension coil is mounted on the crankcase below the cylinder. The breaker points and condenser are mounted at the rear of generator.

Breaker point gap should be 0.014 in. (0.35mm) at maximum opening. Ignition timing should occur (points just open) when mark on generator rotor cooling fin aligns with mark on stator as shown at (A—Fig. HN3-6). If ignition timing is incorrect, loosen the two mounting screws and move the condenser, breaker points and mounting plate. Timing marks should align when the piston is 13-17 degrees BTDC, on earlier models. On later models, E300, ED250 and ER400, timing marks align (fixed) at 19° BTDC, ±2°.

LUBRICATION. Crankcase capacity is 0.61 pint. Recommended motor oil is API classification DG or MS. New API code may be SC or SD. Use SAE 20 or 20W oil for tempera-

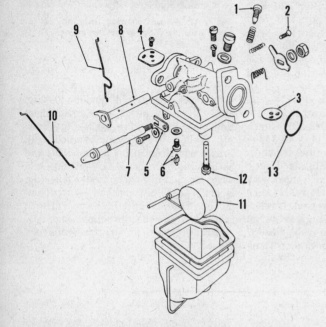

Fig. HN3-1–Exploded view of carburetor. When installing control rods, governor rod (10) should be outside of choke rod (9).

1. Idle mixture needle
2. Idle speed stop screw
3. Throttle plate
4. Choke plate
5. Throttle shaft retainer
6. Fuel inlet needle
7. Throttle shaft
8. Choke shaft
9. Choke rod
10. Governor rod
11. Float
12. Main jet
13. "O" ring

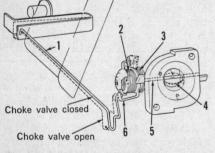

Fig. HN3-2–View showing position of carburetor idle mixture needle (1) and idle speed stop screw (2).

Fig. HN3-4–Exploded view of governor assembly. Rod (10) is also shown at (10– Fig. HN3-1).

10. Governor rod
14. Flyweights
15. Retainer ring
16. Governor slider
17. Lever and shaft
18. Governor spring
19. Lower lever
20. Screw
21. Spring lever
22. Adjuster
23. Speed control lever

Fig. HN3-4A–Governor used on models E300, ED250 and ER400. Note overall similarity to previous design.

1. Carburetor
2. Throttle shaft
3. Governor arm
4. Governor spring
5. Throttle control
6. Governor arm shaft
7. Governor slider
8. Governor weight holder
9. Governor weight
10. Choke lever

Choke valve closed

Choke valve open

Fig. HN3-3–Automatic choke used on model ER400. Expansion and contraction of "U"-shaped bi-metallic strip opens and closes choke valve. See text.

1. Choke rod
2. Relief spring
3. Return spring
4. Choke valve
5. Choke shaft
6. Choke lever

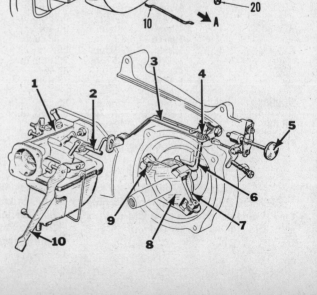

tures between 32° F. and 59° F. For temperatures below 32° F. use SAE 10W and for temperatures over 59° F., use SAE 30 oil. SAE 10W30 may be used in all seasons. Oil should be maintained above bottom of dipstick on filler plug. NOTE: Filler plug must not be screwed in when checking oil level. Engine oil should be changed every 100 hours of operation.

REPAIRS

CYLINDER HEAD. When removing the cylinder head, loosen screws in reverse of sequence shown in Fig. HN3-8 to prevent distorting cylinder head. When cleaning carbon, be careful not to damage the sealing surfaces. Cylinder head stud nuts should be tightened in sequence shown in Fig. HN3-8 to 5.7-6.5 Ft.-Lbs. torque.

Fig. HN3-5—Maximum engine speed is adjusted at screw (HS). The lock spring is located in threaded hole under screw.

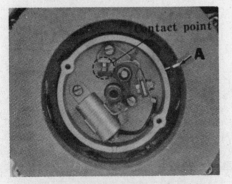

Fig. HN3-6—The ignition breaker points should just open when generator rotor cooling fin mark aligns with mark on stator at (A).

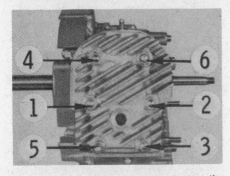

Fig. HN3-8—To prevent damage, loosen the cylinder head retaining stud nuts in reverse of order shown. Tighten in sequence shown.

PISTON, PIN AND RINGS. To remove the piston, it is necessary to remove the cylinder head and generator stator. Unbolt cover (21—Fig. HN3-12) from crankcase and lift the cover and generator end of crankshaft off engine. The piston and connecting rod assembly can then be withdrawn from top of cylinder. Later model engines, E300, ED250 and ER400 also require that generator be removed followed by crankcase cover (5—Fig. HN3-13). For easier access to cap of connecting rod (A) it is advisable, though not absolutely necessary, to remove both valves and camshaft (3) after removing camshaft reservoir (2). With cap of connecting rod unbolted, piston and connecting rod can be removed from cylinder. Refer to the following specification data:

Piston pin to connecting rod bore—
  Desired clearance .. 0.016-0.040mm
                            0.0006-0.0016 inch
  Wear limit ....0.16mm (0.006 inch)

Fig. HN3-9—Timing marks on the camshaft drive pulleys must be aligned as shown at (T).

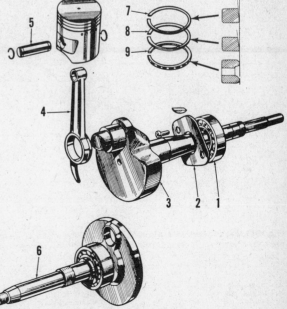

Fig. HN3-10—Exploded view of the crankshaft and associated parts of earlier type engine. The generator and ignition breaker points are located around crankshaft half (3). Engine cooling fan, starter and camshaft drive are at end of half (6).

1. Ball bearing
2. Retainer
3. Crankshaft half
4. Connecting rod
5. Piston pin
6. Crankshaft half
7. Top ring (chrome)
8. Second compression ring
9. Oil control ring

Piston pin to bore in piston—
  Desired clearance 0-0.012mm
                            0-0.0005 inch
  Wear limit ....0.13mm (0.005 inch)

Piston diameter, bottom of skirt at right angles to piston pin—
  Desired 41.995-42.015mm
                        1.6533-1.6541 inch
  Minimum limit 41.35mm (1.628 inch)

Cylinder bore—
  Standard diameter 42.005-42.025mm
                        1.6537-1.6545 inch
  Maximum taper and/or
    out-of-round 0.01mm (0.0004 inch)

Piston ring side clearance in groove—
  Top, desired 0.01-0.04mm
                        0.0004-0.0016 inch
  Wear limit ...0.08mm (0.0032 inch)
  Second (compression) and bottom (oil),
    desired 0.005-0.035mm
                        0.0002-0.0014 inch
  Wear limit ...0.08mm (0.0032 inch)

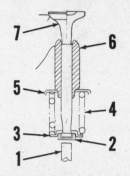

Fig. HN3-11—Cross-section of valve showing adjuster cap (2). Refer to text when adjusting valve clearance.

1. Cam follower (tappet)
2. Adjuster cup
3. Spring retainer cap
4. Valve spring
5. Spring seat
6. Valve guide
7. Valve

Piston ring end gap in cylinder bore—
All rings, desired 0.1-0.3mm
                        0.004-0.012 inch
Wear limit ...... 1.0mm (0.04 inch)
When assembling, manufacturer's marks on side of all piston rings should be toward top of piston. The top compression ring is chrome plated and second ring is unplated. Face of second compression ring is also angled more as shown in Fig. HN3-10. Dipper on connecting rod and arrow on top (head) of piston should both be down. Tighten the cylinder head retaining nuts in sequence shown in Fig. HN3-8 to 5.7-6.5 Ft. Lbs. torque. Tighten the Phillips head screws and one cap screw (C—Fig. HN3-12) that attach cover (21) to crankcase to 2.9-3.6 Ft.-Lbs. torque. Refer to Fig. HN3-13 for later engines. Tighten these assembly screws to 3.6-4.4 Ft.-Lbs. torque.

CRANKSHAFT. The generator end of early model crankshaft can be removed as follows: Remove the generator stator and rotor (permanent magnet), then unbolt cover (21—Fig. HN3-12) from the crankcase.

NOTE: Cover is attached with six Phillips head screws and one cap screw (C).

Crankshaft half (3—Fig. HN3-10) and ball bearing (1) can be removed after unbolting the bearing retainer (2) from inside of cover. The crankpin diameter should be 17.973-17.984mm (0.7076-0.7080 inch) for all engines. If crankpin diameter is less than 17.9mm (0.7047 inch), the crankshaft half or entire crankshaft should be renewed. Desired diameter of connecting rod lower bearing bore on all engines is 18.000-18.001mm (0.70866-0.70869 inch). If connecting rod bore is more than 18.06mm (0.7110 inch) diameter, renew connecting rod.

To remove the cooling fan and starter end of crankshaft of older style engines, it is necessary to remove the connecting rod and piston assembly, engine cooling fan, rewind starter assembly, starter pawl holder, camshaft drive belt and crankshaft timing pulley. When installing the camshaft drive belt, timing marks must be aligned as shown at (T—Fig. HN3-9).

Refer to Fig. HN3-13 and note that entire one-piece crankshaft of later model engines may be removed after generator assembly, crankcase cover (5), camshaft (3) and reservoir (2) are removed as previously covered. During reassembly, be sure that "O" mark on crankshaft timing gear is aligned with index mark on camshaft gear.

Fig. HN3-13A relates to specifications of crankshaft journals which appear in table following:

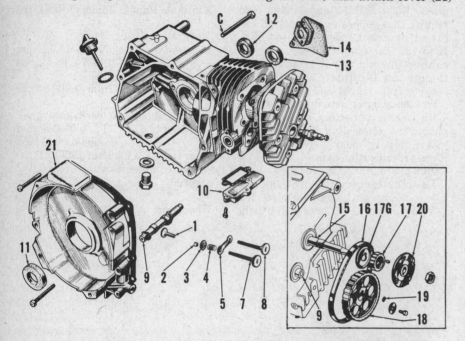

Fig. HN3-12–Exploded view of E-300 crankcase and valve system. Timing marks on camshaft drive pulleys (17 & 18) are shown in Fig. HN3-9.

1. Cam followers (tappet)
2. Adjuster cup
3. Spring retainer cap
4. Valve spring
5. Spring seat
7. Exhaust valve
8. Inlet valve
9. Camshaft
10. Cover
11. Oil seal
12. Oil seal
13. Oil seal
14. Insulator and gasket
15. Crankshaft
16. Drive belt
17. Drive pulley
17G. Belt guide
18. Driven pulley
19. Drive pin
20. Starter pawls and holder

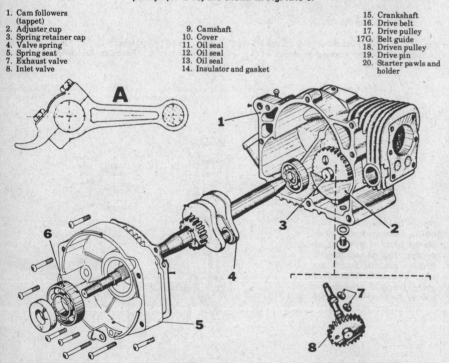

Fig. HN3-13–Exploded view of crankcase and crankshaft of models E300, ED250 and ER400. Note one-piece crankshaft (4) and that connecting rod (A) has removable cap, and that camshaft (3) is driven by spur gears.

1. Crankcase/cylinder
2. Cam gear reservoir
3. Camshaft
4. Crankshaft
5. Crankcase cover
6. Crankshaft bearing
7. Valve lifters
8. Camshaft/camgear

E-300 models (I thru V)
Fan side
15.007-15.025mm
(0.5907-0.5913 inch)
Bearing No. 6002
Renew under 14.95mm (0.5880 in.)

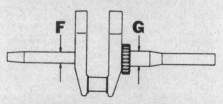

Fig. HN3-13A–View of late style crankshaft to show main bearing journal arrangement. See table in text for specifications.

F. Fan side
G. Generator side

Generator side
19.987-20.003mm
(0.7668-0.7875 inch)
Bearing No. 6204
Renew under 19.95mm (0.7855 in.)

E300, ED250, ER400
Fan side
15.007-15.025mm
(0.5907-0.5913 inch)
Bearing No. 6002
Renew under 14.95mm (0.5880 in.)

Generator side
17.007-17.025mm
(0.6694-0.6700 inch)
Bearing No. 6203
Renew under 16.95mm (0.6672 in.)

CAMSHAFT AND TAPPETS. The camshaft of early style engines (Fig. HN3-12) can be removed after removing the generator drive half of crankshaft, engine cooling fan, rewind starter assembly, starter pawl holder, camshaft drive belt and the camshaft pulley. Tappets can then be removed from bores in crankcase.

Clearance between camshaft and bearing bore in crankcase (at drive end) should be 0.016-0.052mm (0.0006-0.0020 inch). If clearance exceeds 0.18mm (0.007 inch), camshaft and/or crankcase should be renewed. Clearance between camshaft and bearing bore in crankcase cover should be 0.013-0.043mm (0.0005-0.0017 inch). If clearance exceeds 0.18mm (0.007 inch), camshaft or cover should be renewed. Maximum cam lobe diameter new is 16.3-16.4mm (0.6417-0.6457 inch). Cam lobe wear limit is 16.15mm (0.6358 inch).

Camshaft of E300, ED250 and ER400 models with integral cam gear is accessible for removal after removal of generator unit and crankcase cover (5—Fig. HN3-13). Cylinder head and valves are also removed to release valve lifters (7), and after cam gear reservoir (2) is unbolted (one cap screw at bottom) camshaft assembly (3) can be withdrawn. Both cam journals are of equal diameter—9.972-9.987mm (0.3924-0.3930 inch) and camshaft assembly should be renewed if either journal is worn under 9.90mm (0.3897 inch) diameter. Cam lobe specifications are unchanged from earlier models.

Valve lifters (tappets) are identical for all engines. Standard tappet stem diameter is 3.978-3.990mm (0.1565-0.1570 inch). Renew if worn to less than 3.95mm (0.1554 inch).

Align timing marks as shown in Fig. HN3-9 when assembling camshaft drive of model E-300 (older style) engines. On later engines, E300, ED250 and ER400, align index mark of camshaft gear with "O" mark on crankshaft timing gear.

VALVE SYSTEM. Valves are removable after removing cylinder head and tappet cover. Face and seat angle for both valves is 45 degrees. Use cutter to dress seats and lap valve directly to seat for proper finish. A 75 degree cutter should be used to narrow valve seats if necessary.

Valve clearance should be checked with piston at TDC on its compression stroke. Valve clearance is increased by careful grinding of valve clearance adjuster (2—Fig. HN3-11) on its flat lower surface. To decrease clearance, reseat valves further into cylinder block. Renew any valve with stem diameter less than 3.94mm (0.155 inch). Springs are interchangeable between valves.

The following specifications apply:

MODEL: E-300 (I-V)
Valve seat width: 0.7-1.0mm
(0.0028-0.0393 inch)

Service limit: 1.8mm
(0.071 inch)

Tappet clearance: ...IN: 0.04-0.08mm
(0.0016-0.0032 in.)
EXH: 0.05-0.07mm
(0.0020-0.0028 in.)

Valve spring
free length: 20mm
(0.787 inch)

Service limit: 18mm
(0.71 inch)

Min. spring pressure @
13.1mm (0.516 in.) ....7.0 kg
(15.47 lbs.)

MODEL: E300, ED250, ER400
Valve seat
width: 0.5-0.98mm
(0.0196-0.0382 inch)

Service limit: 1.0mm
(0.0393 inch)

Tappet clearance ...IN: 0.04-0.06mm
(0.0016-0.0024 in.)
EXH: 0.03-0.07mm
(0.0012-0.0028 in.)

Valve spring
free length: 21.7-21.9mm
(0.854-0.862 inch)

Service limit: 20mm
(0.787 inch)

Min. Spring pressure @
13.1mm (0.516 in.) ....5.0 kg
(11.0 lbs.)

REWIND STARTER. To remove the starter, from model E-300, remove the governor assembly and fan housing. On later models, begin removal with fan cover. Remove the cooling fan using a suitable puller, then remove four retaining screws and lift off the starter assembly. NOTE: Be careful not to damage the choke link when removing starter from model E-300. The starter can be disassembled after removing snap ring (1—Fig. HN3-14).

When assembling, the starter pulley should be rotated two turns to provide tension for pulling rope back in. Preloading the spring two turns is accomplished after rope is wound on pulley and spring is attached by leaving end of rope out notch (N) then turning the pulley. End of rope can be guided through hole in housing after preloading the spring. The four screws that attach starter housing to crankcase should be tightened to 2.9-3.6 Ft.-Lbs. torque. The flywheel retaining nut should be torqued to 12.7-14.1 Ft.-Lbs. Capscrew used on later models is torqued to 9-11 Ft.-Lbs.

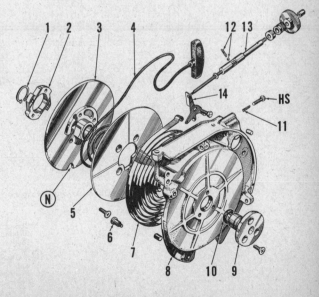

Fig. HN3-14—Exploded view of typical rewind starter. Pawls (20—Fig. HN3-12) engage ratchet (2). High speed stop screw (Fig. HN3-5) is shown at (HS).

1. Snap ring
2. Ratchet
3. Pulley half
4. Rope
5. Pulley half
6. Spring anchor screw
7. Rewind spring
8. Starter housing
9. Bushing
10. Felt ring
11. Lock spring
12. Choke detent spring and ball
13. Choke and throttle control shaft
14. Choke lever

GENERATOR. To remove the generator stator and rotor from model E-300 (I-V), remove the engine covers, fuel tank, bottom cover and frames. Remove the muffler, ignition breaker point assembly and reactor. Remove the four stator retaining screws and withdraw the stator. The rotor (magnet) can be removed using a suitable puller after removing the retaining nut.

When reassembling, make certain that wires are connected correctly. Refer to wiring diagram Fig. HN3-16.

On 50 hertz units, wires must be connected differently than for 60 hertz operation. Wires from the reactor (17) and generator field (10) are marked with tape coded black on white background and black on yellow background. The three wires (B/W1 & B/W3) coded black on white background should be used for 60 hertz operation and engine speed should be 3600 RPM. The three wires (B/Y2 & B/Y4) coded black on yellow background should be used on 50 hertz operation and engine speed should be 3000 RPM.

On all models, the DC system is protected by a three amp (orange) fuse in a brown holder (F1—Fig. HN3-17). The AC system 7 amp. fuse in a black holder is located at (F2). Pilot light (1—Fig. HN3-16) is 6 Volt, 3 Watt.

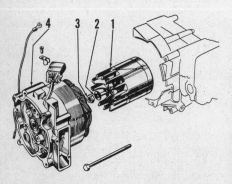

Fig. HN3-15—The generator rotor (1) is a permanent magnet. Make certain that unit is clean and does not have anything clinging to it before installing.

1. Rotor
2. Washer
3. Nut
4. Stator assembly

Fig. HN3-17—The DC system fuse is in brown holder (F1) and AC fuse is in black holder (F2).

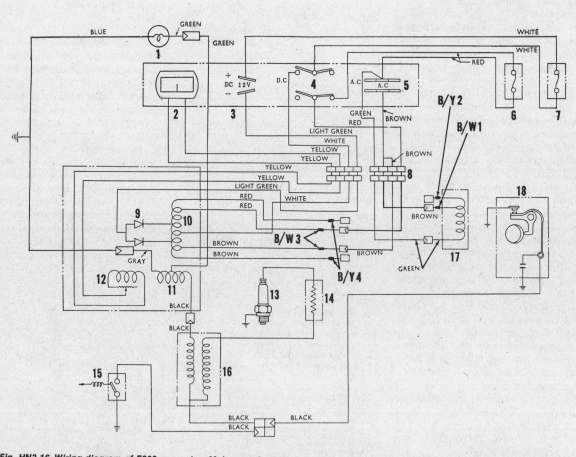

Fig. HN3-16—Wiring diagram of E300 generator. Make certain that wires (B/W1, B/Y2, B/W3 & B/Y4) are connected as described in text.

1. Pilot light
2. Frequency meter
3. DC 12 Volt connection
4. DC or AC switch
5. AC connection
6. AC fuse
7. DC fuse
8. Connector plug terminals
9. Diodes
10. Generator field
11. Ignition generator coil
12. Frequency meter field
13. Spark plug
14. Noise suppressor
15. Engine switch
16. Ignition high tension coil
17. Reactor
18. Ignition breaker points and condenser

HONDA

HONDA MOTOR COMPANY, LTD.
Tokyo, Japan

U. S. Distributor is:
AMERICAN HONDA MOTOR CO., INC.
100 W. Alondra Blvd.
Gardena, California 90247

MODEL	Cyls.	Bore	Stroke	Displ.	H.P.
G40 (E1000)	1	66 mm	50 mm	170 cc	3.3
		2.6 in.	2 in.	10.4 cu. in.	
G65 (E2000)	1	72 mm	59 mm	240 cc	5
		2.83 in.	2.32 in.	14.6 cu. in.	

MAINTENANCE

SPARK PLUG. Recommended spark plug for model G40 is NGK type B-6H. G65 uses B-7H spark plug. Set electrode gap at 0.7 mm (0.028 inch).

CARBURETOR. A float-type, vacuum-controlled variable venturi carburetor is used for both engines. Carburetor is identified as CV (constant vacuum) type. Refer to Figs. HN4-1 and HN4-2.

Idle mixture is adjusted at needle valve (4—Fig. HN4-3). To adjust idle, it is necessary to alternately adjust throttle stop idle speed screw (S) with mixture screw (4) for desired idle speed. Idle speed must be slow enough that automatic centrifugal clutch of models so equipped will disengage so that output shaft is not turning. When required idle speed is set, idle mixture screw may be adjusted ⅛ to ¼-turn rich.

Higher operating range speeds are controlled by varying size of main jet (1

—Fig. HN4-2) by lifting of valve needle (9) as venturi slide (6) opens. Operating RPM limits are determined by setting of governor control knob. When over-rich mixture condition is indicated, as by plug fouling, a main jet with smaller orifice should be installed. Main jet size should also be reduced for operation at high elevations.

Carburetor float level setting calls for use of a special gage which bridges over floats to measure height of float pontoons above float bowl flange. Bend float arm so that it barely touches seated needle valve. This needle valve contains a spring-loaded plunger, and if float arm exerts any pressure, a high fuel level and resultant flooding condition will result.

In later production of G40 engine (after serial number 1112157) another style carburetor has been used. Refer to Fig. HN4-4. This carburetor does not have vacuum operated variable venturi or double pontoon float as in the

CV type but maintenance services are essentially similar. Adjust idle speed and mixture screws by the same procedure except that idle mixture adjustment screw (5—Fig. HN4-4) is also used to smooth out engine operation when throttle/governor is opened to rated RPM with no load. This screw performs an air bleed function and should be adjusted for smooth performance whether engine is idling or with open throttle. Best indication of a good adjustment is a uniform transition from idle to running speed with no surge or flutter.

Float level adjustment requires use of a template type gage. To adjust, invert carburetor body and lift float arm (20) so that very slight clearance (0.01 mm or 0.0004 in.) is evident between tip of float valve (23) and contact point on float arm with float and gage in place. Bend float arm close to pin (19) to adjust. Float level is critical to performance of this engine so great care should be taken with this adjustment. Number 78 main jet (21) is standard size with numbers 68 thru 85 available for substitution as required.

GOVERNOR. A mechanical, fly-weight governor is used. Governor weights are mounted on the camshaft gear as shown in Fig. HN4-5. The camshaft must be removed to service governor weights or slider. Engine speed is adjusted by turning control knob (K—Fig. HN4-6) to increase or decrease governor spring tension. Length of governor rod (R) should be so that movement of the lever (L) will completely open and close the carburetor throttle.

Engine governed speed should be 3600 RPM for all models. High speed limiting nuts (N) should be adjusted so that engine speed is 3600 RPM with full load and controls set at maximum speed position. Generator (armature) RPM should be 3000 RPM for 50 cycle units (E1000E, E1000T, E1000U, E2000E, E2000T & E2000U). Gener-

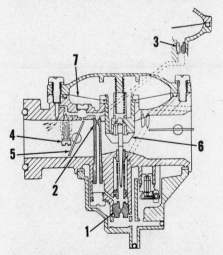

Fig. HN4-1—Cross-sectional view of carburetor at low operating speed. Refer also to Fig. HN4-2.

1. Main jet
2. Idle jet
3. Air jet
4. Idle mixture needle
5. Throttle plate
6. Venturi slide
7. Diaphragm

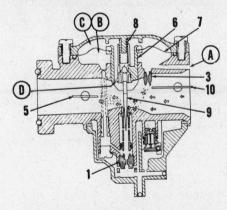

Fig. HN4-2—Cross-sectional view of carburetor at high operating speed. Air enters port (A) into chamber (B) and vacuum at venturi enters chamber (C) through port (D). The higher pressure in chamber (B) under diaphragm (7) raises venturi slide (6) against pressure of spring (8). Tapered needle (9) changes size of main nozzle opening as venturi and needle move up.

1. Main jet
3. Air jet
5. Throttle plate
6. Venturi slide
7. Diaphragm
8. Spring
9. Valve needle
10. Choke plate

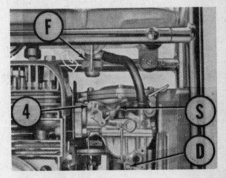

Fig. HN4-3—Idle mixture is adjusted at needle (4) and idle speed at screw (S). Fuel can be drained from float bowl at screw (D). Fuel filter and shut off valve is shown at (F).

RPM should be 3600 RPM for 60 hertz units (E1000A, E1000S, E2000A & E2000S).

IGNITION. The magneto breaker points, coil and condenser are located under the flywheel. On generator units, the external exciter coil is also located under flywheel.

Breaker point gap should be approximately 0.3-0.4 mm (0.012-0.016 inch); however, gap should be adjusted to provide correct ignition timing. To set timing, remove recoil starter, cooling shroud, pulley cup and screen from flywheel side of engine. Turn flywheel until "F" mark on side of flywheel is aligned with crankcase joint on muffler side as shown in Fig. HN4-8. Move the small breaker point cover out of the way and adjust breaker points to just open when "F" mark aligns with crankcase joint. If breaker points open too soon, decrease gap. Breaker point gap (timing) can be adjusted through hole in flywheel, but flywheel must be removed to remove breaker points or

condenser. Timing marks are aligned when piston is 20 degrees BTDC on model G40. Model G65 is correctly aligned at 25 degrees BTDC.

Correct breaker point spring tension is 700-900 gr. (25-32 oz.). Condenser capacitance is 0.24 microfarads (± 10%). Coil output is adequate if spark length is 8mm (0.32 in.) at 300 RPM. Renewal of coil should be considered if spark length falls below 7 mm (0.27 in.).

LUBRICATION. Crankcase capacity of model G40 is 1.2 pints. Model G65 requires 1.7 US pints. Recommended motor oil is API classification DG or MS. Newer API designation may be SC or SD; do not use oils identified as SA or SB in new API codes. Use SAE 20 or 20W for temperatures between 32°F and 59°F. For colder temperatures, use SAE 10W and for temperatures over 59°F, use SAE 30 or SAE 40. SAE 10W-30 weight may be used in all seasons. Oil should be maintained between marks on filler plug dipstick if

engine has this optional item. NOTE: Do not screw filler plug in when checking oil level. Engine oil should be changed after first 20 hours operation of a new or rebuilt engine and at 100 hour intervals thereafter unless extremely dusty conditions are encountered.

REPAIRS

CYLINDER HEAD. The cylinder head can be removed after removing muffler, fuel tank, air cleaner, fan cover and the cylinder and head cooling shroud. When installing head, tighten cylinder head retaining screws in sequence shown in Fig. HN4-10 to torque of 15.7-17.0 Ft.-Lbs.

PISTON, PIN AND RINGS. To remove the piston, the crankcase halves must be separated, then the piston together with connecting rod and crankshaft can be withdrawn from

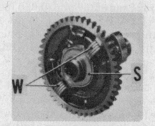

Fig. HN4-5—As engine speed increases, governor weights (W) push the slider (S) out against governor rod.

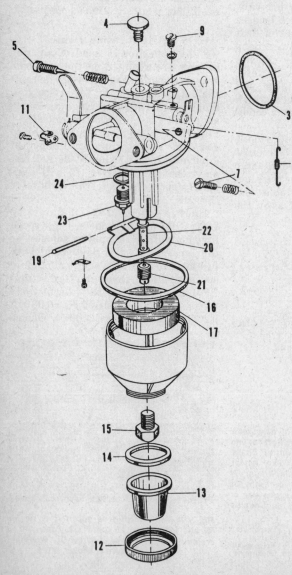

Fig. HN4-4—Exploded view of carburetor fitted to G40 engines serial number 1112158 and after.

2. Throttle return spring
3. Manifold "O" ring
4. Rubber cap
5. Idle mixture needle
7. Idle speed screw
9. Throttle shaft retainer
11. Clip plate
12. Bulb retainer ring
13. Sediment bulb
14. Gasket
15. Assembly bolt
16. Float chamber gasket
17. Float
19. Float pin
20. Float arm
21. Main jet
22. Main nozzle
23. Float valve assembly
24. Fiber washer

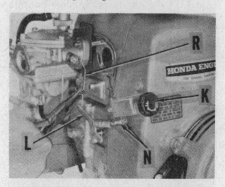

Fig. HN4-6—View of governor external parts. Governor control link rod is shown at (R).

Fig. HN4-8—Ignition breaker point gap (timing) can be set through hole in flywheel. Inset shows timing "F" mark on side of flywheel aligned with joint (J) between halves of crankcase (muffler side).

bottom. Refer to CRANKSHAFT section for removal procedure. The following specification data applies:

Piston pin bore in piston:
G40 Standard 18.000-18.006mm
(0.7086-0.7089 inch)
G65 Standard 19.000-19.006mm
(0.7480-0.7483 inch)
Pin clearance in bore:
G40 & G65 .... 0.012-0.070mm
(0.0005-0.0028 inch)
Piston pin bore in connecting rod:
G40 Standard 18.010-18.033mm
(0.7090-0.7100 inch)
G65 Standard 19.007-19.028mm
(0.7483-0.7491 inch)
Maximum bore I.D.
G40 .... 18.08mm
(0.7118 in.)
G65 .... 19.08mm
(0.7512 in.)
Cylinder bore diameter:
G40 Standard 66.00-66.01mm
(2.5984-2.5988 inch)
G65 Standard 72.00-72.01mm
(2.8346-2.835 inch)
Maximum bore I.D.,
G40 .... 66.15mm (2.6043 in.)
G65 .... 72.15mm (2.8405 in.)
Piston to cylinder,
Clearance 0.07-0.10mm
(0.0028-0.0039 in.)
Wear limit ...0.25mm (0.0098 inch)
Piston ring clearance in ring groove:
Top ring 0.02-0.06mm
(0.0008-0.0024 inch)
Wear limit ....0.15mm (0.006 inch)
Second ring 0.01-0.05mm
(0.0004-0.0019 in.)
Wear limit ....0.15mm (0.006 inch)
Third (oil) ring 0.01-0.05mm
(0.0004-0.0019 in.)
Wear limit ....0.15mm (0.006 inch)
End gap (all rings) 0.2-0.4mm
(0.008-0.016 in.)
May not exceed ..... 1.5mm (0.06 in.)

When assembling, manufacturer's marks on side of all piston rings should be toward top of piston. Pistons and rings are available in standard size and oversizes of 0.010, 0.020 and 0.030 inch (0.25, 0.50 and 0.75 mm). The top com-

pression ring is chrome plated and the second compression ring is parkerized. Refer to the CRANKSHAFT section for installing crankshaft, rod and piston assembly and the lower half of crankcase. Tighten the cylinder head retaining screws in sequence shown in Fig. HN4-10 to torque of 15.7-17.0 Ft.-Lbs.

CRANKSHAFT AND CONNECTING ROD. The connecting rod, crankshaft and piston can be removed after separating the crankcase halves. Connecting rod and crankpin bearing are removed by pressing crankshaft apart.

NOTE: The crankshaft should be disassembled ONLY if required tools are available to correctly check and align the reassembled crankshaft.

Crankshaft and connecting rod specifications:
Inside diameter, small end:
G40 .,........... 18.010-18.033mm
(0.709-0.710 inch)
Max. I. D. ..... 18.08mm (0.718 in.)
G65 .... 19.007-19.028mm
(0.7483-0.7491 inch)
Max. I. D. .... 19.08mm (0.7512 in.)
Inside diameter, large end:
G40 .... 30.999-31.014mm
(1.2204-1.2210 inch)
Max I. D. ...... 31.05mm (1.222 in.)
G65 .... 35.569-35.589mm
(1.4003-1.4011 inch)
Max. I. D. ..... 35.64mm (1.403 in.)
Crankpin O.D. specifications:
G40 .... 26.035-26.045mm
(1.0249-1.0253 in.)
Min. O.D. .... 25.99mm (1.0232 in.)
G65 .... 29.565-29.575mm
(1.1639-1.1643 in.)
Min. O. D. ..... 29.52mm (1.162 in.)
Connecting rod end play:
G40 .... 0.004-0.006mm
(0.00015-0.00024 in.)
G65 .... 0.008-0.016mm
(0.0003-0.0006 in.)
Connecting rod side (axial) play:
All 0.10-0.35mm
(0.004-0.014 in.)
Eccentricity at ends with crankshaft supported at main bearings should not

exceed 0.2 mm (0.008 in.). The connecting rod, bearing and/or crankpin should be renewed if the top (piston pin) end of connecting rod rocks (shakes) back and forth more than 3.0 mm (0.12 inch).

To separate the crankcase halves, remove the muffler, carburetor, cooling shrouds, fan (flywheel), magneto and cylinder head. Remove the eight cap screws that attach the lower half of crankcase to the upper half and cylinder. Turn engine upside down and lift lower half of crankcase off locating dowels. NOTE: Be careful not to damage sealing surface between crankcase halves.

When reassembling, install crankshaft with "O" marks on camshaft and crankshaft gears aligned. The set ring in top half of crankcase should correctly engage groove (G—Fig. HN4-11). Oil seals should be positioned on crankshaft before seating crankshaft in the top half of crankcase. No gasket is used between crankcase halves and sealing surfaces must be smooth and flat. Coat mating surface of lower half of crankcase with a non-hardening sealer The four 6 mm crankcase retaining screws should be torqued to 5.8-6.5 Ft.-Lbs. and the four 8 mm screws should be torqued to 14.5-15.2 Ft.-Lbs. Recheck several times to make certain that final torque is correct.

CAMSHAFT AND TAPPETS. The camshaft and cam followers (tappets) can be removed after separating the crankcase halves as outlined in the CRANKSHAFT section. The camshaft holder (center shaft) can be withdrawn from magneto end after removing the retaining screw. Refer to the following specification data:
Camshaft bore to holder clearance—
Both ends, desired ..0.016-0.061 mm
0.0006-0.0024 in.
Wear limit ...... 0.1 mm (0.004 in.)
Camshaft end clearance in crankcase—
Desired .... 0.1-0.5 mm
0.004-0.020 in.
Wear limit .... 1.0 mm (0.04 in.)
Maximum lobe diameter—
Wear limit ...... 29.0 mm (1.14 in.)
Align "O" marks (Fig. HN4-11) on camshaft and crankshaft gears when reassembling. Refer to CRANKSHAFT section when installing lower crankcase half. Refer to VALVE SYSTEM section for adjusting valve clearance.

VALVE SYSTEM. Valves are removable after removing cylinder head and tappet cover. Valve face and seat angle for both valves is 45 degrees. Desired seat width is 0.7-1.0 mm (0.028-0.039 inch). Narrow seats using a 75 degree cutter if width exceeds 2.0 mm (0.08 inch). Valve clearance should be 0.07-0.1 mm (0.003-0.004 inch) for both inlet and exhaust valves.

Fig. HN4-10–Cylinder head retaining screws should be tightened in sequence shown. Make certain that screws (6, 7 & 8) are special type.

Fig. HN4-11–The "O" marks on camshaft timing gears must be aligned when assembling. Set ring in crankcase top half should completely engage groove (G) in bearing.

Valve clearance should be checked when piston is at TDC on compression stroke. Clearance is increased by carefully grinding end of valve stem. To decrease clearance, reseat valve further in cylinder. Inlet and exhaust valve springs are interchangeable. Model G40 valve spring should be renewed if free length is less than 26 mm (1.02 in.). G65 valve springs should have a minimum free length of 30 mm (1.2 in.). Minimum pressure tests of valve springs are as follows.

G40, more than 13 lbs. at 22.5 mm (0.886 in.)

G65, more than 10.6 lbs. at 27.6 mm (1.087 in.)

G40, more than 27.6 lbs. at 16.7 mm (0.657 in.)

G65, more than 27.6 lbs. at 20.6 mm (0.812 in.)

Inlet valve heads are larger than

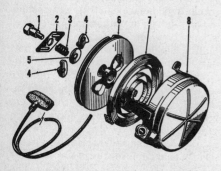

Fig. HN4-12–Exploded view of the rewind starter assembly. Starter cup (attached to engine flywheel) is not shown.

1. Special bolt
2. Friction plate
3. Friction spring
4. Ratchet pawls
5. Washer
6. Rope pulley
7. Rewind spring
8. Housing

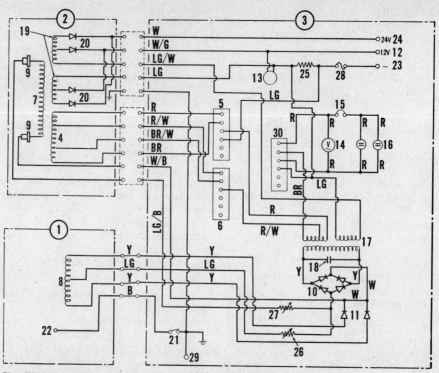

Fig. HN4-20—Wiring diagram for E1000 generator. External exciter coil (8) is under engine flywheel. Plug (30) is attached to connection (5) for 50 hertz operation or connection (6) for 60 hertz operation. Drive pulleys are also different for 50 and 60 hertz operation.

1. Engine
2. Generator
3. Control box
4. AC generator coil
5. Connector (for 50 Hz)
6. Connector (for 60 Hz)
7. Armature
8. External exciter coil (engine)
9. Brushes
10. Bridge rectifier (4 diodes)
11. External exciter diodes
12. DC (12 Volt) positive connection
13. Pilot light
14. Voltmeter
15. AC circuit breaker
16. AC outlet connections
17. Transformer
18. Condenser
19. DC generator coils
20. Diodes for DC output
21. Engine stop (kill) switch
22. Ignition breaker points
23. DC ground connection
24. DC (24 volt) positive connection
25. Resistor
26. Variable resistor
27. Voltage regulator (resistor)
28. DC fuse
29. Ground terminal
30. Plug

those of exhaust valves by design. Valve stem to valve guide clearance of all engines should be 0.02 to 0.05 mm (0.0008-0.002 in.). Valve and/or valve guide should be renewed if clearance exceeds 0.12 mm (0.005 inch).

REWIND STARTER. Refer to Fig. HN4-12 for exploded view of the rewind starter assembly used on some models. Starter can be disassembled as follows: Pull rope out slightly and untie knot at handle end while holding the rope pulley (6) from turning. Remove handle from rope and allow spring to unwind slowly. Remove cap screw (1), friction plate (2), spring (3) and friction disc (5). Remove ratchets (4) from pulley and remove pulley and spring from housing. Reassemble by reversing disassembly procedure and check action of starter before reinstalling on engine.

GENERATOR

Typical generator wiring diagram is shown in Fig. HN4-20. The exciter coil (8) is located under the engine flywheel and uses the permanent magnet in the flywheel to generate initial exciter current. This initial exciter current is changed to DC by diodes (11) then routed to the rotating field (7) of the armature through brushes (9) and slip

Fig. HN4-13–Exploded view of speed reduction unit furnished with some G40 and G65 engines. Reduction ratio is designed to lower governed engine speed of nominal 3600 rpm to 1860 rpm, comparable to standard electric motor speed at reduction unit pto shaft. Clutch is automatic.

C. Centrifugal clutch
1. Left crankshaft
2. Thrust washer
3. Drive sprocket
4. Sprocket key
5. Drain plug gasket
6. Lube drain plug
7. Outer housing
8. Oil seal
9. Ball bearing
10. PTO shaft & sprocket
11. Drive chain
12. Inner housing
13. Housing gasket
14. Dipstick "O" ring
15. Oil level gage
16. Filler cap

rings. The current through field (7) causes the armature to become a rotating electro-magnet. As the armature (electro-magnet) turns, AC current is generated in the stator windings. AC current generated in windings (19) is changed to DC by the four diodes (20). AC current generated in winding (4) is connected to the AC output connection (16).

On all 60 hertz generators, the generator armature should turn 3600 RPM when the engine crankshaft is operating at 3600 RPM. On all 50 hertz generators, the generator armature should be rotating at 3000 RPM when engine output shaft is operating at 3600 RPM. The generator drive belt should have 3/8 to 7/16-inch belt flex between the pulleys. To tighten the drive belt, loosen the four generator mounting screws, loosen the tension screw lock nut and turn the tension adjusting screw at the outside of generator frame. Make certain that the four generator mounting screws and lock nut are retightened after belt tension is set.

The engine can be unbolted and removed from generator frame after the fuel line and wires are disconnected. Make certain that the light green wire from engine is connected to the light green wire to the control box. Each of the two yellow wires from engine should be connected to one of the yellow wires to the control box.

TEST AND REPAIR. To check the engine exciter coil, disconnect the two yellow wires and one light green wire between engine and control box. Resistance of coil (under engine flywheel) should be checked with an ohmmeter as shown in Fig. HN4-21. Resistance between each of the yellow wires and the light green wire should be 9-11 ohms. Engine should not be running when checking resistance. If resistance is correct, start engine and operate at 3500 RPM. Output between each of the yellow wires and the light green wire should be 58-72 volts (AC). NOTE: Resistance and voltage tests are all made between one yellow wire and the green wire. Do not check between the two yellow wires. If resistance and/or voltage is incorrect, remove the engine flywheel and renew the exciter coil Reconnect wires after tests are made.

Operate engine at rated speed without load and measure the voltage (DC) between the two brush terminals at end of generator. Voltmeter should indicate 26-32 volts.

To check condition of diodes, shown in Fig. HN4-22, it is necessary to disconnect one end of each and check individually. Check resistance between ends of each diode with an ohmmeter, then reverse the ohmmeter leads. Diode should have infinite resistance with one connection and little resistance with leads reversed. If resistance is the same (either high or low) in both

directions, diode is faulty.

Capacity of the current transformer secondary circuit condenser between points (1 & 2—Fig. HN4-23) should be 4 mfds. Capacity of the exciter condenser (point 3 & 4) should be 2 mfds. When checking the condenser, make certain that leads are disconnected. Condenser condition can usually be considered satisfactory if needle moves slightly when ohmmeter is first connected.

The voltage adjuster knob on the control panel varies the resistance across the variable resistor (27—Fig. HN4-20). With the adjuster knob set at minimum position, resistance should be 597-603 ohms. If resistance is incorrect, renew the variable resistor. Resistor (26—Fig. HN4-20) is adjustable. Resistance should be set at approximately 100 ohms. If resistance can not be correctly set, renew the resistor.

Refer also to the following specification data:

Slip rings—
  Standard diameter . . 38 mm (1½ in.)
  Minimum diameter 36 mm (1.42 in.)
  Out-of-round limit 0.1 mm (0.004 in.)
Brushes—
  Standard length . . . 18 mm (0.71 in.)
  Wear limit . . . . 10 mm (0.4 in.)
Armature coil—
  Resistance . . . . 60-70 ohms

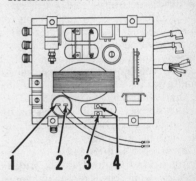

Fig. HN4-23–Drawing of the control box showing location of parts. Refer to text for testing.

Fig. HN4-21–View showing method of checking the exciter coil (on engine). Refer to text.

Fig. HN4-22–View of diodes installed. To test, one end of each must be disconnected.

JACOBSEN

JACOBSEN MANUFACTURING CO.
1721 Packard Ave.
Racine, Wisconsin 53403

MODELS	Cyls.	Bore	Stroke	Displ.
J-100	1	2	1½	4.71
J-150	1	2¼	1¾	6.96
J-200	1	2	2	6.28

Models with letter "V" suffix have vertical crankshafts.
Models with letter "H" suffix have horizontal crankshafts.

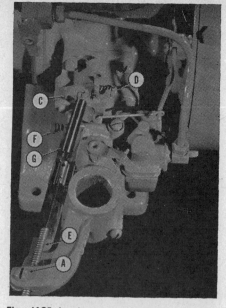

Fig. JAC5—Jacobsen model J-200 carburetor and governor linkage.

A. Screw	E. Cable housing
C. Throttle lever	F. Idle needle
D. Throttle stop screw	G. Governor spring

MAINTENANCE

SPARK PLUG. A 14mm spark plug designed for 2-cycle engine operation with a ⅜-inch thread reach should be used. Heat range will depend upon engine application; however, the following plugs can generally be used: AC-M46; Auto-Lite-A9X; Champion-J11J. Electrode gap should be 0.035.

CARBURETOR. Float feed type carburetors are used and their applications are as follows:

J-100 ...Tillotson MT-52A or MT-77A
J-150 .... Tillotson MT-4A
J-200 ...Tillotson MT-26A or MT-36A

Clockwise rotation of the knurled head idle needle and of the T-head main jet needle leans the mixture. Initial needle settings are: ¾-turn open for the idle needle; 1¼ turns open for the main jet needle. With engine warm and running at ¼ to ½ open throttle, lean the main jet until engine speed drops off, then enrich by ¼-turn. Adjust the idle needle until engine speed drops off, then enrich by ⅛-turn. Adjust the throttle stop screw to obtain the lowest smooth idle that will still permit engine to propel lawn mower.

Carburetor inlet needle is of the spring loaded type. Float setting is 3/32-inch from bowl cover flange to nearest edge of float when bowl cover assembly is in inverted position.

GOVERNOR. Speed control on all models is maintained by a pneumatic (air vane) type governor. The air vane which is linked directly to the carburetor upper throttle lever is actuated by air from the flywheel fan. Make certain that linkage does not bind in any position when moved through full range of travel. To adjust the governor linkage refer to the appropriate paragraph which follows:

MODELS J-100 and J-150. Refer to Fig. JAC4. To check and/or adjust the linkage, proceed as follows: With engine stopped, place the throttle control knob in the closed position; at which time, the upper throttle shaft lever (2) should be in the ½ open position. If lever is not in the ½ open position, bend the balance spring (1), at upper end, until the desired condition is obtained. The lower throttle shaft lever is connected by linkage to the governor balance spring (1). A small anti-surge spring (5) is used in conjunction with this linkage arrangement. Correct installation of the spring is accomplished by hooking one end into the inner hole in the lower throttle shaft lever from the top side; then, hook the other end into loop of governor balance spring so it is underneath the throttle lever link as shown.

MODEL J-200. Refer to Figs. JAC5 and JAC6. To check and/or adjust the linkage, proceed as follows: With engine stopped, place the throttle control in the closed position and adjust the throttle stop screw (D) so that 3/32-inch of the screw protrudes beyond the boss as shown. With all parts so positioned, the governor spring should pull the throttle lever (C) open a minimum of 3/16-inch from stop screw (D) as shown in Fig. JAC6. If adjustment is not as specified, loosen screw (A—Fig. JAC5) and move cable housing (E) in or out as required.

MAGNETO AND TIMING. Flywheel type magnetos are used and their applications are as follows: Early J-100 engines use Wico FW-1753, whereas later production models use Wico FW-2124. Some special engines designated as J-100A were equipped with Jack & Heintz H23-370 and H28-

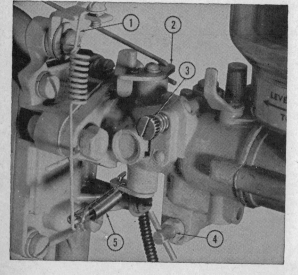

Fig. JAC4—Jacobsen models J-100 and J-150 carburetor and governor linkage.

1. Balance spring
2. Upper throttle shaft lever
3. Idle needle
4. Main jet needle
5. Anti-surge spring

Fig. JAC6—Jacobsen model J-200 governor linkage details. See Fig. JAC5 for legend.

118 magnetos. Latest J-100 engines use Wico FW-2489 magnetos. Wico FW-1754 is used on the J-150 engine and Wico FW-2259 is used on the J-200 series. Breaker contact gap is 0.020. Recommended timing is 30 degrees BTDC on the J-150 and the J-100 series. The J-200 series is timed at 29 degrees BTDC.

Ignition timing is satisfactory if breaker contacts just begin to open when piston is on compression stroke and ⅛-inch before the top dead center position. Shift the magneto stator plate to obtain the desired timing. Note: Piston position can be determined by inserting a scale through spark plug hole.

LUBRICATION. Gasoline and oil should be thoroughly mixed, using one part S.A.E. No. 30 non-detergent oil with sixteen parts regular grade gasoline. Use S.A.E. No. 10 oil in the gear reduction unit.

REPAIRS

CYLINDER HEAD AND CARBON. It is recommended that the muffler, exhaust manifold and cylinder head be removed and the carbon cleaned after each 25 hours of operation. Crank engine until piston is in bottom dead center position and thoroughly clean carbon from the exhaust and intake ports.

Caution: Be sure all carbon particles are removed from cylinder bore before reassembly.

CONNECTING ROD. Rod and piston unit is removed from above on all engines. Crankshaft crankpin diameter is as follows:

J-100	0.623
J-150	0.7475
J-200	0.750

On J-100 and J-150 engines, the forged bronze connecting rod rides directly on the crankshaft crankpin with a recommended diametral clearance 0.0015-0.0025 on models J-100H and J-150 engines, 0.0025-0.0035 on model J-100V. Obtain the recommended clearance by filing rod and cap and re-reaming the bearing to proper size. Recommended rod side play is 0.005-0.015. When reassembling, make certain that index marks on rod and cap are in register.

Series J-200 engines have a jeweled rod with 28 needle bearings inserted between rod and crankpin. The rod is a single steel forging and the cap is broken free after machining; therefore, rod and cap can be assembled in one position only.

PISTON, PIN, RINGS. The cam and taper ground piston is equipped with three ⅛-inch wide compression rings which have an end gap of 0.005-0.010 and a side clearance of 0.004-0.006. Renew rings if end gap exceeds 0.020; renew piston if side clearance of new rings exceeds 0.010. Piston and rings are available in oversizes of 0.010 and 0.020 for J-100 engines; 0.010, 0.020 and 0.030 for J-150 and J-200 engines.

Piston skirt clearance, when checked 90 degrees to piston pin at bottom of skirt should be as follows:

J-100H	0.004-0.005
J-100V	0.005-0.006
J-150	0.002-0.0035
J-200	0.003-0.004

The piston pin should have 0.0002-0.0004 tight fit in piston and 0.0005-0.0015 loose fit in connecting rod. Piston pin is available in oversizes of 0.002, 0.003, 0.005 and 0.010 for J-150 and J-200 engines, 0.002, 0.003 and 0.005 for the J-100 engines.

On all models, the long taper on head of piston should face exhaust side of engine.

CRANKSHAFT & SEALS. The crankshaft is carried in two ball bearings which are a press fit on the shaft. When installing new bearings, be sure crankshaft is supported between the throws and/or the bearings heated in oil to avoid bending the shaft.

On direct drive engines, install crankcase seals so that lips face toward inside of engine. On engines having a speed reduction unit, the crankcase oil seal on the speed reducer side should be installed with lip facing the reducer.

CARBURETOR REED VALVE. The carburetor is mounted on an adapter plate which, on the engine side, carries a small spring steel leaf or reed that acts as an inlet valve. Blow back through carburetor can be caused by grit or foreign matter holding reed open or by an improperly installed reed. Reed has a bend in it and must be installed so as to force reed firmly against mounting plate.

REDUCTION UNIT. Reduction gear cover and gear must be removed before housing can be removed from engine. Crankcase oil seal on the speed reducer side should be installed with the lip facing the reducer. On the power take off side of the reduction unit, the oil seal lip faces the reduction unit.

JACOBSEN

JACOBSEN MANUFACTURING CO.
1721 Packard Ave.
Racine, Wisconsin 53403

MODELS	Cyls.	Bore	Stroke	Displ.
J-125	1	2	1½	4.71
J-175	1	2-1/8	1¾	6.21
J-225	1	2¼	2	7.95
J-321	1	2-1/8	1¾	6.21
J-501	1	2-1/8	1¾	6.21

Models with letter "V" suffix have vertical crankshafts.
Models with letter "H" suffix have horizontal crankshafts.

Maintenance

SPARK PLUG. A 14 mm., 3/8-inch reach spark plug is used in all models. Heat range of spark plug used depends upon engine model and application. Refer to following chart for recommended Champion spark plug type number. Set electrode gap to 0.030 for all models and applications.

Engine Model & Application	Recommended Champion Spark Plug
J-125, rotary mower	J-12J
J-125, reel mower	UJ-12
J-175, rotary mower	J-8J
J-225, rotary mower	J-8J
J-321 & J-501, rotary mower	J-17LM
J-321 & J-501, reel mower*	UJ-12
*For short spark plug, use	TJ-8

CARBURETOR. Float feed type carburetors are used and their applications are as follows:

J-125	Tillotson MT58A
J-175	Tillotson MT59A
J-225	Tillotson MT54A
J-321 & J-501	Walbro LMB or LMG

TILLOTSON CARBURETORS. The Tillotson carburetors used on these engines have three points of adjustment: main adjustment screw (26—Fig. JAC8) idle mixture screw (23) and idle speed screw (18). To adjust carburetor, proceed as follows:

Initial needle settings are: one turn open for the idle mixture needle; 1¼ turns open for the main jet needle. Clockwise rotation of the idle mixture screw and main adjustment screw leans the mixture.

With engine warm and running at approximately one-half open throttle, turn main jet adjustment screw in until engine loses speed. Back out until max-

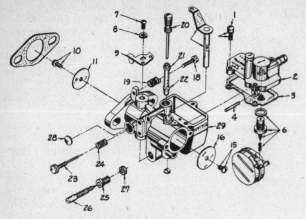

Fig. JAC8–Exploded view of typical Tillotson carburetor.

1. Screw & lockwasher
2. Bowl cover
3. Gasket
4. Lever pin
6. Inlet needle assy.
9. Throttle stop lever
10. Shutter screw
11. Throttle shutter
15. Shutter screw
16. Choke shutter
18. Idle speed screw
19. Spring
20. Idle tube
21. Main nozzle
22. Gasket
23. Idle mixture screw
24. Spring
25. Packing nut
26. Main adjusting screw
27. Packing
28. Welch plug
29. Carburetor body

lowing paragraphs for carburetor adjustments on carburetors equipped with idle adjusting needle and/or main fuel needle.

For initial adjustment, open the idle and/or main fuel adjustment needles 1 to 1¼ turns. Make final adjustment with engine running at operating temperature.

With throttle at "FAST" position, slowly turn main fuel needle clockwise until engine begins to lose speed; then, turn the main needle back ⅛ to ¼-turn counter-clockwise.

Move the throttle to "IDLE" position and slowly turn idle fuel needle on carburetors so equipped, clockwise until engine begins to lose speed; then, turn needle back counter-clockwise ⅛ to ¼-turn.

imum power and speed are obtained.

Make idle mixture adjustment only AFTER the MAIN JET ADJUSTMENT in preceding paragraph has been accomplished. Close throttle and increase engine idle speed to slightly faster than normal by turning idle speed regulating screw inward at throttle stop boss. Turn idle mixture screw in until engine loses speed and misses; then back screw out until engine operates steadily and smoothly.

Idle speed adjustment is made only AFTER the preceding adjustments are completed. Engine will be idling faster than normal at this point. Back out idle speed regulating screw until desired idle speed is obtained.

Carburetor inlet needle is of the spring loaded type. Use idle tube as a gage of the 1/16 to 3/32-inch distance between bowl cover flange and nearest edge of float when bowl cover assembly is in the inverted position. Refer to Fig. JAC9. Float level should be 5/16-inch if a plastic float is used. Bend tab on float as necessary to obtain correct setting.

WALBRO CARBURETOR. Refer to Figs. JAC10, JAC11, and JAC12 for exploded view of typical Walbro carburetors used on J-321 and J-501 engines.

Walbro carburetor shown in Fig. JAC12 does not have adjustable idle or main fuel orifices. Note that some carburetors shown in Fig. JAC10 or JAC11 are not equipped with an idle mixture adjusting needle. Refer to fol-

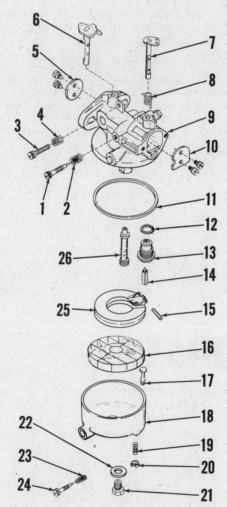

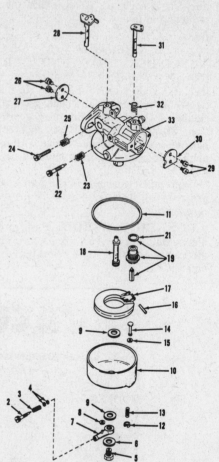

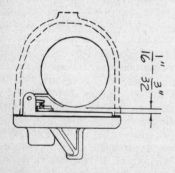

Fig. JAC9–Distance between bowl cover flange and nearest edge of float when bowl cover assembly is inverted should be 1/16-3/32-inch.

Fig. JAC10—Exploded view of Walbro series LMB float carburetor used on some J-321 and J-501 models. Note the fuel bowl screen (16) used on this type carburetor.

1. Idle fuel needle
2. Spring
3. Idle speed screw
4. Spring
5. Throttle disc
6. Throttle shaft
7. Choke shaft
8. Choke return spring
9. Carburetor body
10. Choke disc
11. Gasket
12. Gasket
13. Inlet valve seat
14. Inlet valve
15. Float pin
16. Fuel bowl screen
17. Drain valve
18. Fuel bowl
19. Spring
20. Retainer
21. Bowl retainer
22. Gasket
23. Spring
24. Main fuel needle
25. Float
26. Main nozzle

Fig. JAC11—Exploded view of typical Walbro series LMG carburetor used on some model J-321 and J-501 engines.

2. Main fuel needle
3. Spring
4. Seals
5. Bowl retainer
6. Washer
7. Adapter
8. Seal
9. Washer
10. Float bowl
11. Gasket
12. Retainer
13. Spring
14. Drain valve
15. Gasket
16. Float pin
17. Float
18. Main nozzle
19. Inlet valve
21. Gasket
22. Idle fuel needle
23. Spring
24. Idle stop screw
25. Spring
27. Throttle disc
28. Throttle shaft
30. Choke disc
31. Choke shaft
32. Choke spring
33. Carburetor body

Engine will have a slight "stutter" or intermittent exhaust sound at both idle and high speed when fuel mixture adjustments are correct. Idle speed is controlled by proper adjustment of the governor rather than by adjustment of the idle speed stop screw on carburetor throttle. This is to prevent engine stalling when traction and/or reel clutch is engaged with engine at idle speed. Refer to GOVERNOR paragraph.

To check float setting on Walbro carburetor, invert the body casting and float assembly. There should be 5/32-inch clearance between carburetor body casting and free side of float except on carburetor with fixed main fuel orifice which should have a float level of 1/16-3/32-inch. Adjust clearance by bending tab on float that contacts fuel inlet needle. Then, check float free travel; there should be 3/16-inch free movement of float. Adjust free travel by bending tab on float that contacts float stop.

Main fuel orifice on carburetor with fixed main fuel orifice may be cleaned with a #62 drill bit. Be careful not to damage orifice during cleaning.

GOVERNOR. Speed control on all models is maintained by a pneumatic (air vane) type governor. The air vane

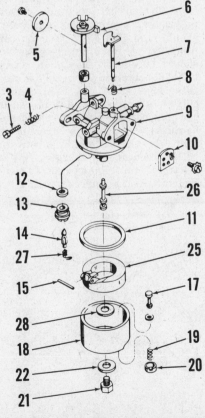

Fig. JAC12–Exploded view of Walbro carburetor with fixed idle and main fuel jets. Refer to Fig. JAC10 for parts identification except for: 27. Retainer; 28. Gasket.

which is linked directly to the carburetor upper throttle lever is actuated by air from the flywheel fan. Make certain that the linkage does not bind in any position when moved through the full range of travel. To adjust the governor linkage, refer to following paragraphs:

RECOMMENDED GOVERNED SPEEDS. When governor linkage has been removed or serviced, engine governed speed should be checked with a tachometer after reassembly. Refer to following table for recommended speeds.

Engine Application	Engine RPM	
	Idle Speed	Top Speed
9" Edge-R-Trim (32A9, 32B9 & 32C9)	1500-2000	3000-3300
9" Edge-R-Trim (50012)	1500-1800	Up to 3600
10" Trimo (3110-8610, 86A & 86B)	1500-2000	3400-3600
10" Trimo (50035)		3500-3700
18" Pacer (52C18, 42D18 & 42E-18)	1300-1600	3500 max.
18" Pacer (11814)	1500-1800	Up to 3600
18" Turbo-Cut (3418, 34B18, 34C18 & 34D18)	1300-1800	3400-3500
18" Turbo-Cut (7518, 75A18 & 75B18)	1500-2000	3400-3500
18" Turbo-Vac (31817)	1500-1800	3200-3400
18" Turbo-Vac (31819)*	1500-1800	3200-3400
18" Turbo-Vac (31819)	2400-2600	3200-3400
18" 4-Blade Rotary (31809)	2400-2600	3200-3400
18" Turbo Cone (117-18)	1500-1600	3200-3400
20" Scepter (8020 & 80A20)	1500-1800	3000-3200
20" Commercial Rotary (35025)	1500-1600	3200-3400
20" Commercial Rotary (32028)	2400-2600	3200-3400
20" Commercial Rotary (32028)*	1500-1600	3200-3400
20" Robust (32031)	1500-1700	3200-3400
20" Snow Jet (9620 & 96A20)	1500-1800	3600-3800
20" Snow Jet (52002, 52003)	1700-1900	3600-3800
21" 4-Blade Rotary (32114)	2400-2600	3200-3400
21" 4-Blade Rotary S.P. (42114, 42118, 42119)	2400-2600	3200-3400
21" Turbo-Cut (3921, 39B21 & 39C21)	1500-1800	3200-3400
21" Turbo Cone (119-21)	1500-1600	3200-3400
21" Turbo-Cut (3521, 35C21, 35D21, 35E21 & 35F21)	1500-1800	3500 max.
21" Turbo Cone (121-21)	1500-1600	3200-3400
21" Lawn Queen (2C21, 2D21 & 2E21)	1300-1600	3500 max.
21" Lawn Queen (12113)	1500-1800	Up to 3600
21" Manor (28F21 & 28G21)	1300-1600	3500 max.
21" Manor (22114, 32121-7B1)	1500-1800	Up to 3600
22" Putting Green (9A22 & 9B22)	1500-1800	3400 max.
22" Greensmower (62203, 62208)	1500-1800	Up to 3800
22" Scepter (8022 & 80A22)	1500-1800	3000-3200
24" Estate (8A24 & 8B24)	1300-1600	3800 max.
24" Rotary S. P. (40A24)	1900-2100	3000 max.
26" Estate (8A26, 8B26, 8C26 & 8D26)	1300-1600	3800 max.
26" Estate R.R. (22601, 22605-7B1)	1500-1800	Up to 3800
26" Estate F.R. (22611, 22615-7B1)	1500-1800	Up to 3800
26" Lawn King (12A26 & 12B26)	1300-1600	3200 max.
26" Lawn King (12601)	1500-1800	Up to 3800

*Speed control on handle.

ADJUSTMENTS, MODELS J-321 AND J-501 WITH FIXED SPEED. Governor adjustment on model J-321 or J-501 with a fixed governed speed is accomplished by turning governor adjustment screw shown in Fig. JAC 13. Turning adjustment screw provides adjustment range of approximately 400 rpm. Refer to recommended governor speeds.

ADJUSTMENTS, MODELS WITH TILLOTSON CARBURETORS. With the engine stopped, close the throttle control lever. The upper throttle shaft lever (2—Fig. JAC14) should be in the ½-open position. If not in this position, bend the balance spring (1) at upper end until the desired position is reached. The lower throttle shaft lever is connected to the governor balance spring (1) by a small anti-surge spring (3). Correct spring installation is accomplished by hooking one end into the

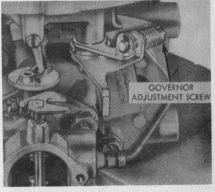

Fig. JAC13—View of governor adjustment screw on model J-321 or J-501 engine.

inner hole of the lower throttle shaft lever from the top side; then hook the other end into the governor balance spring loop so it is underneath the throttle lever link.

ADJUSTMENTS, MODELS WITH REMOTE-CONTROL WALBRO CARBURETOR. Set the "CHOKE-FAST-IDLE-STOP" control to "FAST" position. The hook in the choke lever (link) should just touch the first loop in choke spring, or clear the first loop by 1/16-inch (Refer to Fig. JAC15). If choke is partially closed, or clearance between hook in link and loop in spring exceeds 1/16-inch, loosen the engine control cable clamp and slide cable back or forward until choke control lever (link) just touches the loop in choke spring; then, tighten the control cable clamp. Test setting by moving control to "STOP" position; the carburetor control lever should touch the contact point of "STOP" switch. Then, move the control to "CHOKE" (START) POSITION; carburetor choke should be completely closed.

MAGNETO AND TIMING.
BREAKERLESS IGNITION. Model J-321 may be equipped with a breakerless ignition system. A Blaser ignition system is used on some engines and may be identified by use of single trigger coil as opposed to two trigger coils used in CD ignition system shown in Fig. JAC16. Individual components and complete assembly are not available for Blaser unit and must be replaced with a standard breaker type ignition system or with CD ignition system used on some J-321 engines. The flywheel must also be replaced if the Blaser ignition system is replaced by another ignition system.

Some J-321 engines are equipped with the CD ignition system shown in Fig. JAC16. Components are available for this ignition and if service is required, the following troubleshooting procedure may be used: Be sure igni-

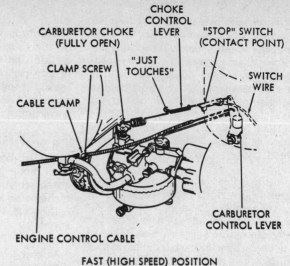

Fig. JAC15 – Drawing showing correct installation of Walbro carburetor controls. Refer to text.

tion is defective by using Wico test plug No. 14281 and rotating engine with starter. If test plug does not fire, ignition should be tested. Remove ignition system from engine. To test high tension coil, connect positive lead of an ohmmeter to coil terminal (B—Fig. JAC16) and connect negative lead to ground screw (C). Ohmmeter should read 0.1-0.5 ohms. Disconnect ohmmeter and connect positive lead to high tension lead of coil and connect negative lead to ground screw (C). Ohmmeter should read 900-1100 ohms. Renew high tension coil if either of the two tests is failed. Disconnect leads to each trigger coil, connect ohmmeter leads to the leads of a trigger coil and read resistance of each coil. Ohmmeter should indicate 15-25 ohms resistance. Renew trigger coil if incorrect reading was obtained. Check connections and leads of trigger coils for continuity. Before checking charging coil and electronics unit, note difference in early and late production units as shown in Fig. JAC17. Remove plug-in terminal (B—Fig. JAC16) from coil tower and

disconnect "ENGINE STOP" wire from terminal (D). Connect positive lead of ohmmeter to terminal (A) and negative lead to terminal (D). Ohmmeter should read 5-25 ohms on early units and 1 Megohm to infinity on late units. Reverse leads of ohmmeter. Ohmmeter should read infinity on early units and 1 Megohm to infinity on late units. Disconnect ohmmeter leads and connect positive meter lead to terminal (D) and negative meter lead to ground screw (C). Ohmmeter should read infinity on early production units and 560-760 ohms on late units. Reverse meter lead connections. Ohmmeter should read 1500-2200 ohms on early units. On late units, ohmmeter reading should be slightly less than reading (560-760) obtained previously. If any of these tests are failed, then charging coil windings are defective and charging coil and electronics unit must be renewed. Electronics circuit of unit cannot be tested except by substitution with a good or new charging coil and electronics unit. Renew unit if ignition system operates correctly with a good

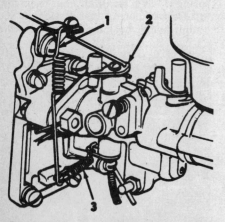

Fig. JAC14–Drawing showing correct installation of Tillotson carburetor controls. Refer to text.

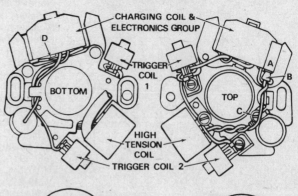

Fig. JAC16–Top and bottom views of CD ignition system used on some J-321 engines.

Fig. JAC17–Location of terminal (D) will identify early and late production CD ignition systems. Refer also to Fig. JAC16 for location of terminal (D).

EARLY PRODUCTION

LATE PRODUCTION

or new charging coil and electronics unit.

Ignition timing on models with CD or Blaser ignition system is fixed and cannot be adjusted.

BREAKER POINT IGNITION. Some J-321 and all other models are equipped with a flywheel magneto system using ignition breaker points. Magneto components are accessible after removing flywheel. Breaker point gap is 0.020 for all models. Recommended ignition timing is 30° BTDC for model J-125, 28° BTDC for model J-175 and 27° BTDC for model J-225. On model J-321 engine used on Snow Jet, rotate stator to full counterclockwise (advanced) position. On J-501 and all other J-321 engines with breaker point ignitions, rotate stator plate to full clockwise (retarded) position.

On J-125, J-175 and J-225 models ignition timing is satisfactory if breaker points just begin to open when piston is on compression stroke and ⅛-inch (0.125) before the top dead center position. Shift magneto stator plate as necessary to obtain desired timing.

NOTE: Piston position at top dead center can be measured by inserting a scale through the spark plug hole.

Magneto output at starting speeds can be checked without removing magneto from engine by using a special Wico Test Plug No. S14281. Refer to Fig. JAC18. Note that the engine spark plug remains in place when using the test plug.

On early models, the manufacturer recommends that a ⅛-inch vent hole be drilled in the lower left hand corner of magneto breaker box to aid in ventilating the contact points (Refer to Fig. JAC19.)

AIR CLEANER. If the engine is operated under dry or dusty conditions, the manufacturer recommends that the air cleaner be serviced after every 25 hours of operation. Refer to following paragraphs for recommended servicing of each type air cleaner used.

FOIL TYPE CLEANER. Wash and rinse thoroughly in gasoline or other

Fig. JAC19–Typical magneto installation. Notice location of ⅛-inch vent hole referred to in text.

solvent. Shake off gasoline or solvent and immerse in clean SAE 30 oil. Allow excess oil to drain off before reinstalling.

PAPER FILTER. Brush or wipe outside of cleaner. Tap gently to loosen dirt from inside of filter. Do not oil or wash filter. Filter can also be cleaned by gently blowing compressed air from the inside. If, after extended use, filter is too dirty to clean properly, renew the filter.

OIL BATH AIR CLEANER. Remove cover from oil reservoir and discard old oil. Wash cleaner in gasoline or other solvent. Dry cleaner thoroughly. Refill to level indicated by arrow with SAE 30 motor oil.

FOAM TYPE FILTER. Remove filter and wash and rinse thoroughly in kerosene or similar solvent. Re-oil with 2 tablespoons of clean SAE 30 oil. Compress filter to distribute oil evenly throughout filter element.

LUBRICATION. Fuel and lubricating oil should be thoroughly mixed in a separate container.

Fuel:oil ratio is 50:1 for J-501 engines; 30:1 for J-321 engines; 16:1 for all other models. Manufacturer recom-

mends Jacobsen two-cycle engine oil. Regular gasoline should be used in all engines.

Use SAE 10 oil in the reduction gear box on models so equipped. Gear box is fitted with an oil level plug.

CLEANING CARBON. Power loss can often be corrected by cleaning carbon from exhaust ports and muffler. To clean, remove spark plug and muffler. Turn engine so that piston is below bottom of exhaust ports and remove carbon from ports with dull knife or similar tool. Clean out the muffler openings, then replace muffler and spark plug.

REPAIRS

TIGHTENING TORQUES. Recommended tightening torques are as follows (values in inch-pounds):

Back plate screws	60-80
Carburetor adapter screws, J-321 & J-501 (with needle bearing connecting rod)	60-80
All other models	30-50
Connecting rod screws, J-321 & J-501 (with needle bearing connecting rod)	45-50
All other models	65-75
Crankcase head (bearing plate) bolts	80-100
Cylinder to crankcase nuts, J-125	150-180
Cylinder head bolts or nuts	150-180
Engine mounting bolts	120-150
Muffler mounting bolts and nuts:	
Rotary mower engines	60-80
Reel mower engines	80-100
Fan housing screws	60-80
Flywheel nut	300-360
Gear box cover, ¼-inch screws	60-80
5/16-inch screws	80-100
Spark Plug	180-200
Stator plate screws	60-80

IF SPARK JUMPS ACROSS TEST PLUG WHEN ENGINE IS CRANKED—MAGNETO IS OK.

Fig. JAC18–View showing use of special Wico Test Plug No. S14281 to check magneto output. Refer to text.

PISTON, PIN AND RINGS. To remove piston, remove gas tank, air cleaner and any shrouding preventing access to cylinder head or carburetor. Disconnect governor link to carburetor and remove carburetor and reed valve plate. Remove cylinder head. Unscrew connecting rod capscrews and remove connecting rod and piston. Be careful not to lose loose bearing rollers on models so equipped. Refer to CONNECTING ROD section to service connecting rod. The cam ground aluminum piston is fitted with either two or three compression rings depending upon engine model. Renew piston if badly worn or scored, or if side clearance of new ring in top ring groove is 0.010 or more. Install top ring with chamfer down and second ring with chamfer up. Piston skirt diameter (measured at right angle to piston pin) is as follows:

J-125 . . . . .1.9965-1.9970
J-175 . . . . .2.1235-2.1240
J-225 . . . . .2.2475-2.2480
J321 (Early) 2.1225-2.1232
   (Late) 2.1220-2.1227
J-501 . . . . .2.1220-2.1227

Piston skirt to cylinder wall clearance (new, measured at right angle to piston pin) should be:

J-125 .0.004-0.005
J-175 .0.002-0.003
J-225 .0.003-0.004
J-321 (Early) 0.0028-0.004
   (Late) 0.0033-0.0045
J-501 . . . . .0.0033-0.0045

Compression ring width is as follows:

J-125 . . . . .0.0890-0.0905
J-175H 0.0615-0.0625
J-175V 0.0925-0.0935
J-225 & J-321 . . . . .0.0925-0.0935
J-501 . . . . .0.0925-0.0935

Piston ring side clearance in groove should be:

J-125 . . . . .0.0035-0.0055

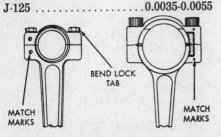

Fig. JAC20—Be sure that match marks are aligned when reassembling cap to connecting rod. Bend lock tab against screw heads on models so equipped.

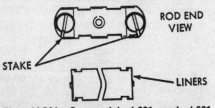

Fig. JAC21—On model J-321 and J-501 engines with aluminum connecting rod, be sure bearing liners fit together as shown. Stake cap retaining screws as shown.

J-175 .0.004-0.006
J-225 .0.002-0.0035
J-321 & J-501 . . . . .0.0015-0.0035

Piston ring end gap should be:

J-125 .0.005-0.010
J-175 (1959 production) 0.005-0.013
J-175 (1960 & later) 0.052-0.060
J-225, J-321 & J-501 . . . . . . .0.005-0.013

NOTE: Wide (0.052-0.060) ring gap on Model J-175 engines refers to units with pinned rings.

Piston diameter on model J-321 and J-501 engines is 0.4999-0.5001; and for all other models, piston pin diameter is 0.49975-0.50025. On model J-225 engines (needle bearing in connecting rod) renew piston if scored or shows any sign of wear. Piston pin to connecting rod clearance for all other models should be:

J-125 . . . . .0.0005-0.0015

J-175 . . . . .0.00055-0.00175
J-321 & J-501 . . . . .0.0007-0.0016

Piston pin fit in pin bore of piston is as follows:

J-321 and J-501 . . . . .0.0003 tight
                                to 0.0002 loose
All other models . . . . .0.00025 tight
                                to 0.00055 loose

Piston pins are available in 0.002, 0.003 and 0.005 oversizes, except on model J-225. If an oversize piston pin is used, pin bores in piston and connecting rod must be reamed accordingly.

CONNECTING ROD. Connecting rod and piston unit can be removed from above after removing cylinder head and carburetor adapter. Connecting rod service data follows:

MODEL J-225. Connecting rod in Model J-225 engine is equipped with

Fig. JAC22—Exploded view of model J-125 engine.

1. Snap ring	15. Lock tab	23. Piston	31. Ball bearing
5. Back plate	16. Rod cap	25. Crankcase head	32. Crankcase
6. Gasket	18. Piston rings	26. Gasket	33. Crankshaft seal
9. Cylinder head	19. Snap ring	27. Crankshaft	34. Needle bearing
10. Gasket	20. Snap ring	28. Ball bearing	35. Crankshaft seal
12. Cylinder	21. Piston pin	29. Bearing race	37. Transfer cover
13. Gasket	22. Connecting rod	30. Spacer	38. Gasket

needle roller crankpin and piston pin bearings. The crankpin needle rollers are separated by a split type cage and use crankpin and connecting rod surfaces as bearing races. The caged piston pin needle bearing is not renewable except by renewing connecting rod assembly.

Renew connecting rod if crankpin bearing surface shows signs of wear or is scored or if any piston pin needle roller has flat spot or any two needles can be separated the width of one needle. Refer to following specifications:

Crankpin diameter 0.750-0.7503
Con. rod bore diameter   0.9399-0.9403
Rod side play on crankpin . 0.008-0.018

MODELS J-321 & J-501. The J321 engine may be equipped with either a plain bearing bronze connecting rod or an aluminum connecting rod with needle roller crankpin bearing and plain piston pin bearing. Model J-501 is equipped with an aluminum connecting rod. The aluminum connecting rod has renewable steel bearing inserts for needle roller outer race. Twenty-eight bearing rollers are used. Bearing guides (10—Fig. JAC25) are used to center bearing rollers on crankpin. Bearing rollers and guides may be held on crankpin with grease before installation of rod. Refer to following specifications:

Piston pin diameter . . . 0.4999-0.5001
Pin to rod
  clearance 0.0007-0.0016
Bronze rod:
  Crankpin diameter . . 0.7485-0.7490
  Crankpin to rod
    clearance 0.0035-0.0045
  Rod side play on
    crankpin 0.004-0.017
Aluminum rod:
  Crankpin diameter . . 0.7496-0.7501
  Con. rod bore diameter 0.9819-0.9824
  Rod side play on
    crankpin 0.005-0.018

ALL OTHER MODELS. A bronze connecting rod with plain crankpin and piston pin bearings is used in all models except J-225, J-501 and some J-321 engines. Refer to following specifications:

Piston pin diameter:
  J-125, J-125V &
    J-175 . . . . 0.49975-0.50025
Pin to rod clearance:
  J-125H & J-125V . . . 0.0005-0.0015
  J-175 . . . . 0.00055-0.00175
Crankpin diameter:
  J-125H 0.6240-0.6245
  J-125V 0.6230-0.6235
  J-175 . . . . 0.7485-0.7490
Crankpin to rod clearance:
  J-125H 0.0015-0.0030
  J-125V 0.0025-0.0040
  J-175 . . . . 0.0035-0.0045
Rod side play on crankpin:

J-125H, J-125V & J-175 0.004-0.017

NOTE: On all models, be sure that match marks on rod and cap are aligned as shown in Fig. JAC20. Bend lock tabs, when used, against cap screw heads. On model J-321 or J-501 with aluminum rod, stake the screw heads as shown in Fig. JAC21; steel bearing inserts must be installed as shown.

CYLINDER. Cylinder bore should be resized if scored, out of round more than 0.0015 or wear has exceeded 0.002. Cylinder bore diameter is 2.0010-2.0015 for model J-125 engines, 2.126-2.1265 for model J-175 engines, 2.2510-2.2515 for model J-225 engines and 2.126-2.1265 for model J-321 and J-501 engines. Oversize pistons of 0.010 and 0.020 are available.

If re-boring is not necessary, the manufacturer recommends deglazing the bore to aid in seating of new rings.

CRANKSHAFT AND SEALS. Except on models J-175, J-321 and J-501, the crankshaft is carried in two ball bearings which are a press fit on the shaft. The crankshaft in model J-175 engines is supported by two needle roller bearings. On model J-321 and J-501 engines, the crankshaft is supported in one ball bearing and one needle bearing. J-125 and J-175 engines also have a third bearing (needle bearing) to support outer end of crankshaft. When removing the bearings, use an approved bearing puller.

After crankshaft has been removed from crankcase, use a dial gage to check straightness.

When installing new bearings, be sure crankshaft is supported between the throws and/or the bearing is heated in oil to prevent bending of the crankshaft.

On model J-321 engines, it is necessary to remove the two bearing retainers (31—Fig. JAC25) before the crankcase head (bearing plate) can be

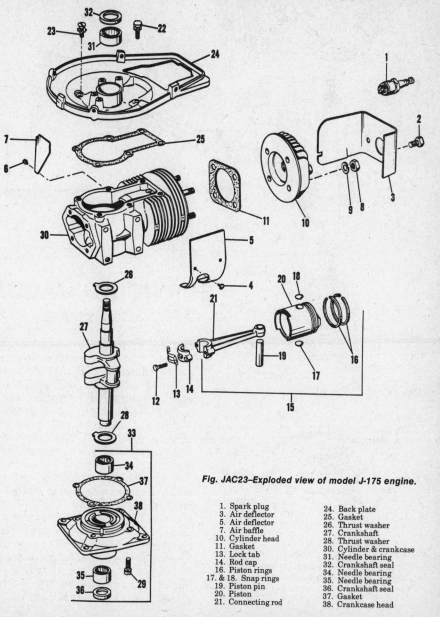

Fig. JAC23—Exploded view of model J-175 engine.

1. Spark plug	24. Back plate
3. Air deflector	25. Gasket
5. Air deflector	26. Thrust washer
7. Air baffle	27. Crankshaft
10. Cylinder head	28. Thrust washer
11. Gasket	30. Cylinder & crankcase
13. Lock tab	31. Needle bearing
14. Rod cap	32. Crankshaft seal
16. Piston rings	34. Needle bearing
17. & 18. Snap rings	35. Needle bearing
19. Piston pin	36. Crankshaft seal
20. Piston	37. Gasket
21. Connecting rod	38. Crankcase head

Fig. JAC24–Exploded view of model J-225 engine.

3. Cylinder head	
4. Gasket	17. Back plate
6. Rod cap	18. Gasket
7. Bearing cage	21. Crankcase head
8. Needle rollers	22. Gasket
10. Piston rings	23. Crankshaft
11. & 12. Snap rings	24. Crankshaft seal
13. Piston pin	25. Ball bearing
14. Piston	26. Ball bearing
15. Connecting rod	27. Crankshaft seal

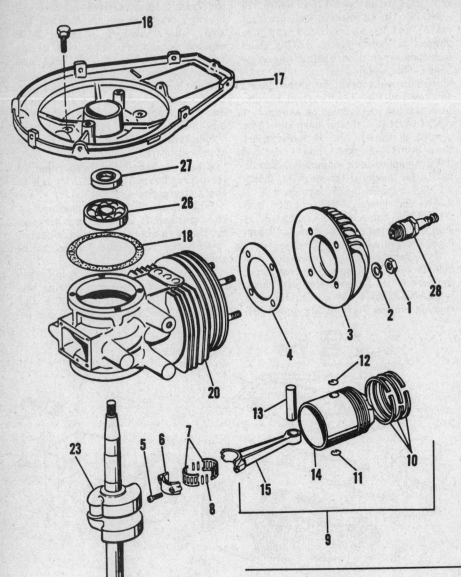

removed from the crankshaft. Remove snap ring which retains bearing on model J-501.

Install crankcase head in crankcase of model J-321 or J-501 so that flat spot on inner portion of crankcase head will be towards cylinder.

On model J-175 engines, maintain crankshaft end play of 0.004-0.018 by renewing thrust washers (26 and 28—Fig. JAC23); or gaskets (25 and 37) are available with less thickness than standard gaskets to reduce crankshaft end play.

On all models with direct drive, install crankcase seals so that lip faces toward inside of engine. On models with speed reducer, the crankcase oil seal on the speed reducer side should be installed with lip facing the reducer.

REED VALVE. On all models the carburetor is mounted on an adapter plate. The plate carries a small spring steel leaf or reed, on the engine side, which acts as an inlet valve. The reed has a bend in it and must be installed so as to force the reed firmly against the mounting plate. Blow-back through the carburetor may be caused by dirt or foreign matter holding reed valve open or by an improperly installed reed.

SERVICING JACOBSEN ACCESSORIES

RECOIL STARTER

Refer to Fig. JAC 26 or JAC 27 for exploded views of starters which may be used. To disassemble dog type starter shown in Fig. JAC 26, remove starter from engine and pull starter rope out of starter approximately 12 inches. Prevent pulley (3) from rewinding and pull slack rope back through rope outlet. Hold rope away from pulley and allow rope pulley to unwind. Unscrew retaining screw (11) and remove dog assembly and rope pulley being careful not to disturb rewind spring (2) in cover. Note direction of spring winding and carefully remove spring from cover. To reassemble starter, reverse disassembly procedure. Rewind spring must be pre-loaded as follows: Install rope through rope outlet of housing and hole in rope pulley. Tie a knot at each end of rope.

Turn rope pulley approximately four turns in direction that places load on rewind spring. Hold pulley and pull remainder of rope through rope pulley. Attach handle to rope end and allow rope to rewind into starter. If spring is properly pre-loaded, rope will fully rewind.

To disassemble starter shown in Fig. JAC 27, remove rope handle and allow rope to wind into starter. Remove roll pin (1) and washers (2 and 3). Remove rope pulley and remainder of starter components. When reassembling starter, turn rope pulley approximately 4 turns counter-clockwise (viewed from open side) before connecting rope to rope pulley. Clip at rope end should have open side facing outward. After assembling starter, check operation of starter and note if rope is fully rewound into starter.

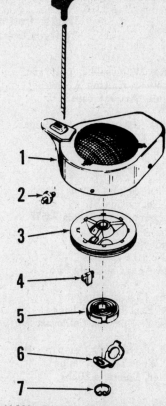

Fig. JAC25—Exploded view of vertical crankshaft model J-321 and J-501 engine; horizontal crankshaft models are similar. Bearing (34) on J-501 is retained by a snap ring and not screw retainer (29, 30 & 31). Note location of bearing rollers (13) and guides (10) in inset. Design of crankcase head (32) will vary with engine application.

1. Spark plug
3. Bracket
4. Air deflector
7. Cylinder head
8. Gasket
9. Breaker cam
10. Bearing roller guides
11. Rod cap
13. Bearing rollers (28)
14. Snap rings
15. Piston pin
16. Connecting rod
17. Piston rings
18. Piston
21. Back plate
22. Crankshaft seal
23. Needle bearing
24. Gasket
27. Cylinder & crankcase
28. Gasket
31. Bearing retainer
32. Crankcase head
33. Crankshaft
34. Ball bearing
35. Crankshaft seal

Fig. JAC28—Exploded view of rewind starter used on some later models.

1. Starter housing	5. Rewind spring & cup
2. Rope guide	6. Pawl plate
3. Rope pulley	7. Snap ring
4. Pawl	

Rewind starter shown in Fig. JAC28 is a pawl type starter with pawl (4) engaging a flywheel fin when the starter rope is pulled. To disassemble starter, remove rope handle and allow rope to rewind into starter. Remove snap ring (7) and remove starter components from starter housing. Inspect components for wear or damage and install in reverse order of disassembly. Spring cup (5) should be installed so that spring attachment point on cup is 180 degrees from rope entry hole in starter housing (1). Turn rope pulley approximately 3½ turns against spring tension before passing end of rope through hole in starter housing. Note that four embossed projections on starter housing adjacent

to rope pulley are friction devices and should not be lubricated.

GEAR REDUCTION UNIT

Before the housing can be removed from the engine, the reduction gear cover and gear must be removed. Crankcase oil seal on the speed reducer

side should be installed with the lip facing the reducer. On the power take off side of the reducer unit, the oil seal lip faces the reduction unit. Refer to Fig. JAC29.

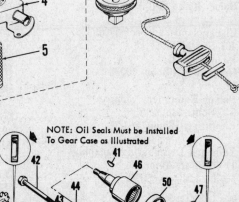

Fig. JAC27—Exploded view of recoil starter used on some engines. Some models use a snap ring in place of pin (1).

1. Pin
2. Washer
3. Washer
4. Cover
5. Spring
6. Washer
7. Rope pulley

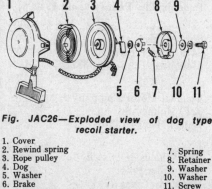

Fig. JAC26—Exploded view of dog type recoil starter.

1. Cover	7. Spring
2. Rewind spring	8. Retainer
3. Rope pulley	9. Washer
4. Dog	10. Washer
5. Washer	11. Screw
6. Brake	

Fig. JAC29—Exploded view of reduction gear assembly used on horizontal crankshaft engines.

40. Drive sprocket
41. Woodruff key
44. Housing
45. Gasket
46. Drive gear
47. Crankcase head
48. Crankshaft seal
49. Needle bearing
50. Needle bearing
51. Oil seal
52. Needle bearing
53. Oil filler plug
54. Oil level plug

NOTE: Oil Seals Must be Installed To Gear Case as Illustrated

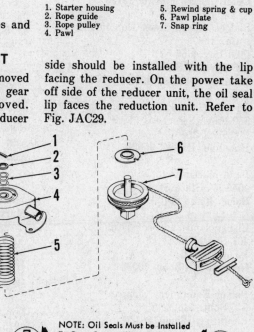

JACOBSEN CENTRAL SERVICE DISTRIBUTORS
(Alphabetically by States)
These franchised firms carry extensive stocks of repair parts.
Contact them for name of nearest dealer who may have the parts
you need.

Dealers Wholesale Supply, Inc.
4040 West Whitton Avenue
Phoenix, Arizona 85019

Lawn & Garden Supply Company
2222 N. 27th Avenue
P.O. Box 11220
Phoenix, Arizona 85017

Bee Tee Engine Sales, Inc.
2424 Teagarden St.
San Leandro, California 94577

Saunders & Company
108 North Sycamore
Santa Ana, California 92701

Jay P. Casteel Company
13536 East Imperial Highway
Santa Fe Springs, California 90670

Boyd Distributing Company, Inc.
1400 West Third Avenue
Denver, Colorado 80223

Mog-All of Florida, Inc.
365 Greco Avenue at Le June Road
Coral Gables, Florida 33146

Blalock Machinery & Equipment
Co., Inc.
P.O. Box 4658
225 Forsyth St. S.W.
Atlanta, Georgia 30302

Lewers & Cooke
550 Paiea Street
P.O. Box 29607
Honolulu, Hawaii 96820

Boyd Martin Company
4550 W. State Street
Boise, Idaho 83703

Chicagoland Jacobsen Dist. Co.
401 South Route 83
P.O. Box 305
Grayslake, Illinois 60030

Power Equipment Company
645 South Route 83
Elmhurst, Illinois 60126

Yeomans Distributing Company
1140 - 50th Avenue
Moline, Illinois 61265

Yeomans Distributing Company
1503 West Altorfer Drive
Peoria, Illinois 61614

Allied Motor Parts Company
1300 Walnut Street
Des Moines, Iowa 50309

Gard'n-Wise Inc.
502 East 33rd Street North
P.O. Box 4097, North Station
Wichita, Kansas 67219

Mid-East Power Equipment Company
185 Lisle Road
Lexington, Kentucky 40502

Southern Specialty Sales Co., Inc.
617 North Broad Avenue
P.O. Box 19965
New Orleans, Louisiana 70119

R. E. Jarvis Company
Route 9
Fayville, Massachusetts 01745

Nelson & Small
P.O. Box 1420
212 Canco Road
Portland, Maine 04103

Ideal Mower Sales, Inc.
811 Woodward Heights
Ferndale, Michigan 48220

Jac Van Distributors, Inc.
4477 East Paris Avenue
Grand Rapids, Michigan 49508

R. L. Gould & Company
3711 North Lexington Parkway
St. Paul, Minnesota 55112

Wilson-Grasser Distributing Company
2301 River Front Drive
Kansas City, Missouri 64120

Disco Distributing Company
11649 Adie Road
Maryland Heights, Missouri 63043

A&I Distributors
2112 4th Avenue, North
P.O. Box 1999
Billings, Montana 59103

Superior Service
4015 Menaul Boulevard, N.E.
Albuquerque, New Mexico 87110

O.P.E. Corporation
1827 Broadway
P.O. Box 952
Albany, New York 12201

Nero Equipment, Inc.
P.O. Box 51
1370 County Road 8
Canandaigua, New York 14424

Crestline Distributors, Inc.
6245 Fly Road
P.O. Box 194
East Syracuse, New York 13057

Ronconi Lawn Mower Service
615 Fifth Avenue
Box 274
Larchmont, New York 10538

Howard J. Premo, Inc.
Sales & Service
South Racquette Street
Massena, New York 13662

Carswell Distributing Company
3750 N. Liberty St.
P.O. Box 4193, North Station
Winston-Salem, North Carolina 27105

Dakota Hardware Company
212 North Pacific Avenue
P.O. Box 789
Fargo, North Dakota 58102

Tecca Distributing Company
4747 Manufacturing Avenue
Cleveland, Ohio 44135

Livingston Seed Company
880 Kinnear Road
P.O. Box 299
Columbus, Ohio 43216

Phillips Machinery Company
8833 East Pine Street
Tulsa, Oklahoma 74115

Lucky JT Distributing Company
4445 N.E. Glisan
Portland, Oregon 97213

Conaway, Inc.
Mayview Road
P.O. Box 303
Lawrence, Pennsylvania 15055

Lawn & Golf Supply Company, Inc.
647 Nutt Road
Phoenixville, Pennsylvania 19460

Shobe, Inc.
2449 Scaper Street
Memphis, Tennessee 38114

Colonial Motor Company
3219 Holmes St.
Dallas, Texas 75215

Al's Wholesale Distributors
6908 Long Point
Houston, Texas 77055

SMALL ENGINES

Hunter Power Saw Company, Inc.
P.O. Box 5889
Texarkana, Texas 75501

Boyd Martin Company
1260 North Temple West
Salt Lake City, Utah 84116

Morse Hardware
1025 State Street
Bellingham, Washington 98225

Pacific Equipment Company
410 10th South at Jackson Street
Seattle, Washington 98104

Engine Sales & Service Company, Inc.
919 Virginia Street
Charleston, West Virginia 25301

Horst Distributing, Inc.
444 North Madison Street
Chilton, Wisconsin 53014

Four Seasons, Inc.
7373 South 6th Street
Oak Creek, Wisconsin 53154

CANADA

Interprovincial Turf Ltd.
4120 - 8th Street Southeast
Box 8218, Station "F"
Calgary, Alberta, Canada

Farm & Tiller Sales, Ltd.
1205 East Hastings Street
Vancouver, B.C., Canada

Consolidated Turf Equipment Ltd.
972 Powell Avenue
Winnipeg, Manitoba, Canada

Halifax Seed Company Ltd.
5860 Kane Street
P.O. Box 338
Halifax, Nova Scotia, Canada

Hilstad Distributors Ltd.
621 Main Street West
North Bay, Ontario, Canada

G.H.L. Distribution
486 Des Moulins
Mont St. Hilaire, Quebec, Canada

Brandt Machine & Mfg. Ltd.
705 Toronto Street
P.O. Box 376
Regina, Saskatchewan, Canada

KOHLER

KOHLER COMPANY
Kohler, Wisconsin

SERIES	Cyls.	Bore	Stroke	Displ.
K90 & K91	1	2⅜	2	8.86

MAINTENANCE

SPARK PLUG. Recommended plug is Champion J-8, AC-C45, Autolite A7 or Prestolite 14-7. Electrode gap is 0.025.

CARBURETOR. Refer to Fig. KO1 for exploded view of Carter Model N carburetor used on early production models. Late production K91 engines are equipped with the Kohler carburetor shown in Fig. KO2.

For initial adjustment, open idle fuel needle 1½ turns and open main fuel needle 2 turns. Make final adjustment with engine warm and running. Place engine under load and adjust main fuel needle for leanest setting that will allow satisfactory acceleration and steady governor operation. Adjust idle speed stop screw to maintain an idle speed of 1000 RPM. Then adjust idle needle for smoothest idle operation. As adjustments affect each other, the adjustment sequence may have to be repeated.

To check float lever, invert the carburetor body casting and float assembly. There should be a 13/64-inch clearance between free side of float and machined surface of body casting. If not, carefully bend float lever tang that contacts inlet valve as necessary to provide correct measurement.

GOVERNOR. A mechanical flyball type governor with external adjustments is used. The governor flyball unit is attached to and rotates with the camshaft gear. Refer to Fig. KO4 for exploded view of the governor flyball unit.

Engine speed is controlled by the tension on the governor spring (B—Fig. KO5). NOTE: Maximum (no load) engine speed is 4000 RPM.

Before attempting to adjust governed speed, synchronize the linkage as follows: Loosen clamp bolt nut (N) and using a pair of pliers, turn shaft (H) counter-clockwise as far as possible. Pull arm (L) completely to the left

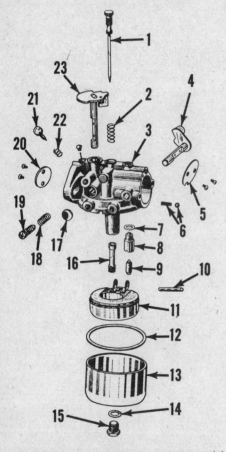

Fig. KO1—Exploded view of typical Carter model N carburetor used on early production K90 and K91 engines.

1. Main fuel needle
2. Spring
3. Carburetor body
4. Choke shaft
5. Choke disc
6. Choke detent
7. Sealing washer
8. Inlet valve seat
9. Inlet valve
10. Float pin
11. Float
12. Gasket
13. Float bowl
14. Sealing washer
15. Retainer
16. Main jet
17. Plug
18. Spring
19. Idle stop screw
20. Throttle disc
21. Idle fuel needle
22. Spring
23. Throttle shaft

Fig. KO2—Exploded view of Kohler carburetor used on late production engines.

1. Main fuel needle
2. Spring
3. Carburetor body assembly
4. Spring
5. Idle speed stop screw
6. Spring
7. Idle fuel needle
8. Sealing washer
9. Inlet valve seat
10. Inlet valve
11. Float pin
12. Float
13. Gasket
14. Float bowl
15. Sealing washer
16. Bowl retainer

Fig. KO3—Early series K90 and K91 engine showing carburetor adjustments and portion of governor linkage. Late production engines are similar.

A. Idle mixture needle
B. Idle stop screw
C. High speed needle
H. Governor arm

(away from carburetor) and tighten the clamp bolt nut. To increase or decrease the maximum engine speed, vary the tension of governor spring (B). On engine with remote throttle control, this is accomplished by moving bracket (F) up or down; on engines without remote throttle control, by rotating disc (D) after loosening bushing (C).

MAGNETO AND TIMING. Bendix Scintilla K1-300 or Phelon model F2100 (now called Repco) is used. Recommended spark timing is 20° BTDC.

On early production engines, adjust point gap to 0.020, (fully opened). No other timing adjustment is required.

On late production engines, a timing port is provided in left side of bearing plate and there are two timing marks on the flywheel. (See Fig. KO6.) Satisfactory timing is obtained by adjusting the breaker contact gap to 0.020. For precision timing, use timing light and adjust breaker gap until the first or "SP" timing mark is centered in timing port, engine running.

On Bendix-Scintilla (Fig. KO7) equipped engines, a wave washer is installed on crankshaft between magneto rotor and flywheel; on Phelon (Fig. KO6) equipped engines, the wave washer is omitted.

LUBRICATION. Crankcase capacity is approximately 1½ pints. Use SAE No. 30 oil when operating in temperatures above 30° F., SAE 10W-30 in

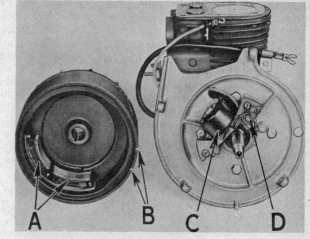

Fig. KO6–Phelon (Repco) magneto installation on K90 and K91 engines. Late production engines have flywheel timing marks shown at "B".

A. Magnets
B. Timing marks
C. Coil
D. Condenser

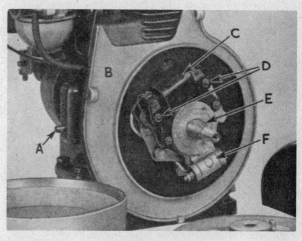

Fig. KO7–Bendix-Scintilla magneto installation on series K90 and K91 engines. Rotating magnet (E) is pressed on crankshaft.

A. Ground button
B. Bearing plate
C. Magneto coil
D. Pole shoes
E. Rotating magnet
F. Condenser

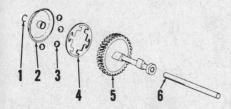

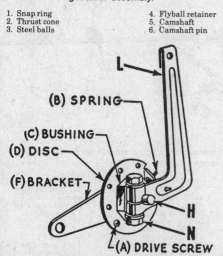

Fig KO4–Exploded view of camshaft and flyball governor assembly.

1. Snap ring
2. Thrust cone
3. Steel balls
4. Flyball retainer
5. Camshaft
6. Camshaft pin

Fig. KO5–Points of adjustment of governor on series K90 and K91 engines.

temperatures between 0° F. and 30° F. and SAE 5W-20 in temperatures below 0° F. Use high quality motor oil having API classification MS or SD. An oil dipper which is attached to the connecting rod cap provides for splash type lubrication. On engines with reduction gear power take-off, use same grade oil in reduction gear housing as used in crankcase.

CRANKCASE BREATHER. The crankcase breather, which serves to eliminate oil leaks at crankcase seals, is attached to cylinder block on carburetor side of engine for early production engines; to valve cover plate on late production engines. On late pro-

duction engines, there should be 1/64-1/32 inch clearance between flapper valve and its seat. If a slight amount of crankcase vacuum is not present, breather valve is faulty or engine has excessive blow-by past rings and/or valves.

AIR CLEANER. Engines may be equipped with either an oil bath type air cleaner shown in Fig. KO8 or a dry element type shown in Fig. KO9.

Oil bath air cleaner should be serviced every 25 hours of operation or more often if operating in extremely dusty conditions. To service the oil bath type, remove complete cleaner assembly from engine. Remove cover and element from bowl. Empty used oil

Fig. KO8–View of oil bath type air cleaner.

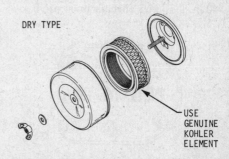

Fig. KO9–Exploded view of dry element type air cleaner.

from bowl, then clean cover and bowl in solvent. Clean element in solvent and allow to drip dry. Lightly re-oil element. Fill bowl to oil level marked on bowl using same grade and weight oil as used in engine crankcase. Renew gaskets as necessary when reassembling and reinstalling unit.

Dry element type air cleaner should be cleaned every 100 hours of operation or more frequently if operating in dusty conditions. Remove dry element and tap element lightly on a flat surface to remove surface dirt. Do not wash element or attempt to clean element with compressed air. Renew element if extremely dirty or if it is bent, crushed or otherwise damaged. Make certain the sealing surfaces of element seal effectively against the back plate and cover.

REPAIRS

TIGHTENING TORQUES. Recommended tightening torques are as follows:

Spark plug .... 325 in.-lbs.
Connecting rod cap screws *140 in.-lbs.
Cylinder head cap screws *200 in.-lbs.
Flywheel retaining nut ... 540 in.-lbs.
*With threads lubricated.

CONNECTING ROD. Connecting rod assembly is removed from above after removing cylinder head and oil pan (engine base). The aluminum alloy connecting rod rides directly on the crankpin. Connecting rod with 0.010 undersize crankpin bore is available for reground crankshaft. Oversize piston pins are also available. Desired running clearances are as follows:

Connecting rod to
  crankpin 0.001-0.0025
Connecting rod to
  piston pin 0.0005-0.001
Rod side play on crankpin .0.005-0.016

Standard crankpin diameter is 0.9355-0.936. Standard piston pin diameter is 0.562.

When reinstalling connecting rod and piston assembly, piston can be installed either way on rod, but make certain the match marks on connecting rod and cap are aligned and are towards flywheel side of engine. Tighten connecting rod cap screws to a torque of 140 in.-lbs. (with threads lubricated).

PISTON, PIN AND RINGS. The aluminum alloy piston is fitted with two 0.093 wide compression rings and one 0.187 wide oil control ring. Renew piston if scored or if side clearance of new ring in piston top groove exceeds 0.005. Pistons and rings are available in oversizes of 0.010, 0.020 and 0.030 as well as standard. Piston pin fit in piston bore should be from 0.0002 interference to 0.0002 loose. Piston pins are available in oversizes of 0.005 and 0.010. Always renew piston pin retaining rings.

Recommended piston to cylinder bore clearance is 0.003-0.004 (measured at thrust face of piston).

Piston ring specifications are as follows:
Ring end gap 0.007-0.017
Ring side clearance:
  Compression rings 0.002-0.004
  Oil control ring 0.0015-0.0035

If compression ring has a groove or bevel on outside surface, install ring with the groove or bevel down. If groove or bevel is on inside surface of compression ring, install ring or bevel up. Oil control ring can be installed either side up.

CYLINDER HEAD. Always use a new head gasket when installing cylinder head. Tighten cylinder head cap screws evenly and in steps using the sequence shown in Fig. KO10 until the tightening torque of 200 in.-lbs. is reached.

CYLINDER BLOCK. If cylinder wall is scored or bore is tapered or out-of-round more than 0.005, the cylinder should be honed to the nearest suitable oversize of either 0.010, 0.020 or 0.030. Standard cylinder bore diameter is 2.375.

CAMSHAFT. The hollow camshaft and integral cam gear (27—Fig. KO11)

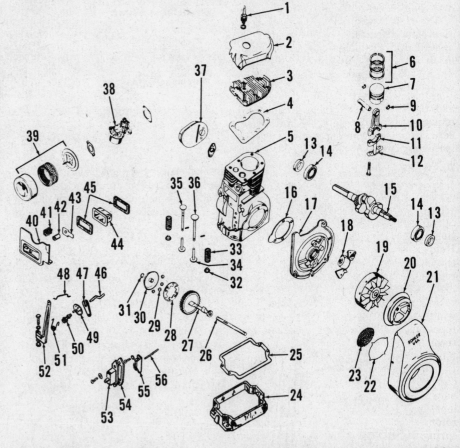

Fig. KO11–Exploded view of K90 and K91 engine. Breaker points (55) are actuated by cam on right end of camshaft (27) through push rod (56).

1. Spark plug	15. Crankshaft	29. Steel balls	43. Breather reed
2. Air baffle	16. Gasket	30. Thrust cone	44. Breather plate
3. Cylinder head	17. Bearing plate	31. Snap ring	45. Gaskets
4. Head gasket	18. Magneto	32. Spring retainer	46. Governor shaft
5. Cylinder block	19. Flywheel	33. Valve spring	47. Bracket
6. Piston rings	20. Pulley	34. Valve tappets	48. Link
7. Piston	21. Shroud	35. Exhaust valve	49. Speed disc
8. Piston pin	22. Screen retainer	36. Intake valve	50. Bushing
9. Retaining rings	23. Screen	37. Muffler	51. Governor spring
10. Connecting rod	24. Oil pan	38. Carburetor	52. Governor lever
11. Rod cap	25. Gasket	39. Air cleaner assy	53. Breaker cover
12. Rod bolt lock	26. Camshaft pin	40. Valve cover	54. Gasket
13. Oil seal	27. Camshaft	41. Filter	55. Breaker points
14. Ball bearing	28. Flyball retainer	42. Breather seal	56. Push rod

Fig. KO10–Tighten cylinder head cap screws to a torque of 200 in.-lbs. in sequence shown.

rotate on a pin (26). Camshaft can be removed after first removing bearing plate (17) and crankshaft, then driving pin out towards bearing plate side of crankcase. Camshaft pin is a press fit in closed (P.T.O.) side of of crankcase and a slip fit (0.0005-0.0012 clearance) in bearing plate side. Camshaft to camshaft pin clearance should be 0.001-0.0025. Desired camshaft end play is 0.005-0.020. Camshaft end play is controlled by installing shim washers between camshaft and bearing plate side of crankcase. Shim washers are available in 0.005 and 0.010 thicknesses. Flyball retainer (28), flyballs (29), thrust cone (30) and snap ring (31) are attached to and rotate with the camshaft assembly.

CRANKSHAFT. The crankshaft is supported in two ball bearing mains. Renew ball bearings (14—Fig. KO11) if excessively loose or rough. Desired crankshaft end play of 0.0038-0.0228 is controlled by thickness of bearing plate gaskets (16). Install one 0.020 thick gasket and 0.010 thick gasket as required.

The crankpin journal may be ground to 0.010 undersize for use of undersize connecting rod if journal is scored or out-of-round. Standard crankpin diameter is 0.9355-0.936. Connecting rod to crankpin journal running clearance should be 0.001-0.0025.

When installing crankshaft, align timing marks on crankshaft gear and camshaft gear. Kohler recommends that crankshaft seals (13) be installed in crankcase and bearing plate after crankshaft and bearing plate are installed. Carefully work seals over the crankshaft with lips to inside and drive seals into place with hollow driver that contacts outer edge of seals.

VALVE SYSTEM. Valve tappet gap (cold) is 0.005-0.009 for intake valve and 0.011-0.015 for exhaust valve. Correct tappet gap is obtained by grinding end of valve stems squarely. Be sure to remove all burrs from end of stem after grinding.

The exhaust valve seats on a renewable seat insert and intake valve seats directly on machined seat in cylinder block. However, intake seats are available for service. Valve face and seat angle is 45 degrees. Desired seat width is 0.037-0.045.

Valve stem clearance in guide should be 0.0005-0.002 for intake valve and 0.002-0.0035 for exhaust valve. Valve guides are not renewable. Excessive valve stem to guide clearance is corrected by reaming guides and installing new valves with 0.005 oversize stems. Standard valve stem diameter is 0.248-0.2485 for intake valve and 0.246-0.2465 for exhaust valve.

SERVICING KOHLER ACCESSORIES

RETRACTABLE STARTERS

Fairbanks-Morse or Eaton retractable starters are used on some Kohler engines. When servicing the starters, refer to appropriate following paragraph.

Fairbanks-Morse

OVERHAUL. To disassemble the starter, remove retainer ring, retainer washer, brake spring, friction washer, friction shoe assembly and second friction washer as shown in Fig. KO12. Hold the rope handle in one hand and the cover in the other and allow rotor to rotate to unwind the recoil spring preload. Lift rotor from cover, shaft and recoil spring. NOTE: Check the winding direction of recoil spring and rope for aid in reassembly. Remove recoil spring from cover and unwind rope from rotor.

When reassembling the unit, lubricate recoil spring, cover shaft and its bore in rotor with Lubriplate or equivalent. Install the rope on rotor and the rotor to the shaft and engage the recoil spring inner end hook. Pre-load the recoil spring four turns and install middle flange and mounting flange. Check friction shoe sharp ends and renew if necessary. Install friction washers, friction shoe assembly, brake spring, retainer ring. Make certain that friction shoe assembly is installed properly for correct starter rotation. If properly installed, sharp ends of friction shoe plates will extend when rope is pulled.

Starter operation can be reversed by winding rope and recoil spring in opposite direction and turning the friction shoe assembly upside down. See Fig. KO13 for counter-clockwise assembly and Fig. KO14 for clockwise assembly.

Eaton

OVERHAUL. To disassemble the

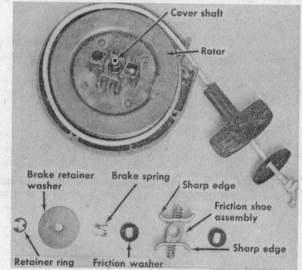

Fig. KO12–Fairbanks-Morse starter with friction shoe assembly removed.

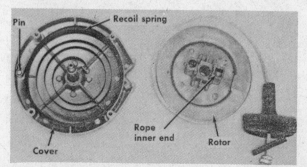

Fig. KO13–View showing recoil spring and rope installed for counter-clockwise starter operation.

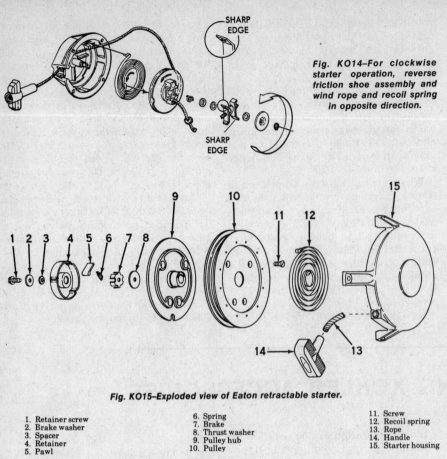

Fig. KO14–For clockwise starter operation, reverse friction shoe assembly and wind rope and recoil spring in opposite direction.

After securing the pulley assembly in housing, align notch in pulley with rope bushing in housing. Engage rope in notch and rotate pulley at least two full turns in same direction it is pulled to properly pre-load starter spring. Pull rope to fully extended position. Release handle and if spring is properly pre-loaded, the rope will fully rewind.

Before installing starter on engine, check teeth in starter driven hub (165 —Fig. KO16) for wear and renew hub if necessary.

12-VOLT STARTER-GENERATOR

The combination 12-volt starter-generator manufactured by Delco-Remy is used on some Kohler engines. The starter-generator functions as a cranking motor when the starting switch is closed. When the engine is operating and with starting switch open, the unit acts as a generator. Generator output and circuit voltage for the battery and various operating requirements are controlled by a current-voltage regulator.

Kohler recommends that starter-generator belt tension be adjusted until about 10 pounds pressure applied midway between pulleys will deflect belt ¼-inch. Refer to Fig. KO17 for exploded view of starter-generator assembly. Parts are available from Kohler as well as authorized Delco-Remy service stations.

Fig. KO15–Exploded view of Eaton retractable starter.

1. Retainer screw
2. Brake washer
3. Spacer
4. Retainer
5. Pawl
6. Spring
7. Brake
8. Thrust washer
9. Pulley hub
10. Pulley
11. Screw
12. Recoil spring
13. Rope
14. Handle
15. Starter housing

starter, first release tension of rewind spring as follows: Hold starter assembly with pulley facing up. Pull starter rope until notch in pulley is aligned with rope hole in cover. Use thumb pressure to prevent pulley from rotating. Engage rope in notch of pulley and slowly release thumb pressure to allow spring to unwind until all tension is released.

When removing rope pulley, use extreme care to keep starter spring confined in housing. Check starter spring for breaks, cracks or distortion. If starter spring is to be renewed, carefully remove it from housing, noting the direction of rotation of spring be-

fore removing. Exploded view of clockwise starter is shown in Fig. KO15.

Check the pawl, brake, spring, retainer and hub for wear and renew as necessary. If starter rope is worn or frayed, remove from pulley, noting the direction it is wrapped on pulley. Renew rope and install pulley in housing, aligning notch in pulley hub with hook in end of spring. Use a wire bent to form a hook to aid in positioning spring on hub.

REDUCTION DRIVE

The reduction drive unit consists of a driven gear (G—Fig. KO18) which is pressed on the power take-off shaft. Drive gear (P) is an integral part of engine crankshaft. The pto shaft is supported by two bushings; one in the housing and the other in the cover. Oil seals are used at both ends of pto shaft. To disassemble the unit, first remove plug and drain the unit. Unbolt and

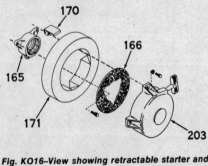

Fig. KO16–View showing retractable starter and starter hub.

165. Starter hub
166. Screen
170. Bracket
171. Air director
203. Retractable starter assembly

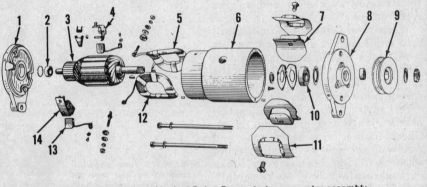

Fig. KO17–Exploded view of typical Delco-Remy starter-generator assembly.

1. Commutator end frame
2. Bearing
3. Armature
4. Ground brush holder
5. Field coil L.H.
6. Frame
7. Pole shoe
8. Drive end frame
9. Pulley
10. Bearing
11. Field coil insulator
13. Field coil R.H.
13. Brush
14. Insulated brush holder

remove the cover, then remove driven gear (G). Remove cap screws securing housing to engine block and lift off housing. Clean and inspect all parts and renew any showing excessive wear or other damage.

When reassembling, use tape or seal protector to prevent damage to oil seals. Use copper washers on two internal cap screws and lockwashers on external cap screws. Adjust gear reduction (pto) shaft end clearance to 0.001-0.006 by varying total thickness of cover gaskets. Fill housing to oil level hole with same grade of oil as used in engine.

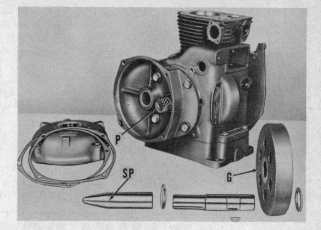

Fig. KO18–Elements of reduction gear unit used on some K90 and K91 engines. Pinion (P) is on crankshaft; internally toothed gear is (G). Seal protecting tool (SP) is used when installing cover to housing.

KOHLER CENTRAL ENGINE DISTRIBUTORS
(Alphabetically by States)
These franchised firms carry extensive stocks of repair parts. Contact them for name of dealer in their area who will have replacement parts.

Auto Elect. & Carb. Co., Inc.
2625 Fourth Avenue, S.
Birmingham, Ala. 35233

B&C Supply Corp.
443 E. Fourth Ave.
Anchorage, Alaska 99501

Charlie C. Jones, Inc.
Battery & Electric Company
2440 W. McDowell Road
P.O. Box 6654
Phoenix, Arizona 85005

Generator Equip. Co.
3409-11 W. Jefferson Blvd.
Los Angeles, Calif. 90018

H. G. Makelim Co.
219 Shaw Road
San Francisco, Calif. 94080

Spitzer Industrial Prod. Co.
43 W. 9th Ave.
Denver, Colo. 80204

Spencer Eng. & Magneto, Inc.
1114 W. Cass St.
Tampa, Fla. 33606

SEDCO, Inc.
3637 Clearview Parkway, N.E.
Atlanta, Georgia 30340

Small Engine Clinic
99-128 Aiea Heights Drive
P.O. Box 98
Aiea, Hawaii 96701

Midwest Engine Warehouse
515 Romans Road
Elmhurst, Ill. 60126

R.P.W., Inc.
2100 E. Broadway
P.O. Box 4826
Des Moines, Iowa 50313

Medart Engines & Parts of Kansas
15500 W. 109th St.
P.O. Box 5515
Lenexa, Kansas 66215

Grayson Co., Inc.
416 Cotton Street
P.O. Box 14
Shreveport, Louisiana 71101

C. V. Foster Equip. Co.
2502 Harford Road
Baltimore, Md. 21218

W. J. Connell Co.
210 Needham Street
Newton Upper Falls, Mass. 02164

Auto Elect. & Serv. Corp.
15550 Woodrow Wilson Ave.
Detroit, Mich. 48238

Carl A. Anderson, Inc. of Minn.
3380 Highway #49
St. Paul, Minnesota 55121

Medart Engines & Parts
3100 Washington Ave.
St. Louis, Missouri 63103

Original Equipment, Inc.
905 Second Ave., North
Billings, Montana 59103

R.P.W., Inc.
7402 "L" Street
Omaha, Nebraska 68127

The Durham Co., Inc.
7 Elkins Road
P.O. Box 620
East Brunswick, N.J. 08816

Spitzer Electrical Co. of N.M.
1023 Third St., N.W. P.O. Box 25065
Albuquerque, N.M. 87102

Automotive Elect. Assoc., Inc.
700 West 28th Street
P.O. Box 1497
Charlotte, N.C. 28206

Gardner, Inc.
1150 Chesapeake Ave.
Columbus, O. 43212

Magneto Ignition Co., Inc.
7450 E. 46th Place
P.O. Box 45324
Tulsa, Okla. 74145

Truck & Ind. Equip. Co.
7 Northeast Oregon St.
Portland, Ore. 97232

Auto Gear & Parts Co., Inc.
1620 Hunting Park Ave.
Philadelphia, Pa. 19140

Pitt Auto Electric Co.
5135 Baum Blvd.
Pittsburgh, Pa. 15224

Automotive Elect. Corp.
3250 Millbranch Road
P.O. Box 4508
Memphis, Tenn. 38116

Tri-State Equip. Co.
1501 E. Paisano Dr.
P.O. Box 771
El Paso, Tex. 79945

Waukesha-Pearce Industries
12320 So. Main
P.O. Box 35068
Houston, Tex. 77035

Diesel Elect. Serv. & Supply Co.
652 West, 1700 South
Salt Lake City, Utah 84104

Richmond Battery & Ign. Corp.
959 Myers Street
Richmond, Va. 23230

Northwest Motor Parts & Mfg. Co.
2930-6th Ave., S.
Seattle, Wash. 98134

Automotive Jobbers Supply Co.
P.O. Box 2200
South 125 Walnut Street
Spokane, Wash. 99204

Wisconsin Magneto, Inc.
4727 N. Teutonia Ave.
Milwaukee, Wisc. 53209

CANADA

Power Elect. & Equip. Co., Ltd.
604 Fourth St. S.E.
Calgary, Alberta

Coast Dieselec Ltd.
1920 Main Street
Vancouver, B.C.

W. N. White Co. Ltd.
2-213-215 Bedford Highway
P.O. Box 1474
Halifax, Nova Scotia

Suntester Equip. (Central) Ltd.
915 Oxford Street
P.O. Box 280
Toronto, Ontario

LAWN BOY

OUTBOARD MARINE CORPORATION
Post Office Box 82409
Lincoln, Nebraska 68501

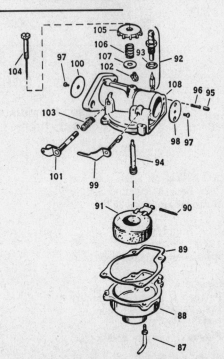

MODELS	Bore	Stroke	Displacement
C-10, C-12, C-20, C-21, C-22, C-70, C-71, C-72, C-73, C-75	1-15/16	1½	4.43
C-13 thru C-17, C-40, C-41, C-42, C-50, C-51, C-60, C-61, C-74, C-76, C-77, C-78, C-80, C-81	2-1/8	1½	5.22
C-18, C-19, C-19B, C-43, C-44, D-400 thru D-408, D-405E thru D-408E, D-409, D-430, D-431, D-433, D-440 thru D-448, D-445E thru D-448E, D-449, D-450, D-451, D-452, D-460, D-461, D-462, D-475, D-476, D-480, D-481, D-600, D-600E, D-601, D-640, D-641, D-641E	2-3/8	1½	6.65

Engines listed have been used on Lawn-Boy rotary lawn mowers, snow blowers, rotary tillers and edger-trimmers. Engine model number and serial number are located on cylinder fin. On 1960 and earlier models, identification will be found on engine shroud or gas tank strap.

Fig. LB1—Exploded view of typical Lawn Boy carburetor used on series C engines. Refer to Fig. LB3 for carburetor used on D series engines.

87. Bowl retaining screws	98. Choke disc
88. Float bowl	99. Choke shaft
89. Gasket	100. Throttle disc
90. Float pin	101. Throttle shaft
91. Float	102. Throttle spring
92. Inlet valve assy.	104. Fuel adjustment needle
93. Gasket	105. Knob
94. Nozzle	106. Spring
95. Choke detent	107. Washer
96. Spring	108. Carburetor body

MAINTENANCE

SPARK PLUG. Electrode gap should be set at 0.025 for all models except D-600 series (solid state ignition) which calls for a gap of 0.035. Champion J-14-J plugs are used in 4.43 CID engines and 5.22 CID engines. Champion CJ-14 is used in 6.65 CID engines. If plugs of another make are installed, make substitution carefully. For example, Autolite A11X is proper equivalent for Champion J-14-J and heat range is correct.

CARBURETOR. Lawn-Boy float-type carburetors are used on all engine models. Style of carburetor used on C-Series engines is shown in exploded view in Fig. LB1. Fig. LB2 shows early D-Series carburetor details. Later D-models do not have a low speed mixture needle (6—Fig. LB3), but are equipped instead with a fixed jet requiring no adjustment. D-600 Series engine carburetors are fully automatic with no external adjustments to regulate normal fuel intake. Altitude com-

pensation needle shown in Fig. LB5 is covered later in this section.

For initial adjustment of Lawn-Boy carburetors so equipped, open idle (low speed) needle about ¾-turn. After engine is started, adjust main fuel needle so that engine runs smoothly until properly warmed up (about five minutes). Then, turn main fuel needle in (clockwise) until engine begins to lose speed, then back out from 1/8 to ¼-turn. Set idle needle when engine is at normal operating temperature for smoothest idle performance. If idle mixture is too lean, engine is likely to surge at low speed.

Float setting on ALL Lawn-Boy Carburetors is 15/32-inch above carburetor body flange as shown in Fig. LB2. Adjust float lever only by bending float arm using needle nose pliers. Do not apply strain or pressure to cork float. If float shows signs of damage or if epoxy varnish is flaked off or chipped, renew float assembly.

Do not use commercial carburetor cleaners. Use a mild solvent to clean

and clear carburetor parts and passages. Do not dry carburetor parts with a cloth. Loose lint may be the

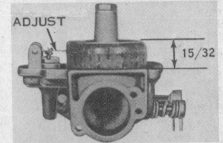

Fig. LB2—Correct float setting for all Lawn Boy carburetors can be checked as shown. D-600 carburetor is illustrated.

ADJUST

15/32

cause of a later problem. Be sure all internal fuel and air passages are clean and open. If compressed air is used, do not direct air flow on reed valves as they will be bent or distorted so as to be made unserviceable.

When reassembling carburetor, re-install main fuel nozzle (94—Fig. LB1 or 23—Fig. LB3) before installing fuel needle (104 or 10) to prevent jamming needle into nozzle seat. Be sure to set a light pre-load on throttle spring (20—Fig. LB3) by adding about ½-turn tension when attaching spring to throttle shaft lever.

See Fig. LB5 for cutaway view of automatic carburetor used on D-600 series engines. Principal difference between this and preceding models is elimination of external adjustments for main and idle circuits. Early 1972 production was fitted with a plastic throttle shaft and disc. If renewal becomes necessary, use assembly No. 681008 which contains bronze parts.

Primer used on this carburetor is a pneumatic bulb type and differs from prior lift-type primer in that air displaced by pressure on primer bulb forces fuel from float chamber through main jet into carburetor venturi. System is highly effective, and it is easy to over-prime. One priming stroke is normally sufficient.

Altitude adjustment shown on carburetor (Fig. LB5) is designed to compensate for differences in atmospheric pressure if engine is to be operated at elevations which are high or low in relation to sea level. For most areas, normal setting is ¾-turn open. At low altitudes, open valve slightly to increase fuel proportion in mixture. At high altitudes, turn valve inward (clockwise) to reduce amount of raw fuel to be mixed with lighter (lower density) intake air.

MODULAR CARBURETOR. In recent production, a modular-type carburetor is offered on engine models D-409, D-481, D-601, D-641 and D-641E. This new style carburetor is shown in exploded view in Fig. LB5B. Parts listed are available at service outlets, however, if carburetor main body (22) is physically damaged, there is no repair. Entire unit, less filter element and cover, is available for renewal. Order as part number 681445.

Note absence of external adjustment points. This carburetor is fully automatic with no preliminary settings required except for altitude compensation air screw (4) which is opened ¾-turn for most elevations, usually 500 to 1500 feet above mean sea level.

GOVERNOR. All models are equipped with a mechanical governor. The governor weight unit is located under the flywheel. Refer to appropriate following paragraphs for information on each unit.

SERIES C ENGINE GOVERNOR. The series C engine governor is shown in Fig. LB6. Engine speed is controlled

by compression of the coil spring under governor weight unit as shown in Fig. LB7. Three different governor springs are available providing governed speeds of 2800 rpm, 3200 rpm and (on older model snow blower engines only) 4000 rpm. Data on governor springs are as follows:

RPM	Free Length	Color
2800	0.750-0.780	Red
3200	0.735-0.765	.....
4000	0.954-0.984	Blue

To check governor adjustment on "C" series engines, special tool No. 602885 must be used. Proceed as follows:

With governor assembly installed, set gauge over crankshaft end and hold

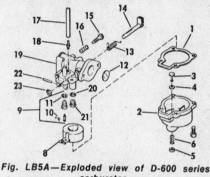

Fig. LB5A—Exploded view of D-600 series carburetor.

1. Gasket		13. Throttle spring
2. Float bowl		14. Throttle shaft
3. Dump valve stem		15. Altitude screw
4. Valve seat		16. Spring
5. Valve keeper		17. Fuel tube
6. Valve spring		18. Connector
8. Float		19. Body assembly
9. Float valve assembly		20. Washer
10. Clip		21. Plug
11. Washer		22. Float pin
12. Throttle disc		23. Throttle shaft retainer

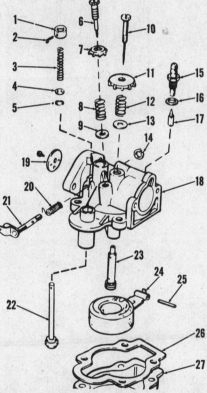

Fig. LB3—Exploded view of carburetor typical of type used on D series engines. Late D models are not equipped with idle fuel needle (6).

1. Knob
2. Cotter pin
3. Spring
4. Washer
5. "O" ring
6. Idle fuel needle
7. Knob
8. Spring
9. Washer
10. Main fuel needle
11. Knob
12. Spring
13. Washer
14. Snap ring
15. Float valve seat
16. Washer
17. Float valve
18. Carburetor body
19. Throttle disc
20. Throttle spring
21. Throttle shaft
22. Primer plunger
23. Nozzle
24. Float
25. Float pin
26. Gasket
27. Float bowl

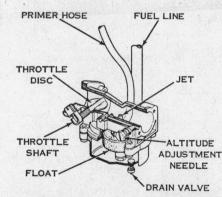

Fig. LB5—Cutaway view of Lawn-Boy carburetor used in D-600, D-640 models. Note absence of choke and high and low speed adjustments. When primer bulb is pressed, fuel charge enters venturi at jet to provide rich mixture for starting. Refer to text.

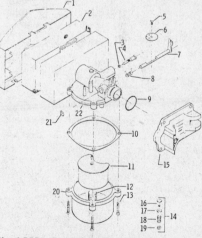

Fig. LB5B—Exploded view of modular carburetor used on some recent models. This carburetor cannot be repaired. See text.

1. Filter cover
2. Filter element
3. "O" ring
4. Air screw
5. Screw
6. Disc
7. Throttle shaft
8. Return spring
9. Retainer
10. Bowl gasket
11. Float
12. Spring
13. Screw
14. Dump valve assembly
15. Reed plate
16. Valve stem
17. Valve seat
18. Valve spring
19. Valve keeper
20. Float bowl
21. Retainer
22. Main body

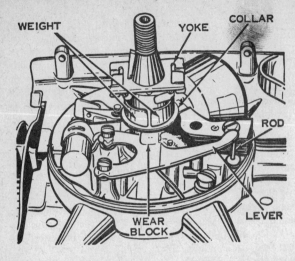

Fig. LB6–Drawing showing governor components of series C engines. Refer also to Fig. LB7.

RPM	Free Length	Color
Variable (2500-3200)	0.735-0.765	Green
3200	0.735-0.765	....
4000 (snow blower)	0.954-0.984	Blue

To check the series D governor, a special tool available through Lawn Boy central parts distributors is used as shown in Fig. LB10. Hold the carburetor throttle shaft in closed position and push governor weight unit as far down on crankshaft as possible using special tool. The gap between the governor lever and end of governor rod should then be 1/16-inch. If not, bend governor lever at crease in lever near point where it contacts governor rod.

D-600 GOVERNOR. Assembly, adjustment and servicing of D-600 series governor corresponds to preceding information for D-400 engines with this major exception:

Refer to Fig. LB11A and note the

down firmly. With throttle shaft held in closed position, check gap between governor rod and lever with lever lifted lightly to its upper limit. Gap should be ⅛-inch. See Fig. LB8.

SERIES D ENGINE GOVERNOR. The governor used on series D engines is similar to those used on series C engines. On all D series engines, (except D-430, D-460 and D-470) a variable spring is located between the

speed control lever and the governor lever (see Fig. LB12) providing a variable speed governor.

Three different governor springs (12 —Fig. LB30) are used. The unpainted spring is used on D-430 and D-460

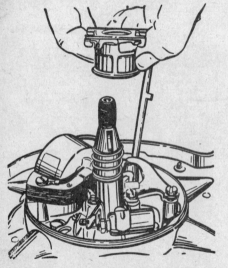

Fig. LB7–Install governor yoke, weights and collar as a unit.

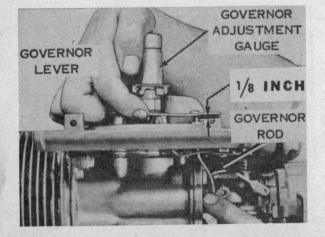

Fig. LB8–Technique for setting C-series governor using Lawn-Boy tool No. 602885. Note that throttle is held in closed position. Refer to text.

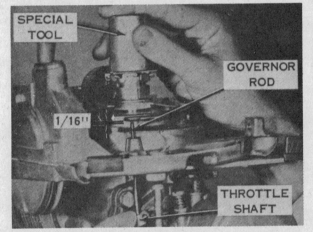

Fig. LB10–Checking governor linkage on series D engine. Refer to text for procedure.

models to provide a governed speed of 3200 RPM. The governor spring used on model D-470 (snow blower engine only) is painted blue and governs engine speed at 4000 RPM. All other models (with variable engine speed) use the governor spring painted green. Refer to the following for spring identification:

Fig. LB11—Installing governor lever on series D engine. Exploded view of governor is shown in Fig. LB30.

Fig. LB11A–D-400 and D-600 governor thrust collars shown for comparison. They cannot be interchanged. Refer to text.

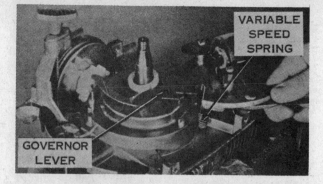

Fig. LB12–Hooking variable speed spring into governor lever on series D engine.

difference between D-600 and D-400 style thrust collars. New D-600 collar is designed to prevent engine from starting and running backward due to pre-ignition, combustion chamber hot spot or other malfunction. D-400 and D-600 thrust collars are NOT interchangeable.

To adjust governor of D-600 series engines after assembly, turn variable speed control to "light" position and rotate thrust collar clockwise against its stop on governor lever. Set gauge (special tool No. 604541) over end of crankshaft as in Fig. LB10, hold gauge firmly in place while holding throttle shaft closed, then check for 1/16-inch gap between tip of governor rod and bottom surface of governor lever as shown. Bend lever along its diagonal crease to adjust gap.

When reassembling governor, place web in groove of plastic thrust collar (See Fig. LB11) between arms on governor lever with lugs on arms inserted in groove of collar. Engage the tabs on governor lever in slots on breaker point dust cover. Hook governor spring into lever as shown in Fig. LB12. Apply light coat of Lubriplate or similar grease to both faces of steel thrust washer and place washer on top of plastic collar. Place governor spring

over crankshaft. Install the governor yoke, weights and collar assembly over end of crankshaft and governor spring as shown in Fig. LB7. Turn flat side of yoke next to keyway in crankshaft as shown in Fig. LB13; then, install key and flywheel. Lug on flywheel drives the governor weight unit of older production models. Later governor yokes have two "dimples" which engage bottom side of flywheel to drive governor. NOTE: Bore in flywheel and end of crankshaft should be clean and dry before installing flywheel.

MAGNETO AND TIMING. Refer to appropriate following paragraphs for magneto service information on each series of Lawn Boy engines.

SERIES C MAGNETOS. All series C engines use basically similar magnetos. Refer to Fig. LB14. On all models, timing is fixed and non-adjustable.

Armature air gap should be 0.010. Air gap can be considered correct if heels of armature core are flush with machined rim on armature plate. See Fig. LB15.

On model C-71 snow blower engine, adjust breaker point gap to 0.010; on all other series C engines, adjust breaker point gap to 0.020. When installing breaker points and/or condenser, wires from coil and stop switch should be installed under the breaker point spring.

If ignition grounding switch has been disassembled, be sure that unit is reassembled as shown in Fig. LB16. Check to see that high tension lead is pushed firmly onto metal needle in the ignition coil as shown in Fig. LB17 and tighten clamp holding high tension lead to armature plate. Also, be sure that ground lead from ignition coil is pressed down flat against armature core so that governor weights will not strike wire.

SERIES D MAGNETO. The magneto breaker cam on series D engines is driven by a flyweight as shown in Fig. LB19 to provide an automatic timing advance. The flyweight is retained in position by a pin through a hole in the crankshaft which engages the small end of the flyweight. A coil spring

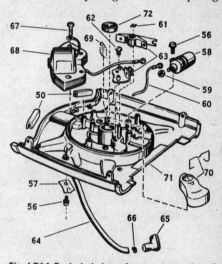

Fig. LB14–Exploded view of magneto used on C series engines. Design of armature plate (71) is different on some models of C engines.

58. Condenser	69. Cam oiler felt
60. Stop switch wire	70. Dust cover
63. Breaker points	71. Armature plate
68. Coil	

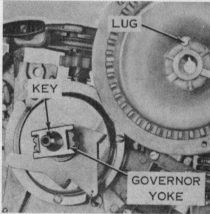

Fig. LB13—Flat side of governor yoke must be aligned with flywheel key as shown before installing flywheel on series D engines. Lug on flywheel drives governor weight unit. In later production, governor is driven as in Fig. LB13A.

Fig. LB13A–More recent production of D-400 governors and all D-600 governors are driven by two "dimples" (arrows) on governor yoke rather than a lug on flywheel. This new style can be used with earlier type flywheels.

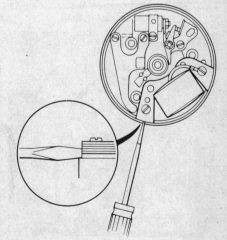

Fig. LB15–To set armature air gap on C-series engines, loosen mounting screws and set coil heels flush with rim of armature plate as shown.

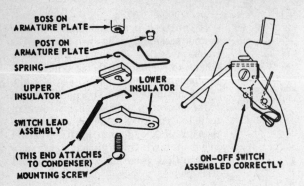

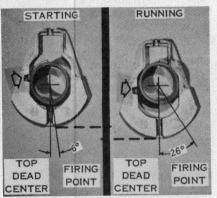

Fig. LB16—Correct assembly of on-off ignition switch on series C engines is important.

surrounds the pin and forces the small end of the flyweight away from the crankshaft when the engine is not running. When engine speed reaches approximately 1000 RPM, centrifugal force moves the flyweight against spring pressure which advances the breaker cam to running position. At starting position, ignition occurs at 6 degrees BTDC; at running position, the timing is advanced to 26 degrees BTDC. See Fig. LB19A.

The breaker points, condenser, cam and flyweight are enclosed by a dust cover under the flywheel and governor assembly. Refer to SERIES D ENGINE GOVERNOR paragraph for information on flywheel and governor removal and replacement.

To remove flyweight and breaker cam, refer to Fig. LB20 and proceed as follows: Push small end of flyweight towards crankshaft, hold pin and spring in this position, then disengage small end of flyweight from pin and remove pin and spring from crankshaft. The flyweight and cam can then be lifted from the crankshaft.

To adjust breaker points, install breaker cam on crankshaft and turn cam to position of widest breaker point gap. Adjust breaker point gap to 0.020 on all models with flywheel part number 678355. Breaker point gap should be 0.016 for early models with flywheel number 678103. Flywheel part number is on flywheel. The later flywheel is used for servicing early engines. When adjusting breaker point gap, pull the upper end of crankshaft toward carburetor.

NOTE: When servicing magneto, always reinstall wire leads on condenser terminal first. Then install breaker point spring and secure with nut. Wire from coil to condenser terminal should be under the breaker point base.

When reinstalling cam and flywheel assembly, hold breaker points open and slip the cam and flyweight as a unit, into place on crankshaft. Turn cam and flyweight so small end of flyweight is on keyway side of crankshaft. Install spring on pin, push small end of flyweight down and insert inner end of pin into hole in crankshaft. Push pin in against spring and engage outer end of pin into small end of flyweight.

Armature air gap should be 0.010. With the flywheel installed, place a piece of 0.010 non-metallic shim stock or air gap gauge No. 604659 as shown in Fig. LB21 between armature core and flywheel magnets. Loosen arma-

MAKE SURE KEY IS INSTALLED CORRECTLY

RIGHT   WRONG

Fig. LB20A—When installing Lawn-Boy flywheels, be sure flat side of woodruff key is placed as shown.

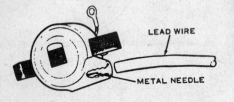

Fig. LB17—Push high tension lead firmly onto metal needle in ignition coil and be sure lead retaining clamp is tight.

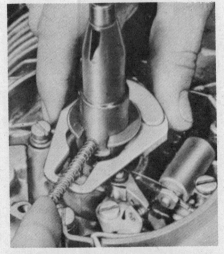

Fig. LB19A—Comparison view to show rotation movement (arrows) of breaker cam as flyweight moves from starting to running position.

Fig. LB21—Use of non-metallic gage, Lawn-Boy No. 604659 to set 0.010 air gap between flywheel magnets and coil heels of D-400 engines. Same tool and procedure is used to set air gap of capacitive discharge system used on D-600 series.

Fig. LB19—Timing on series D engines is automatically advanced when engine speed reaches 1000 RPM. Dotted line shows position of flyweight at speeds above 1000 RPM.

Fig. LB20—Removing flyweight pin and timing advance spring on series D engine. Refer to Fig. LB30.

ture core mounting screws and allow magnets to pull core against flywheel. Tighten armature core mounting screws and remove shim stock.

NOTE: Excessive clearance between the crankshaft and the top main bearing will affect the armature air gap and breaker point gap resulting in faulty ignition. The top main bearing on 1965 and later models is a renewable needle bearing. The bushing, integral with the armature plate on earlier production models, is serviced by installing the late type armature plate and needle bearing.

Coat end of high tension wire with silicon lubricant for waterproofing and push wire firmly onto metal pin in ignition coil as shown in Fig. LB17. Secure high tension wire to armature plate with clamp and screw.

D-600 IGNITION SYSTEM. Lawn-Boy's "Solid state" (capacitive discharge) ignition design eliminates all moving parts which are normally associated with magneto ignition. On D-600 models, there is no spark advance assembly, breaker cam, breaker point set, condenser or coil. Complete system is electronic, contained in a single, sealed module which is dust and moisture proofed and serviced only as an assembly.

Maintenance is confined to setting air gap between flywheel magnets and CD module, checking for spark output by use of a test spark plug grounded to cylinder and isolation test of ignition switch for continuity. No procedures for trouble shooting or testing ignition pack are offered by manufacturer. If unit will not produce a spark at electrodes of test spark plug and ignition switch and spark plug cable check out as serviceable, renewal of module assembly is necessary. Substitution of a spare ignition pack known to be good is an ideal test procedure.

Ignition timing is fixed. System design is set up for 9° retarded spark timing for ease of starting. After engine starts, spark is advanced electronically to 29° BTDC as crankshaft speed reaches 800 RPM.

To service ignition module, remove three screws holding air baffle to armature plate and separate kill switch lead from ignition switch. Primer and starter need not be removed. With CD ignition pack exposed, 0.010 air gap may be checked. To do so, rotate flywheel to align its magnets on laminated core heels of ignition module and use non-metallic gage No. 604659 as shown in Fig. LB21. With gage in position, when module mounting screws are loosened, magnets will pull module snug against gage. Retighten screws and remove gage.

Operators of this engine should be cautioned to allow 10-15 seconds after shut-down before removing spark plug lead so that high voltage (approximately 30,000 volts) from CD pack secondary can leak off.

LUBRICATION. Engine is lubricated by pre-mixing oil in fuel in separate container before filling engine tank. Use of Lawn-Boy lubricant is preferred, in mixing ratio of 32:1 or ½ pint Lawn-Boy lubricant to 2 gallons of regular grade leaded gasoline.

If other oils are substituted, mix ½ pint of SAE 40, SA or SB (formerly ML or MM) with one gallon of regular leaded gasoline for a mixing ratio of 16:1. API service SB (MM) two-stroke non detergent oil may also be used. DO NOT USE multiple viscosity oils: 10W40, etc.

Do not use any gasoline or oil additive but OMC 2+4 Fuel Conditioner. If strong anti-gum solvents are added to fuel, it is likely that epoxy varnish coating of carburetor float will be damaged resulting in flooding or over-rich fuel mixtures. Currently, manufacturer recommends use of leaded regular grade gasoline only.

CARBON. If ignition, fuel supply to combustion chamber, and compression check out as satisfactory, but engine will not run or runs badly, it is likely that there is a heavy carbon build-up in exhaust ports and muffler. A common symptom is "four-cycling" or firing every other power stroke.

Carbon clean out is recommended by manufacturer for every 35 hours operation. Proceed as follows:

On all models except D-600, remove two retaining nuts and muffler cover. D-600 muffler cover is secured by four nuts and mower blade and stiffener must first be removed from lower end of crankshaft on this model. Rotate crankshaft so that piston wall blocks exhaust ports and use a ⅜-inch wooden dowel to break carbon away from port openings. Clean carbon from muffler chamber and cover plate before reassembling.

REPAIRS

TIGHTENING TORQUES: Recommended tightening torques for principal assemblies are shown. Values are given in inch-pounds.

Engine Tightening Torques

Carburetor to reed plate	63-75
Reed to reed plate	10-13
Reed plate to crankcase	63-75
Breaker point base	20-25
Coil to armature	20-25
Condenser to armature	20-25
High tension cable clamp screw	20-25
Armature to crankcase	63-75
Shroud to armature (front)	25-30
Shroud to armature (side)	10-15
Connecting rod	58-70
Cylinder to crankcase	105-115
Engine mounting screws	142-170
Tank to shroud	63-75
Flywheel, "C" series	190-225
Flywheel, "D" series	335-400
Spark plug	150-180
Starter mounting	58-63
Starter pulley	16-19

Mower Tightening Torques

Blade nut	450-550
Wheel bolts	200-240
Engine to muffler plate	142-170
Muffler to muffler plate	58-63

CONNECTING ROD. Rod and piston assembly can be removed after removing reed valve plate and cylinder from crankcase. Early C series engines were equipped with an aluminum connecting rod with cast-in crankpin bearing surfaces in rod and cap. Late C series engines and all D series engines have a needle roller crankpin bearing; the aluminum connecting rod is fitted with renewable steel inserts. Bearing dimensions and clearances are as follows:

"C" Series Engines:
Crankpin dia.
(plain bearing) 0.7495-0.7500
   Desired clearance . 0.0025-0.0035
Crankpin dia.
(needle bearing) 0.7425-0.7430

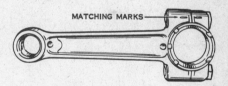

Fig. LB22–When reassembling cap to connecting rod, be sure that match marks are aligned as shown.

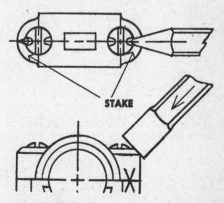

Fig. LB23–Connecting rod screws on some engines have recesses into which cap metal can be staked to lock screw after it has been tightened to proper torque value.

All "D" Series Engines:

Crankpin dia.

(needle bearing) 0.7425-0.7430

When reassembling plain bearing connecting rod to crankpin, oil the bearing surfaces and be sure that match marks on rod and cap are aligned as shown in Fig. LB22. After tightening cap retaining screws, be sure rod is free on crankpin. If screws have recesses in head in addition to screwdriver slot, stake cap metal into recesses with dull screwdriver as shown in Fig. LB23.

If installing new needle roller set, lay the strip of 33 rollers on forefinger and carefully peel backing off of rollers. Curl forefinger around crankpin to transfer rollers from finger to crankshaft. Grease on the rollers will hold them together and to the crankpin.

If reinstalling used needle rollers, be sure that none of the 33 rollers are damaged. Coat surfaces with a layer of light grease such as Lubriplate and stick the rollers to the connecting rod and cap. Fit 17 rollers to rod cap and 16 to rod.

Press the needle bearing liners into rod and cap so that the dovetail ends of liners (8L—Fig. LB25 or LB30) will fit together when match marks on rod and cap are aligned. Carefully fit rod and cap to crankpin bearing and install cap retaining screws and screw lock plates. After tightening the screws, check to be sure that rod assembly is free on the crankpin and that none of the rollers dropped out on assembly. Then, bend the lock plates up against the flats of the screw heads.

PISTON, PIN AND RINGS. Piston, pin and rings are available in standard size only. Recommended piston to cylinder clearance for different cylinder bore diameters is as follows:

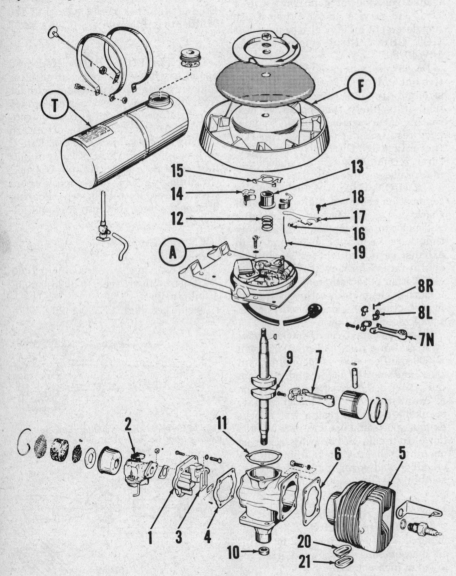

Fig. LB25–Exploded view of C-20, C-21 and C-22 engine. Armature plate (A) is different on other C series engines. Refer to Fig. LB26 or LB27. Other series C engines are similar. Some models use needle bearings in connecting rod as shown at 7N, 8L and 8R.

A. Armature plate	7. Connecting rod (plain bearing)	13. Governor collar
F. Flywheel	7N. Connecting rod (needle bearings)	14. Governor weight
T. Fuel tank	8L. Bearing liners	15. Governor yoke
1. Reed plate	8R. Bearing rollers (33 used)	16. Wear block
2. Carburetor	9. Crankshaft	17. Governor lever
3. Valve reeds	10. Lower seal	18. Screws
4. Gasket	11. Shim	19. Carburetor link rod
5. Cylinder	12. Governor spring	20. Sleeve
6. Gasket		21. Gasket

Fig. LB26–Exploded view of armature plate, flywheel and shroud used on some C model engines. Starter is attached to top of shroud.

A. Armature plate	23. Starter pin
F. Flywheel	24. Flywheel pulley
T. Fuel tank	25. Cooling shroud
22. Spring	26. Tank bracket

Fig. LB27–Exploded view of armature plate, fuel tank and shroud used on some C model engines. Starter is shown at (S). Refer to Fig. LB26 for legend.

Nominal Cyl. Bore	Recommended Piston to Cylinder Clearance
1 15/16	0.004-0.0055
2⅛	0.0045-0.006
2⅜	0.005-0.0065

Piston pin is retained by snap rings at each end of pin bore in piston. Heat piston to facilitate removal and installation of pin in push fit bore. Piston pin diameter and desired clearances are as follows:

Cyl. Bore (Nominal)	Pin Dia.	Desired Clearance Rod Bore	Piston Bore
1 15/16	0.4270-0.4272	0.0003-0.0010	0-0.0005
2⅛ & 2⅜ ..	0.4898-0.4900	0.0003-0.0010	0-0.0007

Piston ring end gap should be 0.015-0.025 for all engine models. Renew piston rings if end gap exceeds 0.025.

Prior to 1970, all engines were equipped with 3-ring pistons and a plain bronze bearing in wrist pin end of connecting rod. Since 1970, two rings are fitted to all pistons and connecting rod small end contains 27 loose needle roller bearings. Great care must be taken to prevent loss of needles during removal as they are not serviced separately.

CYLINDER. Piston and rings are available in standard size only. Renew cylinder if bore is excessively worn or scored. Standard and (new) cylinder bore diameters are as follows:

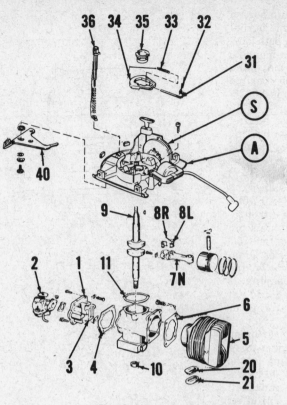

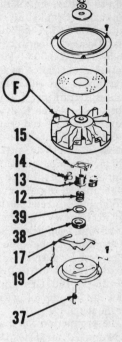

Fig. LB30—Exploded view of typical series D engine.

1. Reed plate		11. Shim		33. Ignition advance spring	
2. Carburetor		12. Governor spring		34. Ignition advance flyweight	
3. Reed valve		13. Governor collar		35. Ignition breaker cam	
4. Gasket		14. Governor weights		36. Primer plunger and shut-off bar	
5. Cylinder		15. Governor yoke		37. Variable speed spring	
6. Gasket		17. Governor lever		38. Thrust collar	
7N. Connecting rod		19. Carburetor link rod		39. Thrust washer	
8L. Bearing liners		20. Sleeve		40. Governor control lever	
8R. Bearing rollers (33 used)		21. Gasket			
9. Crankshaft		31. Flyweight pin			
10. Seal		32. Retainer			

Nominal Bore Size	Cylinder Bore Diameter
1 15/16	1.940-1.941
2⅛	2.125-2.126
2⅜	2.377-2.378

In 1967 production only, model C-78 and entire "D" series had 2.380-2.381 cylinder bore.

When reinstalling cylinder, be sure that the new cylinder to crankcase gasket is properly aligned so that it will not close the transfer ports. Loose cylinder retaining screws can cause considerable power loss. Lawn Boy recommends use of regular split type lock washers under screw heads even if screw is fitted with a serrated type washer.

Because of similarity of appearance, it is possible that cylinders for D-400 and D-600 engines might be confused. D-600 (high compression) cylinders have an "H"-shaped web cast between horizontal and vertical cooling fins. If this cylinder were installed on a D-400 engine, overheating and seizure would result.

CRANKSHAFT AND SEALS. All series C engines have plain non-renewable main bearings; magneto end bearing is plain bore in armature plate

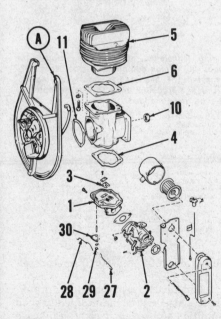

Fig. LB28—Partially exploded view of C-72 engine used on Hobby Gardner rotary tiller.

A. Armature plate	10. Seal
1. Reed plate	11. Shim
2. Carburetor	27. Bellcrank to carburetor rod
3. Reed valves	28. Governor to bellcrank rod
4. Gasket	29. Snap ring
5. Cylinder	30. Bellcrank
6. Gasket	

Fig. LB30A—New style piston and connecting rod assembly with needle bearing set in small end of connecting rod. Assembly shown is interchangeable for all "C" and "D" engines, but components (wrist pin, bearings, etc.) DO NOT interchange. Service as a complete assembly.

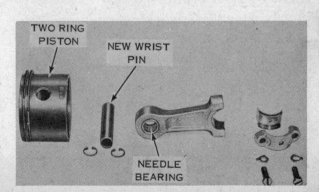

and pto end bearing is in plain bore of crankcase. Crankshaft main journal diameter is 0.8737-0.8742 for both journals. Desired clearance for magneto end bearing is 0.002-0.0033; maximum allowable clearance is 0.005. Desired clearance for pto end bearing is 0.0038-0.0068. Crankpin diameter for 4.43 cubic inch series C engines having plain connecting rod crankpin bearing is 0.7495-0.7500; desired connecting rod to crankpin clearance is 0.0025-0.0035. On 5.22 cubic inch series C engines with plain bearing connecting rod, crankpin diameter is also 0.7495-0.7500, but desired clearance is 0.0025-0.0036. Renew crankshaft if crankpin out-of-round condition exceeds 0.0015.

Crankpin diameter for series D engines and for series C engines having needle roller crankpin bearing is 0.7425-0.7430. Crankpin should not show any signs of wear, scoring or overheating.

The production top main bearing on 1964 and earlier series D engines was a non-renewable bronze bushing in the armature plate (A—Fig. LB30). Excessive clearance between the crankshaft and the top main bearing will affect both armature air gap and breaker point gap and result in faulty ignition. If the early bushing type top main bearing is worn, the later armature plate and needle bearing should be installed. Refer to Fig. LB31 for current change in armature plate bearings. Bearing removal tool No. 605082 is recommended for driving out old bearings. Hold armature plate in palm of hand for support, not on hard surface during removal to prevent breakage. Use tool No. 605081 to install new bearing assembly. Crankshaft main journal diameter is 0.8737-0.8742 for both journals on all models. Desired clearance for bushing type top main bearing is 0.002-0.0033. Maximum allowable clearance is 0.005. Desired clearance for pto end main bearing is 0.0038-0.0068 for all models.

On series C and series D engines, recommended crankshaft end play is 0.012; gasket (11—Fig. LB25, LB28 or LB30) used between crankcase and armature plate is available in thick-

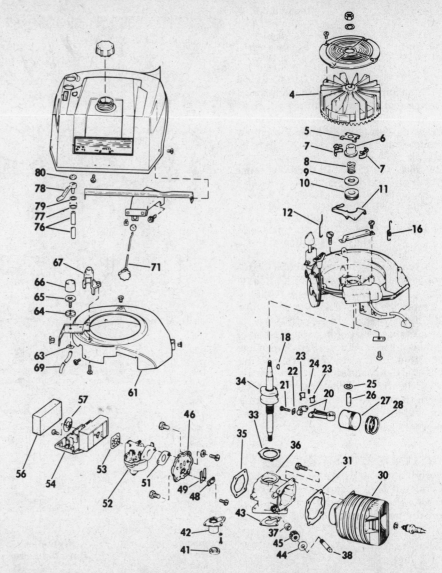

Fig. LB32–Exploded view of typical D-600, D-640 engine. If installed, electric starter mounts on crankcase directly opposite recoil-type starter. Cylinder (30) is high compression type. Note "H"-shaped web cast between fins at top of cylinder. Crankshaft (34) has integral worm gear to mesh with gear (45) to turn drive shaft (38) for new shaft driven self-propelled units. Primer (66) and fuel shut-off (78) are also different on these models.

4. Flywheel	23. Bearing liners	37. Driveshaft seal
5. Governor yoke	24. Needle bearings (33)	38. Driveshaft
6. Governor collar	25. Piston pin retainer	41. Crankshaft seal
7. Governor weights	(2)	42. Cover
8. Governor spring	26. Piston (wrist) pin	43. Gasket
9. Washer	27. Piston	44. Thrust washer
10. Thrust collar	28. Piston rings (2)	45. Pinion gear
11. Governor lever	30. Cylinder	46. Reed plate
12. Governor rod	31. Cylinder gasket	48. Retainer
16. Variable speed spring	33. Armature plate	49. Reed assembly
18. Flywheel key	gasket	51. Carburetor gasket
20. Connecting rod	34. Crankshaft	52. Carburetor
assembly	35. Reed plate gasket	53. Gasket
21. Screw	36. Crankcase (incl. brgs.	54. Air filter case
22. Lockplate	& seal)	56. Filter element

57. Washer
61. Air baffle
63. Fastener
64. Cap
65. Primer base
66. Primer bulb
67. Mounting bracket
69. Fuel line
71. Control rod & knob
76. Fuel line
77. Spring clip
78. Fuel shut-off
79. Washer
80. Gasket

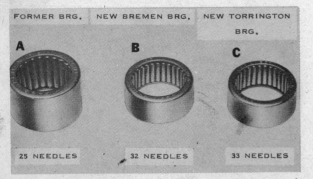

Fig. LB31–Needle roller bearing A (25 needles) was installed in armature plates through 1969 production. Bearings B and C have been used since 1970. Note that new Bremen bearing has 32 needles and that Torrington bearing has 33. Be sure to place installing tool against lettered side of cage.

nesses of 0.005 and 0.010 for controlling end play.

As in all two cycle engines, crankshaft seals must be maintained in good condition to prevent loss of crankcase compression and resulting loss of power. Install new seals with lips (grooved side of seal) to inside of crankcase. When installing crankshaft, use an installing sleeve or wrap tape over keyways and sharp shoulders on crankshaft.

REED VALVE. Reed valves which do not seat properly can cause hard starting and loss of power. Reed valve unit can be removed and inspected after removing carburetor. Reeds do not have to be absolutely flat but must close and seal completely under pressure. Do not use compressed air on reeds. Smooth side of reed valve must

Fig. LB33–View of reed plate assembly. Clearance of 0.015 measured as shown is allowable. Renew reed valve if clearance is excessive or if bent or distorted so as to prevent sealing under pressure.

be installed toward reed plate. See Fig. LB33.

NOTE: Do not use washer under head of capscrew directly behind throttle shaft arm. Clearance must be

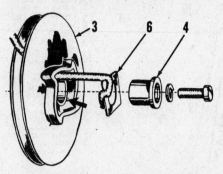

Fig. LB35–When renewing rope in early rewind starter, it is recommended that rope retainer plate (clamp) be installed. To install clamp, first remove 3/64-inch material from boss indicated by arrow; then assemble unit as shown.

Fig. LB36–Old and new rewind spring installations for starter (C-10) shown in Fig. LB34. Note change of spring attachment for C-12 spring shown in Fig. LB37.

maintained between arm and screw.

STARTERS

RECOIL STARTERS (Series C Engines). On early recoil starters, the rope should be attached with retainer as shown at (6—Fig. LB35). Rope installation on late type starters is shown in Fig. LB38. Refer to Fig. LB36 when installing late type recoil spring in early type starter.

On QUIETFLITE mowers, the starter is similar to that shown in Fig. LB37; however, the top cover (1) is not used. The rewind spring is anchored on starter bracket as shown in Fig. LB39.

Be sure that rewind spring is not over-tightened. Never wind pulley over two turns after spring tension begins to be felt. Very important: Drive pin or pins on flywheel pulley must be outside

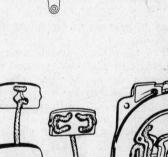

C-10   C-12

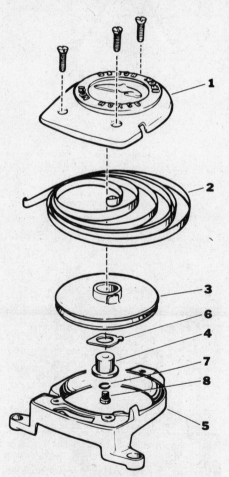

Fig. LB34–Exploded view of early type rewind starter used on some models. Very early models used bead on rope as retainer instead of plate (6). Refer to Fig. LB35 for method of adapting rope retaining plate to early production units.

1. Cover	5. Housing
2. Rewind spring	6. Rope retainer
3. Rope pulley	7. Lockwasher
4. Pulley bearing	8. Screw, pulley to cover

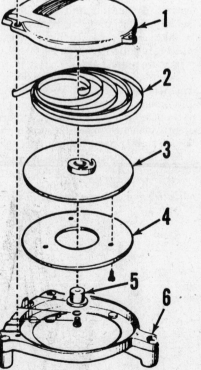

Fig. LB37–Exploded view of later type rewind starter. Refer to Fig. LB38 for rope installation.

1. Cover	4. Plate
2. Rewind spring	5. Bushing
3. Rope pulley	6. Housing

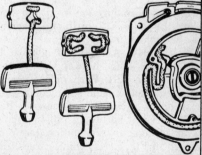

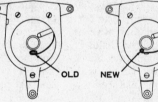

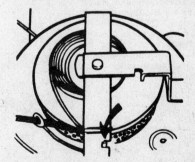

Fig. LB38–View showing method of retaining rope ends in rewind starter shown in Fig. LB37. Singe (heat) about ¾-inch of each end of nylon rope to be sure it will hold securely.

Fig. LB39–On QUIETFLITE models, be sure outer end of rewind spring is anchored at position indicated by arrow.

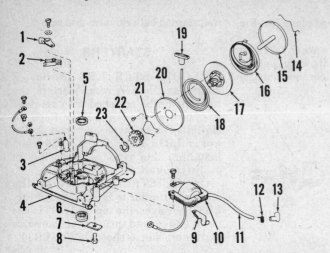

1. Breaker point base
2. Breaker point arm
3. Condenser
4. Armature plate
5. Crankshaft oil seal
6. Needle bearing
7. Starter pin clamp
8. Clamp screw
9. High tension wire clip
10. Coil & lamination assembly
11. High tension wire
12. Spring terminal
13. Spark plug cover
14. Rope retainer spring
15. Starter spring cup
16. Starter spring
17. Starter pulley
18. Starter rope
19. Starter handle
20. Starter pulley plate
21. Starter pinion spring
22. Starter pinion
23. Push-on retainer

Fig. LB41–Exploded view of series D engine starter and magneto assembly. Starter pinion (22) engages teeth in lower side of flywheel; refer to view of flywheel in Fig. LB13. Needle bearing (6) is used in late engines; early production engines have plain bearing bore in armature plate (4) for upper crankshaft journal.

starter pulley ratchet before screws holding starter to shroud are tightened.

RECOIL STARTERS (Series D Engines). To remove recoil starter, remove cooling shroud and starter handle, then allow rope to recoil slowly through hole in top of armature plate. Remove screw (8—Fig. LB41) and clamp (7), then lift out starter assembly. NOTE: Hold assembly together to prevent recoil spring from unwinding.

When assembling, attach inner end of spring (16) to pulley (17) and position on spring cup (15) with outer end of spring through slot in spring cup. Turn the pulley (17) until end of spring is against slot in cup as shown in view S Fig. LB44. Attach end of rope to pulley (17—Fig. LB41) and install pulley plate (20). With pinion spring (21) removed, ends of spring should be less than ¼-inch apart as shown in Fig. LB43. Install spring in pinion groove with prongs toward pinion teeth as shown in Fig. LB44, being careful not to spread ends of spring too far. Position pinion (22—Fig. LB41) on pulley (17) with spring (21) toward pulley,

then install snap ring (23). Wind rope around pulley and install the assembly as shown in Fig. LB44. Wind rope around pulley until end of recoil spring is against cup; plus 1 to 1½ additional turns to pre-load spring, then guide rope through hole in armature plate and install handle.

STARTER (D-600). Service to manual pull-up starter used on D-600 models is basically similar to procedures outlined for other D-models with some noteworthy exceptions:

In order to remove starter from engine for renewal of starter cord or recoil spring, carburetor and reed plate assembly must first be removed from crankcase in order to have access to starter retainer screw in bottom side of armature plate.

See Fig. LB42 for minor change in recoil spring design and method of placement on rear of worm gear plate. Also note that rope retainer is permanently attached to starter cup. Identify D-600 starter parts by reference to Fig. LB42. No lubrication should ever be used on starter worm gear or nylon pinion. If recoil spring is renewed, it should have a thin coat of lightweight

grease before being wound into starter cup. When manual starter of D-600 series is reinstalled, two full turns of starter pulley are required to pre-load recoil spring.

12-VOLT ELECTRIC STARTER.

Some series D engines with letter "E" following model No., are equipped with a battery operated electric starter. The electric starter pinion (27—Fig. LB48) is located across from the recoil starter pinion (22). The electric starter pinion assembly can be removed after removing drive belt, flywheel and set screw (24—Fig. LB49). When installing, clearance between snap ring and pulley should be 0.010 inch. Clearance is adjusted by moving pulley shaft before tightening set screw (24). The starter drive belt should have ⅛-inch deflection with 1½ lbs. pressure between pulleys. Adjustment is accomplished by moving the starter and

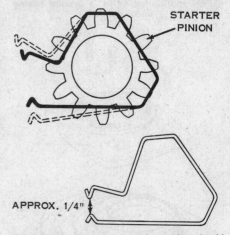

Fig. LB43–Ends of starter pinion spring should be less than ¼-inch apart when spring is removed.

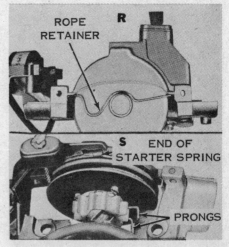

Fig. LB44–View R shows placement of D-400 series starter rope retainer locked in position with starter installed in armature plate. View S shows correct installation of starter pinion spring with one prong above and one below armature plate. Note location of end of recoil spring.

Fig. LB42–Exploded view of armature plate and starter used on D-600 and D-640 models. When installed, electric starter is fitted to crankcase, engaging flywheel directly opposite manual starter.

2. CD ignition pack
4. Spark plug boot
5. Armature plate
6. Crankshaft seal
7. Upper main bearing
8. Starter clamp
9. Clamp screw
10. Rope clip
11. Retainer
13. Plate
14. Rope
15. Pulley
16. Recoil spring
17. Cup & pin
18. Pinion spring
19. Pinion
20. Rope handle
21. Shorting switch
23. Knob

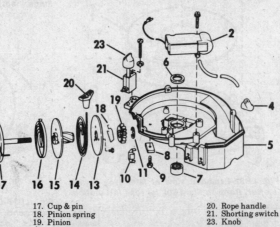

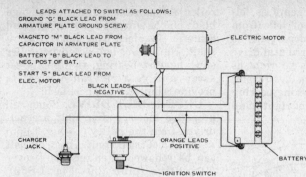

LEADS ATTACHED TO SWITCH AS FOLLOWS:
GROUND "G" BLACK LEAD FROM
ARMATURE PLATE GROUND SCREW

MAGNETO "M" BLACK LEAD FROM
CAPACITOR IN ARMATURE PLATE

BATTERY "B" BLACK LEAD TO
NEG. POST OF BAT.

START "S" BLACK LEAD FROM
ELEC. MOTOR

ELECTRIC MOTOR

BLACK LEADS
NEGATIVE

CHARGER
JACK

ORANGE LEADS
POSITIVE

BATTERY

IGNITION SWITCH

Fig. LB45–Starter circuit with 12-V battery. Some models do not have charger jack circuit. Refer to text.

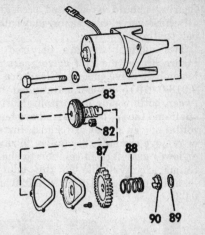

Fig. LB47–View of electric starting motor and drive used on D-600E and D-640E. See text for service.

82. Motor pinion	88. Spring
83. Driven gear	89. Retainer
87. Starter pinion	90. Pinion stop washer

bracket after loosening the three screws.

To charge battery, connect trickle charger leads (red to positive post) to battery before connecting charger to 110-V outlet. Some later models have a charger connecting jack installed in battery case. Plug charger cable into jack of these models before connecting charger cord to power outlet. Refer to Fig. LB45 for starter-battery circuit layout.

ELECTRIC STARTER, D-600, D-640. See Fig. LB46 for wiring diagram of starter—battery—charger circuits with ignition switch. On these models, ignition key must be "ON" if manual starter is used and will then function as a kill switch.

Arrangement of starter and drive is shown in Fig. LB47. Pinion (82) and driven gear (83) enclosed in case require light lubrication—use OMC Type A lube. No lubrication should be applied to starter worm gear or nylon starter pinion gear (87). Note that

Fig. LB48–Exploded view of armature plate and starter pinions used on models with 12-volt electric starter. Refer to Figs. LB41 or LB42 for legend except the following.

24. Set screw
25. Starter shaft
26. Snap ring
27. Starter pinion
28. Pinion spring
29. Pulley
30. Pulley plate
31. Pulley bearing
32. Snap ring

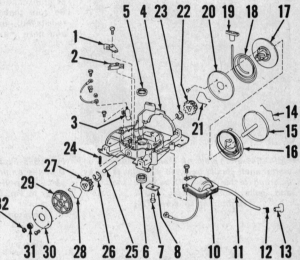

starter motor housing has three mounting legs which attach by long cap screws to engine crankcase. Two of these three bolt holes are oversized so that casting can be pivoted to adjust depth of pinion mesh in flywheel. Allow a small amount of backlash when mounting starter assembly so that pinion can engage teeth of flywheel without clashing or binding.

SELF PROPELLED MOWERS
LOWER BELT DRIVE MODELS.
Some self propelled mowers are driven by a pulley on bottom of crankshaft. Misalignment of drive pulleys, incorrectly installed sub-base (10—Fig. LB52) or failure of needle bearing (12) may cause enough heat to melt the pulley (3). On later models, the sub-base is equipped with a grease fitting as shown in Fig. LB53. When installing needle bearing, make certain that hole in bearing outer race is aligned with grease hole in base.

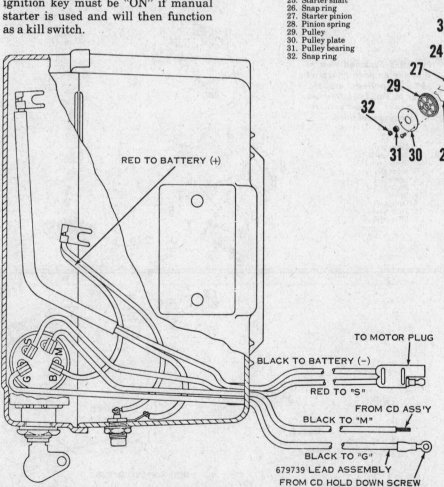

RED TO BATTERY (+)

TO MOTOR PLUG

BLACK TO BATTERY (−)

RED TO "S"

FROM CD ASS'Y

BLACK TO "M"

BLACK TO "G"

679739 LEAD ASSEMBLY
FROM CD HOLD DOWN SCREW

Fig. LB46–Wiring diagram for electric start models, D-600E and D-640E. Note charging jack adjacent to ignition key switch. Refer to text.

Bearing should be greased occasionally; however, over-greasing may cause belt to slip.

Two adjustments are required to insure proper mesh of drive gears on lower belt drive models: Clearance of 0.018-0.019 must be maintained between bottom side of horizontal drive shaft and face of bevel gear above horizontal driven pulley. To adjust, install or remove shims under pulley to raise or lower gear face in relation to shaft. Shims are available for this adjustment in thicknesses of 0.010, 0.020 and 0.025.

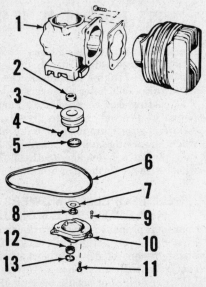

Fig. LB49–End play of starter assembly on starter shaft should be 0.010. End play is set by inserting feeler gage (F) between snap ring and pulley then pushing shaft in before tightening set screw (24).

Adjust mesh of bevel gears as follows: Loosen set screw of left (from operator's position) hand drive roller so that roller is loose on horizontal drive shaft, then move shaft as far right as possible and hold. Insert a 0.010 feeler gage between nylon bushing-bearing assembly and inner side of right hand

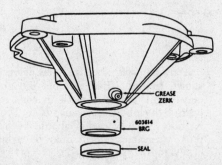

Fig. LB53–Sub-base shown above fits to bottom of crankcase on early self-propelled mowers. Be sure that sub base is not cocked when reinstalled; machined surfaces of crankcase and base must fit evenly or severe damage may result.

roller. Adjust roller snug against gage blade and be sure set screw is tight and centered in place over flat sector of shaft. Now bring left side drive roller snug against bearing, tighten its set screw and gear clearance is set to provide required 0.010 backlash.

UPPER BELT DRIVE. Some self propelled mowers after 1967 are belt driven from the pulley (1—Fig. LB55) at top end of crankshaft. The drive belt can be renewed after removing cover (10), drive roller (20—Fig. LB56), washer (16) and sleeve (15) from left side. Withdraw belt from opening in handle bracket where sleeve (15) was installed.

Due to changes in design of idler bracket (2—Fig. LB55) there are two belt alignment procedures. Refer to Fig. LB55A to determine if unit being serviced has old or new style bracket.

To correctly align the drive belt with old style bracket installed, position a straight edge against edge of driven pulley as shown at (Y—Fig. LB57). Locate driven pulley (12) on drive shaft

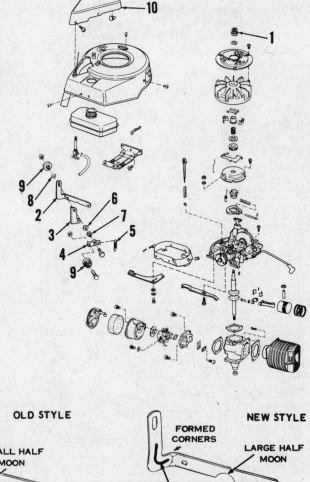

Fig. LB55–Exploded view of D series engines typical of self propelled models. Refer to Fig. LB56 for view of mower base and remainder of drive.

1. Drive pulley
2. Idler bracket
3. Spring retainer bracket
4. Lever
5. Spring
6. Shim
7. Grommet
8. Lock washer
9. Idler pulleys
10. Belt cover

Fig. LB52–Exploded view of self propelled drive used on early models.

1. Crankcase
2. Seal
3. Drive pulley
4. Set screw
5. Retainer
6. Belt
7. Washer
8. Felt seal
9. Sub-base to muffler plate screws
10. Sub-base
11. Sub-base to crankcase screws
12. Needle bearing
13. Seal

Fig. LB55A–Comparison views of old and new style idler brackets used on self-propelled models with upper belt drive. Refer to text for details.

OLD STYLE

SMALL HALF MOON

NO REINFORCEMENT RIB

NEW STYLE

FORMED CORNERS

LARGE HALF MOON

REINFORCEMENT RIB

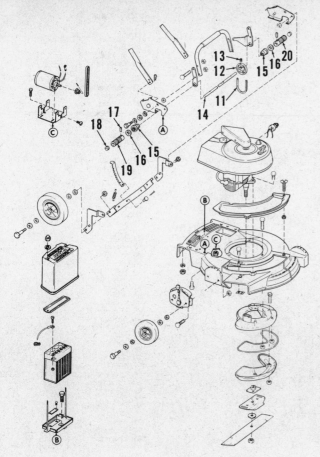

11. Self propelled drive belt
12. Driven pulley
13. Set screw
14. Drive shaft
15. Sleeve and bearing
16. Washer
17. Roll pin
18. Grease plug
19. Drive roller (right side)
20. Drive roller (left side)

Adjustments for correct operation of this drive are limited to control of side play of roller drive shaft and end play of drive tube between tee drive housing and engine.

To adjust drive shaft side play, measure between drive roller (54) and washer (56) for 0.062 (1/16-inch) play at each side. If play exceeds 0.062, add an additional washer (56), part No. 603037, between roller (54) and bearing (57) on right hand side. End play of drive tube (38) should measure between 0.035 and 0.135. If end play of tube measures from 0.136 to 0.235, add one "O" ring, part No. 303067, between nylon bushing (37) and square-end driven shaft (50). If measurement exceeds 0.236, add an "O" ring at each end of drive tube. If nylon bushings (37) are worn to such extent that tube is loose in rotation, renew bushings.

If bronze driven gear is to be separated from worm gear of engine crankshaft, it must be marked for reinstallation exactly as removed. If not, a new gear must be installed. If bevel gear set in roller shaft transmission is worn or damaged, renew both gears. Needle bearings (46, 47, 48 & 49) are individually renewable. These bearings must not be driven in or out. Use a press.

ROLLER ADJUSTMENT. On all self-propelled models, adjust clutch control to provide ¼-inch space between drive roller and driven wheel tread with control in "out-of-drive" position. Readjust whenever handle or wheel height is changed.

(14) so that straight edge is aligned with inside of pulley (9S) as shown at (X). Distance between straight edge and belt at point where belt just enters movable pulley (9M) should be 15/32-inch as shown at (A). If clearance (A) is incorrect, move pulley (12) either way as necessary. Minimum clearance between belt and fuel tank (B) should be 3/32-inch when mower is in drive position. If belt is too close to tank, loosen mounting bracket and move tank.

If new style bracket is used, procedure steps are as before, except that dimension (A—Fig. LB57) becomes 1/8 to 5/32-inch.

It may not be possible to adjust drive belt correctly due to excessive end play in drive shaft (14—Fig. LB57). If this condition appears, particularly in 1968-69 models, remove wave washers fitted to shoulder bolt which holds bearing carrier bracket to handle bracket and substitute plain washers for use as spacers to eliminate end play. If this does not serve to correct looseness, install new type shoulder bolt, part No. 606672.

GEAR DRIVE MODELS. Using Fig. LB58 as a guide to parts arrangement, disassembly and assembly of this type self-propelled drive, introduced in 1972 models is generally apparent.

Fig. LB57–Self propelled drive belt should be aligned as described in text.

9M. Movable idler pulley
9S. Stationary idler pulley
11. Drive belt
12. Driven pulley
13. Set screw
14. Drive shaft
W. Straight edge
X. Inside edge of pulley
Z. Ruler

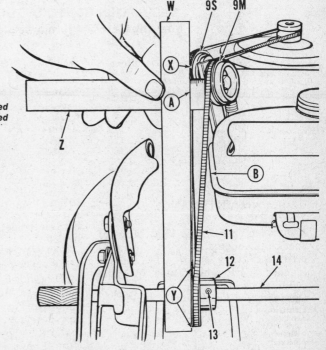

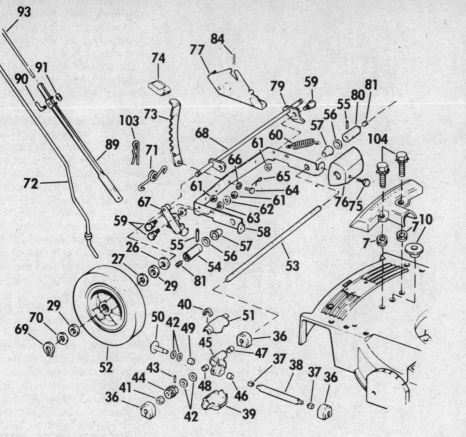

7. Grommet
26. Washer
27. Felt washer
29. Spacer
36. Seal
37. Bushing
38. Drive tube
39. Bottom gear cover
40. Clamp
41. Felt washer
42. Thrust washer
43. Roll pin
44. Driven gear
45. Bracket & bearing
46. Sealed bearing
47. Sealed bearing
48. & 49. Needle bearing
50. Drive gear
51. Gear top cover
52. Rear wheel
53. Drive shaft
54. Drive roller (RH)
55. Spirol pin
56. Washer
57. Sleeve & bearing
58. Bracket
59. Shoulder bolt
60. Spring
61. Nut
62. Washer
63. Washer
64. Pin
65. Cotter pin
66. Washer
67. Clutch
68. Axle
69. Retainer
70. Washer
71. Spring
72. Grass bag rod
73. Lever
74. Knob
75. Screw
76. Roller guard
77. Handle bracket
79. Bracket
80. Drive roller (LH)
81. Plug
84. Clip
89. Control lever
90. Screw
91. Nut
93. Control rod
103. Hairpin
104. Screw

Fig. LB58—Exploded view of self-propelled drive used on 1972 models D-600 and D-640. Tubular drive shaft (38) connects to drive shaft (38—Fig. LB32) at rear of crankcase of these models. Service is covered in text.

McCULLOCH

McCULLOCH CORPORATION
Los Angeles, California 90045

MODEL	Bore	Stroke	Displacement
MC-2	2.165	1.635	6.05
MC-5	2.125	1.375	4.9
MC-6	2.125	1.500	5.3
MC-7	2.165	1.635	6.05
MC-8, MC-9	2.165	1.635	6.05
MC-10	2.125	1.500	5.3
MC-20	2.125	1.635	5.8
MC-30	2.165	1.635	6.05
MC-40, MC-45	2.165	1.635	6.05
MC-70	2.217	1.835	7.08
MC-75	2.250	1.835	7.29

MAINTENANCE

SPARK PLUG. Use a 14 mm., ⅜-inch reach spark plug. Heat range of spark plug should be selected for specific operating conditions; recommended spark plug type for various conditions is as follows:

Operating Condition	Champion Plug No.	AC Plug Number
Average driving ...	J-6J	M-44C
Light racing ...	J-4J	M-42K
Lengthy racing ...	J-2J	M-41K

Set electrode gap to 0.025 on all models.

CARBURETOR. Models MC-5 and MC-6 use Tillotson Series HL carburetors as shown in Fig. MC1. All other models use McCulloch carburetors as shown in Fig. MC2 or Fig. MC3. All carburetors are diaphragm type with integral fuel pump.

Initial adjustment for models MC-40 and MC-70 is 2 turns open on both idle and main fuel mixture needles on both carburetors. On other models, initial adjustment is 1¼ turns open on idle fuel mixture needle and 1½ turns open on main fuel mixture needle. Make final adjustments with engine warm and running. Place kart on blocks so that rear wheels can turn freely. Adjust idle speed regulating screw so that engine idles at 1500-1700 RPM. Turn idle fuel needle slowly in clockwise direction until engine idles smoothly. If engine starts to accelerate while turning needle in clockwise direction, turn the needle back counter-clockwise until engine slows down. Take kart off blocks and test for acceleration. If engine mis-fires during acceleration, richen fuel mixture by turning idle fuel needle counter-clockwise a small fraction of a turn at a time until engine accelerates smoothly and rapidly. If engine appears sluggish on acceleration, a leaner fuel mixture may be required. Turn idle needle a small fraction of a turn at a time in clockwise direction until acceleration of engine is at maximum. As main fuel needle has not had final adjustment at this time,

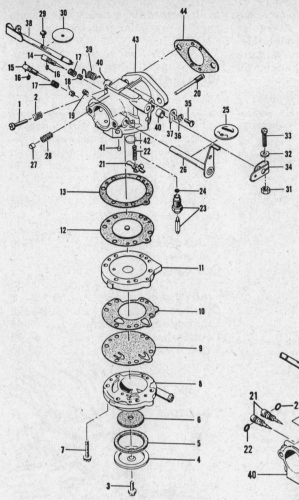

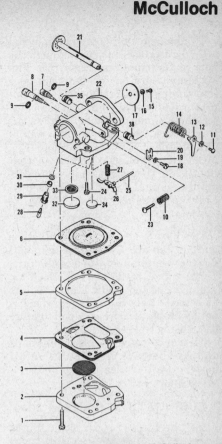

Fig. MC1–Exploded view of typical Tillotson carburetor used on models MC-5 and MC-6.

1. Idle speed screw
2. Spring
4. Strainer cover
5. Gasket
6. Strainer screen
8. Fuel pump body
9. Pump diaphragm
10. Gasket
11. Diaphragm cover
12. Diaphragm
13. Gasket
14. Idle fuel needle
15. Main fuel needle
16. Washer
17. Spring
18. Packing
20. Inlet lever pin
21. Inlet lever
22. Spring
23. Inlet needle & seat
25. Choke disc
26. Choke shaft & lever
27. Friction pin
30. Throttle disc
34. Throttle lever
37. Clip
38. Throttle shaft & lever
39. Spring
40. Bushing
41. Plug
42. Plug
43. Carburetor body
44. Gasket

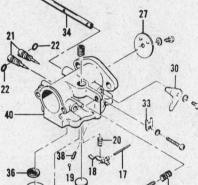

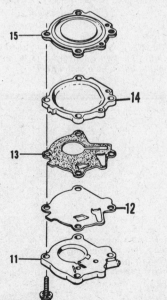

Fig. MC3–Exploded view of McCulloch carburetor used on MC-7, MC-8, MC-20, MC-30, MC-40 and MC-70 models. Carburetors used on models MC-2, MC-45 and MC-75 are similar.

2. Fuel pump body		22. Carburetor body
3. Fuel pump filter		23. Idle speed screw
4. Pump diaphragm		25. Inlet lever pin
5. Diaphragm plate		26. Inlet lever
6. Diaphragm		27. Spring
7. Idle fuel needle		28. Needle valve
8. Main fuel needle		29. Needle body
9. "O" ring		30. Needle seat
10. Spring		31. Valve washer
13. Throttle arm		32. Expansion plug
14. Spring		33. Capillary seal
17. Throttle disc		34. Expansion plug
20. Clip		35. Bushing
21. Throttle shaft		38. Bushing

acceleration may not be at maximum peak.

Test engine at high speed under load. If engine four-cycles (fires every other stroke), lean the fuel mixture by turning the main fuel needle in small increments in clockwise direction until engine fires on every stroke at peak RPM. Never attempt to adjust the main fuel mixture needle unless engine is under load.

After adjusting the main fuel needle, it may be necessary to readjust the idle fuel needle as previously described.

MAGNETO AND TIMING. The magnet is cast into the flywheel on all models. The breaker points and condenser on the model MC-10 are mounted in a breaker box outside the engine crankcase. The flywheel must be removed on all other models to gain access to the breaker points and condenser. Breaker point gap on all models is 0.018.

11. Fuel pump body	22. "O" rings
12. Pump diaphragm	27. Throttle disc
13. Pump gasket	30. Throttle shaft arm
14. Diaphragm plate	33. Clip
15. Carburetor diaphragm	34. Throttle shaft
	35. Expansion plug
17. Inlet lever pin	36. Filter
18. Inlet control lever	37. Expansion plug
19. Ball, ⅛ inch	38. Ball check seat
20. Inlet lever spring	40. Carburetor body
21. Metering needles	

Fig. MC2–Exploded view of McCulloch 50070C diaphragm carburetor and diaphragm type fuel pump assembly used on MC-10 kart engine.

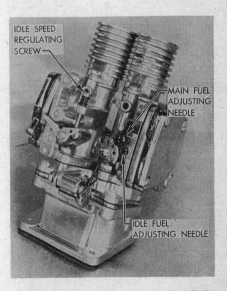

IDLE SPEED REGULATING SCREW

MAIN FUEL ADJUSTING NEEDLE

IDLE FUEL ADJUSTING NEEDLE

Fig. MC4–View of dual carburetor installation on models MC-40 and MC-70 showing carburetor adjustment points. Main fuel adjusting needle and idle fuel adjusting needle are on rear side of left carburetor.

To adjust breaker point gap on model MC-10, insert a ¼-inch pin through the hole in the crankcase cover (See Fig. MC8) and turn engine until pin goes into timing hole in flywheel. Disconnect primary lead from breaker point terminal. Connect timing light in series between breaker point terminal and engine ground as shown in Fig. MC9. Adjust breaker points so that light is on, then slowly adjust breaker points so that light just goes out. Tighten breaker point mounting screws.

To adjust breaker points on all other models, remove flywheel and install degree wheel on engine crankshaft. Turn engine to 25° BTDC. Hook up timing light and adjust breaker points as described above. If degree wheel is not available, set breaker point gap to 0.018 using feeler gage.

Clearance between coil laminations and flywheels is 0.007-0.012 on all models. Desired clearance of 0.010 is set as shown in Fig. MC10.

LUBRICATION. For model MC-2,

mix one pint of SAE 40 two-cycle engine oil with each gallon of regular gasoline. For all other models McCulloch recommends fuel-oil mixture of one part SAE 40 two-cycle engine oil

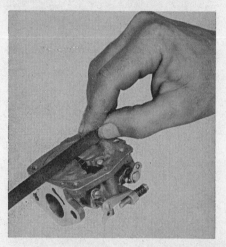

Fig. MC7—On McCulloch carburetors, be sure that diaphragm lever is flush with machined gasket surface of carburetor body as shown.

to 10 parts of 100 octane white marine gasoline or regular grade gasoline.

CARBON. Lack of power may indicate exhaust ports need cleaning. Clean ports with wooden scraper.

REPAIRS

TIGHTENING TORQUES. Recommended tightening torques are as follows. All values are in inch-pounds.

Breaker points screw	30-35
Carburetor to adapter	90-100
Carburetor adapter to manifold	60-65
Carburetor manifold to cylinder	60-65
Coil and lamination screws	55-60
Condenser screw	30-35
Connecting rod, MC-70 & MC-75	90-95
All other models	65-70
Crankcase bottom screws	95-100
Crankcase end cover screws	60-65
Cylinder head screws	55-60
Exhaust stack	55-60

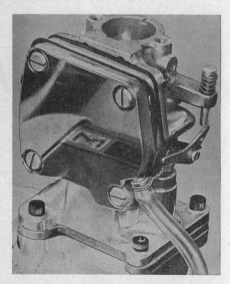

Fig. MC5—Always secure fuel tube with wire at each end as shown.

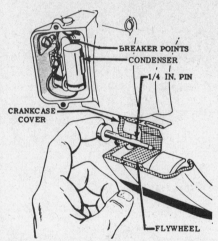

Fig. MC8—On MC-10 engines, crankshaft can be locked in firing position by inserting a ¼-inch pin into bored hole in flywheel.

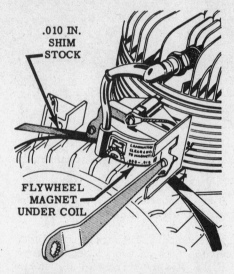

Fig. MC10—Recommended magneto air gap is obtained by shifting coil on mounting screws.

Fig. MC6—On Tillotson carburetor, be sure that diaphragm lever is flush with diaphragm chamber surface as shown.

Fig. MC9—Illustrating proper use of timing light in adjusting breaker point gap on McCulloch kart engines.

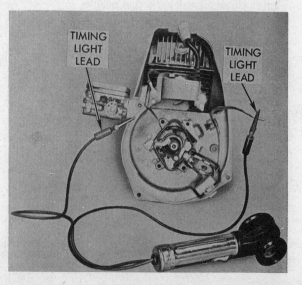

Fan housing 55-60
Flywheel nut 300-360
Reed valve clamp 30-35
Spark plug 216-264
Clutch or sprocket nut 260-300

CONNECTING ROD. On models MC-2 and MC-70, the cylinder head is non-removable and the piston and connecting rod assembly must be removed from the bottom. Remove engine bottom cover, detach rod from crankshaft and remove crankshaft and engine cover assembly. Then withdraw rod and piston through bottom opening. On all other models, rod and piston assembly are removed from above.

The crankpin bearing on model MC-2 is a two-piece floating bushing. On all other models, 24 uncaged needle roller bearings are used. Renew rod, bushings, or crankshaft on model MC-2 if scored or worn excessively. On all other models, crankpin nominal diameter is 0.6298. Clearance between end of rollers and side of crankpin journal (needle end clearance) should be 0.008-0.018. Accumulative clearance between rollers should be 0.008-0.010. Side clearance between rod and crankshaft should be 0.100-0.110. Renew rod and/or crankshaft if scored or if any wear spots are visible.

Install crankpin needle rollers by sticking 12 rollers in the rod and 12 in the rod cap with grease. Align "pips" (See Fig. MC12) on rod and cap when installing on crankpin. Parting faces of connecting rod and cap are fractured (not machined) to provide the dowel effect on the meshing of the consequent uneven surface. It is advisable to wiggle the rod cap back and forth while tightening to make sure the interstices of the fractured joint are in perfect mesh. When properly meshed, no "catch points" will be felt when finger nail is rubbed along parting line of rod and cap. See Fig. MC13.

PISTON, PIN AND RINGS. Piston in early model MC-5 and MC-10 engines was fitted with two thick compression rings. Ring end gap should be 0.007-0.010. If piston skirt to cylinder wall clearance exceeds 0.005 or ring end gap exceeds 0.010 with new piston ring, hone or rebore cylinder to next oversize or renew cylinder. If ring side clearance in top ring groove exceeds 0.004, renew the piston. Piston rings should always be renewed whenever engine is disassembled for service. Piston and rings are available in oversizes of 0.010, 0.020 and 0.030 as well as standard size. Install the chrome plated ring in top ring groove and install cast iron ring in second ring groove.

In late production MC-5 and MC-10 engines and all other models, piston is fitted with two thin chrome compression rings. Ring end gap should be 0.051-0.091 on models MC40, MC-45, MC-70 and MC-75 which have ring retaining pins in the ring grooves. Ring end gap on all other thin-ring pistons is 0.004-0.050. If piston skirt to cylinder wall clearance exceeds 0.007 or new rings cannot be fitted with end gap tolerance, hone or rebore cylinder to next oversize or renew cylinder. If ring side clearance in top ring groove exceeds 0.004 with new piston ring, renew the piston. Piston rings should always be renewed whenever engine is disassembled for service. Piston and rings are available in standard size and 0.010 oversize only for models MC-2, MC-7 and MC-30. For other models, piston and rings are available in oversizes of 0.010, 0.020 and 0.030 as well as standard size; in addition, 0.040 and

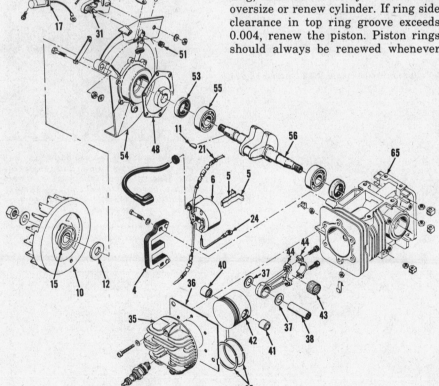

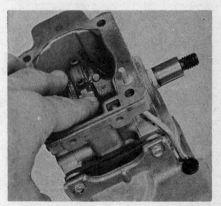

Fig. MC12–Install cap on connecting rod with "pips" on rod and cap aligned as shown.

Fig. MC11–Exploded view of MC-10 engine. Note external breaker box on crankcase cover (54) and push rod (32) that actuates breaker points.

4. Coil laminations	31. Breaker assembly	43. Needle rollers (24 used)
5. Coil retainers	32. Push rod	44. Connecting rod
6. Coil	35. Cylinder head	48. Gasket
10. Flywheel	36. Gasket	51. Bushing
11. Woodruff key	37. Thrust washers	53. Crankcase seal
12. Felt dirt shield	38. Piston pin	54. Crankcase cover
14. Breaker box cover	39. Rings	55. Ball bearing (2 used)
17. Condenser	40. Open needle bearing	56. Crankshaft
24. Ground wire	41. Closed end needle bearing	65. Crankcase and cylinder
29. Eccentric screw	42. Piston	

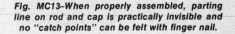

Fig. MC13–When properly assembled, parting line on rod and cap is practically invisible and no "catch points" can be felt with finger nail.

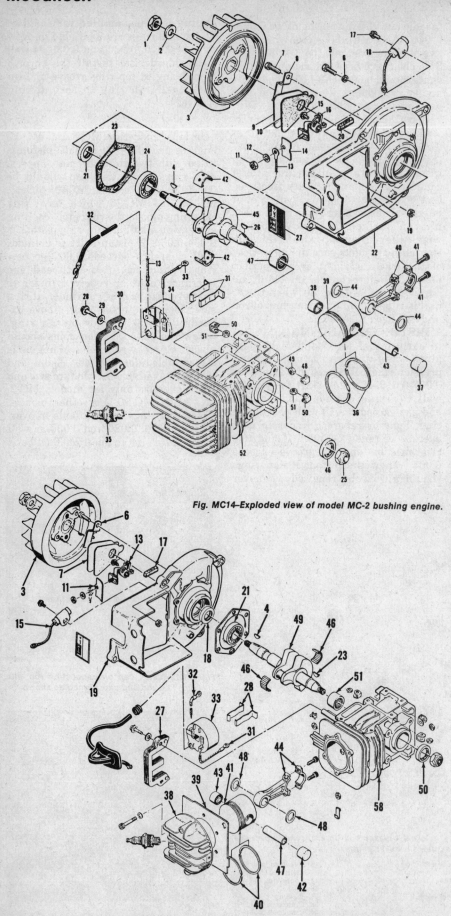

3. Flywheel
4. Woodruff key
8. Retainer
9. Breaker box cover
10. Gasket
16. Breaker assembly
18. Condenser
20. Felt wiper
21. Oil seal
22. Crankcase cover
23. Gasket
24. Ball bearing
26. Woodruff key
30. Coil lamination
31. Coil retainers
34. Coil assembly
35. Spark plug
36. Piston ring set
37. Closed end bearing
38. Open end bearing
39. Piston
40. Connecting rod
42. Floating rod bushing
43. Piston pin
44. Thrust washers
45. Crankshaft
46. Oil seal
47. Needle bearing
52. Crankcase

Fig. MC14–Exploded view of model MC-2 bushing engine.

Fig. MC15–Removing connecting rod and piston assembly from model with removable cylinder head. It is not necessary to remove crankcase cover or crankshaft to remove piston and rod on models with removable cylinder head.

3. Flywheel
4. Woodruff key
6. Breaker box cover retainer
7. Breaker box cover
11. Insulator
13. Breaker points
15. Condenser
17. Felt wiper
18. Crankcase seal
19. Crankcase cover
21. Ball bearing
23. Woodruff key
27. Coil laminations
28. Coil retainers
31. Ground wire
32. Primary wire
33. Coil
38. Cylinder head
39. Gasket
40. Rings
41. Piston
42. Closed end needle bearing
43. Open needle bearing
44. Connecting rod
46. Needle rollers (24 used)
47. Piston pin
48. Thrust washers
49. Crankshaft
50. Crankcase seal
51. Needle bearing
58. Crankcase and cylinder

Fig. MC16–Exploded view of MC-6 engine; MC-5, MC-7 and MC-8 are similar except that MC-7 and MC-8 use an "O" ring in place of crankcase cover gasket shown adjacent to ball bearing (21).

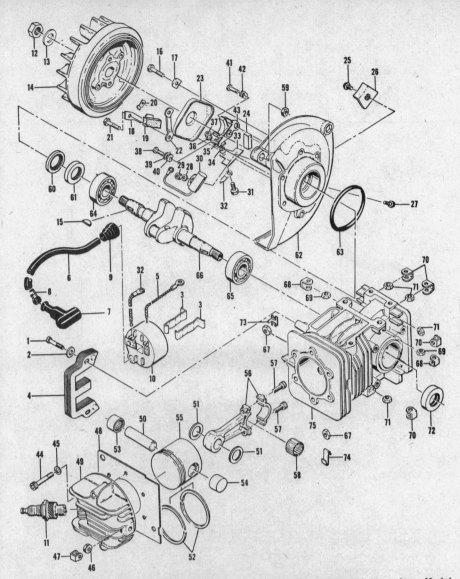

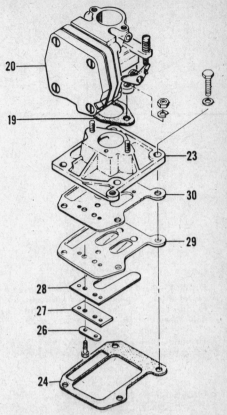

Fig. MC17–Exploded view showing construction of models MC-20, MC-30, MC-40 engines. Model MC-45 is similar except for nine-port crankcase. Model MC-75 is also similar except for nine-port crankcase and gasket is used instead of "O" ring (63).

4. Coil laminations	51. Thrust washers
5. Grounding wire	52. Piston rings
6. Spark plug wire	53. Needle bearing
10. Coil assembly	54. Needle bearing
11. Spark plug	55. Piston
14. Flywheel	56. Connecting rod
23. Breaker box cover	58. Needle rollers
24. Felt cam wiper	60. Oil seal
30. Condenser	62. Crankcase cover
32. Primary coil wire	64. Ball bearing
43. Breaker point assy.	65. Ball bearing
49. Cylinder head	66. Crankshaft
50. Piston pin	75. Crankcase

0.050 oversize piston and rings are available for model MC-20 engine. The two compression rings are interchangeable on all thin-ring pistons.

CAUTION: Never install piston rings with end gap less than specified tolerance; this will result in cylinder wall scuffing and possible engine sei-

3. Carburetor	12. Valve reed
6. Inlet manifold	13. Reed plate
7. Gasket	14. Gasket
8. Reed valve assy.	17. Crankcase bottom
10. Lockplate	18. Gasket
11. Reed guard	21. Exhaust header

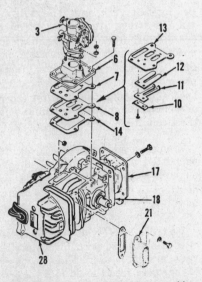

Fig. MC18–View of MC-6 reed assembly.

Fig. MC19–Carburetor mounting and inlet reed valve system on models MC-2 and MC-20. Some other models are similar except that reed guards are used.

19. Gasket	26. Lockplate
20. Carburetor	27. Reed clamp
23. Intake manifold	28. Reed valve
24. Gasket	29. Reed plate

zure. Ring end gap is measured with ring positioned just above the transfer ports.

Piston pin is a press fit in connecting rod of all models. Model MC-5 piston has non-renewable oilite bushings in piston pin bore; all other models use one open and one closed end needle bearing in piston. Piston must be supported in special support block available from McCulloch Corporation when

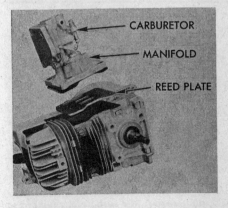

Fig. MC20–View of carburetor and manifold removed from model MC-8 engine showing reed plate. Refer to Fig. MC19 for exploded view of reed plate assembly.

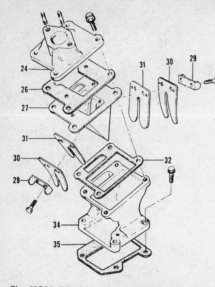

Fig. MC21–Reed inlet valve installation used on
model MC-30. Two sets of reed valves are used
to increase intake capacity. Installations on
dual carburetor MC-40 and MC-70 models are
similar. Refer to Fig. MC-22.

24. Carburetor adapter
26. Gasket
27. Reed valve block
29. Lockplate
30. Reed valve guard
31. Reed valve
32. Gasket
34. Manifold body
35. Gasket

pressing pin in or out of piston and rod.
The closed end needle bearing used in
the piston of all models except MC-5
must be placed in the side of the piston
towards the exhaust port in cylinder
wall.

CRANKSHAFT. The crankshaft is
supported by a ball bearing at the
flywheel end and a caged needle roller
bearing at the pto end on models MC-2,
MC-5, MC-6, MC-7 and MC-8. On
models MC-10, MC-20, MC-40 and MC-
70, the crankshaft is supported by ball

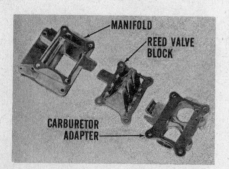

Fig. MC22–View of manifold, reed valve block
with six reeds and carburetor adapter used
with dual carburetor MC-40 and MC-70 models.
Refer to Fig. MC21 for exploded view of reed
valve block for single carburetor MC-30 engine
which is of similar construction.

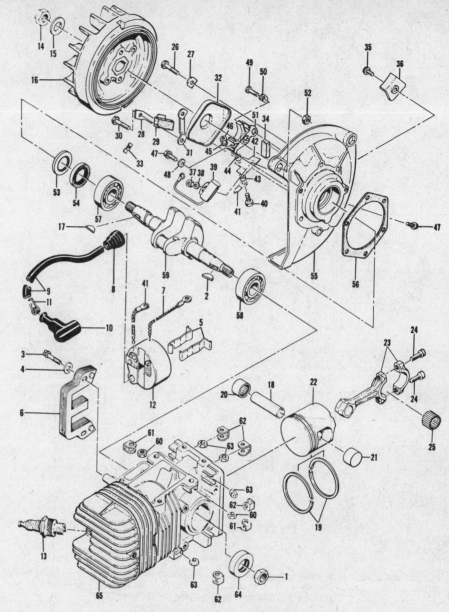

Fig. MC23–Exploded view of model MC-70 engine.

bearings at each end. The ball type
main bearings are a press fit on the
crankshaft and both the ball and
needle type main bearings are a press
fit in the crankcase or cover. Inspect
pto end journal where needle bearing is
used and crankpin journal for scoring
or wear spots and renew crankshaft if
these conditions are noted.

Crankcase and crankcase cover must
be heated to 180-200° F. in an oven
when installing ball or needle type
bearings to prevent damage to bearing
bore.

VALVE SYSTEM. A combination
of reed and third port (piston porting)
valve system is used. The smooth side
of the valve reed should face the valve
plate.

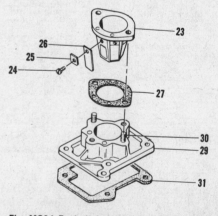

Fig. MC24–Exploded view of pyramid type reed
inlet valve assembly and carburetor adapter
used on models MC-45 and MC-75. Six steel
reeds (26) are used.

23. Valve block
24. Screws
25. Reed clamp plate
26. Reed valves
27. Gasket
29. Adapter
30. Stud bolts
31. Gasket

McCULLOCH

McCULLOCH CORPORATION
Los Angeles, California 90045

MODEL	Bore	Stroke	Displacement
MC-49	2.125	1.375	4.9
MC-49C	2.125	1.375	4.9
MC-49E	2.125	1.375	4.9
MC-90	2.165	1.635	6.05
MC-91	2.165	1.635	6.05
MC-91A	2.165	1.635	6.05
MC-91B	2.165	1.635	6.05
MC-91C	2.165	1.635	6.05
MC-100	2.250	1.835	7.29
MC-101	2.280	1.835	7.5
MC-101A	2.280	1.835	7.5
MC-101C	2.280	1.835	7.5

Illustrations Courtesy of McCulloch Corporation

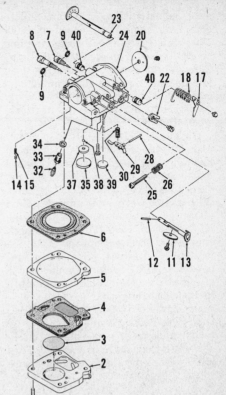

MAINTENANCE

SPARK PLUG. For normal operating conditions, models MC-49, MC-49C and MC-49E are equipped with Champion J-8J, models MC-91B and MC-101A are equipped with Champion L-78 and all other models use Champion J-4J. However, certain operating conditions may require use of a different heat range. Examination of plug will indicate whether plug was of suitable heat range, or if a hotter or colder plug should be installed. If plug is fouled, install a new plug of hotter heat range; whitish deposits on insulator and burned electrodes indicates a colder plug should be installed. Brown to grayish-tan deposits around insulator indicates that plug was of proper heat range. Refer to the following heat range chart for selection of plug to suit operating conditions.

Champion plug with ⅜-inch reach

Heat Range	Plug Number
Hotter	J-8J
	J-6J
	J-4J
	J-2J
Colder	J-58R

Champion plug with ½-inch reach

Heat Range	Plug Number
Hotter	L-88
	L-81
	L-78
	L-87R
Colder	L-84R

Set electrodes gap to 0.025 for all models and operating conditions. Note that use of Champion J-58R or L-84R plug may require warming engine up on a hotter plug as plug may foul in cold engine.

CARBURETOR. McCulloch diaphragm or pressure pulse type carburetors are used on these models. Refer to Figs. MC25, MC26, MC27 and MC28 for exploded view of carburetors.

ADJUSTMENT. On models MC-49, MC-49C, MC-90 and MC-100, turn fuel adjusting needles clockwise until they are lightly seated. Open idle mixture needle (7—Fig. MC25) 1¼ turns and main fuel needle (8) 1½ turns. With engine warm and running, adjust idle speed screw (25) until engine idles at a speed of 1500-1700 rpm. Check engine for acceleration and open main fuel needle a slight amount if engine misfires, or turn needle in a slight amount if engine smokes and is sluggish on acceleration.

On model MC-49E, lightly seat idle mixture needle (19—Fig. MC26), then open the needle 1¼ turns. Main fuel jet is non-adjustable. Standard jet (17) has an orifice diameter of 0.031 in. Optional jets with orifice diameters of 0.028 (lean), 0.029 and 0.033 (rich) are available. With engine warm and run-

Fig. MC25–Exploded view of McCulloch diaphragm type carburetor with integral fuel pump used on models MC-49, MC-49C, MC-90 and MC-100. On some models, a screen (capillary seal) is used instead of check valve ball (38) and seat (37). Some carburetors do not have choke.

2. Fuel pump body
3. Fuel pump filter
4. Fuel pump diaphragm
5. Carburetor diaphragm plate
6. Carburetor diaphragm
7. Idle fuel needle
8. Main fuel needle
9. "O" ring
11. Choke plate
12. Groove pin
13. Choke shaft
14. Choke friction pin
15. Choke friction spring
17. Throttle shaft arm
18. Throttle return spring
20. Throttle plate
22. Throttle shaft clip
23. Throttle shaft
24. Carburetor body
25. Idle speed screw
26. Idle speed screw spring
27. Inlet lever pin
29. Inlet control lever
30. Inlet lever spring
32. Inlet needle valve
33. Valve body
34. Washer
35. Expansion plug
37. Valve seat
38. Check valve ball
39. Expansion plug
40. Throttle shaft bushings

1. Cover
2. Gasket
3. Check valve diaphragm
4. Fuel pump diaphragm
5. Fuel screen
6. Choke plate
7. Carburetor body
8. Choke shaft
9. Throttle shaft clip
10. Fuel inlet needle
11. Lever pin
12. Inlet lever
13. Gasket
14. Carburetor diaphragm
15. Cover
16. Lever spring
17. Main fuel orifice
18. Throttle plate
19. Idle mixture needle
20. Throttle shaft
21. Throttle plate
22. Throttle return spring
23. Idle speed screw

Fig. MC26–Exploded view of McCulloch diaphragm type carburetor used on model MC-49E.

ning, adjust idle speed screw (23) to obtain an engine idle speed of 1500-1700 rpm. Place a load on engine and check engine for acceleration. If engine falters or misfires on acceleration, open idle mixture needle a small amount. If engine runs rough and smokes heavily on acceleration, turn needle in (clockwise) slightly.

On models MC-91, MC-91A, MC-91C, MC-101 and MC101C, turn both fuel adjusting needles in until they are lightly seated, then open both fuel needles (16 and 20—Fig. MC27) 1 turn. With engine warm and running, adjust idle speed screw (8) to obtain an engine idle speed of 1500-1700 rpm. Check engine for acceleration and if engine falters or misfires, open main fuel needle slightly. If engine smokes and is sluggish on acceleration, turn main fuel needle in slightly.

On models MC-91B and MC-101A, turn idle mixture needle (23—Fig. MC28) and main fuel needle (24) clockwise until they are lightly seated. Turn idle mixture needle counter-clockwise

1-1¼ turns, then turn main fuel needle counter-clockwise 1½-2 turns. With engine warm and running, adjust idle speed screw (14) until engine idle speed is 1500-1700 rpm. Place a load on engine and check engine acceleration. If engine runs rough or smokes heavily on acceleration, close main fuel needle a slight amount. If engine falters or misfires on acceleration, open main fuel needle a slight amount.

CAUTION: On all models, avoid carburetor settings that will run the engine too lean. If setting is too lean, overheating and lack of lubrication will seriously damage the engine.

MAGNETO AND TIMING. Proper ignition timing is obtained by adjusting breaker point gap. If degree wheel and static timing light are available, adjust breaker points so they start to open at 25 degrees BTDC on models MC-49, MC-49C and MC-90, 26 degrees BTDC on models MC-49E, MC-91, MC-91A, MC-91B and MC-91C, or 22 degrees BTDC on models MC-100, MC-101, MC-101A and MC-101C. An alternate method of setting timing is to adjust breaker point opening to 0.018 on models MC-49, MC-49C and MC-90, 0.019 on models MC-49E, MC-91, MC-91A, MC-91B and MC-91C, or 0.015 on models MC-100, MC-101, MC-101A and MC-101C, using a feeler gage.

Refer to Figs. MC30 for magneto used on models MC-49, MC-49C, MC-49E, MC-90, MC-91, MC-91A, MC-91B and MC-91C. Models MC-100, MC-101, MC-101A and MC-101C use magneto shown in Fig. MC31.

Fig. MC28–Exploded view of McCulloch pressure pulse type carburetor used on models 91B and 101A.

2. Fuel pump body	14. Idle speed screw
3. Fuel filter	15. Spring
4. Fuel pump diaphragm	16. Throttle shaft clip
5. Diaphragm plate	17. Throttle shaft arm
6. Carburetor diaphragm	18. Spring
7. Circuit plate	19. Bushing
8. Check valve diaphragm	20. Carburetor body
9. Gaskets	21. Throttle plate
10. Inlet lever	22. Throttle shaft
11. Lever pin	23. Idle mixture needle
12. Fuel inlet needle	24. Main fuel needle
13. Lever spring	25. Spring
	26. "O" ring washer
	27. "O" ring
	28. One-way valve

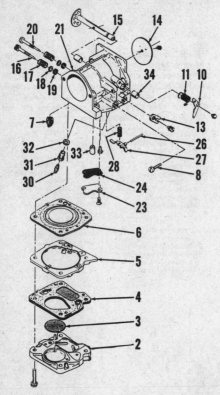

Fig. MC27–Exploded view of McCulloch pressure pulse type carburetor used on models MC-91, MC-91A, MC-91C, MC-101 and MC-101C.

2. Fuel pump body	17. Needle spring
3. Fuel pump filter	18. "O" ring washer
4. Fuel pump diaphragm	19. "O" ring
5. Diaphragm plate	20. Idle fuel needle
6. Carburetor diaphragm	21. Carburetor body
7. One-way "duck-bill" valve	23. Idle cluster cover
8. Idle speed screw	24. Gasket
10. Throttle shaft arm	26. Control lever pin
11. Throttle shaft spring	27. Inlet lever
13. Throttle shaft clip	28. Inlet lever spring
14. Throttle plate	30. Inlet valve needle
15. Throttle shaft	31. Inlet valve body
16. Main fuel needle	32. Inlet valve gasket
	33. Check valve
	34. Throttle shaft bushing

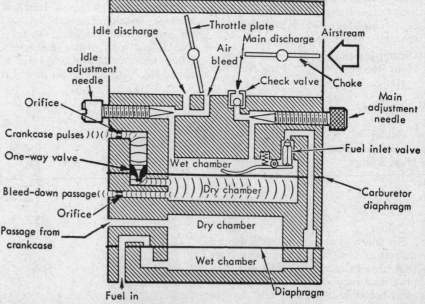

Fig. MC29–Cross-sectional diagram of McCulloch pressure pulse type carburetor. Note straight bore through carburetor; venturi is not required as fuel is ejected into carburetor bore under pressure from fuel pump. Pulse pressure from engine crankcase works against fuel pressure and force of inlet lever spring to regulate inlet valve opening, thus metering fuel ejected into carburetor bore to meet engine requirements.

Adjust armature air gap to 0.010. No condenser test specifications are available; McCulloch recommends renewing the condenser whenever installing a new set of breaker points.

LUBRICATION. Mix one part of McCulloch oil or SAE 40 2-cycle engine oil with 20 parts of regular grade automotive gasoline or 100 octane white marine gasoline.

CARBON. Exhaust ports should be cleaned regularly using a wood scraper to avoid loss of power due to clogged exhaust ports.

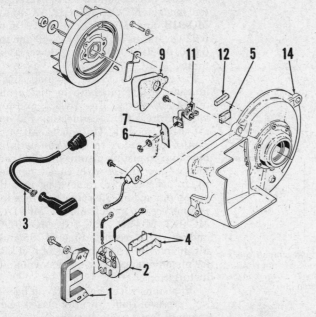

1. Armature core
2. Ignition coil
3. Spark plug wire
4. Coil retainer clips
5. Breaker box felt
6. Primary wire
7. Insulator
9. Breaker box cover
11. Breaker points
12. Cam wiper felt
14. Crankcase cover

Fig. MC30 – Exploded view of typical magneto ignition system used on models MC-49, MC-49C, MC-49E, MC-90, MC-91, MC-91A, MC-91B and MC91C. Tab on breaker box cover (9) can be used as feeler gage to adjust breaker point gap.

REPAIRS

TIGHTENING TORQUES. Recommended tightening torques are as follows. All values are in inch-pounds.

Breaker point screw	30-35
Carburetor to adapter nuts	90-100
Carburetor adapter to manifold	60-65
Carburetor manifold to cylinder	60-65
Coil and lamination screws	55-60
Condenser screw	30-35
Connecting rod, MC-100, MC-101, MC-101A & MC-101C	90-95
MC-91, MC-91A, MC-91B & MC-91C	105-110
All other models	65-70
Crankcase end cover screws	60-65
Crankcase bottom screws	95-100
Cylinder head screws	55-60
Exhaust stack screws	55-60
Fan housing screws	55-60
Flywheel nut	300-360
Reed valve clamp screws	30-35
Spark plug	216-264
Sprocket or clutch nut	260-300

CONNECTING ROD. On models MC-49, MC-49C and MC-49E, the cylinder head is not removable and the piston and connecting rod assembly must be removed from bottom of crankcase after removing bottom cover, crankcase cover and the crankshaft. On other models, piston and connecting rod assembly can be removed after removing bottom cover and cylinder head.

On all models, 24 uncaged needle

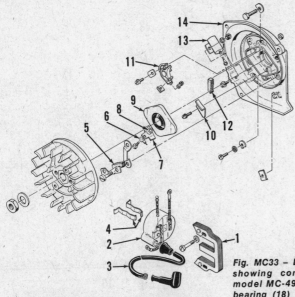

Fig. MC-31 – Exploded view of magneto ignition system as used on models MC-100, MC-101, MC-101A and MC-101C.

1. Armature core
2. Ignition coil
3. Spark plug wire
4. Coil retaining clips
5. Breaker box felt
6. Primary wire
7. Insulator
8. Insulator
9. Breaker box cover
10. Wire retaining clip
11. Breaker points
12. Cam wiper felt
13. Condenser
14. Crankcase cover

Fig. MC33 – Exploded view showing construction of model MC-49 engine. Ball bearing (18) and seal (23) are supported in crankcase cover (14 – Fig. MC30). Models MC-49C and MC-49E are similar except for piston, pin and bearings; refer to Fig. MC34 for view of piston assembly.

3. Piston rings
4. Piston pin
6. Piston
7. Connecting rod
8. Crankpin needle rollers
9. Expansion plug
12. Crankshaft seal
13. Crankcase
18. Ball bearing
19. Needle roller bearing
20. Crankshaft
23. Crankshaft seal
24. Snap rings

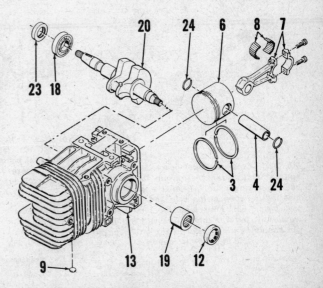

Fig. MC32 – When installing connecting rod cap, pips on rod and cap must be aligned. If pips are not aligned as shown at right, rod and bearing failure will result.

PIPS (ALIGNED)

PIP (NOT ALIGNED)

rollers are used for crankpin bearing. Renew the needle rollers as a complete set if any roller has flat spot, or if it has burn or score marks. Renew crankshaft and/or connecting rod if bearing surfaces are scored or rough. When reassembling, use light grease to stick 12 needle rollers in connecting rod and 12 needle rollers in cap. Fit connecting rod to crankpin, then install cap with "pips" aligned as shown in Fig. MC32.

PISTON, PIN AND RINGS. Piston is fitted with two thin steel rings. Ring end gap should be 0.004-0.050 on pistons that do not have ring locating pin, or 0.051-0.091 on pistons with pinned rings. If ring side clearance in groove exceeds 0.004 with new ring, the piston should be renewed. Also, renew piston

if scored or if cylinder to piston skirt clearance exceeds 0.007. Piston and rings are available in standard size for

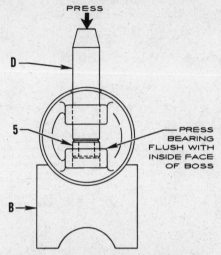

Fig. MC36–Using driver (D) and support block (B) to install piston pin needle bearings. After bearings are installed, a similar driver can be used to install piston pin.

all models as well as in 0.010, 0.020 and 0.030 oversizes for models MC-49C, MC-49E, MC-100, MC-101 and MC-101C, in 0.005 and 0.010 oversizes for models MC-90, MC-91, MC-91A, MC-91B and MC-91C, in 0.010 and 0.020 oversizes for model MC-49 and in 0.010, 0.020, 0.030 and 0.050 oversizes for model MC-101A.

Piston pin is retained by snap rings at each end of pin bore in piston on model MC-49 (see Fig. MC33), and by being a press fit in connecting rod on all other models. On model MC-49, piston pin rides in non-renewable bushings in piston; pistons on all other models are fitted with caged needle roller bearings. To remove or install piston pin and needle roller bearings in pistons used in models MC-91, MC91A, MC-91B, MC-91C, MC-101, MC-101A and MC-101C, refer to Figs. MC35 and MC36 for views showing use of tool kit for piston pin and bearing removal and installation.

On pistons with one closed end bearing, press pin out towards closed end bearing, forcing the bearing out with pin. Then, press open end bearing from

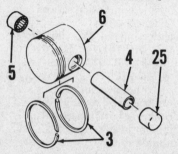

Fig. MC34–View showing type of piston, pin and piston pin bearings used on models MC-49C, MC-90 and MC-100. Refer to Fig. MC33 for view showing construction, except for piston assembly, typical of models MC-49C and MC49E and to Fig. MC37 for view of assembly typical of models MC-90 and MC-100 except for piston.

3. Piston rings
4. Piston pin
5. Open end needle bearing
6. Piston
25. Closed end needle bearing

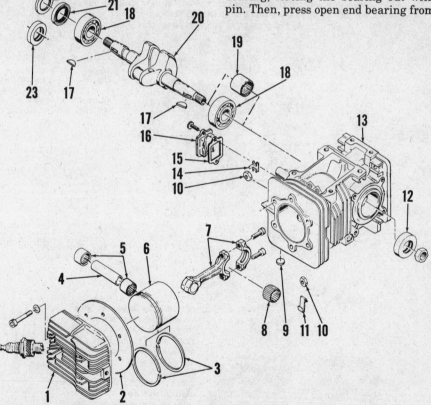

Fig. MC37–Exploded view showing typical construction of models MC-91, MC-91A, MC-91B, MC-91C, MC-101, MC-101A and MC-101C. Models MC-90 and MC-100 are of similar construction except that piston assembly shown in Fig. MC34 is used and models MC-90 and MC-100 do not have port cover (16). Needle bearing (19) is used at output end of crankshaft on all models except MC-100, MC-101, MC-101A and MC-101C. Latest type crankshaft seals (12 and 23) are installed with sealing lip outward instead of towards crankpin.

Fig. MC35–Cross-sectional view showing use of special McCulloch piston pin and needle bearing removal tool. A small washer (W) is inserted between piston skirt and pin boss to pull piston pin. After removing pin, a larger washer is used with tool to remove blind piston pin needle bearing. Refer to Fig. MC36 for pin and bearing installation.

B. Support block
G. Swivel guide
N. Nut
S. Puller shaft
W. Horseshoe washer

1. Cylinder head	8. Crankpin needle rollers	16. Port cover plate
2. Head gasket	9. Expansion plug	17. Woodruff keys
3. Piston rings	10. Nuts	18. Ball bearing
4. Piston pin	11. Nut retainer	19. Needle roller bearing
5. Open end needle bearings	12. Crankshaft seal	20. Crankshaft
6. Piston (exhaust side blind)	13. Crankcase	21. Inner crankshaft seal
7. Connecting rod	14. Nut retainer	22. Outer crankshaft seal
	15. Gasket	23. Single crankshaft seal

piston. Install new bearings in piston so that inner ends of bearing cages are flush with piston pin boss. Insert piston pin through open bearing and press through connecting rod until end of pin is flush with outer end of open end needle bearing cage. Always support piston in fixture when pressing pin in or out. Heating the connecting rod to about 180° F. will permit easier piston pin installation.

CRANKCASE. Where cylinder is worn so that piston skirt to cylinder clearance is 0.007 or more with new

piston or ring end gap is excessive with new piston rings, the cylinder must be rebored to next oversize or a new crankcase must be installed. Refer to previous paragraph for piston and ring oversizes available.

CRANKSHAFT. On models MC-100, MC-101, MC-101A and MC-101C, crankshaft is supported in ball bearings at each end. On other models, flywheel end of crankshaft is supported in a ball bearing and output end is supported in a needle roller bearing. The ball bearings are a press fit on crankshaft and both the needle and ball bearings are a press fit in crankcase and crankcase cover. Inspect output end main journal for scoring or wear spots on models with needle bearing.

Crankcase and crankcase cover must be heated to temperature of 180-200° F. prior to installing crankshaft and ball bearing assembly, or installing needle bearing in crankcase on models so equipped.

REED VALVES. Flat valve reeds as shown in Fig. MC38 are used on models MC-49, MC-49C and MC-49E. Models MC-90 and MC-100 are equipped with pyramid reeds as shown in Fig. MC39. Models MC-91, MC-91A, MC-91B, MC-91C, MC-101, MC-101A and MC-101C, which use McCulloch pressure pulse type carburetor, are equipped with V-type reed block as shown in Fig. MC40.

Correct seating of reed valves is essential to maintain crankcase pressure. Be sure that reeds and seats are clean and reeds lay flat against seat. Renew any broken or chipped reeds. Renew reed plate, pyramid seat or reed block if worn in seat area.

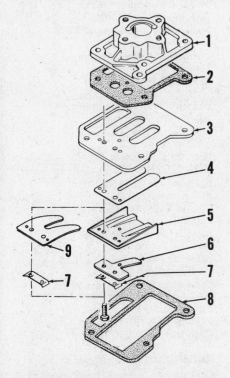

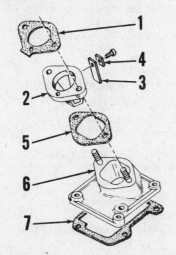

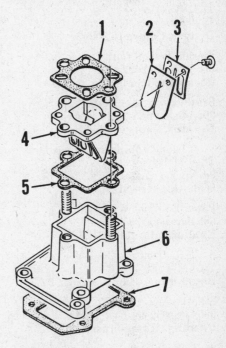

Fig. MC38–Exploded view of carburetor adapter and reed valve plate assembly used on models MC-49, MC-49C and MC-49E. Model MC-49C and MC-49E use reed guard (9); model MC-49 is equipped with fuel deflector (5) and reed clamp (6).

1. Carburetor adapter
2. Gasket
3. Reed plate
4. Valve reeds
5. Fuel deflector
6. Reed clamp
7. Lockplate
8. Gasket
9. Reed guard

Fig. MC39–Models MC-90 and MC-100 are equipped with pyramid reed intake valve.

1. Gasket
2. Pyramid reed seat
3. Valve reeds
4. Reed clamp
5. Gasket
6. Carburetor adapter
7. Gasket

Fig. MC40–Exploded view of V-block reed valve assembly used on models MC-91, MC-91A, MC-91B, MC-91C, MC-101, MC-101A and MC-101C.

1. Gasket
2. Valve reeds
3. Reed clamp plate
4. Valve block
5. Gasket
6. Adapter manifold
7. Gasket

SERVICING McCULLOCH ACCESSORIES

RECOIL STARTER

To disassemble the recoil starter, first unbolt and remove starter assembly from engine. Refer to Fig. MC41, hold handle (4) and remove cover (5). Allow rope pulley to rotate slowly until tension is removed from recoil spring. Remove ratchet (11), then carefully withdraw rope pulley from starter base (10). Recoil spring (8) should remain in starter base. Renew

rope or recoil spring as necessary and reassemble starter. Preload recoil spring about two turns. Inspect the two spring loaded pawls which are pinned to the flywheel and renew any parts that show excessive wear or other damage. Reinstall starter assembly.

Fig. MC41–Exploded view of recoil starter assembly used on some McCulloch engines. A kit is available for installation of similar recoil starter on other models.

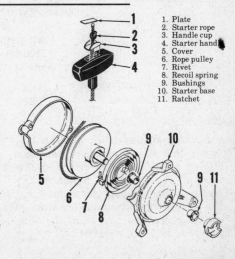

1. Plate
2. Starter rope
3. Handle cup
4. Starter handle
5. Cover
6. Rope pulley
7. Rivet
8. Recoil spring
9. Bushings
10. Starter base
11. Ratchet

McCULLOCH DISTRIBUTORS

(Arranged Alphabetically by States)

These franchised firms carry extensive stocks of repair parts. Contact them for name of nearest dealer who may have the parts you need.

McCulloch Distributing Co.
4201 Park Ave. S.W.
Birmingham, Alabama 35221

Leavitt Power Tool Co.
P.O. Box 214287
Sacramento, California 95821

Coast-McCulloch Co.
855 Bryant Street
San Francisco, California 94103

California-McCulloch Equip. Co., Inc.
22425 South Vermont
Torrance, California 90502

M. L. Foss, Inc.
1900 Lawrence
Denver, Colorado 80202

Florida Tractor Corp.
5th St. at McDuff Ave.
Jacksonville, Florida 32205

Southeast Tractor Corp.
2935 East Ponce de Leon Ave.
Decatur, Georgia 30030

Inter Island Equipment, Division
Theo. H. Davies and Co., Ltd.
94-031 Farrington Hwy.
Waipahu, Hawaii 96797

Power Equipment Company
645 South Rt. 83
Elmhurst, Illinois 60126

S & S Distributing Co.
1307 Main St.
Baton Rouge, Louisiana 70802

Stantial-McCulloch Company
335 Main Street
Reading, Massachusetts 01867

Langford McCulloch Co.
22310 Telegraph Rd.
Southfield, Michigan 48075

Power Tools, Inc.
3771 Sibley Memorial Highway
St. Paul, Minnesota 55111

Contractors Supply Co.
620 E. 18th St.
Kansas City, Missouri 64108

Twin "C" McCulloch Co.
310 Scott Avenue
St. Louis, Missouri 63122

Log Cutters Supply Co.
2120 Claremont Ave.
Albuquerque, New Mexico 87107

Eaton Equipment Corp.
23 Lake St.
Hamburg, New York 14075

Ronconi Equipment Co., Inc.
615 Fifth Avenue
Larchmont, New York 10538

Porter Brothers, Inc.
1005 East Dixon Blvd.
Shelby, North Carolina 28150

Hayward Distributing Co.
460 Neilston Street
Columbus, Ohio 43215

Lucky-JT Distributing Co.
4445 N.E. Glisan St.
Portland, Oregon 97213

Ronconi Equipment Co., Inc.
Route 309
Hatfield, Pennsylvania 19440

Conaway, Incorporated
Mayview Rd.
Lawrence, Pennsylvania 15055

Shobe, Incorporated
2449 Scaper St.
Memphis, Tennessee 38114

The Bill Voorhees Co., Inc.
700-8th Avenue South
Nashville, Tennessee 37203

Timberland Saw Company
1603 East Houston
Marshall, Texas 75670

Wilson's Transport Supply
1055 South 6th West
Salt Lake City, Utah 84104

Ronconi Equipment Co., Inc.
8815 Telegraph Rd.
Lorton, Virginia 22079

Pacific Equipment, Inc.
410-10th Avenue South
Seattle, Washington 98104

Spokane McCulloch Co., Inc.
4230 East Mission Ave.
Spokane, Washington 99202

Engine Sales & Service Co., Inc.
919 Virginia St., East
Charleston, West Virginia 25301

Rapids Distributing Co., Inc.
Highway 51 & 54
P.O. Box 405
Plover, Wisconsin 54467

O&R ENGINES

(FORMERLY OHLSSON & RICE)

O&R ENGINES, INC.
3340 Emery Street
Los Angeles, California 90023

MODEL SERIES	Bore	Stroke	Displacement
Compact I	1.250	1.032	1.26
Compact II, III	1.250	1.096	1.34
13A, 13B	1.250	1.096	1.34

Starting in mid-1967, a three-digit type number is stamped on crankcase flange opposite spark coil and carburetor; or on large cylinder cooling baffle. Starting about the same time, the serial number indicates time of manufacture, the first digit denoting the year and the next two digits the month.

Engine may be equipped with direct drive, centrifugal clutch, or centrifugal clutch and gear reduction. Rated engine speed is 6300 rpm, and reduction units are available with output shaft speeds of 3300 rpm, 1700 rpm or 900 rpm.

MAINTENANCE

SPARK PLUG. On models using a 10 mm. spark plug, use a Champion UY-6 or equivalent; the Champion UY-6 is a ¼-inch reach plug with auxiliary spark gap.

On engine models using a 14mm. spark plug, use a Champion CJ-8 or equivalent on heavy duty applications or Champion CJ14 or equivalent for normal or light use.

Adjust spark plug electrode gap to 0.030 for normal usage and 0.025 for heavy duty.

CARBURETOR. A diaphragm type carburetor is used. Carburetor is equipped with only one mixture adjusting screw. On later carburetors, the adjusting screw has a spring to keep it from turning due to vibration; on some early models, the adjusting screw is held with a lock nut.

248

On early production models with screw head type jet instead of hex needle valve housing (3—Fig. O&R1), adjust carburetor as follows: For initial adjustment, turn fuel mixture adjusting screw in until seated (do not force) and then back screw out 1½ to 2 turns. Final adjustment should be made with engine running under normal load. To adjust, turn screw in or out until engine fires on every stroke and is running at maximum RPM; then, turn screw out until engine slows down slightly. This will provide a fuel-air mixture rich enough for proper engine lubrication. If fuel mixture cannot

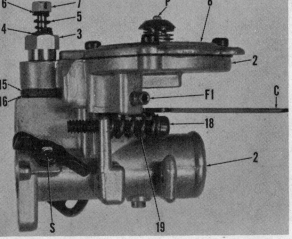

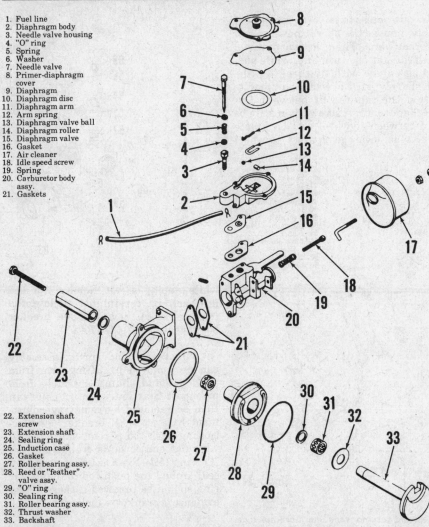

1. Fuel line
2. Diaphragm body
3. Needle valve housing
4. "O" ring
5. Spring
6. Washer
7. Needle valve
8. Primer-diaphragm cover
9. Diaphragm
10. Diaphragm disc
11. Diaphragm arm
12. Arm spring
13. Diaphragm valve ball
14. Diaphragm roller
15. Diaphragm valve
16. Gasket
17. Air cleaner
18. Idle speed screw
19. Spring
20. Carburetor body assy.
21. Gaskets

22. Extension shaft screw
23. Extension shaft
24. Sealing ring
25. Induction case
26. Gasket
27. Roller bearing assy.
28. Reed or "feather" valve assy.
29. "O" ring
30. Sealing ring
31. Roller bearing assy.
32. Thrust washer
33. Backshaft

Fig. O&R2—Exploded view of carburetor, induction housing and backshaft unit. Refer to Fig. O&R1 for view of carburetor assembly. Refer also to Fig. O&R6.

Fig. O&R1–View of late production diaphragm carburetor. New cover (8) with primer unit (P) can be installed on some earlier carburetors; a conversion kit is available. Flat end of governor vane shaft fits in slot (S) in carburetor throttle shaft. Fuel inlet is (FI), choke lever is (C); refer to Fig. O&R2 for remainder of legend.

be adjusted under load, adjusting screw should be turned to the position that will give smooth and rapid acceleration from low idle RPM to maximum governed speed. After adjusting carburetor, be sure that adjusting screw lock nut, if so equipped, is tightened securely. Idle speed should be 2200-2500 RPM.

On later production models with mixture adjusting needle and hex needle housing (3—Fig. O&R1) adjust carburetor as follows: For initial adjustment, turn adjusting screw (7) in until lightly seated and open screw ½-turn. Final adjustment should be made with engine warm and running under normal load. Turn screw in or out until engine fires on every stroke and is running at maximum RPM. Then, turn screw out slightly until engine starts to slow down; this will provide a sufficiently rich mixture for proper engine lubrication. If mixture cannot be adjusted under load, adjust needle to position that will give smoothest and most rapid acceleration from low idle speed to maximum RPM. Idle speed should be 2200-2500 RPM.

When removing the carburetor, first remove needle valve (7—Fig. O&R2) and housing (3), and the nearest (long) screw retaining diaphragm cover (8); then lift off diaphragm body (2) as an assembly. Fuel line will not need to be disconnected. Carefully disconnect governor vane shaft from slot (S—Fig. O&R1) in throttle shaft.

To reassemble diaphragm assembly, proceed as follows: Place diaphragm roller in housing as shown in Fig. O&R3 and install spring (2) so that bend in each end of spring is pointing down and closed end is adjacent to ball seat. Move spring away from roller (3) until diaphragm ball can be placed in seat while holding spring. Insert short end of diaphragm arm (11—Fig. O&R2) under closed end of spring and hook arm over pivot pin. Move spring

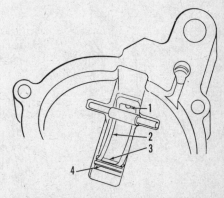

Fig. O&R3–Install diaphragm arm as outlined in text.

1. Ball recess
2. Spring
3. Roller
4. Ridge

onto arm as far as it will go and move roller (3—Fig. O&R3) to small cavity on other side of ridge (4). Be sure both ends of spring still contact roller after moving roller. Measure height of diaphragm arm by placing a straight edge across diaphragm housing and measure gap between straight edge and highest point on diaphragm arm. Gap should be 0.017-0.022.

GOVERNOR. An air-vane type governor is used on all models. To remove or inspect the air vane (44—Fig. O&R4), remove the blower housing as follows: Remove screws retaining cylinder baffles to blower housing. Remove screws retaining blower housing to engine and lift blower housing from engine.

The governor air vane should be held against the stop (43) by very light spring pressure from the coil spring on the carburetor throttle shaft. The vane and throttle shaft should work freely and return to position against the vane stop if released from any other position. Check for and remove any binding condition.

To renew governor spring, slide open end of new spring over throttle shaft and secure inner end of spring behind hook that is cast on the carburetor body. Slide a few coils of the outer end of spring off of the throttle shaft and twist spring clockwise only far enough to insert the straight outer end in the first hole in the throttle shaft. Be sure that none of the coils of the spring overlap when spring is in place.

Fig. O&R5—Exploded view of crankcase and cylinder assembly. Cylinder (71) is threaded into crankcase (83). Additional muffler sections (67) may be used on some engines. For exploded view of later production engine, refer to Fig. O&R6.

57. "O" rings	70. Gasket
58. Breaker pushrod	71. Cylinder
59. Roller bearing assy.	72. Gasket
60. Thrust washer	73. Exhaust collector
61. Flywheel key	74. Gasket
62. Crankshaft	75. Spacers
63. Roller bearings	76. Spacer washer
64. Retainer washers	77. "O" rings
65. Retainer washers	78. Piston rings
66. Roller bearing	79. Piston
67. Muffler sections	80. Piston pin
68. Muffler cup	81. Snap ring
69. Muffler bolt	82. Connecting rod

The flat end of the governor vane shaft should engage the slot in the carburetor throttle shaft so that the throttle disc is wide open when the governor vane is against the stop.

MAGNETO AND TIMING. A flywheel type magneto is used. The breaker contact points are enclosed in a box under the flywheel. The armature, coil and condenser are mounted outside the flywheel.

To gain access to the breaker contact points, remove the blower housing and governor vane. Then, loosen flywheel retaining nut one turn and, while supporting engine with flywheel, tap the nut sharply with a small hammer to unseat the tapered fit between flywheel and shaft. A screwdriver may be used between flywheel and backplate to provide leverage against flywheel

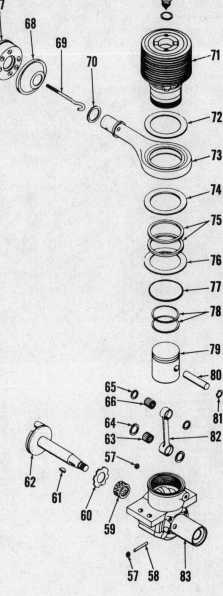

while tapping on nut. Remove nut and flywheel. Be careful not to lose the flywheel drive key. Remove breaker box cover (45—Fig. O&R4).

Contact arm and spring assembly can be removed by lifting arm from push rod and sliding assembly from pivot post. Stationary contact point can then be removed by removing adjustment lock screw. If breaker point actuating push rod is removed, reinstall with flat end towards crankshaft. An "O" ring (57—Fig. O&R5) is used as a seal around the push rod (58) and "O" ring should be renewed if there is any evidence of crankcase leakage.

On early production models, spring on breaker arm fits in slot of terminal

34. Flywheel nut	45. Breaker cover
35. Washer	46. Breaker point arm
36. Starter dogs	47. Insulators
37. Flywheel	48. Breaker point base
38. Seal	49. Breaker post
39. Retainer	50. Insulator
40. Roller bearing	51. Backplate
41. Armature & coil assy.	52. Insulated washer
42. Grommet (vane shaft)	53. Nut
43. Guard	54. Magneto short-out spring
44. Governor vane	55. Nut
	56. Condenser

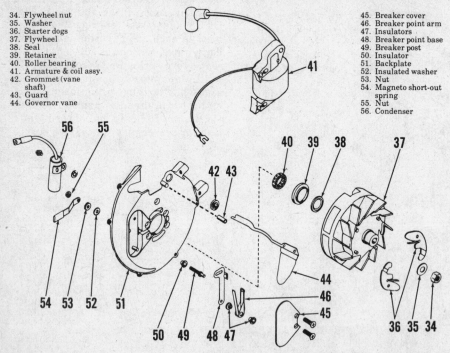

Fig. O&R4—Exploded view of magneto, backplate, flywheel and governor vane unit. Governor vane guard tube (43) is not used on later models. Bearing and seal retainer (39) is pressed onto crankcase (83—Fig. O&R5).

post (49—Fig. O&R4); on later production, the post is not slotted and spring rests against the post. The post must be insulated from the magneto backplate as it carries the primary ignition current.

If necessary to renew the magneto backplate, disconnect governor linkage, pry flywheel shaft seal and bearing retainer (39) from crankcase and remove backplate retaining screws. Flywheel nut tightening torque is 100 in.-lbs.

Adjust breaker contact gap to 0.020. Adjust armature air gap to 0.010.

LUBRICATION. Engine is lubricated by mixing SAE 30 API classification "MS" motor oil with regular gasoline. Fuel-oil ratio is 16:1. Mix thoroughly in a separate container.

CARBON. The engine cylinder should be removed (see Fig. O&R5), and any carbon present be scraped from exhaust ports, exhaust collector ring, piston, rings, ring grooves and muffler after each 30 to 100 hours of use. Use a dull tool and be careful not to damage cylinder bore.

REPAIRS

NOTE: When repairing engine, care should be exercised during disassembly that none of the bearing rollers from the connecting rod, crankshaft, clutch or gearbox are lost; and on reassembly that all bearing rollers are in their proper place and are not intermixed.

PISTON, PIN, RINGS AND CYLINDER. Lower end of cylinder is threaded into crankcase. To remove cylinder, first remove cylinder baffles, blower housing and governor vane shaft. Then, unscrew spark plug and using proper size drag link socket, unscrew cylinder from crankcase. Hold exhaust collector from turning when unscrewing cylinder. When threads are disengaged, lift cylinder straight up off of piston and rings.

Piston is equipped with two unpinned piston rings. Recommended piston ring end gap is 0.010 for early production wide rings and 0.005 for later production narrow rings. Narrow rings only are available for service; if end gap of early model with wide rings exceeds 0.010, install new narrow type rings with late type piston. Side clearance of either the wide or narrow rings in piston grooves should not exceed 0.005. Parts are available in standard size only.

Piston rings should be installed with end gaps 180 degrees apart. On early models with plain bearing piston pin, install pin with plugged end towards retaining snap ring.

Cylinder inside diameter is 1.2490

(top)-1.2505 (bottom) new. Renew cylinder if scored, cracked or if taper exceeds 0.005.

When installing cylinder, use new gaskets and "O" ring. Lubricate gasket and "O" ring, assemble exhaust collector on cylinder with gaskets, spacers and "O" ring as in Fig. O&R5 or O&R6. While holding piston at top dead center, push cylinder down over piston and rings. Carefully engage threads of cylinder and crankcase. Hold collector ring from turning while screwing cylinder into place. Be sure that exhaust collector ring is properly positioned and screw cylinder down snugly using drag link socket.

NOTE: The original cylinder used on COMPACT I Series engines is no longer available for service. If cylinder must be renewed, the factory recommends installation of latest cylinder, exhaust collector ring and associated parts.

CONNECTING ROD. Piston and rod assembly may be removed after removing cylinder and induction housing. On models with a clutch or gearbox, remove extension shaft, gearbox cover or clutch cover and clutch; then, remove screws retaining induction housing, clutch housing,

radial mount or gear case to engine crankcase. Complete assembly with carburetor attached may then be removed as a unit. Using tweezers, remove outer half of connecting rod bearing retainer and bearing rollers (early production models) or outer connecting rod retaining washer (later models). Slide connecting rod off of crankpin and remove rod and piston unit from engine. Remove inner half of bearing retainer (early models) or remaining retainer washer (late models). Be sure to remove any loose rod bearing rollers from crankcase before proceeding further.

To remove connecting rod from piston, remove snap ring at end of piston pin and push pin out of piston and connecting rod. On early production models with plain bearing piston pin, be careful not to push plug out of closed end of pin. On later engines with roller piston pin bearing, be careful not to lose any of the loose rollers and bearing retainer washers.

Renew any parts that are excessively worn or scored. Parts are available in standard size only.

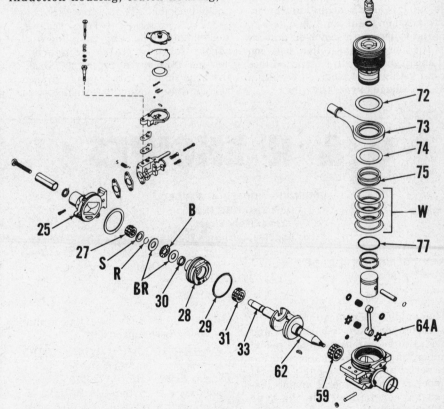

Fig. O&R6–Exploded view of late production engine; refer to Fig. O&R2 and Fig. O&R5 for earlier production engine, and for identification of parts not having call-out numbers in above view.

B.	Thrust bearing
BR.	Bearing races
R.	Retaining ring
S.	Spacer
W.	Heat-sink washers
25.	Induction housing

27.	Roller bearing
28.	Reed (feather) valve assembly
29.	"O" ring
31.	Roller bearing
33.	Backshaft

59.	Roller bearing
62.	Crankshaft
72.	Gasket
73.	Exhaust collector
74.	Gasket
75.	Spacers
77.	"O" ring

To reassemble piston to connecting rod, proceed as follows: On early models with plain bearing in upper end of connecting rod, insert the pin, open end first, through piston and connecting rod and install snap ring. On later models, stick the loose needle rollers in upper end of connecting rod with a light coat of heavy grease. Slide piston pin slightly through pin bore in piston and place one retainer washer over inner end of pin. Insert connecting rod with roller bearings into piston and carefully push piston pin most of the way through rod. Slide remaining pin bearing retainer washer between rod and piston and push the pin fully into place. Install piston pin retaining snap ring.

To reinstall piston and rod unit on early production models, place half of rod bearing retainer on crankpin. Insert rod into crankcase and slide open end over bearing retainer and crankpin. Insert bearing rollers into retainer using tweezers; then, place outer half of bearing retainer over crankpin.

On later production units with loose roller crankpin bearing, install piston and rod unit as follows: Install one retainer washer on crankpin with flat side out (towards bearing). Place connecting rod on crankpin, lubricate rod, pin and rollers with motor oil and insert the loose bearing rollers between rod and crankpin with tweezers. Place second retaining washer on crankpin with flat side in towards bearing.

NOTE: New piston pin and crankpin roller sets are furnished in wax strips for easy assembly. **Do not** remove wax from rollers; install the waxed roller strips in eyes of connecting rod and complete the assembly as described in preceding paragraphs.

CRANKSHAFT, BEARINGS AND SEALS. A two-piece crankshaft is used; refer to Figs. O&R2, O&R5 and O&R6. The flywheel crankshaft (62) with integral crankpin rides directly in two caged roller bearings located in the engine crankcase. The backshaft (33), or output shaft, rides directly in one caged roller bearing (31) located in the reed valve and in one caged roller bearing (27) located in the induction housing. The flywheel end shaft is sealed with a lip type seal (38—Fig. O&R4) located directly behind the flywheel and seal is renewable after removing flywheel. The backshaft is sealed with an "O" ring (30—Fig. O&R2) located in the bore of the reed valve unit and "O" ring is renewable after removing the backshaft.

REMOVE BACKSHAFT. First, remove clutch or gearbox cover if so equipped and remove clutch drive hub or drive gear hub from tapered outer end of backshaft. Then, after removing induction housing retaining screws, work induction housing (complete with carburetor and clutch or gearbox housing) from engine crankcase. Backshaft can then be withdrawn from reed valve unit and induction housing. Reed

valve unit may also be removed at this time.

Induction housing is sealed to reed valve unit and reed valve unit is sealed to engine crankcase with thin paper gaskets. Fuel-air induction passage is sealed with a lip type seal in induction housing and an "O" ring in reed valve unit which seat against backshaft. One induction housing retaining screw also has a small sealing "O" ring that fits into recess in induction housing.

REMOVE FLYWHEEL END SHAFT. To remove the flywheel end of the crankshaft, flywheel, connecting rod and piston unit must be removed from engine. Then, turn flywheel shaft so that ignition contact points are open (milled flat on shaft is away from pushrod) and withdraw shaft from engine. Reverse disassembly procedures and use all new gaskets and "O" rings to reassemble.

INTAKE VALVING. The reed valve assembly contains the inner bearing race for the engine backshaft and fits over the backshaft as shown in Fig. O&R6. Protrusion on reed valve unit fits into induction housing. Early models were fitted with metal reeds; later models have plastic reeds ("feather" valve).

If the reed valve is not functioning properly, the complete valve assembly must be renewed as individual parts are not available. The reed valve assembly can be renewed after removing the engine backshaft. Refer to exploded views in Figs. O&R2 and O&R6.

O & R ENGINES

(FORMERLY OHLSSON & RICE)
O&R ENGINES, INC.
3340 Emery Street
Los Angeles, California 90023

MODEL SERIES	Bore	Stroke	Displacement
20A	1.437	1.250	2.0

The engine identification plate is attached to the magneto back plate and includes three numbers: engine model number, engine type number and engine serial number. The engine model number indicates general engine features for servicing while the type number identifies specific engine features and must be used when obtaining parts.

MAINTENANCE
SPARK PLUG. Recommended spark plug is Champion CJ6 for normal

use and CJ4 for heavy use. Spark plug electrode gap should be 0.025.

CARBURETOR. A Walbro HDC diaphragm carburetor is used on all models. Refer to Fig. O&R10 for exploded view of carburetor. Initial setting of mixture screws is 1¼ turn open for idle mixture screw and 1 turn open for high speed screw. Idle speed should be approximately 2500 rpm. When installing carburetor, be sure crankcase pulse passages are aligned and clear in gaskets and reed valve housing.

GOVERNOR. An air vane governor

is used on some engines. As engine speed varies the air vane turns the governor shaft. The governor link (10 —Fig. O&R11) between the governor shaft lever (15) and carburetor throttle will transmit variations in engine speed and open or close carburetor throttle. A governor spring (11) is connected between governor shaft lever and speed setting bracket (1). Spring may be connected to one of three holes to obtain desired governed engine speed.

Governor assembly should be inspected to be sure linkage does not bind or is restricted. Right angle end of governor link (10) is connected to carburetor throttle lever. Opposite end of governor link is connected to one of two holes in governor shaft (15) lever. Installing link in inner hole will increase governor sensitivity while installation in outer hole decreases sensitivity.

To adjust governed speed, refer to Fig. O&R12 and connect governor spring in hole of desired governed rpm range. Loosen governor plate screw (S) and run engine under load. Move governor plate until desired governed rpm is obtained and retighten retaining screw. If engine "hunts", readjust carburetor. If carburetor adjustment will not correct hunting, alter governor sensitivity by moving governor link (10 —Fig. O&R11) to alternate hole in governor shaft (15) lever.

MAGNETO AND TIMING. A flywheel type magneto is used. The breaker contact points are enclosed in a box under the flywheel and actuated by

a cam on crankshaft. Armature and ignition coil are mounted outside flywheel. Refer to Fig. O&R13.

To obtain access to breaker points, recoil starter assembly, blower housing and flywheel must be removed. On models with a kill switch mounted on blower housing, ground wire must be disconnected to remove blower housing. Tighten flywheel retaining nut to 120 in.-lbs.

Ignition timing is fixed. Breaker point gap should be 0.015-0.018 and must be correct, as incorrect point gap will affect ignition timing. Armature air gap should be 0.010. Set air gap by loosening armature mounting screws and place 0.010 shim stock between armature and flywheel. Position armature against shim and tighten armature mounting screws. Remove shim stock.

LUBRICATION. The engine is lubricated by mixing oil with fuel. A good quality SAE 30 oil with classification MS should be mixed with fuel at ratio of 16:1. Oil designed for air-cooled engines should be used.

Gear reduction unit is lubricated with a Lubri-Plate type grease or equivalent. Oil should not be used as clutch action will be affected.

REPAIRS

PISTON, PIN, RINGS AND CYLINDER. Model 20A is equipped with a chrome plated cylinder. To remove cylinder, remove blower housing, flywheel and magneto back plate. Note position of exhaust so that cylinder may be reinstalled correctly depending on engine application.

Inspect cylinder for excessive wear or damage to chrome bore. Excessive wear may be checked by placing a new piston ring in cylinder bore and measuring ring end gap. If gap exceeds 0.077, cylinder should be renewed. Remove, clean and inspect piston. Piston ring side clearance should be 0.0015-0.0035. Piston ring end gap should be 0.067-0.077. Piston rings are non-directional. Install piston with

piston ring locating pins towards flywheel side of engine. Tighten cylinder retaining nuts to 50 in.-lbs.

CONNECTING ROD. To remove connecting rod, remove cylinder and piston as previously outlined. Remove carburetor and reed valve assembly. Hold connecting rod cap (13—Fig. O&R14) by placing a finger through intake port and remove rod capscrews. Remove connecting rod, being careful not to lose bearing rollers. Use a suitable press to remove and reinstall small end bearing.

Connecting rod is fractured and serrations of rod and cap must mesh during assembly. Rod and cap have match marks as shown in Fig. O&R15 which must be aligned. To reinstall connecting rod, hold 14 bearing rollers in connecting rod cap with heavy grease and hold cap and rollers on crankshaft. New bearing rollers are on wax strips which may be used in place of grease. Place remaining 14 bearing rollers in rod with heavy grease, align match marks and serrations on rod and cap and install rod on crankshaft.

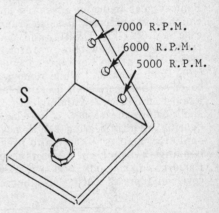

Fig. O&R12–Governed speed is determined by location of governor spring in one of three holes in governor plate and repositioning plate by loosening screw (S).

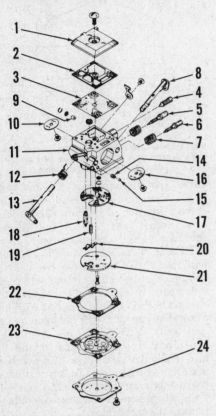

Fig. O&R10–Exploded view of Walbro HDC carburetor.

1. Cover	12. Spring
2. Gasket	13. Throttle shaft
3. Fuel pump diaphragm	14. Spring
	15. Choke friction ball
4. Idle speed screw	16. Choke plate
5. Idle mixture screw	17. Gasket
6. High speed mixture screw	18. Fuel inlet valve
	19. Spring
7. Spring	20. Metering lever
8. Choke shaft	21. Circuit plate spring
9. Limiting jet	22. Gasket
10. Throttle plate	23. Metering diaphragm
11. Body	24. Cover

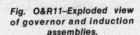

Fig. O&R11–Exploded view of governor and induction assemblies.

1. Governor plate
2. Governor bracket
3. Air filter housing
4. Gasket
5. Carburetor
6. Gasket
7. Reed valve seat
8. Reed petal
9. Gasket
10. Governor link
11. Governor spring
12. Bushing
13. Retainers
14. Pin
15. Governor shaft & lever
16. Crankcase
17. Magneto back plate

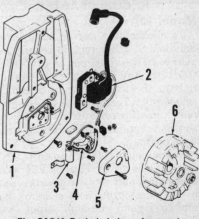

Fig. O&R13–Exploded view of magneto.

1. Magneto back plate	4. Breaker points
2. Armature and coil	5. Point box
3. Condenser	6. Flywheel

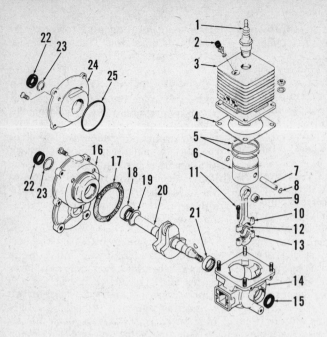

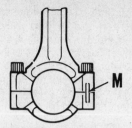

Fig. O&R14—Exploded view of engine. Crankcase cover (16) is used with gear reduction unit. Cover (24) may be used with direct drive or clutch.

1. Spark plug
2. Compression release
3. Cylinder
4. Gasket
5. Piston rings
6. Piston
7. Piston pin
8. Retainer
9. Bearing
10. Connecting rod
11. Capscrew
12. Bearing rollers (28)
13. Rod cap
14. Crankcase
15. Seal
16. Crankcase cover
17. Gasket
18. Bearing
19. Snap ring
20. Crankshaft
21. Bearing
22. Seal
23. Snap ring
24. Crankcase cover
25. "O" ring

Fig. O&R15—Connecting rod match marks (M) must be aligned during assembly.

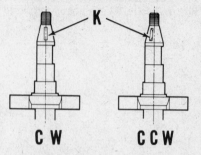

Fig. O&R16–Crankshaft for clockwise (CW) or counterclockwise (CCW) rotation may be identified by keyway (K) location.

Tighten connecting rod capscrews to 40-50 in.-lbs.

CRANKSHAFT AND CRANKCASE. To remove crankshaft, remove connecting rod as previously outlined. Remove gear reduction assembly and clutch if so equipped. Remove crankcase seal (22—Fig. O&R14) and snap ring (23). Unscrew three retaining screws and remove crankcase cover (16). Hold crankshaft while removing cover so that crankshaft does not fall against crankcase. Withdraw crankshaft being careful not to lose loose bearing rollers in bearing (21). Remove seal (15), heat crankcase and press bearing (21) race out of crankcase. Remove snap ring (19), heat crankcase cover and press bearing (18) out of

cover.

Note different locations of keyway on crankshaft used for clockwise or counterclockwise engine rotation. See Fig. O&R16. Engine rotation is determined by rotation of output end of crankshaft and not gear reduction output shaft. Correct engine rotation is listed in parts book for each engine type number.

Inspect components for wear or damage. Heat crankcase cover, press in bearing (18—Fig. O&R14) and install snap ring (19). Heat crankcase and press in bearing (21) race so that letters on race are to inside of crankcase. Install 18 bearing rollers in race with grease to hold rollers in place. Install crankshaft, gasket and crankcase

cover. Install snap ring (23) and seal (22). Turn crankshaft and check for correct location of bearing (21) rollers and install seal (15). Reinstall remainder of engine components.

REED VALVE. Model 20A is equipped with a reed valve. Reed valve should be inspected for damage to reed valve petal or seat. Reed valve petal (8—Fig. O&R11) should seat flat with an allowable gap of 0.010 between petal and seat. Reed petals are available separately. Install gaskets (6 and 9) and reed valve seat (7) so that notches are aligned with notch in top of intake passage of crankcase (16). The notches form a passage for crankcase pulsations to the carburetor.

SERVICING O&R ACCESSORIES

RECOIL STARTER
Model 20A

To disassemble starter, remove rope handle and allow rope to rewind into starter. Remove cover (12—Fig. O&R20). Rewind spring (11) should remain in cover but care should be taken when removing cover as spring may uncoil and could cause injury. Remove remainder of starter assembly from engine.

To reassemble starter, install starter dogs as shown in Fig. O&R21. Note that crankshaft rotation is determined by viewing output end of crankshaft and NOT gear reduction output shaft. Place end of rope through hole in rope pulley and tie knot. Pass other end of rope through rope outlet in housing (9

Fig. O&R20–Exploded view of starter assembly. Housing (9) or (9A) may be used.

1. Flywheel
2. Spring
3. Starter dog
4. "E" ring
5. Blower housing
6. Bushing
7. Rope pulley & hub
8. Handle
9. & 9A. Housing
10. Washer
11. Rewind spring
12. Cover

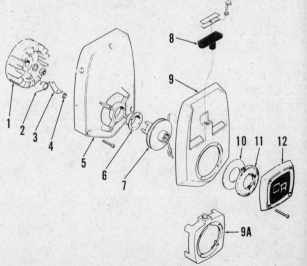

SMALL ENGINES

or 9A—Fig. O&R20). Assemble components (1 thru 9). Pull rope out of starter so that it is fully extended and attach rope handle so that there is 28 inches from starter housing to bottom of rope handle. Wind rope on pulley by turning pulley in direction that does not engage starter dogs. Install rewind spring in cover as shown in Fig. O&R21. Lubricate spring with a suitable lubricant. To preload starter rope, install spring and cover so that inner hook of spring engages notch in rope pulley and turn cover 1-1½ turns in direction that will wind spring. Install cover screws.

All Other Models

On late models, the starter reel is retained in blower housing by a snap ring as shown in Fig. O&R22. On early models, the reel is not secured and is retained only by its close fit on bearing (87—Fig. O&R23) and by rope and recoil spring.

To disassemble the starter, unseat the retaining snap ring if so equipped, and remove knob from rope if rope is not broken; then allow spring to slowly unwind. Lift out the reel, being careful to disengage hooked inner end of recoil spring from reel hub. Spring should remain in recess in blower housing when reel is removed.

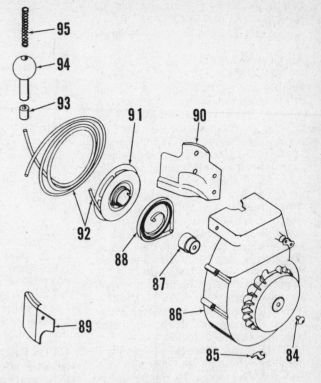

Fig. O&R23–Exploded view of blower housing and recoil starter assembly. Screw (84) retains starter bearing (87) in blower housing.

84. Screw
85. Spring retainer (not used on late models)
86. Blower housing
87. Starter bearing
88. Starter spring
89. Cylinder baffle
90. Cylinder baffle
91. Starter reel assy.
92. Starter cord
93. Cushion
94. Knob
95. Spring (not used on late models)

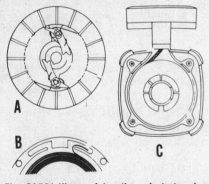

Fig. O&R21–Views of location of starter dogs (A), rewind spring (B) and rope (C) on clockwise rotating engine. Reverse positions of starter dogs, rewind spring and rope shown above for counterclockwise rotating engine.

Fig. O&R22–On late models, except model 20A, starter reel is retained to blower housing by a snap ring which must be removed as shown.

Early models use a 44-inch nylon starter cord and hooked outer end of spring engages a slot in outside of blower housing. Late models use a 54-inch cord and outer end of recoil spring contains a riveted loop. Cord and/or spring cannot be interchanged. On all models, rope is anchored to reel hub by a twisted soft iron wire.

When reinstalling the reel, proceed as follows: Unwind rope from reel sheave and pull entire rope out between spokes of reel. Install reel, making sure inner end of spring engages slot in reel hub. Install retaining snap ring if so equipped, making sure end gap is NOT positioned in wide slot where rope emerges. On all models, turn reel counter-clockwise until recoil spring is completely wound, then clockwise one turn. Feed starter rope back through reel spokes and out through opening in blower housing. Pull rope tight through guide rollers and tie a slip knot in rope until knob is reinstalled.

Starter dogs (36—Fig. O&R4) mount on pins on outer face of flywheel. On early models, dogs were retained by a machined slot in flywheel hub. On late models, a retaining washer is used. Washer is a press fit on flywheel and a new washer should be installed each time starter dogs are removed. Check to be sure starter dogs do not bind or are not unduly worn. Stake new retaining washer in two places on models so equipped.

DIRECT DRIVE CLUTCH
Model 20A

Clutch hub may be screwed on crankshaft if clutch sprocket is mounted inboard, or clutch may be retained on crankshaft with a snap ring. To unscrew hub, place blade of screwdriver in slot of clutch shoe as shown in Fig. O&R24 and tap on screwdriver while holding flywheel. Disassemble clutch assembly and inspect components. Renew clutch shoes if grooves in rubbing surface are worn away or shallow. Renew clutch shoes in pairs. Inspect clutch drum for concentricity. If clutch engagement speed occurs at lower than desired rpm, renew clutch springs. Clutch springs must be renewed as a unit to obtain uniform clutch engagement.

Install clutch shoes on hub so that relieved end of shoe is trailing surface. Install clutch springs in shoes with "V" of springs bent back against block on

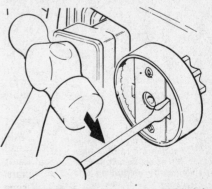

Fig. O&R24–Remove threaded clutch hub by inserting screwdriver blade as shown and tapping with hammer.

hub as shown in Fig. O&R26. Secure retainer plate (11—Fig. O&R25) screws with Loc-Tite.

All Other Models

EARLY PRODUCTION. To disassemble the early production direct drive clutch, proceed as follows: Loosen the extension shaft retaining cap screw (2—Fig. O&R27) one turn. While supporting engine by holding extension shaft (4), tap loosened cap screw sharply with a small hammer to loosen taper fit of shaft to clutch shaft. Remove extension shaft, clutch cover, thrust washer and roller bearing. If clutch drum (6) will not pull out of clutch bearing easily, reinstall extension shaft on clutch shaft and, while supporting engine with extension shaft, drive die-cast clutch bearing (8) off of clutch drum with screwdriver and a small hammer. CAUTION: Be careful that engine does not drop when clutch bearing and drum separate. Hold engine close to bench.

Clutch shoes (7) can then be removed from clutch hub. Renew shoes if linings are excessively worn. To remove clutch hub from engine backshaft, loosen Phillips head screw (10) one turn, and support engine by holding clutch hub. Set screwdriver against loosened screw and tap screwdriver sharply with small hammer to loosen tapered fit between clutch hub and backshaft.

Fig. O&R27–View showing direct drive clutch drum and shoes removed.

1. Clutch cover
2. Cap screw
3. Clutch cover seal
4. Extension shaft
5. Outer clutch bearing
6. Clutch drum
7. Clutch shoes and spring assembly
8. Inner clutch bearing
9. Clutch hub
10. Clutch hub retaining screw

Lubricate clutch parts with SAE30 oil and use new paper gasket between clutch housing and cover during reassembly. Reverse disassembly procedure to reassemble.

NOTE: Parts are no longer available for early production clutch. Install complete later production clutch if clutch renewal is necessary.

LATE PRODUCTION. To disassemble the late production direct drive clutch (See Fig. O&R28), proceed as follows: Loosen extension shaft retaining capscrew (1) one turn. While supporting engine by holding extension shaft (2), tap loosened capscrew sharply with small hammer to loosen taper fit of shaft to clutch shaft. Remove extension shaft, clutch cover (3)

and roller bearing retainer assembly (4). If clutch drum (5) will not pull out of clutch bearing easily, reinstall extension shaft and while supporting engine with extension shaft, lightly tap clutch bearing (7) off of clutch drum with screwdriver and small hammer. Caution: Be careful that engine does not drop when clutch bearing and drum separate. Hold engine close to bench.

Clutch shoes and hub assembly (6) can then be removed from engine backshaft. Loosen Phillips head screw (in end of backshaft) one turn and support engine by holding clutch bearing (7). Set screwdriver against loosened screw and tap screwdriver sharply with small hammer to loosen tapered fit between clutch hub and backshaft.

Lubricate clutch parts with grease and use new paper gasket between clutch housing and cover during reassembly. Reverse disassembly procedure to reassemble unit.

GEAR REDUCTION UNIT
Model 20A

Disassemble gear reduction assembly by removing gear cover (2—Fig. O&R25) being careful not to lose bearing rollers in bearing (3). Withdraw output gear and shaft (5). Remove snap ring (8) and remove clutch assembly. Refer to previous section to

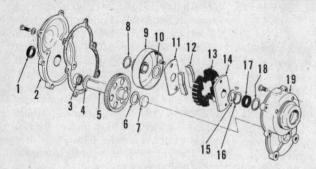

Fig. O&R25–Exploded view of gear reduction unit. Clutch components may be used without gear reduction as direct drive.

1. Seal
2. Gear cover
3. Bearing
4. Thrust washer
5. Output gear & shaft
6. Thrust washer
7. Bearing
8. Snap ring
9. Clutch housing
10. Washer
11. Retainer plate
12. Clutch springs
13. Clutch shoes
14. Clutch hub
15. Washer
16. Snap ring
17. Seal
18. Snap ring
19. Crankcase cover

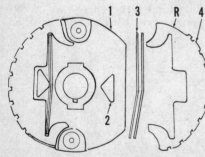

Fig. O&R26–Install clutch springs (3) so that arch of spring will be bent back against anchor block (2) when installed. Clutch shoe recess (R) should be on trailing end of shoe when installed.

R. Recess
1. Clutch hub
2. Anchor block
3. Clutch springs
4. Clutch shoe

Fig. O&R28–Exploded view of late production direct drive clutch assembly. Refer to Fig. O&R27 for view of early type clutch.

1. Extension shaft screw
2. Extension shaft
3. Clutch cover
4. Roller bearing
5. Clutch drum
6. Clutch drum and shoe assy.
7. Clutch bearing
8. Engine backshaft

service clutch. To remove crankcase cover (19), remove snap rings (16 and 18) and seal (17). Unscrew retaining screws and remove cover while supporting crankshaft end. Refer to CRANKSHAFT section to service crankcase cover. When reassembling unit, lubricate bearings and seals with a Lubri-Plate type grease; do not use oil. Be sure bearing rollers are correctly installed. Note that gear reduction unit can be mounted on crankcase in three different positions.

All Other Models

Models with reduction gear drive (gearbox) may be equipped with or without centrifugal clutch. Models with 900 RPM output shaft speed have a compound gearbox. To disassemble gear reduction drive, proceed as follows:

Loosen cap screw retaining extension shaft (L.H. threads on 1700 and 3300 RPM models, R.H. thread on 900 RPM models) and, while supporting engine with extension shaft, tap loosened screw sharply with small hammer to loosen tapered fit of shaft. On 900 RPM models, remove compound gear cover, extension shaft and gear assembly. On 1700 RPM and 3300 RPM models, remove extension shaft and gearbox cover.

Loosen the screw retaining clutch hub or pinion gear to engine backshaft and, while supporting engine with clutch hub or pinion gear, tap loosened screw sharply with a small hammer and screwdriver to loosen taper fit of hub or gear to shaft. Remove pinion gear or clutch hub and large driven gear. Gear housing, induction housing and carburetor may now be removed from engine as a unit.

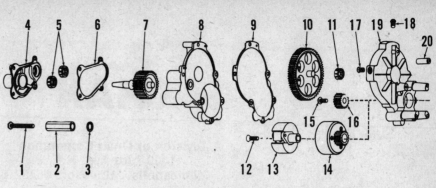

Fig. O&R29—Exploded view of double reduction gear unit. On models without clutch (13 & 14), drive gear (16) is used.

1. Extension shaft screw
2. Extension shaft
3. Sealing ring
4. Reduction gear cover
5. Roller bearings
6. Gasket
7. Output gear
8. Gear housing cover
9. Gasket
10. Intermediate gear
11. Roller bearing
12. Phillips head screw
13. Clutch hub and shoe assy.
14. Clutch drum & drive gear
15. Phillips head screw
16. Drive gear
17. Plug
18. Plug
19. Gear housing
20. Spacer (reverse position gear case models only)

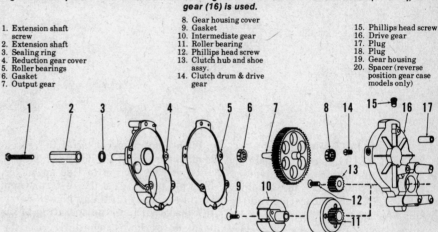

Fig. O&R30—Exploded view of single reduction gear unit. Drive gear (13) is used on models without clutch (10 & 11). Spacer (17) is used on reverse position gear case installation only.

1. Extension shaft screw
2. Extension shaft
3. Sealing ring
4. Gear case cover
5. Gasket
6. Roller bearing
7. Output gear
8. Roller bearing
9. Phillips head screw
10. Clutch hub & shoe assy.
11. Clutch drum & drive gear
12. Phillips head screw
13. Drive gear
14. Plug
15. Plug
16. Gear housing
17. Spacer

Reverse disassembly procedures to reassemble. Lubricate gear box with steel gears with two tablespoons of heavy grease such as Union Oil Unoba F-1 or equivalent. One tablespoon of grease should be added any time gear cover is removed. On models without steel gears, lubricate unit with one tablespoon of SAE 30 oil. One teaspoon of oil should be added after each 10 hours of use. CAUTION: Do not overfill gearbox as this will cause overheating. Gearbox is provided with a screw plug for lubricating gears.

ONAN

Division of Onan Corporation
1400 73rd Ave. N.E.
Minneapolis, Minnesota 55432

Model	Cyls.	Bore	Stroke	Displ.
AJ	1	2¾	2½	14.9
AK	1	2½	2½	12.2

MAINTENANCE

SPARK PLUG. Recommended plug is 14mm Champion H-8 or equivalent. Electrode gap is 0.025 for gasoline; 0.018 for LP-Gas or natural gas fuel.

CARBURETOR (GASOLINE).

Refer to Fig. O1 for exploded view of typical Carter model N carburetor used on models AJ and AK Onan engines. Clockwise rotation of main fuel needle (10) and idle fuel needle (7) leans the fuel mixture.

For initial adjustment, open main fuel needle approximately 2½ turns and open idle fuel needle about one turn. Make final adjustments with engine running at operating temperature.

With engine operating at full rated load, turn main fuel needle in slowly until engine begins to lose speed (or light plant voltage starts to drop), then turn needle out until engine will carry full load. With engine operating at no load, or at lowest charging rate for battery charging plant, turn idle fuel needle in slowly until engine loses speed, then turn needle out to point of smoothest engine operation.

To help prevent governor "hunting" under changes in load, adjust throttle stop screw (2) as follows: With engine operating at rated speed at no load, turn throttle stop screw in until it just touches throttle lever, then turn screw out one turn.

For float level setting, refer to Fig. O2.

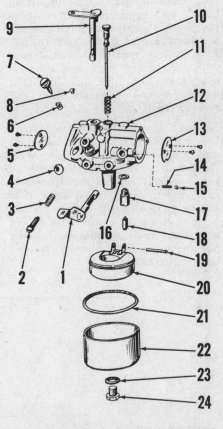

Fig. O1–Exploded view of typical Carter model N carburetor as used on gasoline fuel engines. Refer to Fig. O2 for checking float level.

1. Choke shaft
2. Throttle stop screw
3. Spring
4. Welch plug
5. Throttle plate
6. Spring
7. Idle fuel needle
8. Idle passage plug
9. Throttle shaft
10. Main fuel needle
11. Spring
12. Carburetor body
13. Choke plate
14. Spring
15. Friction ball, choke shaft
16. Gasket
17. Inlet valve seat
18. Inlet valve
19. Float pin
20. Float
21. Gasket
22. Float bowl
23. Gasket
24. Screw

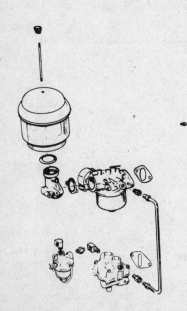

Overall view of fuel system components typical of those used on Onan models AJ, AK.

AUTOMATIC CHOKE. Some gasoline fuel models are equipped with an automatic electrically operated choke. Refer to exploded view of the choke assembly in Fig. O3. When cold, the bimetal element (2) turns the carburetor choke to closed position. After engine is started, heat from electric heating coil in cover (1) causes bimetal element to move choke to open position.

At a temperature of 70° F., the choke should be approximately ⅛-inch from fully closed position. Extreme temperature variation may require adjustment of the choke; refer to Fig. O4 for choke adjustment.

FUEL PUMP. Refer to Fig. O5 for exploded view of the gasoline fuel lift pump assembly. All parts except upper and lower bodies (1 and 14) are serviced separately. Actuating primer lever (10) will pump fuel into carburetor.

CARBURETOR (LP-GAS OR NATURAL GAS). When equipped to burn LP-Gas or natural gas, an Ensign single diaphragm model F regulator and a carburetor as shown in Fig. O6 are used. The regulator shown in Fig. O7 automatically shuts off the fuel supply when engine is stopped and is provided with idle fuel mixture adjusting needle (I). Gas from the supply line enters inlet (A) at 4 to 6 ounces pressure, but is prevented from entering the regulator due to valve (C) being closed by spring (B) when engine is not running. When engine is started, vacuum from the carburetor is transmitted via the outlet (E) and regulator passage (F) to the right side of the diaphragm (G) causing diaphragm and lever (H) to move to the right thus opening the valve (C) to control flow of gas to carburetor. At slow idling speeds the movement of the diaphragm (and the quality of the idling mixture) is controlled by the idle mixture adjusting needle (I). An idle tube from the carburetor is connected to the regulator at (J). A primer (P) instead of a choke is provided to facilitate starting.

Regulator may be disassembled for overhaul. Carefully inspect all parts and renew any that show wear. The diaphragm is bulged and cemented between gaskets at the factory. Do NOT attempt to flatten it. When reassembling valve (C) and lever (H) do not tighten the pivot block screw (L) more than enough to hold the block in position. If screw is tightened too much it will bind the lever.

Adjust carburetor in normal manner keeping in mind that idle mixture is controlled by needle (I) mounted on the regulator while power mixture is controlled by the knurled adjusting needle

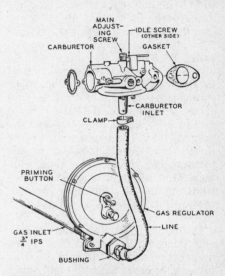

Fig. O6—View of carburetor and pressure regulator used on LP-Gas or natural gas engines.

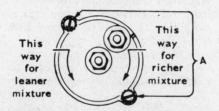

Fig. O4—To adjust gasoline carburetor automatic choke unit, loosen cover retaining screws and turn cover as required. Refer to text.

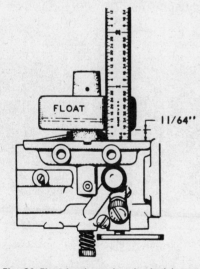

Fig. O2—Float level can be checked by measuring distance between free end of float and carburetor body as shown when body and float assembly are held in inverted position.

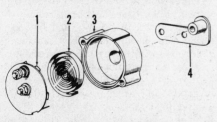

Fig. O3—Exploded view of automatic choke unit available on gasoline models. Refer to Fig. O4 for adjusting unit.

1. Cover & heating element assy.
2. Bimetal element
3. Housing
4. Mounting bracket

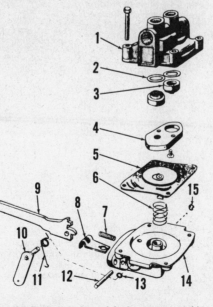

Fig. O5—Exploded view of fuel pump assembly used on some models.

1. Upper body
2. Gaskets
3. Valves
4. Valve retainer
5. Diaphragm
6. Spring
7. Spring
8. Link
9. Arm
10. Primer lever
11. Spring
12. Pin
13. "O" ring
14. Lower body
15. Snap ring

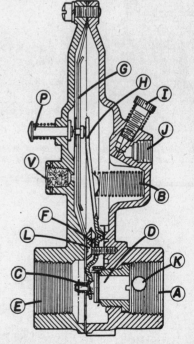

Fig. O7—Cross-sectional view of pressure regulator (see Fig. O6) used on LP-Gas or natural gas engines. Idle fuel mixture adjusting screw is (I).

A. Inlet
B. Spring
C. Valve
D. Valve seat
E. Outlet
F. Passage
G. Diaphragm
H. Lever
I. Idle mixture adjustment
J. Idle connection
L. Pivot screw
P. Primer
V. Vent

on the carburetor.

Choke position is determined by counterweight on choke shaft. On some models, a choke adjusting screw is provided; refer to Fig. O8. The weighted choke should just close, but be free to open with air stream through carburetor when engine is running. Turn adjusting screw in to reduce choking.

GOVERNOR. Engines which drive electric plants are governed at 1500, 1600, 1800, 2400, 2600, 3000 or 3600 RPM as indicated on generating plant nameplate. Industrial engines are usually governed at 2400 rpm.

To adjust governor linkage, proceed as follows: On models with automatic idle control (Fig. O10), move control toggle switch to "off" position. With engine stopped, the tension of the governor spring should hold the throttle arm in the wide open position and the throttle lever on the carburetor throttle shaft should just clear the carburetor body by not more than 1/32-inch. This setting can be obtained by adjusting the ball joint on the governor control linkage shown at upper left in Fig. O9.

On industrial engines, start engine and adjust no load speed 50-100 rpm higher than desired full load speed by turning the speed adjusting nut. Apply

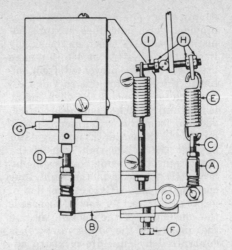

Fig. O10–View of automatic idle control used on some generating plants. Adjustment procedure is outlined in text.

full load and if speed drop is too great correct by adjusting sensitivity screw to move end of governor spring closer to governor shaft. If engine tends to hunt, adjustment is too close. Any change in sensitivity adjustment will require a speed readjustment. For governor repairs refer to CAMSHAFT and GOVERNOR paragraph.

On AC generating plants, connect a voltmeter across generator output terminals. With plant operating at no load, adjust engine speed so that voltmeter reading is 126 volts on 120 volt plant, or 252 volts on a 240 volt plant. Then, when a full rated load is connected to generator, voltmeter reading should not fall below 108 volts on a 120 volt plant, or 216 volts on a 240 volt plant. If voltage drop is excessive, turn sensitivity adjustment screw (See Fig. O9) in (clockwise) to increase governor sensitivity. If voltage remains above limits at full load, but voltmeter reading is unsteady (governor "hunts"), turn sensitivity adjustment screw out (counter-clockwise) to decrease governor sensitivity. Any change in the sensitivity adjustment screw will require a compensating change in the speed adjustment nut. On 115-volt DC direct service plants, governor can be adjusted following procedure outlined for AC generating plants.

On models with automatic idle control, refer to Fig. O10 and proceed as follows: Set idle control to "OFF" position and loosen screw (F) so there is no tension on spring (E). Slip socket of flexible joint (A) from ball on lever (B). With lock nuts (H) loosened, adjust governor for normal 3600 RPM operation as outlined in previous paragraph for AC generating plants. Then, tighten locknuts (H) with spring (E) as

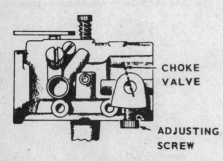

CHOKE VALVE

ADJUSTING SCREW

Fig. O8–View showing choke adjusting screw location on some LP-Gas or natural gas carburetors.

Fig. O11–View of magneto ignition system. Timing is adjustable by rotating magneto assembly on slotted mounting holes.

STOP LEAD
BREAKER POINT SET
TIMING ADJUSTING SCREW
TUCK PRIMARY COIL WIRE UNDER INSULATION STRIP
HIGH TENSION LEAD
ADVANCE TIMING
RETARD TIMING
LOOSEN THIS SCREW TO SHIFT POINT SET FOR 0.022" GAP AT FULL SEPARATION. RETIGHTEN SCREW SECURELY.
OIL WICK
CONDENSER
COIL INSULATED FROM SHOE. HELD TIGHT BY ONE LAMINATION.
TIMING ADJUSTING SCREW
POLE SHOE AND BACKPLATE

close as possible to end of sensitivity lever.

MAGNETO AND TIMING. Refer to Fig. O11 for view of flywheel type magneto used on some engines. Breaker points are located under flywheel. Recommended breaker point gap of 0.022 can be obtained by loosening the points assembly retaining screw and shifting the point set. Timing on engines operated at 1800 rpm or less should be 19 degrees BTC; engines operated above 1800 rpm should be timed at 25 degrees BTC. Magneto back plate has elongated mounting screw holes to permit timing adjustment. Breaker points should just start to open when index mark on flywheel is aligned with the correct de-

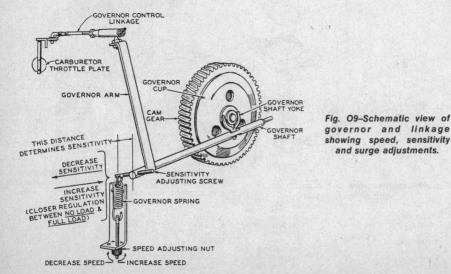

GOVERNOR CONTROL LINKAGE
CARBURETOR THROTTLE PLATE
GOVERNOR ARM
GOVERNOR CUP
CAM GEAR
GOVERNOR SHAFT YOKE
GOVERNOR SHAFT
THIS DISTANCE DETERMINES SENSITIVITY
DECREASE SENSITIVITY
SENSITIVITY ADJUSTING SCREW
INCREASE SENSITIVITY (CLOSER REGULATION BETWEEN NO LOAD & FULL LOAD)
GOVERNOR SPRING
SPEED ADJUSTING NUT
DECREASE SPEED   INCREASE SPEED

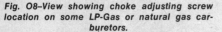

Fig. O9–Schematic view of governor and linkage showing speed, sensitivity and surge adjustments.

gree mark on gear cover. Air gap between coil pole shoes and flywheel should not be less than 0.010 and not more than 0.015.

BATTERY IGNITION AND TIMING. Some engines are equipped with a battery ignition system. The ignition breaker points and condenser are located on side of engine. Timing is adjusted by varying the breaker point gap. The point gap can be varied from 0.016 to 0.024 in order to attain a spark advance of 19 to 25 crankshaft degrees BTC. Recommended timing is 19 degrees BTC on engines that run at speeds of 1800 rpm and slower; 25 degrees BTC on engines that run above 1800 rpm. Decreasing the point gap retards timing and increasing gap advances timing. A reference mark and 19 and 25 degree marks on flywheel can be seen through an opening in the blower housing.

LUBRICATION. Recommended oil is API classification SE. During break-in or for operation in temperatures below 32°F, CC rated oils may be used. With air temperatures below 0°F, use SAE 5W-30 weight oil. From 0°F to 32°F, use 5W-30 or 10W-30, and from 32°F to 90°F use SAE 30.

Crankcase capacity is 3 pints. Pressure lubrication is optional. Pressure lubricated engines utilize a gear type oil pump, an oil intake cup and a non-adjustable oil pressure relief valve. If pump is to be removed it must be turned off the intake pipe. If the oil pump fails install a complete new pump.

REPAIRS

TIGHTENING TORQUES. Recommended tightening torque values are as follows. All values are in Ft.-Lbs.

Connecting Rod 10-12
Cylinder Head 24-26
Gear Cover 15-20
Oil Base 25-30
Oil pump mounting screws 7-9

PISTON, PIN AND RINGS. The aluminum piston is fitted with two compression rings and one oil control ring. Tapered compression rings should be installed with word "TOP" or other identifying mark up. Recommended

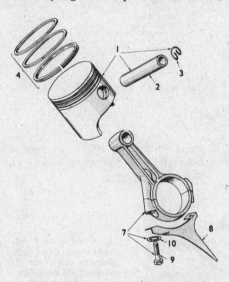

Fig. O13–Exploded view of piston and connecting rod assembly. Note position of oil dipper (8).

1. Piston & pin assy.
2. Piston pin
3. Retaining rings
4. Piston rings
7. Connecting rod assy.
8. Oil dipper
9. Rod cap screws
10. Lock washers

piston ring end gap for all rings is 0.007-0.017.

Desired piston skirt to cylinder bore clearance is 0.0015-0.0035 for model AK engines and 0.0025-0.0045 for model AJ engines. Standard cylinder bore is 2.5005-2.5015 for model AK and 2.7505-2.7515 for model AJ engines. Pistons and piston rings are available in oversizes of 0.010, 0.020, 0.030 and 0.040 and in standard size for both models.

The floating type piston pin is retained by snap rings. Pin should be a hand push fit in piston and a thumb push fit in connecting rod at 72° F. Piston pin is available in standard size and in 0.002 oversize.

CONNECTING ROD. Rod and piston unit is removed from above. The aluminum rod rides directly on the crankshaft crankpin. Crankpin diameter is 1.3745-1.3750. Recommended bearing clearance is 0.0015-0.0025. Rod assembly is available in undersizes of 0.010, 0.020 and 0.030 as well as standard size. Side play on the crankpin should be 0.012-0.035. Note that dipper is installed so as to splash oil towards the camshaft side of engine on splash lubricated models.

CRANKSHAFT, BEARINGS AND SEALS. The crankshaft rides in two renewable sleeve type bearings. Some models require flange type bearings (bushings) which must be pressed into bore from inside of block or bearing plate. Bearings used in early production engines required line boring or reaming after installation;

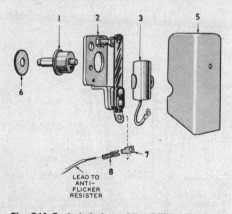

Fig. O12–Exploded view of "anti-flicker" points used on some generating plant engines. Lead is attached to anti-flicker resister in generator and has no connection with engine ignition system. Adjust anti-flicker breaker point (2) gap to 0.020.

1. Plunger assembly
2. Point set
3. Condenser (0.5 mfd.)
5. Cover
6. Gasket
7. Terminal
8. Terminal

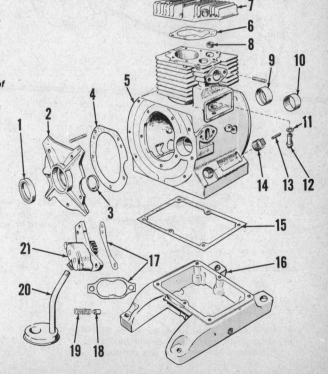

Fig. O14–Exploded view of crankcase assembly.

1. Oil seal
2. Bearing plate
3. Plug
4. Gaskets
5. Cylinder block
6. Gasket
7. Cylinder head
8. Exhaust valve seat insert
9. Crankshaft bearings
10. Camshaft bearings
11. Gasket
12. Valve guides
13. Dowel pin (timing gear cover)
14. Oil filler plug
15. Gasket
16. Oil pan
17. Gaskets
18. Oil pressure relief valve
19. Relief valve spring
20. Oil intake tube & screen
21. Oil pump assembly

however, current service parts are precision type bearings which require no reaming and are used to renew the earlier type bearings.

Crankshaft main bearing journal diameter is 1.6860-1.6865; desired journal to bearing running clearance is 0.003-0.004. Renew bearings if clearance is excessive. If crankshaft main journals are worn, journals may be ground undersize as bearings are available in undersizes of 0.002, 0.010, 0.020 and 0.030 as well as standard size. Desired crankshaft end play is 0.008-0.012 on industrial engines and 0.010-0.015 for generating plant engines. Obtain desired end play by varying thickness of gaskets (4—Fig. O14) used between bearing plate and crankcase.

When installing new crankshaft main bearings, be sure oil hole in bearing sleeve is aligned with oil supply hole in bearing bore. On splash lubricated engines, oil hole will be upward. On pressure lubricated engines, oil hole will be opposite from the camshaft. Bearing plate and crankcase

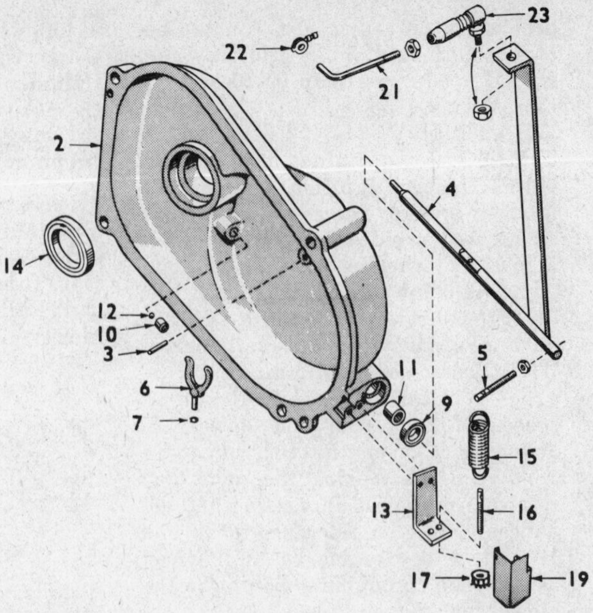

Fig. O17–Exploded view of timing gear cover assembly. Pin (3) engages a hole in governor cup.

2. Cover
3. Roll pin
4. Governor arm & shaft
5. Sensitivity adjustment stud
6. Yoke
7. Snap ring (not all models)
9. Oil seal
10. Bearing
11. Bearing
12. Thrust ball
13. Spring bracket
14. Crankshaft oil seal
15. Governor spring
16. Spring adjusting stud
17. Adjusting nut
19. Spring cover
21. Governor link
22. Clip
23. Ball joint

should be heated 200° F. in oven or in hot water before pressing bearings into place.

Renewal of front oil seal requires removal of the timing gear cover. Rear oil seal removal requires removal of bearing plate. Open side (lip) of oil seals must be installed to inside of engine. Rear seal should be flush with face of boss. Use shim stock or pilot sleeve to avoid damage to seals when installing timing gear cover or bearing plate. Seal the mating surface of seal and seal bore with Permatex.

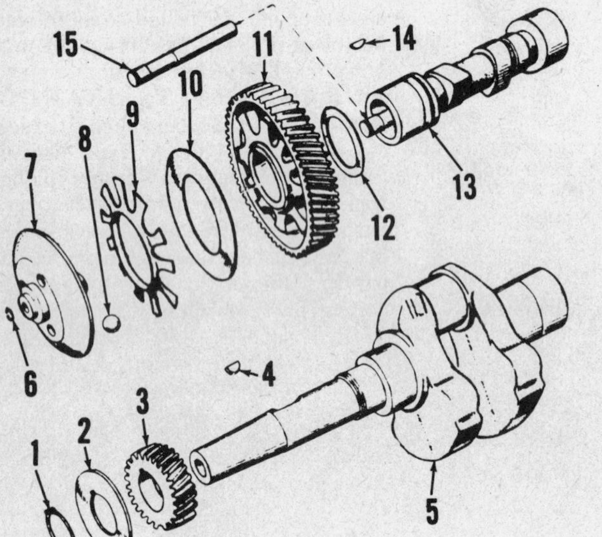

CAMSHAFT AND GOVERNOR. Cam gear is a tight press fit on shaft and should be removed from engine as a single unit with shaft. Unit can be removed after first removing cylinder head, gear cover, valves, tappets (fuel pump if used) and the crankshaft gear lock ring and washer. Early camshaft bearings were babbitt-lead lined bushings which can be renewed using latest precision type bearings that do not need to be align bored or reamed after

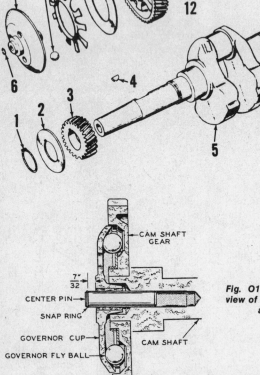

Fig. O15–Exploded view of crankshaft, camshaft and governor units. Pin (15) is pressed into camshaft (13); refer to Fig. O16. Items (9) and (10) not used on all models.

1. Snap ring
2. Washer
3. Crankshaft gear
4. Woodruff key
5. Crankshaft
6. Snap ring
7. Governor cup
8. Steel balls
9. Spacer
10. Plate
11. Camshaft gear
12. Thrust washer
13. Camshaft
14. Woodruff key
15. Pin

Fig. O16–When governor cup is pushed in tight against camshaft gear, there should be 7/32-inch clearance between snap ring and cup.

CAM SHAFT GEAR

CENTER PIN

SNAP RING

GOVERNOR CUP

GOVERNOR FLY BALL

CAM SHAFT

Fig. O18 – Cross-sectional view of engine valve system and breather.

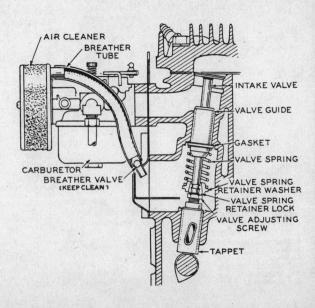

AIR CLEANER
BREATHER TUBE
INTAKE VALVE
VALVE GUIDE
GASKET
VALVE SPRING
VALVE SPRING RETAINER WASHER
VALVE SPRING RETAINER LOCK
VALVE ADJUSTING SCREW
TAPPET
CARBURETOR
BREATHER VALVE (KEEP CLEAN)

installation. Recommended running clearance is 0.0015-0.0030. Install bushings with oil groove at top. Front bushing should be installed flush with cylinder block; rear bushing flush with bottom of counter bore for expansion plug. Shaft should have minimum end play of 0.003 (measured at front bearing) which is controlled by a thrust washer behind the cam gear.

Governor weight unit is mounted on front face of cam gear as shown in Fig. O16. Make sure the distance from outer face of cup sleeve (bushing), or cup itself if bushing is flush, to inner face of snap ring is 7/32-inch as shown when cup is held against fly balls. If less than specified amount, grind end of sleeve as required being sure to remove all burrs from sleeve bore after grinding. If dimension is more than specified amount, press pin further into camshaft. Engines designed for 3600 rpm have 5 fly balls; others have 10.

When installing the gear cover, make sure pin (3—Fig. O17) in cover engages any one of the 3 holes in governor cup (7—Fig. O15).

TIMING GEARS. Timing gears should always be renewed in pairs, never separately. To remove cam gear first remove camshaft and gear as a unit as per preceding paragraph then press gear off shaft. Crankshaft gear can be removed by using two No. 10-32 screws threaded into holes in gear to push gear from shaft. The "O" marks on gears must be in register for correct valve timing.

VALVE SYSTEM. Valve tappet clearance for both intake and exhaust valves is 0.010-0.012 cold. Obtain recommended clearance by turning the self locking adjusting screws as needed. Valve face angle is 44°, valve seat angle is 45° and the seat width 1/32-3/64 inch. Renewal of valve seat inserts requires the use of special equipment and should not be attempted unless same is available. Valve stem clearance in guides is 0.0010-0.0025 for intake valves; 0.0025-0.0040 for exhaust valves. Install valve guides so that shoulder on guide is flush against gasket at valve guide openings in cylinder block casting. Valve tappets are also replaceable from the valve chamber after removing the valve assemblies. Valves are properly timed when timing mark on crankshaft gear registers with timing mark on camshaft gear.

SERVICING ONAN ACCESSORIES

RECOIL STARTER

Refer to Fig. O19 for exploded view of friction shoe type recoil starter. To disassemble starter, hold rope pulley (17) securely with thumb and remove four screws securing ring (3) and flange (5) to cover (20). Remove ring and flange and release thumb pressure enough to allow spring to rotate pulley until spring (18) is unwound. Remove snap ring (6), washer (7), spring (8), slotted washer (9), and fiber washer (10). Lift out friction shoe assembly (11, 12, 13 and 14), then remove remaining washers. Withdraw rope pulley (17) from cover. Remove rewind spring from cover if necessary and note direction of windings.

When reassembling, lubricate rewind spring, cover shaft and center bore in rope pulley with a light coat of Lubriplate or equivalent. Install rewind spring so that windings are in same direction as removed spring. Install rope on pulley and place pulley on cover shaft. Make certain that inner and outer ends of spring are correctly hooked on cover and rotor. Pre-load the rewind spring by rotating the rope pulley two full turns. Hold pulley in pre-load position and install flange (5) and ring (3). Check sharp end of friction shoes (12) and sharpen or renew as necessary. Install washers (9 and 10), friction shoe assembly, spring (8), washer (7) and snap ring (6). Make certain that friction shoe assembly is installed properly for correct starter rotation. Refer to Fig. O20. If properly installed, sharp ends of friction shoes will extend when rope is pulled.

Remove brass centering pin (19) from cover shaft, straighten pin if necessary, then reinsert pin 1/3 of its length into cover shaft. When installing starter on engine, centering pin will align starter with hole in starter cup retaining capscrew.

GENERATOR

Refer to Fig. O21 for exploded view of typical generator unit. Armature (3) has tapered shaft which fits into tapered socket in end of engine crankshaft and is retained to crankshaft by through bolt (8). Generator must be disassembled and the armature removed from engine crankshaft to remove crankshaft or service crankshaft rear oil seal.

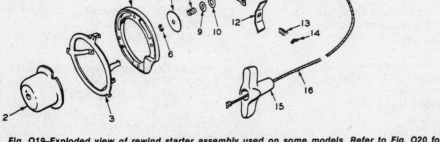

Fig. O19–Exploded view of rewind starter assembly used on some models. Refer to Fig. O20 for installation of friction shoes (12).

2. Starter cup	9. Brake washer
3. Adapter ring	10. Friction washer
5. Flange	11. Brake lever
6. Snap ring	12. Friction shoes
7. Brake washer	13. Friction shoe springs
8. Brake spring	14. Spring retainers

15. Rope handle
16. Starter rope
17. Rope pulley
18. Rewind spring
19. Centering pin
20. Starter cover

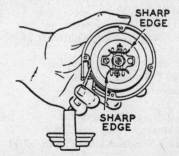

Fig. O20–Install friction shoe and lever assembly with sharp edges of friction shoes pointing in direction shown.

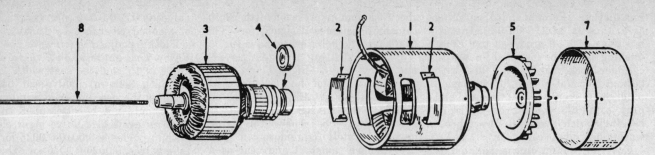

Fig. O21—Exploded view of typical generator unit. Generator must be disassembled to service engine crankshaft.

1. Frame assembly
2. Air opening covers
3. Armature
4. Bearing
5. Fan
7. End cover
8. Through bolt

ONAN CENTRAL PARTS DISTRIBUTORS
(Alphabetically by States)
These franchised firms carry extensive stocks of repair parts. Contact them for name and address of nearest dealer who may have the parts you need.

Atchison Equipment Co., Inc.
4501 First Ave., North
Birmingham, Alabama 35212

Kennedy Engine Company
261 South Water Street
Mobile, Alabama 36602

Equipment Sales Company
720 South 19th Avenue, P.O. Box 6188
Phoenix, Arizona 85005

Equipment Sales Co.
600 West 25th St.
Tucson, Arizona 85713

Capital Equipment Company
1007 Center Street
Little Rock, Arkansas 72202

Equipment Service Company
3431 Cherry Avenue
Long Beach, California 90801

California Electric Works
4567 Federal Blvd.
San Diego, California 92112

Cal-West Electric, Inc.
1341 San Mateo Avenue
So. San Francisco, California 94080

C. W. Silver Company, Inc.
4995 Colorado Boulevard
Denver, Colorado 80216

GLT Industries, Inc.
29 Mascolo Road
South Windsor, Connecticut 06074

Marine Industrial Equipment Corp.
710 Haines Street
Jacksonville, Florida 32206

R. B. Grove, Inc.
261 S. W. Sixth Street
Miami, Florida 33130

Tampa Armature Works, Inc.
5862 South Tampa Ave.
Orlando, Florida 32809

Kennedy Florida Engine Company, Inc.
P.O. Box 1387, 3011 West 12th Street
Panama City, Florida 32401

Tampa Armature Works, Inc.
P.O. Box 3381
440 South 78th St.
Tampa, Florida 33601

Blalock Machinery & Equipment Co.
848 Oglethorpe Avenue, P.O. Box 155
Albany, Georgia 31701

Blalock Machinery & Equipment Co.
P.O. Box 4658
225 Forsyth St. S.W.
Atlanta, Georgia 30303

Atlas Electric Company, Inc.
645 Halekauwila Street
Honolulu, Hawaii 96813

Power Systems
Boise Industrial Park
4499 Market St.
Boise, Idaho 83705

C. W. Silver Co., Inc.
255 Ash Street, So.
Twin Falls, Idaho 83301

Forces, Incorporated
4040 Washington Blvd.
Hillside, Illinois 60162

National Industrial Supply Company
Div. of National Auto Supply Co.
1100 Martin Luther King Drive
East St. Louis, Illinois 62201

Service Automotive Warehouse, Inc.
111 Fourth Ave.
Rock Island, Illinois 61201

Workinger Electric Inc.
1704 West Bristol Street
Elkhart, Indiana 46514

Evansville Auto Parts, Inc.
5 East Riverside Drive
Evansville, Indiana 47713

Demco Incorporated
610 West Main Street, P.O. Box 307
Indianapolis, Indiana 46142

Electrical Engineering & Equip. Co.
1201 Walnut Street
Des Moines, Iowa 50307

Anderson Equipment Co., Inc.
300 South Virginia St.
Sioux City, Iowa 51102

Virgil Heck Equipment Company
2438 Crittenden Drive
Louisville, Kentucky 40217

Delhome Industries, Inc.
1500 Fulton Street
New Iberia, Louisiana 70560

Electrical Industries, Inc.
2311 Tchoupitoulas St.
New Orleans, Louisiana 70130

Menge Pump and Machinery Co., Inc.
2740 North Arnoult Road, Box 215
New Orleans, Louisiana 70004

Menge Pump and Machinery Co., Inc.
1510 Grimmet Drive
Shreveport, Louisiana 71107

Leen's Electric Motor Service
54 Wilson Street
Brewer, Maine 04412

Stanley J. Leen Company, Inc.
52 Union Street
Portland, Maine 04103

Curtis Engine & Equipment Co.
6120 Holabird Avenue
Baltimore, Maryland 21224

Generator Power Equipment, Inc.
3703 42nd Avenue
Brentwood, Maryland 20722

J. H. Westerbeke Corporation
Avon Industrial Park
Boston, Massachusetts 02322

General Electric Truck & Diesel
   Equip. Serv.
1264 Union Street
Springfield, Massachusetts 01089

Carroll Stuart Corp.
Div. of Hunt Wood, Inc.
23820 Telegraph Rd.
Detroit, Michigan 48075

Morley-Murphy Company
400 Ludington Street
Escanaba, Michigan 49829

Don F. Nickel Equipment Company
1006 South Division Avenue
Grand Rapids, Michigan 49507

E. W. Henry Co.
1620 South Airport Rd.
Traverse City, Michigan 49684

Flaherty Equipment Corp.
2525 East Franklin Avenue
Minneapolis, Minnesota 55460

Horvick Electric Motor Company
305 Main Avenue
Moorhead, Minnesota 56560

Kennedy Marine Engine Company
P.O. Box 167, Reynoir & Jackson
   Streets
Biloxi, Mississippi 39530

Energy Equipment Company
1623 South Gallatin
Jackson, Mississippi 39202

Kennedy Marine Engine Co.
   of Pascagoula
137 Delmas Avenue
Pascagoula, Mississippi 39567

Comet Electronics, Inc.
4800 Deramus Avenue
Kansas City, Missouri 64120

Universal Engineering Corp.
Mile 214.5 (Portage Island)
Portage des Sioux, Missouri 63373

Automotive & Industrial Distributors
2112 Fourth Avenue North
Billings, Montana 59101

Automotive & Industrial Distributors
610 East Platinum
Butte, Montana 59701

Automotive & Industrial Distributors
807 South 2nd Street
Great Falls, Montana 59401

Anderson Equipment Company
5532 Center Street
Omaha, Nebraska 68106

Constructor Equipment Service
   & Supply
2314 Western Avenue
Las Vegas, Nevada 89102

Air Service Co.
2505 Mill Street
Reno, Nevada 89502

R. C. Equipment Co., Inc.
522 South Broadway
Gloucester City, New Jersey 08030

GLT Industries, Inc.
411 Clinton Avenue
Northvale, New Jersey 07647

Desert Industrial, Inc.
531 Haines Ave. N.W.
Albuquerque, New Mexico 87103

Geils & Foerst Marine Electric, Inc.
197 City Island Avenue
City Island, New York 10464

Power Plant Equipment Corp.
6 Northway Lane
Latham, New York 12110

Ronco Communications &
   Electronics, Inc.
1475 East Henrietta
Rochester, New York 14623

Power Plant Equipment Corp.
929 South Salina Street
Syracuse, New York 13202

Ronco Communications &
   Electronics, Inc.
595 Sheridan Drive
Tonawanda-Buffalo, New York 14150

H. B. Owsley & Son, Inc.
5701 Old Pineville Road
Charlotte, North Carolina 28201

H. B. Owsley & Son, Inc.
Box 8627, Interstate 40
Greensboro, North Carolina 27410

Bemco, Inc.
Beaufort Morehead Causeway
Morehead City, North Carolina 28557

Cincinnati Electric Equipment Co.
16 East 72nd Street
Cincinnati, Ohio 45216

McDonald Equipment Co.
37200 Vine Street
Cleveland, Ohio 44094

Tuller Corporation
947 West Goodale Blvd.
Columbus, Ohio 43212

Mechanical & Electrical Equip. Co.
712 South Wheeling
Tulsa, Oklahoma 74150

Electrical Construction Co.
2121-2147 NW Thurman Street
Portland, Oregon 97208

Joseph C. Schultz
2123 Parade Street
Erie, Pennsylvania 16503

A. F. Shane Company
1343 Old Freeport Road
Pittsburgh, Pennsylvania 15238

Winter Engine Generator Service
1321 West Poplar Street
York, Pennsylvania 17404

Shakstad Electric & Machine Works
1400 Industrial Avenue
Sioux Falls, South Dakota 57101

Osborne Equipment Company
6207 Provence Street
Chattanooga, Tennessee 37421

Osborne Equipment Company
4311 Paper Mill Road
Knoxville, Tennessee 37902

Maritime & Industrial, Inc.
P.O. Box 9397, 292 East Mallory
Memphis, Tennessee 38109

Stephens Distributing Company
1201 Dickerson Pike
Nashville, Tennessee 37207

Lightbourn Equipment Company
13649 Beta Street
Dallas, Texas 75240

Harrison Equipment Company
1616 McGowen
Houston, Texas 77001

McEntyre Brothers
2705 Kermit Highway
Odessa, Texas 79760

Sabine Propeller & Marine Serv. Co.
945 Houston Avenue, P.O. Box 1057
Port Arthur, Texas 77640

Lightbourn Equipment Co.
102 W. Turbo
San Antonio, Texas 78216

C. W. Silver Company
550 West 7th South
Salt Lake City, Utah 84101

T&L Electric Company, Inc.
Sykes Avenue, Box 835
White River Junction, Vermont 05001

Paxton Company
1111 Ingleside Road
Norfolk, Virginia 23502

J. P. Long Company
1811 Roseneath Road
Richmond, Virginia 23230

Fremont Electric Company
744 North 34th Street
Seattle, Washington 98103

West Virginia Tractor & Equip. Co.
P.O. Box 473, 1701 Fifth Avenue
Charleston, West Virginia 25322

West Virginia Tractor & Equip. Co.
P.O. Box 587
Clarksburg, West Virginia 26301

Morley-Murphy Company
700 Morley Road
Green Bay, Wisconsin 54303

Clymar, Incorporated
2310 Pennsylvania Avenue
Madison, Wisconsin 53700

Clymar, Incorporated
N. 55 W. 13787 Oak Lane
Milwaukee, Wisconsin 53225

Morley-Murphy Co.
1111 McLeary
Wausau, Wisconsin 54401

Power Service Company
P.O. Box 2880
5201 West Yellowstone Hwy.
Casper, Wyoming 82601

CANADA

Simson Maxwell
6121 Centre Street
South Calgary, Alberta

Simson Maxwell
10375 59th Avenue, Box 4446
South Edmonton, Alberta

Simson Maxwell
729 Fourth Avenue
Prince George, British Columbia

Simson Maxwell
1380 West 6th Avenue
Vancouver, British Columbia

Kipp Kelly, Ltd.
68 Higgins Avenue
Winnipeg, Manitoba

Sansom Equipment, Ltd.
Woodstock Road, Box 1263
Fredericton, New Brunswick

George G. R. Parsons, Ltd.
96 Elizabeth Avenue
St. Johns, Newfoundland

Wilson Equipment, Ltd.
46 Elm St., Box 340
Truro, Nova Scotia

J. A. Faguy & Sons, Ltd.
36 Murray St.
Ottawa, Ontario

Algoma Truck & Tractor Sales Ltd.
815 Great Northern Road, Box 391
Saulte Ste. Marie, Ontario

Burlec Sales, Ltd.
125 Nantucket Blvd.
Scarborough, Ontario

Dixon Bros. Electric, Northern, Ltd.
1146 Lorne Street
Centennial Industrial Park
Sudbury, Ontario

J. A. Faguy & Sons Ltd.
750 Montee de Liesse
Montreal, Quebec

Davies Electric Co. Ltd.
347 2nd Avenue South
Saskatoon, Saskatchewan

PINCOR

PIONEER GEN-E-MOTOR CORPORATION

5841 West Dickens Ave.

Chicago, Illinois 60639

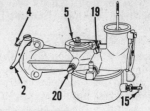

MODEL	Cyls.	Bore	Stroke	Displ.
4V & 4VR	1	2 5/16	1⅝	6.8
7V & 7VR	1	2 5/16	1⅝	6.8
8V & 8VR	1	2 5/16	1¾	7.4
9V & 9VR	1	2½	1¾	8.6

All models listed are vertical crankshaft engines of 4-stroke cycle design. Engine crankcase is of die cast aluminum alloy with a cast iron cylinder liner. Main bearings are either plain aluminum bore of crankcase or engine base or a bronze bushing in crankcase and/or engine base.

MAINTENANCE

SPARK PLUG. A Champion J-8 or equivalent spark plug is recommended

Fig. P4—Assembled view of float type carburetor shown in Fig. P3.

2. Lever	15. Main fuel needle
4. Lever stop	19. Idle stop screw
5. Throttle arm	20. Idle fuel needle

for all models. Set electrode gap to 0.025. Tighten spark plug to a torque of 25-27 ft.-lbs.

CARBURETOR. Carburetor may be either float or suction type. Refer to Figs. P1 through P6 for exploded views and adjustment points of typical carburetors.

FLOAT TYPE CARBURETORS.

Early type float carburetors were equipped with separate idle and high speed fuel mixture jets. When overhauling these early carburetors, Pioneer Gen-E-Motor recommends that a

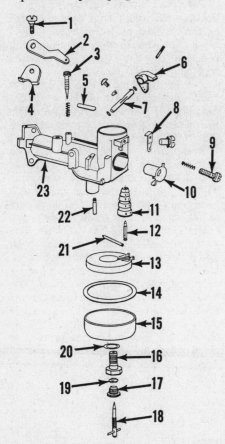

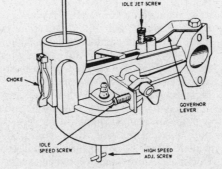

Fig. P2—Assembled view of a Pincor float carburetor showing fuel mixture adjustment needles, etc. Refer to Fig. P1 for exploded view of this carburetor.

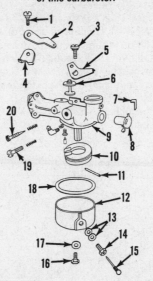

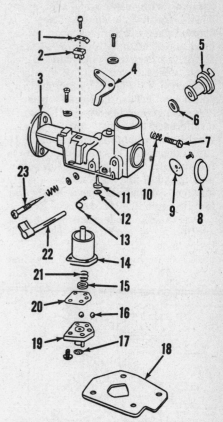

Fig. P1—Exploded view of one type of float carburetor used on Pincor engines. Choke details may be similar to that shown in Fig. P5 for suction type carburetor. Refer to Fig. P3 for exploded view of second type of float carburetor.

1. Shoulder screw	13. Float
2. Lever	14. Gasket
3. Idle fuel needle	15. Bowl
4. Lever stop	16. Retainer
5. Plug (or idle jet)	17. Nut
6. Throttle arm	18. Main fuel needle
7. Throttle shaft	19. Packing
8. Retainer	20. Gasket
9. Idle stop screw	21. Float pin
10. Choke	22. Main jet
11. Inlet valve seat	23. Body casting
12. Inlet needle	

Fig. P3—Exploded view of a second type Pincor float carburetor. Choke details may be similar to that shown in Fig. P5 for suction carburetor. Refer to Fig. P1 for another type of float carburetor used.

1. Shoulder screw	11. Float pin
2. Lever	12. Bowl
3. Screw	13. Gaskets
4. Throttle stop	14. Nut
5. Throttle arm	15. Main fuel needle
6. Throttle valve	16. Nut
7. Retainer	17. Gasket
8. Choke	18. Gasket
9. Body casting	19. Idle stop screw
10. Float	20. Idle fuel needle

Fig. P5—Exploded view of Pincor suction type carburetor.

1. Ground strap	13. Choke spring
2. Nylon grommet	14. Pump housing
3. Body casting	15. Pusher ring
4. Lever	16. Check valves
5. Throttle valve	17. Screen
6. Felt washer	18. Gasket
7. Idle stop screw	19. Pump cover
8. Plug	20. Pump diaphragm
9. Choke disc	21. Spring
10. Spring	22. Choke shaft
11. Fuel tube	23. Fuel mixture needle
12. Screen	

later type carburetor body casting incorporating a single fuel jet be installed.

For initial adjustment of all float type carburetors, open both the idle and high speed fuel needles approximately 2 to 2½ turns. Make final adjustments with engine running at operating temperature. Set throttle approximately ¾-turn open; then, turn high speed fuel needle in slowly until engine begins to slow down. Then, turn the high speed needle out until engine runs unevenly from an over-rich fuel mixture. Correct high speed needle adjustment is midway between these two settings.

Return throttle to idle speed position and turn idle fuel needle in until engine idles roughly; then, back needle out slowly until engine idles smoothly. Set idle speed adjustment screw so that slow idle speed is just above 2000 RPM.

To adjust carburetor float level, bend tang on float so that when body and float assembly is inverted, upper surface of float and body are parallel.

SUCTION TYPE CARBURETOR. The suction type carburetor is equipped with only one fuel adjustment needle. Initial adjustment of needle is approximately 2¾ turns open. Make final adjustment with engine at operating temperature and running at about 3000 RPM. Fuel tank should be approximately ½-full when making adjustments. Turn fuel needle in until engine begins to lose speed; then, turn needle back out slowly until fuel mixture is rich enough to cause engine to run unevenly. This should provide a fuel mixture rich enough for full power under load; if not, open needle slightly further. Adjust idle speed stop screw for minimum idle speed of 2000 RPM.

Fuel tank on models equipped with a suction type carburetor is vented through the carburetor and no vent is provided in fuel tank cap. The fuel pump in suction type carburetors may be primed by filling the fuel tank; however, do not over-fill tank up into filler neck as this will cause over-rich carburetor operation.

GOVERNOR. All models are equipped with an air-vane type governor. Be sure that air vane, carburetor throttle valve and linkage operate freely. To adjust maximum governed speed, refer to Fig. P7 and proceed as follows: Loosen screw (1) and move the stop washer (4) until desired maximum speed is obtained with speed control lever (2) against stop. Recommended high idle no load speed is 3300 RPM. Do not set maximum high idle speed above 3600 RPM. Slow idle speed of 2000 RPM is obtained by adjusting throttle stop screw on carburetor.

MAGNETO AND TIMING. A flywheel type magneto is used on all models. Breaker points and condenser are located under the flywheel. Breaker point gap on all models is 0.023-0.025 and condenser capacity on all models is 0.18-0.25 mfd. Timing on these engines is fixed and non-adjustable. Check air gap between armature legs and magnets on flywheel. Air gap should be 0.010-0.012. To adjust air gap, loosen armature mounting screws and move armature away from flywheel. Place feeler gages or correct thickness shim stock between armature legs and magnets on flywheel. Hold armature tight against feeler gages or shim stock, then tighten mounting screws.

LUBRICATION. Crankcase capacity on all models is 1¼ pints. Use SAE 30 oil when operating in temperatures above 32° F. and SAE 10W oil in temperatures below 32° F. Use high quality motor oil having API classification MS or SD.

CRANKCASE BREATHER. When cleaning crankcase breather, be sure that inner plate (25—Fig. P9) is installed with reed valve pointing down and that outer plate is installed with breather hole to top. A breather pad (24) is placed between the inner plate and center gasket (30).

REPAIRS

TIGHTENING TORQUES. Recommended tightening torque values are as follows:

Connecting rod .... 42-54 inch-lbs.
Cylinder head ...... 180-190 inch-lbs.
Engine base bolts .... 72 inch-lbs.
Flywheel nut .... 60-70 Ft.-Lbs.
Spark plug .... 25-27 Ft.-Lbs.

CYLINDER HEAD. The removable cylinder head is retained by eight 5/16-inch cap screws and flat washers. When reinstalling cylinder head, be sure gasket surfaces are clean, use new gasket and tighten retaining cap screws to a torque of 180-190 inch-pounds in sequence shown in Fig. P8.

CONNECTING ROD. The connecting rod and piston assembly are removed from cylinder head end of block. The aluminum alloy connecting rod rides directly on the heat treated steel alloy crank.

The connecting rod should be rejected if the crankpin hole is worn to a diameter of 0.880 or larger, or if the piston pin hole is worn to a diameter of 0.5567 or larger.

Reassemble cap to connecting rod with the "flats" on rod and cap aligned and towards camshaft side of engine. Tighten the cap retaining screws to a torque of 42-54 inch-lbs. and bend ears of lock strap against screw heads.

PISTON, PIN AND RINGS. The aluminum alloy piston is fitted with two compression rings and one oil control ring. Clearance between piston skirt and cylinder wall should be 0.007-0.010. Reject piston if scored or scuffed or if skirt to cylinder wall clearance is excessive. Also, reject piston if side clearance of new piston ring is 0.005 or more in top ring groove.

Reject piston pin if 0.0005 or more

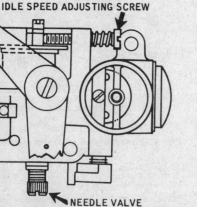

Fig. P6—View showing location of idle speed adjusting screw and fuel mixture needle valve on Pincor suction type carburetor.

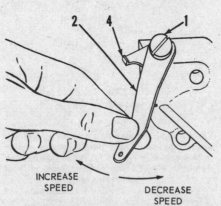

Fig. P7—To change maximum governed speed on Pincor engines, loosen screw (1) and move stop (4) so that lever (2) contacts stop at desired engine speed.

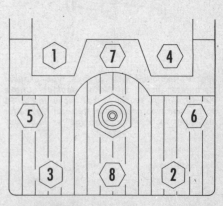

Fig. P8—Drawing showing sequence for tightening cylinder head retaining cap screws.

out-of-round or if worn to a diameter of 0.5503 or smaller. The floating type piston pin is retained by a snap ring at each end of pin bore in piston.

Piston ring end gap should be 0.007-0.017; reject rings if end gap is 0.035 or more. Install top compression ring with groove on inside diameter of ring towards top of piston. Install second ring with groove on outside diameter of ring towards bottom of piston. The oil control ring may be installed either side up.

Piston rings and piston are available in standard size and oversizes of 0.005, 0.010 and 0.015. Piston pin is available in standard size only.

CYLINDER AND CRANKCASE. The die-cast aluminum crankcase and cylinder unit is equipped with an integral cast iron cylinder liner. If cylinder wear is 0.003 or more or if cylinder out-of-round condition is 0.0025 or more, reject cylinder or rebore to next oversize. Standard cylinder bore diameter on 9V models is 2.4990-2.5000; standard cylinder bore diameter for all other models is 2.3115-2.3125. Piston and rings are available in standard size and oversizes of 0.005, 0.010 and 0.015. Always rebore cylinder to exact oversize for proper fit of piston and rings.

Press new crankshaft oil seals into crankcase and engine base with spring loaded lip of seal to inside of engine.

When reassembling engine base to crankcase, note that one of the retaining bolts extends into the engine breather chamber. Before installing this bolt, coat threads with sealer to prevent oil leakage at this point.

Thickness of gasket used between crankcase and engine base determines crankshaft end play. Refer to following CRANKSHAFT AND MAIN BEARINGS paragraph for selection of correct gasket thickness.

Tighten alternate engine base retaining bolts to a torque of 72 inch-pounds until all bolts are tight.

CRANKSHAFT AND MAIN BEARINGS. The crankshaft rides directly in the unbushed bores of aluminum crankcase and engine base on some models, and in bronze bushings in the crankcase and/or engine base on other models.

Reject the crankshaft if the crankpin or either main bearing journal is worn to a diameter of 0.8715 or smaller. Crankshaft end play should be 0.004-0.010, and is controlled by thickness of gasket or gaskets used between crankcase and engine base. Gaskets are available in the thicknesses of 0.015 and 0.020 and at least one 0.015 thick gasket must be used.

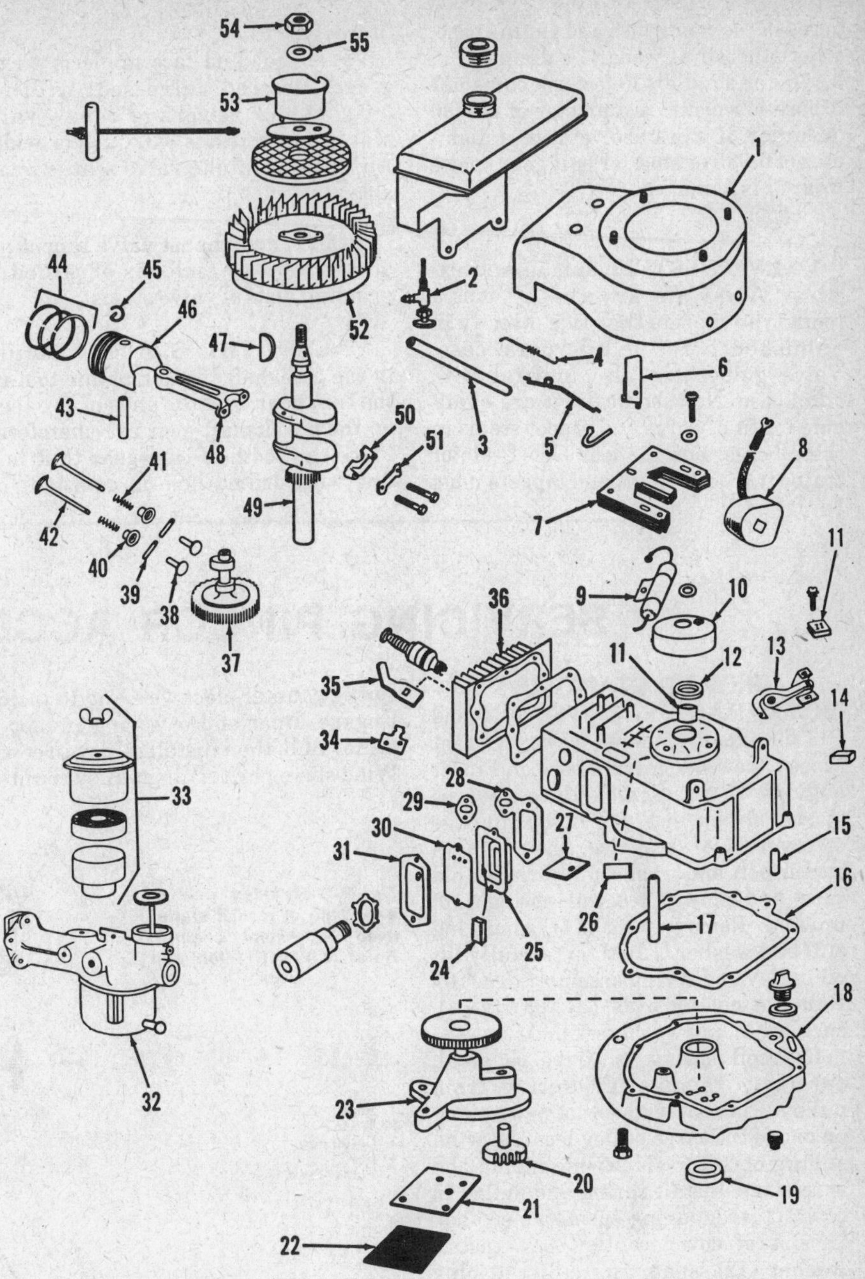

Fig. P9–Exploded view of Pincor engine. The construction of this engine is typical of all models.

1. Blower housing	15. Dowel pin	29. Gasket	43. Piston pin
2. Fuel tank valve	16. Gasket	30. Gasket	44. Ring set
3. Fuel line	17. Camshaft pin	31. Breather cover	45. Snap rings
4. Governor spring	18. Engine base	32. Carburetor	46. Piston
5. Governor link	19. Oil seal	33. Air cleaner	47. Woodruff key
6. Governor vane	20. Oil pump gear	34. Spring clip	48. Connecting rod
7. Armature core	21. Oil pump base	35. Stop spring	49. Crankshaft
8. Ignition coil	22. Oil filter	36. Cylinder head	50. Connecting rod cap
9. Condenser	23. Oil pump	37. Camshaft	51. Lock strap
10. Breaker cover	24. Breather pad	38. Tappets	52. Flywheel
11. Bushing	25. Breather assembly	39. Retainer pins	53. Starter pulley
12. Oil seal	26. Grommet	40. Spring retainers	54. Flywheel nut
13. Breaker points	27. Baffle	41. Valve springs	55. Lockwasher
14. Felt wick	28. Gasket	42. Valves	

Renew the main bearing bushings on models so equipped if worn to a diameter of 0.8795 or larger. If bearing bore in crankcase or engine base in models not originally equipped with bushings is worn to a diameter of 0.8795 or larger, the bearing can be reamed and a bushing installed by using Pioneer Gen-E-Motor tool kit No. 60-1391

along with Briggs & Stratton tool kit No. 19158.

Before installing crankshaft, be sure that any burrs that would damage crankshaft seals are removed from ends of crankshaft.

CAMSHAFT AND PIN. The hollow camshaft and gear unit (37—Fig. P9) rides on a pin (17) which is a loose fit in bores in the crankcase and engine base. Reject the pin if worn to a diameter of 0.3705 or smaller. Reject the camshaft if bore is worn to a diameter of 0.3790 or larger, if lobes are worn to a diameter of 0.885 or smaller or if gear shows wear or is damaged.

VALVE SYSTEM. Intake and exhaust valves are actuated by mushroom type tappets that ride directly in unbushed bores in the crankcase. Valve guides are also integral with crankcase. No specifications are available for fit of valve and tappet stems in their bores, but Pioneer Gen-E-Motor states that the valves and tappets must

fit freely.

Valve seat and face angle is 45 degrees. Desired valve seat width is 0.047-0.062; rework or renew valve seat if seat width is 3/32-inch or wider. An oversize intake valve seat is available.

Intake and exhaust valve tappet gap of 0.003-0.011 (cold) is obtained by grinding ends of valve stems.

VALVE TIMING. A hole is drilled in the camshaft in back of one tooth of the cam gear, and the ends of two teeth on the crankshaft gear are chamfered. Place the tooth of cam gear that is in line with drilled hole in camshaft be-

tween the two chamfered teeth of the crankshaft gear to properly time engine.

OIL PUMP. Engine is splash lubricated by a jet of oil from a gear type pump (earlier production engines) or a "splasher" (late production engines) that is attached to engine base. Parts are available for service.

When reassembling gear type pump, be sure that oil intake hole in pump base plate (21—Fig. P9) is aligned over the "U" shaped cut in base of pump body. End play of gear assembly should be 0.005-0.014. New engine bases will be fitted with a "splasher instead of a pump; discard pump when installing new type base.

SERVICING PINCOR ACCESSORIES

REWIND STARTERS

OVERHAUL. Refer to Fig. P10 and P11 for exploded views of two different types of rewind starters used on Pincor engines. To disassemble the early type starter shown in Fig. P10, clamp edge of cover (11) in a vise, then remove center bolt and washer (8). Remove old rope and slowly let coil spring (10) unwind. Remove plug (14), snap ring (13) and washer (12), then carefully lift off pulley and spring assembly (9 & 10). Remove cotter pins (3), pawls (4), springs (6) and washers (7).

If recoil spring is to be renewed, carefully remove old spring from pulley. Place outer hook of new spring on one of the three pulley legs and wind spring counter-clockwise inside the three legs. Install spring and pulley in cover (11), engaging spring inner hook in slot of cover center boss. Install washer (12), snap ring (13) and plug (14).

Wind recoil spring by turning pulley counter-clockwise until spring is tight, then back off pulley 1 to 2 turns, aligning rope pulley slot with rope guide in cover. Install new rope and secure with center bolt and washer (8). Allow rope to wind on the pulley.

To disassemble the late type rewind starter shown in Fig. P11, clamp edge of cover (9) in a vise and remove screw (3), washer (4), spring (5), pawl retainer (6), pawls (7) and friction washer (11). Pull rope out as far as possible and wedge pulley to prevent the spring from turning it. Remove old rope, then remove pulley wedge and allow pulley (8) and coil spring (10) to slowly unwind. Carefully remove pulley and old spring.

When reassembling, hook loop of spring over post inside of cover. Wind

spring counter-clockwise and to inside. Engage inner end of spring in slot in pulley hub, then install pulley in cover. Wind spring by turning pulley counter-

clockwise until spring is tight. Back pulley off 1 to 2 turns, aligning rope hole in pulley with rope guide in cover. Wedge pulley to prevent it from turn-

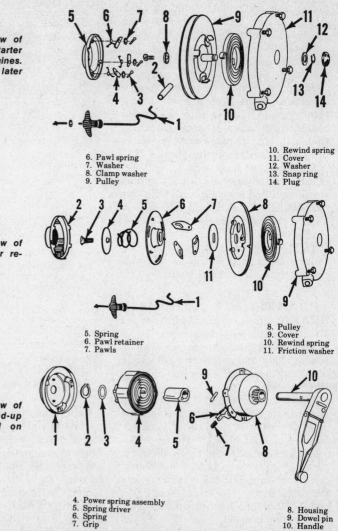

Fig. P10—Exploded view of early type of rewind starter used on Pincor engines. Refer to Fig. P11 for later type.

1. Rope
2. Tubing
3. Cotter pin
4. Pawl
5. Flange & pin assy.
6. Pawl spring
7. Washer
8. Clamp washer
9. Pulley
10. Rewind spring
11. Cover
12. Washer
13. Snap ring
14. Plug

Fig. P11—Exploded view of late production Pincor rewind starter.

1. Rope
2. Flange
3. Screw
4. Washer
5. Spring
6. Pawl retainer
7. Pawls
8. Pulley
9. Cover
10. Rewind spring
11. Friction washer

Fig. P12—Exploded view of early production wind-up (snap) starter used on Pincor engines.

1. Driver cup
2. Snap ring
3. Washer
4. Power spring assembly
5. Spring driver
6. Spring
7. Grip
8. Housing
9. Dowel pin
10. Handle

ing, then install new rope. Hold rope and remove wedge, allowing rope to wind on pulley. Install friction washer (11), pawls (7), pawl retainer (6), spring (5), washer (4) and screw (3).

WIND-UP (SNAP) STARTER

OVERHAUL. Refer to Figs. P12 and P13 for exploded views of two different types of wind-up starters that have been used on Pincor engines. Disassembly of either starter is obvious after an examination of the unit and reference to Fig. P12 or P13.

CAUTION: When servicing wind-up

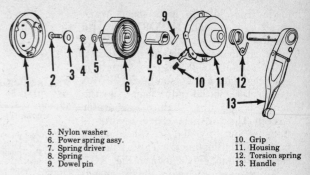

Fig. P13–Exploded view of later production Pincor wind-up (snap) starter assembly.

1. Driver cup
2. Screw
3. Washer
4. Lock washer
5. Nylon washer
6. Power spring assy.
7. Spring driver
8. Spring
9. Dowel pin
10. Grip
11. Housing
12. Torsion spring
13. Handle

starters, do not attempt to remove power spring from the steel cup. A rapidly uncoiling power spring could cause serious injury. Power spring and spring cup are serviced as an assembly only.

PIONEER GEN-E-MOTOR CENTRAL DISTRIBUTORS

These franchised firms carry extensive stocks of repair parts. Contact them for name and address of nearest service distributor who may have the parts you need.

C. C. Jones Battery & Elect.
320 W. Jefferson
Phoenix, Arizona 85003

J. F. Dixon Co.
1835 S. Hope St.
Los Angeles, California 90015

Spencer Engine & Magneto, Inc.
1214 West Cass
Tampa, Florida 33606

John E. Connor Co.
30 Asinof Ave.
Chicopee, Massachusetts 01013

Electrical & Magneto Service Co.
1600 Campbell
Kansas City, Missouri 64108

Wollgast Supply Co.
2783 Dunn Road
St. Louis, Missouri 63136

Strauss Bros. Engine and Equip.
399 Dewolfe Place
Hackensack, New Jersey 07601

Carolina Rim & Wheel Co.
321 S. Blount St.
Raleigh, North Carolina 27601

Williams Service & Supply
1411 North Sheridan
Tulsa, Oklahoma 74115

Tracey & Co., Inc.
N.W. 10th & Glisan St.
Portland, Oregon 97209

Sullivan Brothers
445 N. 63rd Street
Philadelphia, Pennsylvania 19151

Master Repair Service
2423 Broadway N.E.
Knoxville, Tennessee 37917

Mapp Caster & Truck Co.
320 N. Sampson St.
Houston, Texas 77003

Bradshaw Auto Parts Co.
359 Pierpont Avenue
Salt Lake City, Utah 85101

Power Tools Sales Co.
E. 7311 Sprague Ave.
Spokane, Washington 99206

ROPER

Roper Corporation, Bradley Division
Bradley, Illinois 60915

Models	Cyls.	Bore	Stroke	Displ.	HP at RPM
1900	1	1-3/8	1-9/32	1.9	1.5-7000
3700	1	1-13/16	1-7/16	3.7	3.1-7500

MAINTENANCE

SPARK PLUG. These lightweight 2-stroke engines are fitted with the following Champion spark plugs for general use: Model 1900 requires a DJ6J and model 3700 calls for a CJ6 plug which may be replaced by a Champion CJ8 for operation in cooler weather or if engine is subjected to long term idling. Required electrode gap is 0.025.

CARBURETOR. Engine model 1900 is equipped with a model HDC5 Walbro diaphragm-type carburetor. See exploded view in Fig. RO1. Initial adjustments of this carburetor are as follows: Main adjustment needle (8—Fig. RO1) is backed off its seat by ¾-turn. Idle mixture needle (7) is backed out one complete turn. Idle speed regulating screw (6) is turned in to just contact throttle stop (4), then add ¾-turn. These settings should serve to get engine to start. After a few minutes

warm-up, if engine will not idle, turn idle speed screw (6) inward (clockwise) about 20° (1/16-turn) at a time until idle speed is maintained. To set smooth engine idle, turn idle mixture needle (7) in by 1/16-turn steps. If engine idle speeds up excessively, back out idle speed screw (6) to correct. When throttle is opened quickly, engine should accelerate smoothly into operating speed range. If it does not, back out idle mixture needle (7) a little bit at a time until a smooth transition is made from idle to high speed when throttle is opened. IMPORTANT: Do not use more than light finger force to close carburetor needles on their seats.

On model 3700 engine, which is equipped with a Tillotson model HS79A carburetor, initial adjustment is the same as for the Walbro carburetor except that idle mixture needle is backed out by 1-1/8 turns as a beginning adjustment. This Tillotson carburetor model is shown in Fig. RO2.

Adjustment of main (high speed) needle is made only under load with engine at normal operating temperature. Because an over-lean mixture will cause engine damage due to lack of lubrication, it is better to allow a slightly rich adjustment.

GENERAL SERVICE NOTES. Diaphragm-type carburetors are relatively trouble-free if clean fuel and high-grade oil are used and if proper adjustments are maintained. If erratic performance occurs and ignition system, exhaust

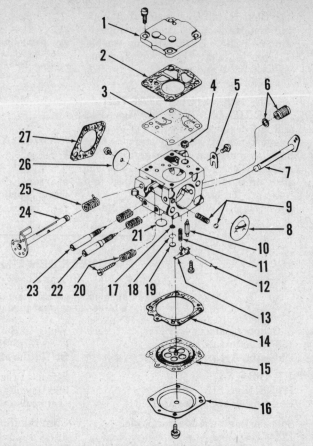

Fig. RO2—Exploded view of Tillotson carburetor model HS79A used on model 3700 engine.

1. Fuel pump cover
2. Fuel pump gasket
3. Fuel pump diaphragm
4. Inlet screen
5. Throttle shaft clip
6. Governor valve/gasket
7. Choke shaft
8. Choke plate
9. Choke detent
10. Inlet needle
11. Inlet control spring
12. Lever pivot pin
13. Inlet control lever
14. Diaphragm gasket
15. Diaphragm
16. Cover
17. Passage screen
18. Retainer ring
19. Welch plug
20. Idle speed screw/spring
21. Welch plug
22. High speed mixture needle
23. Idle mixture needle
24. Throttle shaft
25. Return spring
26. Throttle plate
27. Flange gasket

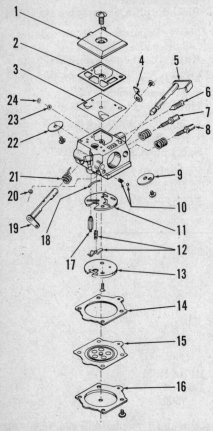

Fig. RO1—Exploded view of Walbro model HDC5 carburetor used on model 1900 engine.

1. Fuel pump cover
2. Fuel pump gasket
3. Fuel pump diaphragm
4. Throttle stop
5. Choke lever
6. Idle speed screw
7. Idle mixture needle
8. Main mixture needle
9. Choke plate
10. Choke detent
11. Circuit gasket
12. Metering lever & spring
13. Circuit plate
14. Metering diaphragm gasket
15. Metering diaphragm
16. Cover
17. Inlet valve
18. Metering rod
19. Throttle shaft
20. Limiting jet
21. Return spring
22. Throttle plate
23. Check valve screen
24. Retainer ring

ports and engine compression are normal, the following points apply in checking out a questionable carburetor. Refer to Figs. RO1 and RO2 for parts arrangement.

If carburetor is running lean:

Check fuel pump diaphragm. Leaking or defective check valves call for renewal of diaphragm. Check diaphragm against light.

Make sure fuel tank vent is clear.

Check for leaking fuel line or connections.

Check for clogged filter screens.

Fuel orifice plugged or dirt in idle

passages. See Fig. RO3. Be sure to check pump pulse passage (P).

Check metering diaphragm for holes or breaks.

Check metering lever adjustment. See Fig. RO4 for Walbro and Fig. RO5 for Tillotson carburetor.

Check for leaks in carburetor/reed valve to manifold mounting gaskets.

Over-rich or flooding condition:

Check fuel pump diaphragm. Renew if leaking.

Check for high setting of metering diaphragm lever. Reset as in Figs. RO4 or RO5.

Check inlet valve needle and seat for dirt or obstruction.

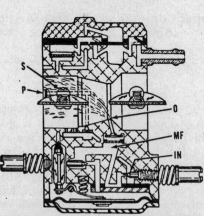

Fig. RO3—Cross-section of typical Walbro HDC carburetor to show internal passages.

P. Pulse passage
S. Throttle shaft
O. Main fuel orifice
MF. Main fuel circuit
IN. Idle fuel needle

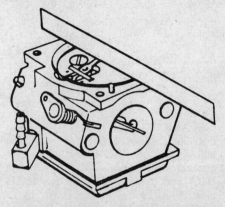

Fig. RO4—Metering diaphragm lever of Walbro HDC carburetor is in correct adjustment when it will just touch a straightedge laid across carburetor body as shown.

Check to determine if metering diaphragm spring is properly seated. Refer to applicable figure.

On Walbro HDC5 carburetor, check for leak in circuit gasket (11—Fig. RO1).

SPECIAL NOTE: Do not use "carburetor cleaner" type solvents on these carburetors. Use regular solvents. Carburetor repair kits are offered which provide new welch plugs, inlet and mixture needles and springs, fuel pump diaphragms, metering diaphragms with levers and springs and all required gaskets. Careful disassembly of carburetor, thorough cleaning and proper reassembly with renewed parts should restore full performance.

REED VALVES. Model 1900 engines are fitted with a wedge reed valve and model 3700 uses pyramid style reed valve. Check for assembly and arrangement in appropriate figures. If reed valves do not seat properly, hard starting and loss of engine power under load will usually be the first indication. Individual reeds need not be perfectly flat, but they must seal completely under pressure when closed. When relaxed, a slight clearance, on the order of 0.010, may appear between reed and seat. This condition is satisfactory, however, if seats are pitted or flawed or if reeds are bent, damaged or otherwise distorted so as to allow for leaks, renewal is necessary. On these engines, reed petals are not serviced separately, and entire reed valve assembly must be renewed. Reed valve units must always be handled with care—never use compressed air in cleaning induction system.

MAGNETO. These engines are fitted with a conventional flywheel magneto. Spark timing is non-adjustable, however, if ignition breaker points are not accurately set to required 0.015 gap, ignition timing will be affected.

Air gap between magneto coil pole pieces and outer circumference of flywheel is specified as 0.008-0.010 inch. Core mounting holes are slotted so that

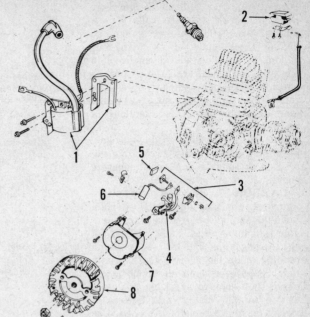

Fig. RO6—Exploded view of magneto ignition components of model 1900 engine. Note slots in coil core (1) to allow for shifting of coil assembly to set air gap between coil poles and magneto-flywheel (8).

1. Coil assembly
2. Shorting switch
3. Stud/insulator assembly
4. Breaker points
5. Cam felt
6. Condenser
7. Dust cover
8. Magneto-flywheel

when mounting screws are loosened, coil can be shifted to set this gap. A common, effective procedure is to place shim stock or plastic of proper thickness between flywheel magnets and coil poles. After adjustment is made, turn engine over by hand to check for clearance completely around flywheel.

For access to condenser and breaker point set, engine flywheel must be removed. Use of a strap wrench or special Roper flywheel wrench to hold flywheel while flywheel nut is backed off is recommended. Wedging a screwdriver between fins to hold flywheel can cause damage or distortion. Retainer nut is 5/16-24 thread (NF) and a knock-out puller or nut can be fitted to protect crankshaft threads for bumping

crankshaft end out of tapered bore of flywheel. Refer to Figs. RO6 or RO7 for parts arrangement if points and condenser are to be removed for renewal. Carefully set breaker point gap to 0.015 and be sure that terminals and insulators are snug and clean. Be sure to reinstall breaker covers. When flywheel is refitted, be sure that Woodruff key is properly engaged in keyway, and torque flywheel retaining lock nut to 130-150 inch-pounds.

All ignition components are available as separate service parts for renewal.

LUBRICATION. All internal lubrication of these engines is by gasoline-oil mix which passes through engine crankcase during operating cycles. For normal break-in period, engine should

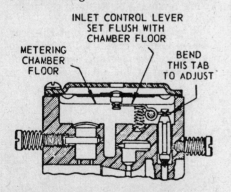

INLET CONTROL LEVER SET FLUSH WITH CHAMBER FLOOR

METERING CHAMBER FLOOR

BEND THIS TAB TO ADJUST

Fig. RO5—Fuel metering diaphragm lever of Tillotson HS carburetor should be adjusted flush with chamber floor as shown.

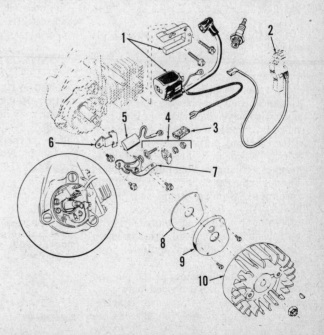

Fig. RO7—Exploded view of ignition system parts used on model 3700 engine.

1. Coil/core assembly
2. Shorting switch
3. Cam felt
4. Stud-insulator
5. Condenser
6. Condenser clip
7. Points assembly
8. Gasket
9. Cover
10. Magneto-flywheel

burn about four gallons of gasoline. Break-in period mixture calls for ¾ pint of two-stroke oil per gallon, so mixing three pints of oil with four gallons of gasoline will cover break-in operation. Thereafter, proper mix is one-half pint per gallon, for a 1:16 ratio. For convenience, this is two pints (one quart) of oil in four gallons of gasoline.

Use clean regular grade gasoline, premixing good quality two-stroke engine oil thoroughly in a clean, separate container, never in unit fuel tank.

CARBON. At regular twenty-five hour intervals of operation, carbon build-up should be removed from engine exhaust ports and mufflers of these engines. To do so, remove muffler mounting screws so that muffler can be disassembled and ports exposed then remove spark plug. Rotate engine so that piston is at bottom of stroke leaving exhaust ports open. Use a hardwood scraper to clear accumulated carbon deposits from exhaust ports. Thoroughly clean up all parts of spark arrestor type muffler. Before refitting muffler to cylinder barrel, pull starter cord a time or two to blow loose carbon particles out of engine combustion chamber. Replace spark plug.

REPAIRS

TIGHTENING TORQUES. Recommended torque values in INCH-POUNDS are shown here for nut and screw sizes used on these engines:

5/16-24 (NF), Flywheel	130-150
¼-28 (NF)	80-100
¼-20 (NC), Muffler	100-130
No. 10-32	30-40
No. 8-32	17-21
No. 6-32	8-10

CYLINDER, PISTON, PIN AND RINGS. Preliminary to disassembly of cylinder and crankcase assemblies of these engines, remove carburetor, muffler, starter housing and flywheel. Engines used to power chain saws must also have crankcase end plate removed. Cylinder barrel can be removed after backing nuts from four studs which align and hold cylinder to crankcase flange. Aluminum cylinders have chromed bores of 0.001-0.002 thickness. Severe wear, scoring or cracks in cylinder wall cannot be corrected by reboring; entire cylinder barrel must be renewed. Always use a new gasket between cylinder and crankcase.

On model 1900, piston, piston pin and connecting rod are serviced only as a complete assembly. Parts are separately available for model 3700. Pistons are

Fig. RO8—Exploded view of crankcase-cylinder assembly parts of model 1900 engine.

1. Muffler assembly
2. Cylinder
3. Gasket
4. Locknuts 10-24 (4)
5. Piston rings
6. Piston pin
7. Piston
8. Connecting rod
9. Needle bearing
10. Crankshaft
11. Seal retainer (2)
12. Crankshaft seal (2)
13. Needle bearings (2)
14. Needle bearings (2)
15. Gasket
16. Bearing carrier
*17. Oil pickup hose
*18. Oil filter
*19. Chain tensioner
* Chain saw application

fitted with two cast iron rings. Be sure that rings are properly fitted to alignment pins during assembly. Pistons must be heated for removal or installation of piston pin which slips through bore of small end of model 1900 connecting rod or through a caged needle bearing in small end of model 3700 connecting rod. Both models use snap rings in piston pin bores.

IMPORTANT NOTE: During assembly, keep in mind that closed end of piston pin is installed toward exhaust port and that "EXH" mark on piston crown is also assembled toward exhaust port side.

When pressing old bearing out or new bearing into small end of model 3700 connecting rod, be sure that connecting rod end is fully supported, especially if lower rod end is attached to engine crankshaft.

CONNECTING ROD. On smaller model 1900 engine, though connecting rod and piston are an assembly for parts renewal purposes, large end bearing may be separately renewed. To do so, first remove cylinder from engine crankcase followed by engine flywheel. Note in Fig. RO8 that crankshaft (10) separates at connecting

rod journal. It will be apparent, after study of illustration, that removal of bearing carrier (16) makes it possible to remove flywheel end of crankshaft. Such disassembly should include plan to renew gasket (15) and probably crankshaft seal (12). With piston and connecting rod at top of stroke, large end of connecting rod can be slipped from connecting rod journal of crankshaft and lifted out of crankcase. Needle roller bearing (9) can now be pressed out of large end of connecting rod (8). Take care to press only on lettered end of roller cage of new bearing during installation.

On model 3700 engine, after removal of cylinder barrel from crankcase, remove snap rings and press piston pin (9—Fig. RO10) from piston (8) after heating. Wrist pin bearing (10) may be loose if engine has been in service for some time, and if so, may be removed with finger pressure. Always check for excessive play in small end bearing before removing piston from connecting rod.

When piston (8) is out of the way, unscrew cap screws at lower end of connecting rod (11) and separate from cap portion of rod taking care not to

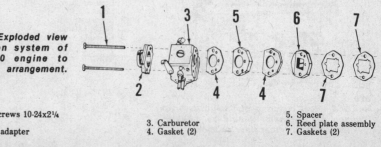

Fig. RO9—Exploded view of induction system of model 1900 engine to show parts arrangement.

1. Assembly screws 10-24x2¼ (2)
2. Air cleaner adapter

3. Carburetor
4. Gasket (2)

5. Spacer
6. Reed plate assembly
7. Gaskets (2)

lose bearing rollers (12). There are thirty-one loose rollers which make up this bearing; renewal bearing is furnished as part of a new connecting rod along with cap screws. If old bearing and connecting rod are to be re-used, hold bearing rollers in place with grease during reassembly. When small end bearing is also renewed, be sure to press on lettered end of bearing cage. Check for match marks on large end of connecting rod and on rod cap and be sure they are in register during reassembly.

CRANKCASE AND CRANKSHAFT.

Both models of these Roper engines are fitted with anti-friction bearings to support their crankshafts. Model 1900 has two sets of caged roller needle bearings (Torrington) and model 3700 uses a ball bearing assembly at pto end and a keystone-type caged roller bearing set at flywheel end of crankshaft. Refer to Fig. RO8 and Fig. RO10 for identification and placement.

When renewal of crankshaft bearings is determined to be necessary, keep these points in mind:

Renew crankshaft seals and retainers (model 1900) as part of bearing service.

Heat is required for expansion of bearing recess areas of crankcase and bearing retainer so that bearing can be pressed or pulled out. Use of open flame devices for heat is not recommended. If available, use a heat gun or heat lamp and before use, apply compressed air to clear residue of fuel-oil mix from bearing races and crankcase interior.

Refer to TIGHTENING TORQUES at beginning of this section for proper tightening of grade five cap screws used for assembly.

Ball bearing (19—Fig. RO10) is pressed on crankshaft. Groove in bearing outer race is placed adjacent to crank throw. When bearing retainers (18) are reinstalled, tighten 10-32 screws to 30-40 in.-lbs. after application of CV grade Loctite to threads. Rotate crank by hand to insure that screw heads are clear of crankshaft.

RECOIL STARTER.

Manual starter used on model 1900 engine is shown in exploded view for parts identification in Fig. RO11. Model 3700 starter is shown in Fig. RO12. All parts are serviced by central distributors and are available through Roper dealers. Service is as follows:

STARTER PAWLS & SPRINGS.

If starter pawls, springs or pivot posts are damaged or worn so as to require renewal, remove attaching screws so that entire housing (8—Fig. RO11) or

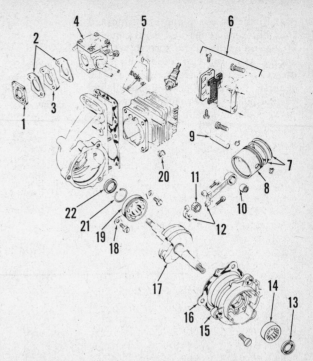

Fig. RO10—Exploded view of crankcase-cylinder assemblies of model 3700 engine to show parts arrangement.

1. Cork gasket
2. Gaskets (2)
3. Heat barrier
4. Carburetor
5. Reed assembly
6. Muffler assembly
7. Piston rings (2)
8. Piston
9. Piston pin
10. Needle bearing
11. Bearing rollers (31)
12. Connecting rod assembly
13. Oil seal
14. Keystone roller bearing
15. Bearing carrier
16. Gasket
17. Crankshaft
18. Bearing retainer (2)
19. Ball bearing
20. Lock nut (4)
21. Retainer ring
22. Oil seal

(10—Fig. RO12) can be lifted away from flywheel. Unscrew pivot posts from flywheel for renewal of broken springs or damaged pawls. Note that on model 3700, screen (4) must be removed first.

RENEW STARTER CORD. (Model 1900).

Remove housing (8—Fig. RO11). Remove knot from starter rope at pulley end and remove rope. Remove "E" ring (3) from starter center post with spacer washer, then lift out starter pulley (4). Tie firm knot in new rope and thread through center of pulley hub so¹ that standing (no knot) end of rope passes outward through pulley sheaves, then reinstall pulley (4) on center post and replace washer and "E" ring (3). Thread loose rope end into starter housing grommet from underside and attach handle (9) and insert (10) to rope as shown. Guide this new rope into pulley and turn pulley clockwise for seven turns. Hold pulley (4) to prevent turning and pull out rope slack by starter handle, then allow rope to retract. Reattach housing and tighten

mounting screws securely.

(Model 3700).

Remove four mounting screws to remove housing assembly (10—Fig. RO12) from engine. Untie or cut knot from old starter rope at pulley and pull out. Fit starter handle (11) to new rope. Now, wind starter pulley (7) against spring (clockwise) for eight full turns, then insert a screwdriver through opening in housing to engage lugs on pulley and prevent spring from unwinding. Insert new rope through housing grommet and into pulley hub and secure with a firm knot. Remove screwdriver from pulley lugs and allow pulley to revolve and wind up starter cord. Reassemble starter housing to engine. Tighten screws securely.

RENEW STARTER SPRING.

On both models, operating spring is coiled within cup portion of housing and is installed relaxed. Refer to applicable figure and remove starter housing. Remove "E" ring from starter body center post and remove pulley. Note that model 1900 has a removable screw

Fig. RO11—Exploded view of recoil starter used on model 1900 engine. Pivot posts and pawls are mounted on engine flywheel.

1. Starter pawls & springs
2. Pivot posts
3. "E" ring
4. Pulley halves
5. Retainer
6. Spacer
7. Recoil spring
8. Housing
9. Pull handle & rope
10. Insert

post to anchor outer end of spring and that different types and arrangements of spacers are used. Be sure to set new spring into its cup coiled in same direction as old spring. Apply a little graphite to center post. Reinstall and rewind pulley as described in preceding paragraphs and refit starter assembly to engine.

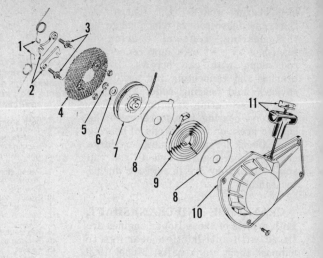

Fig. RO12—Exploded view of recoil starter used on model 3700 engine.

1. Pawl springs
2. Starter pawls
3. Pivot posts
4. Screen
5. "E" ring
6. Washer
7. Starter pulley
8. Spacers
9. Recoil spring
10. Housing
11. Handle & rope insert

METRIC CONVERSION

MM.	INCHES			MM.	INCHES			MM.	INCHES			MM.	INCHES		
1	0.0394	1/32	+	26	1.0236	1 1/32	−	51	2.0079	2.0	+	76	2.9921	3.0	−
2	0.0787	3/32	−	27	1.0630	1 1/16	+	52	2.0472	2 1/16	−	77	3.0315	3 1/32	+
3	0.1181	1/8	−					53	2.0866	2 3/32	−				
				28	1.1024	1 3/32	+					78	3.0709	3 1/16	+
4	0.1575	5/32	+	29	1.1417	1 5/32	−	54	2.1260	2 1/8	+	79	3.1102	3 1/8	−
5	0.1969	3/16	+	30	1.1811	1 3/16	−	55	2.1654	2 5/32	+	80	3.1496	3 5/32	+
6	0.2362	1/4	−					56	2.2047	2 7/32	−				
				31	1.2205	1 7/32	+					81	3.1890	3 3/16	+
7	0.2756	9/32	−	32	1.2598	1 1/4	+	57	2.2441	2 1/4	−	82	3.2283	3 7/32	+
8	0.3150	5/16	−	33	1.2992	1 5/16	−	58	2.2835	2 9/32	+	83	3.2677	3 9/32	−
9	0.3543	11/32	+					59	2.3228	2 5/16	+				
				34	1.3386	1 11/32	−					84	3.3071	3 5/16	−
10	0.3937	13/32	−	35	1.3780	1 3/8	+	60	2.3622	2 3/8	−	85	3.3465	3 11/32	+
11	0.4331	7/16	−	36	1.4173	1 13/32	+	61	2.4016	2 13/32	−	86	3.3858	3 3/8	+
12	0.4724	15/32	+					62	2.4409	2 7/16	+				
				37	1.4567	1 15/32	−					87	3.4252	3 7/16	−
13	0.5118	1/2	+	38	1.4961	1 1/2	−	63	2.4803	2 15/32	+	88	3.4646	3 15/32	+
14	0.5512	9/16	−	39	1.5354	1 17/32	+	64	2.5197	2 17/32	−	89	3.5039	3 1/2	+
15	0.5906	19/32	−					65	2.5591	2 9/16	−				
				40	1.5748	1 9/16	+					90	3.5433	3 17/32	+
16	0.6299	5/8	+	41	1.6142	1 5/8	−	66	2.5984	2 19/32	+	91	3.5827	3 19/32	−
17	0.6693	21/32	+	42	1.6535	1 21/32	−	67	2.6378	2 5/8	+	92	3.6220	3 5/8	−
18	0.7087	23/32	−					68	2.6772	2 11/16	−				
				43	1.6929	1 11/16	+					93	3.6614	3 21/32	+
19	0.7480	3/4	−	44	1.7323	1 23/32	+	69	2.7165	2 23/32	−	94	3.7008	3 11/16	+
20	0.7874	25/32	+	45	1.7717	1 25/32	−	70	2.7559	2 3/4	+	95	3.7402	3 3/4	−
21	0.8268	13/16	+					71	2.7953	2 25/32	+				
				46	1.8110	1 13/16	−					96	3.7795	3 25/32	−
22	0.8661	7/8	−	47	1.8504	1 27/32	+	72	2.8346	2 27/32	−	97	3.8189	3 13/16	+
23	0.9055	29/32	−	48	1.8898	1 7/8	+	73	2.8740	2 7/8	−	98	3.8583	3 27/32	+
24	0.9449	15/16	+					74	2.9134	2 29/32	+				
				49	1.9291	1 15/16	−					99	3.8976	3 29/32	−
25	0.9843	31/32	+	50	1.9685	1 31/32	−	75	2.9528	2 15/16	+	100	3.9370	3 15/16	+

NOTE. The + or − sign indicates that the decimal equivalent is larger or smaller than the fractional equivalent.

SOLO

SOLO MOTORS, INC.
5100 Chestnut Avenue
Copeland Industrial Park
Newport News, Virginia 23605

Model	Cyls.	Bore	Stroke	Displ.
206	1	2.56	2.13	10.9
209	1	2.80	2.13	13.4

MAINTENANCE

SPARK PLUG. Recommended spark plug is Bosch W175T1, Champion L-85, AC 42F, Autolite AE3 or equivalent. Electrode gap is 0.018-0.020.

CARBURETOR. Tillotson model HR19A carburetor is normally used; however, some motors may be equipped with model HL287A Tillotson carburetor. Initial adjustments are as follows: Lightly seat both mixture needles. Open idle mixture needle (24—Fig. S1) 1 turn and main fuel mixture needle (23) 1½ turns. Final adjustments should be made with engine running at normal operating temperature. Adjust idle speed stop screw (4) to obtain engine idle speed of 1800-2200 rpm. Readjust idle mixture needle to obtain smooth and even idle speed operation. Adjust main fuel mixture needle so engine will accelerate without hesitation and will run smoothly without smoking.

To disassemble the carburetor, remove idle mixture needle (24) and main fuel needle (23). Remove cover (12), gasket (11) and screen (10), then unbolt and remove fuel pump body (9), valve diaphragm (8), pulse diaphragm (7) and gasket (22). Remove diaphragm cover (21), metering diaphragm (20) and gasket (19). Remove the control lever retaining screw, control lever pin (18), control lever (16) and spring (15). NOTE: Care must be used while removing parts due to spring pressure on inlet control lever. The spring must be

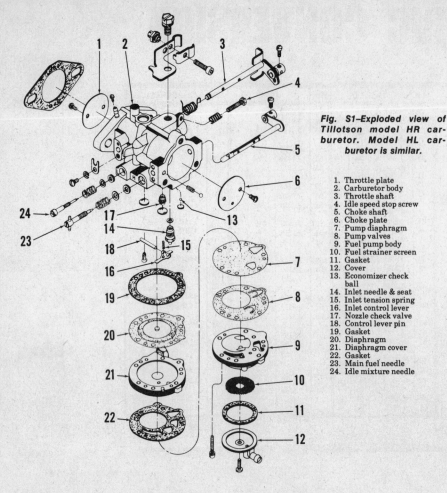

Fig. S1—Exploded view of Tillotson model HR carburetor. Model HL carburetor is similar.

1. Throttle plate
2. Carburetor body
3. Throttle shaft
4. Idle speed stop screw
5. Choke shaft
6. Choke plate
7. Pump diaphragm
8. Pump valves
9. Fuel pump body
10. Fuel strainer screen
11. Gasket
12. Cover
13. Economizer check ball
14. Inlet needle & seat
15. Inlet tension spring
16. Inlet control lever
17. Nozzle check valve
18. Control lever pin
19. Gasket
20. Diaphragm
21. Diaphragm cover
22. Gasket
23. Main fuel needle
24. Idle mixture needle

LUBRICATION. The engine is lubricated by mixing oil with the fuel. A suitable two-cycle, SAE30, air cooled engine oil is recommended. Fuel and oil should be mixed in ratio of 25:1. Mix fuel and oil thoroughly in separate container before pouring mixture into fuel tank. For cold weather blending, pre-mix the oil with a small amount of gasoline and shake thoroughly, then blend with remainder of fuel. Do not use kerosene or fuel oil for pre-mixing.

REPAIRS

CYLINDER HEAD. Cylinder head (26—Fig. S4) is removable from all models. When reinstalling cylinder head, always use new head gasket (26G) and tighten head retaining cap screws evenly.

PISTON, PIN, RINGS & CYLINDER. To remove the cylinder (27—Fig. S4), unbolt and remove the carburetor, exhaust manifold and air shrouds. Remove the four cylinder retaining nuts and washers, then pull cylinder straight out from crankcase until free from piston. Inspect cylinder for scoring, cracks, excessive wear or other damage.

Remove retaining rings (21), piston pin (20) and withdraw piston (19). Inspect piston pin (20), piston pin bearing (18) and side washers (17) for excessive wear. Check piston for scoring, excessive wear or other damage.

Check ring end gap as shown in Fig. S5. Ring end gap should be 0.012-0.015 in. Remove all carbon from ring grooves in piston, install new rings and measure ring side clearance as shown in Fig. S6. Recommended side clearance is 0.002-0.003 in. Place piston (without rings) in cylinder close to top dead center position. Using a feeler gage, measure piston side clearance in

handled carefully to prevent stretching or compressing. Any alteration to the spring will cause improper carburetor operation. If in doubt as to its condition, renew it.

Remove inlet needle and seat assembly (14), using a 5/16-inch thin wall socket. If necessary to remove nozzle check valve (17) or economizer check ball (13), drill through welch plugs with a ⅛-inch drill. Allow drill to just break through welch plugs. If drill travels too deep in cavity, the casting may be ruined. Pry welch plugs out of seats, using a small punch.

Throttle and choke shafts (3 and 5) can be removed for inspection if there is evidence of wear on these parts. Mark throttle and choke plates (1 and 6) so they can be reassembled in their

original positions.

Clean and inspect all parts and renew any showing excessive wear or other damage. When reassembling, tighten fuel inlet needle cage to a torque of 25-30 in.-lbs. Adjust inlet control lever (16) so that diaphragm end of lever is flush with metering chamber floor as shown in Fig. S2. Use Fig. S1 as a guide to assemble gaskets, diaphragms and castings in the correct order.

MAGNETO AND TIMING. A Bosch flywheel type magneto is used on all models. Breaker point gap can be checked or adjusted after removing the recoil starter, cooking fan, felt ring, inner fan cover and flywheel. Breaker point gap should be 0.014-0.018 in. To adjust ignition timing, position piston 0.118 in. BTDC, loosen stator plate mounting screws and rotate stator plate until breaker points just begin to open. (A 0.001 in. feeler gage should just slide between points). Tighten plate mounting screws. Also, at this time the edge gap (distance between flywheel pole edge and ignition armature pole edge) should be 0.3-0.4 in.

When reassembling, install cooling fan so that arrow (A—Fig. S3) is toward top of cylinder when piston is at TDC.

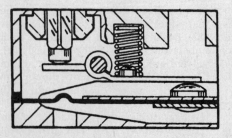

Fig. S2—Diaphragm end of fuel inlet lever must be flush with metering chamber floor as shown. Adjust by bending control lever.

Fig. S3—Arrow (A) on fan should point toward top of cylinder when piston is at Top Dead Center.

cylinder, which should be a minimum of 0.006 in. Piston and rings are available in standard size only. Grooves in pistons are equipped with pins and rings must be correctly installed to engage the pins. Install piston on rod so that arrow on top of piston is pointed toward exhaust side of cylinder. A drop of sealant should be applied to crankcase joints before installing new gasket (27G—Fig. S4) and cylinder.

CONNECTING ROD, CRANK-SHAFT & CRANKCASE. To remove the connecting rod and crankshaft assembly (16—Fig. S4), it is necessary to separate the crankcase halves. After removing the cylinder, piston and magneto assemblies, remove cap screws securing case halves together,

heat drive side of crankcase (13P) around bearing area to approximately 350-400° F. and carefully remove the crankcase half. Heat and remove flywheel side of crankcase (13F). Crankshaft and connecting rod are available only as an assembled unit and disassembly is not recommended. Use a suitable puller to remove main bearings (14) from crankshaft using extreme care not to distort the crankshaft. Main bearings are a tight fit on crankshaft journals. Bearings should be heated to approximately 300° F. before installing. Allow bearings to cool before assembling into heated crankcase halves. Always renew gaskets and seals (12). Lips of seals should be toward inside and outside edge of seal should be flush with crankcase flange.

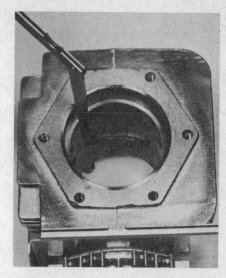

Fig. S5–Piston ring end gap should be 0.012-0.015, measured just above ports as shown.

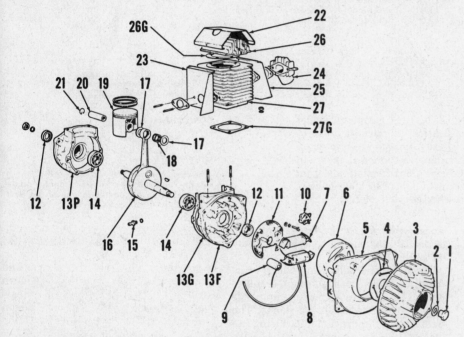

Fig. S4–Exploded view typical of models 206 and 209 engines. Seals (12) and main bearings (14) are identical at both ends of crankshaft.

Fig. S6–Use a feeler gage to measure piston ring side clearance in grooves. Recommended clearance is 0.002-0.003.

1. Flywheel nut	13F. Crankcase half (flywheel side)
2. Washer	13G. Gasket
3. Cooling fan	13P. Crankcase half (output side)
4. Felt ring	14. Main bearing
5. Fan cover	15. Crankcase pulse fitting
6. Flywheel	16. Crankshaft assembly
7. Lighting coil	17. Side washers
8. Ignition coil	18. Piston pin bearing
9. Condenser	19. Piston
10. Breaker points	20. Piston pin
11. Stator plate	
12. Crankcase seals	

21. Retaining ring (2 used)
22. Top air shroud
23. Air shroud (inlet side)
24. Exhaust manifold
25. Air shroud (exhaust side)
26. Cylinder head
26G. Gasket
27. Cylinder
27G. Gasket

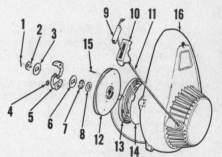

Fig. S7–Exploded view of recoil starter used on Solo models 206 and 209 engines. Washers (3) and (6) are identical.

1. Pin	9. Anchor
2. Spring washer	10. Handle
3. Thrust washer	11. Rope
4. Snap rings (2 used)	12. Pulley
5. Pawls	13. Recoil spring
6. Thrust washer	14. Washer
7. Snap ring	15. Pin
8. Washer	16. Starter housing & fan cover

SERVICING SOLO ACCESSORIES

RECOIL STARTER

OVERHAUL. To disassemble the recoil starter, refer to Fig. S7 and proceed as follows: Remove pin (1), spring washer (2), thrust washer (3), snap rings (4) and lift off pawls (5) and thrust washer (6). Remove anchor (9) and handle (10). Allow rope to rewind into housing, remove snap ring (7) and

washer (8), then lift pulley (12) out. Remove spring (13) and washer (14).

Clean and inspect all parts and renew any showing excessive wear or other damage. When reassembling, install washer (14), spring (13) and pulley (12) in housing (16). Turn pulley counter-clockwise (as viewed from engine side) approximately 5 turns and

insert rope through pulley and exit hole in housing. Rope (11) should be approximately 43 inches long. Press knot (at pulley end of rope) into recess in pulley until knot is flush with face of pulley. Install handle (10), anchor (9), washer (8) and snap ring (7). Assemble thrust washer (6), pawls (5) and snap rings (4). Install thrust washer (3), spring washer (2) and pin (1). Check operation before installing starter on engine.

TECUMSEH 4-CYCLE

Tecumseh Products Company
Grafton, Wisconsin

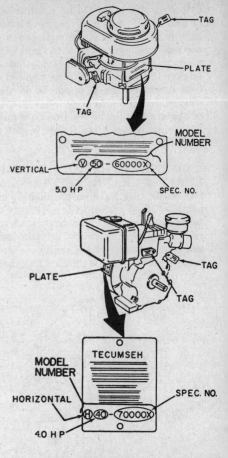

LIGHT FRAME MODELS

Reference Code	Bore In.	Stroke In.	Displ. Cu. In.	Rated HP
A	2 1/8	1 3/4	6.207	1.7, 2.0, 2.25
B	2 5/16	1 3/4	7.35	2.25, 2.5
C	2 5/16	1 13/16	7.61	3.0
D	2 5/16	1 27/32	7.75	2.25, 2.5, 3.0
E	2 1/2	1 13/16	8.9	3.2, 3.5
F	2 1/2	1 27/32	9.06	3.5 (Model ECH90)
G	2 5/8	1 27/32	10.0	(Model ECV100)
H	2 5/8	1 15/16	10.5	4.0 (Model ECV105)
I	2 3/4	1 15/16	11.0	(Model ECV110)
J	2 13/16	1 15/16	12.0	5.0 (Model ECV120)

MEDIUM FRAME MODELS

K	2 1/2	2 1/4	11.04	4.0, 4.5
L	2 5/8	2 1/4	12.176	4.5, 5.0, 5.5
M	2 5/8	2 1/2	13.53	4.5, 5.5, 6.0

Engines must be identified by the complete model number, including the specification number in order to obtain correct repair parts. These numbers are located on the name plate and or tags that are positioned as shown in Fig. T1. It is important to transfer identification tags from the original engine to replacement short block assemblies so that unit can be identified when servicing later.

Fig. T1—Tags and plates used to identify model will most often be located in one of the positions shown.

MAINTENANCE

SPARK PLUG. The spark plug electrode gap should be 0.030 for engines with gasoline and kerosene fuel; 0.020 for LP gas. Most engines use a 14 MM, ⅜-inch reach plug, however other sizes are also used.

14 MM—⅜-inch reach
Gasoline J-8
LP-Gas J-8
Kerosene UJ-12
18 MM—½-inch reach
Gasoline . . . . D-16 or MD-16
Kerosene D-21
All ⅞-inch thread size W-18

CARBURETOR. Several different carburetors are used on these engines. Refer to the appropriate following paragraph for service and adjustment.

TECUMSEH DIAPHRAGM CARBURETOR. Idle mixture is adjusted at needle (10—Fig. T2). High speed mixture is adjusted at main fuel needle (14). Initial setting is 1 turn open for both needles and clockwise rotation will lean the mixture. Make final mixture adjustment with engine warm and operating with the normal amount of load. Adjust the main fuel needle (14) for smoothest operation at governed speed, then adjust idle needle (10) for smoothest operation at idle (slow) speed. Idle speed is adjusted at stop screw (9) and should be approximately 1800 RPM.

Observe the following when overhauling Tecumseh diaphragm carburetors: The carburetor model number is stamped on the mounting flange. The fuel strainer in the fuel inlet fitting can be cleaned by reverse flushing with compressed air after the inlet needle and seat (19—Fig. T2) are removed. The inlet needle seat fitting is metal with a neoprene seat, so the fitting (and enclosed seat) should be removed before carburetor is cleaned with a commercial solvent. The stamped line on carburetor throttle plate should be toward top of carburetor, parallel with throttle shaft and facing OUTWARD

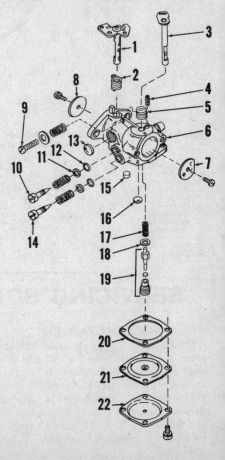

Fig. T2—Exploded view of typical Tecumseh diaphragm carburetor.

1. Throttle shaft
2. Return spring
3. Choke shaft
4. Choke stop spring
5. Return spring
6. Carburetor body
7. Choke plate
8. Throttle plate
9. Idle speed screw
10. Idle mixture needle
11. Washers
12. "O" rings
13. Welch plug
14. Main fuel needle
15. Cup plug
16. Welch plug
17. Inlet needle spring
18. Gasket
19. Inlet needle & seat assembly
20. Gasket
21. Diaphragm
22. Cover

as shown in Fig. T3. Flat side of choke plate should be toward the fuel inlet fitting side of carburetor. Mark on choke plate should be parallel to shaft and should face INWARD when choke is closed. Diaphragm (21—Fig. T2) should be installed with rounded head of center rivet up toward the inlet needle (19), regardless of size or placement of washers around the rivet. On carburetor models 0234-252, 265, 266, 269, 270, 271, 282, 293, 303, 322, 327, 333, 334, 344, 345, 348, 349, 350, 351, 352, 356, 368, 371, 374, 378, 379, 380, 404 and 405, gasket (20) must be installed between diaphragm (21) and cover (22). All other models are assembled as shown, with gasket between diaphragm and carburetor body.

TECUMSEH STANDARD FLOAT CARBURETOR. Idle mixture is adjusted at needle (12—Fig. T4) and high speed mixture at main fuel needle (34). Initial setting is 1 turn open for both needles and clockwise rotation will lean the mixture. Make final mixture adjustment with engine warm and operating with the normal amount of load. Adjust the main fuel needle (34) for smoothest operation at governed

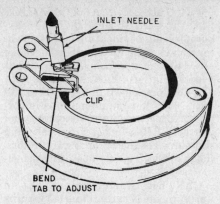

INLET NEEDLE

CLIP

BEND TAB TO ADJUST

Fig. T4A–View of float and fuel inlet valve needle. The valve needle shown is equipped with resilient tip and a clip. Bend tab shown to adjust float height.

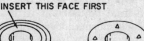

INSERT THIS FACE FIRST

GROOVE

INLET NEEDLE TIP SEATS AT THIS POINT

Fig. T4B–The Viton seat used on some Tecumseh carburetors must be installed correctly to operate properly. All metal needle is used with seat shown.

speed, then adjust idle needle (12) for smoothest operation at idle (slow) speed. Idle speed is adjusted at stop screw (1) and should be approximately 1800 RPM.

Observe the following when overhauling: Disassemble the carburetor before attempting to clean. Most commercial cleaners will damage neoprene and Viton rubber parts. Do not attempt to reuse any expansion plugs. Install new plugs if any are removed for cleaning. The fuel inlet needle valve closes against a neoprene or Viton seat which must be removed before cleaning in most commercial solvents.

Three types of fuel inlet valves are used. Some carburetors are equipped with a resilient tip on the fuel inlet needle (Fig. T4A). The soft tip contacts the seating surface machined into the carburetor body to shut off the fuel. Do not attempt to remove the inlet valve seat. Some carburetors are equipped with a Viton seat (21—Fig. T4) that is located in bore of carburetor body. The rubber seat can be removed by blowing compressed air in from the fuel inlet fitting or by using a hooked wire. The grooved face of valve seat should be IN toward bottom of bore and the valve

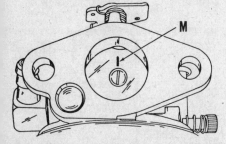

M

Fig. T3–The mark (M) on throttle plate should be parallel to the throttle shaft and outward as shown. Some models may also have mark at 3 o'clock position.

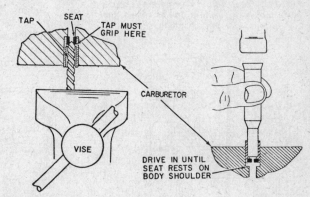

TAP   SEAT

TAP MUST GRIP HERE

CARBURETOR

VISE

DRIVE IN UNTIL SEAT RESTS ON BODY SHOULDER

Fig. T4C–A 10-24 or 10-32 tap is used to pull the brass seat fitting and fuel inlet valve seat from some carburetors. Use a close fitting flat punch to install new seat and fitting.

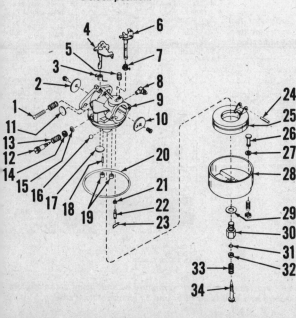

Fig. T4–Exploded view of standard Tecumseh float type carburetor.

1. Idle speed screw
2. Throttle plate
3. Return spring
4. Throttle shaft
5. Choke stop spring
6. Choke shaft
7. Return spring
8. Fuel inlet fitting
9. Carburetor body
10. Choke plate
11. Welch plug
12. Idle mixture needle
13. Spring
14. Washer
15. "O" ring
16. Ball plug
17. Welch plug
18. Pin
19. Cup plugs
20. Bowl gasket
21. Inlet needle seat
22. Inlet needle
23. Clip
24. Float shaft
25. Float
26. Drain stem
27. Gasket
28. Bowl
29. Gasket
30. Bowl retainer
31. "O" ring
32. Washer
33. Spring
34. Main fuel needle

needle should seat on smooth side of the Viton seat. Refer to Fig. T4B. On some carburetors, the Viton seat is contained in a brass seat fitting. Use a 10-24 or 10-32 tap to pull the seat and fitting from carburetor bore as shown in Fig. T4C. Use a flat, close fitting punch to install new seat and fitting.

Install the throttle plate (2—Fig. T4) with the two stamped marks out and at 12 and 3 o'clock positions. The 12 o'clock line should be parallel with the throttle shaft and toward top of carburetor. Install choke plate (10) with flat side down toward bottom of carburetor. Float setting should be 0.200-0.220 and can be measured with a No. 4 drill as shown in Fig. T4D. Remove float and bend tab at float hinge to change float setting. The fuel inlet fitting (8—Fig. T4) is pressed into body on some models. Start fitting, then apply a light coat of "Loctite" (grade A) to shank and press fitting into position. The flat on fuel bowl should be under the fuel inlet fitting. Refer to Fig. T4E.

Be sure to use correct parts when servicing the carburetor. Some gaskets used as (20) are square section, while others are round. The bowl retainer (30) contains a drilled passage for fuel to the high speed metering needle (34). A diagonal port through one side of the bowl retainer is used on carburetors with external vent. The port is through both sides on models with internal vent. Refer to Fig. T4F.

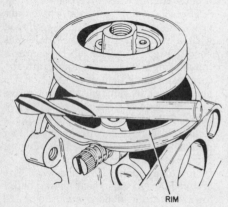

Fig. T4D–Float height can be measured on some models by using a drill as shown. Refer to text for correct setting height.

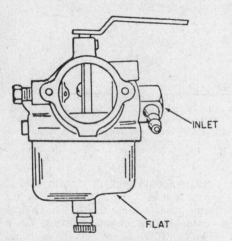

Fig. T4E–Flat part of float bowl should be located under the fuel inlet fitting.

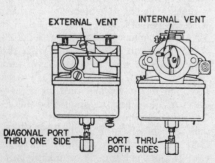

Fig. T4F–The bowl retainer contains a drilled fuel passage which is different for carburetors with external and internal fuel bowl vent.

TECUMSEH "AUTOMAGIC" FLOAT CARBURETOR. The carburetor can be identified by the absence of the idle mixture needle, choke and the main mixture adjustment needle (Fig. T5). Float setting is with No. 4 drill as shown in Fig. T4D (0.210 inch). Air filter maintenance is important in order to obtain the correct fuel mixture. Refer to notes for servicing standard Tecumseh float carburetors. Refer to Fig. T5A for operating principles.

CARTER. Initial adjustment of Carter model N carburetors is 1½ turns open for the idle mixture needle (9—Fig. T6) and 1¾ turns open for the main adjusting needle (4). Clockwise rotation of both needles leans the mixture. Make final adjustment with engine running at normal operating temperature. Adjust main fuel needle for smoothest engine operation at high idle RPM and adjust idle mixture needle for smoothest low idle operation. Engine should now have a smooth acceleration from low idle to high idle speed and steady governor operation.

To check float level invert carburetor body and float assembly. There should be 11/64-inch clearance between free side of float and machined surface of body casting. Bend float lever tang to provide correct measurement.

MARVEL-SCHEBLER. On series AH Marvel Schebler carburetors, clockwise rotation of both the idle mix-

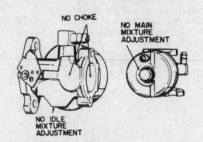

Fig. T5–Tecumseh "Automagic" carburetor is similar to standard float models, but can be identified by absence of choke and adjusting needles.

ture needle (18—Fig. T7) and main fuel adjusting needle (13) leans the mixture. Initial adjustment is 1 turn open for the idle mixture needle and 1¼ turns open for the main fuel adjusting needle. Make final adjustment with

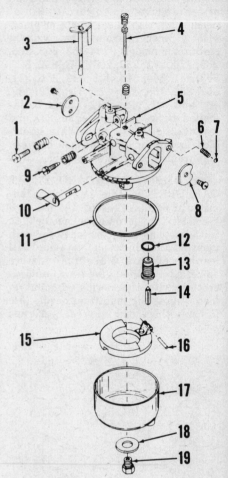

Fig. T6–Exploded view of typical Carter N carburetor.

1. Idle speed screw	10. Choke shaft
2. Throttle plate	11. Bowl gasket
3. Throttle shaft	12. Gasket
4. Main adjusting	13. Inlet valve seat
needle	14. Inlet valve
5. Carburetor body	15. Float
6. Choke shaft spring	16. Float shaft
7. Ball	17. Fuel bowl
8. Choke plate	18. Gasket
9. Idle mixture needle	19. Bowl retainer

Fig. T5A–The "Automagic" carburetor provides a rich starting mixture without using a choke plate. Mixture is changed by operating with a dirty air filter and by incorrect float setting.

engine running at normal operating temperature. With engine running at recommended high idle (governed) speed, adjust main fuel adjusting needle for smoothest engine operation. Then, back out idle speed screw (1), hold throttle to slowest engine speed possible without stalling, and adjust idle speed mixture needle for smoothest engine operation. Readjust

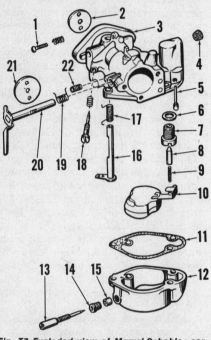

Fig. T7–Exploded view of Marvel-Schebler carburetor.

1. Idle speed screw	12. Fuel bowl
2. Throttle plate	13. Main adjusting
3. Carburetor body	needle
4. Fuel screen	14. Retainer
5. Float shaft	15. Packing
6. Gasket	16. Throttle shaft
7. Inlet valve seat	17. Throttle spring
8. Inlet valve	18. Idle mixture needle
9. Spring	19. Choke spring
10. Float	20. Choke shaft
11. Gasket	21. Choke plate
	22. Choke ratchet spring

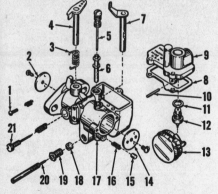

Fig. T8–Exploded view of typical Tillotson MT carburetor.

1. Idle speed screw	12. Inlet needle & seat
2. Throttle plate	assy.
3. Throttle spring	13. Float
4. Throttle shaft	14. Choke plate
5. Idle tube	15. Friction pin
6. Main nozzle	16. Choke shaft spring
7. Choke shaft	17. Carburetor body
8. Gasket	18. Packing
9. Bowl cover	19. Retainer
10. Float shaft	20. Main adjusting
11. Gasket	needle
	21. Idle mixture needle

Fig. T9–Exploded view of typical Tillotson E carburetor.

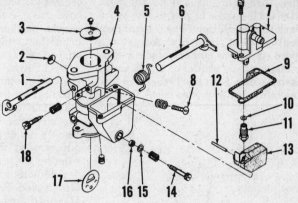

Fig. T9–Exploded view of typical Tillotson E carburetor.

1. Throttle shaft
2. Welch plug
3. Throttle plate
4. Carburetor body
5. Return spring
6. Choke shaft
7. Bowl cover
8. Idle speed stop screw
9. Bowl gasket
10. Gasket
11. Inlet needle & seat assy.
12. Float shaft
13. Float
14. Main fuel needle
15. Washer
16. Packing
17. Choke plate
18. Idle mixture needle

idle speed screw to obtain a low idle speed of 1800 RPM. To adjust float level, hold carburetor body and float assembly in inverted position. Bend tang on float to obtain a clearance of 3/32-inch between free end of float and machined surface of carburetor body.

TILLOTSON TYPE "MT" CARBURETOR. Clockwise rotation of both the idle mixture needle (21—Fig. T8) and main fuel adjusting needle (20) leans the mixture. Initial setting for idle mixture needle should be ¾-turn open and for the main adjusting needle, 1 turn open. Start engine and run until normal operating temperature is reached. Then, readjust main fuel needle for smoothest operation at high idle RPM. Adjust idle speed screw (1) for low idle speed and adjust idle mixture needle if necessary for best idle operation. Float setting should be 1 13/32 inches as measured, with bowl cover and float assembly turned upside down, from top of float to gasket surface of bowl cover.

TILLOTSON TYPE "E" CARBURETOR. Clockwise rotation of both

the idle mixture needle (18—Fig. T9) and main fuel needle (14) leans the mixture. Initial setting for idle mixture needle is ¾-turn open and for main fuel needle, 1 turn open. With engine running at normal operating speed, turn main fuel needle clockwise until engine begins to lose speed. Then, slowly back needle out (usually ⅛ to ¼-turn) until maximum speed and power is obtained. Operate engine at idle speed,

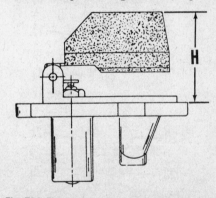

Fig. T9A–Float height (H) should be measured as shown for Tillotson type "E" carburetors. Gasket should not be installed when measuring.

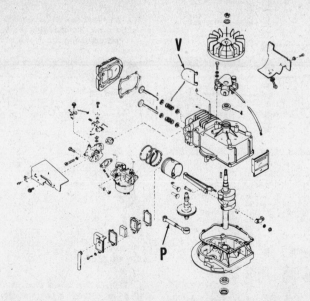

Exploded view of Light Frame vertical crankshaft engine. Model shown has plunger type oil pump (P) and air vane (V) governor.

then turn idle mixture needle clockwise until engine begins to lose speed. Back the needle out (¼ to ½-turn) until engine idles smoothly. Adjust idle speed stop screw for desired idle speed.

Float setting should be 1 5/64 inches as measured, with bowl cover and float assembly turned upside down, from top of float at free end to gasket surface of bowl cover. Refer to Fig. T9A. Gasket should not be installed when measuring float height. Carefully bend tang on float to adjust float height.

WALBRO. On Walbro carburetors, clockwise rotation of both the low idle mixture needle (9—Fig. T10) and the main fuel adjusting needle (33) leans the mixture. Initial setting for both needles is 1 turn open. Make final adjustment with engine warm and running. Adjust main fuel needle until engine runs smoothly at normal operating speed. Back out idle speed screw (7), hold throttle to slowest engine speed possible without stalling and adjust idle mixture needle for smoothest operation. Readjust idle speed screw so engine idles at 1800 RPM.

To check float setting, hold carburetor body and float assembly in inverted position. A clearance of ⅛-inch should exist between free end of float and machined surface of carburetor body. Refer to Fig. T10A. Bend tab on float as necessary to provide correct measurement.

NOTE: If carburetor has been disassembled and main nozzle (19—Fig. T10) removed, do not reinstall the original equipment nozzle; obtain and install a new service nozzle. Refer to Fig. T10B for differences between original and service nozzles.

PNEUMATIC GOVERNOR. Some engines are equipped with a pneumatic (air vane) type governor. On fixed linkage hookups, the recommended idle speed is 1800 RPM. Standard no-load speed is 3300 RPM. Operating speed range is 2600 to 3600 RPM. On engines not equipped with slide control (Fig. T17), obtain desired speed by varying the tension on governor speed regulating spring by moving speed adjusting lever (Fig. T15) in or out as required. If engine speed fluctuates due to governor hunting or surging, move carburetor end of governor spring into next outer hole on carburetor throttle arm shown in Fig. T16.

A too lean fuel mixture or friction in governor linkage will also cause hunting or unsteady operation.

On engines with slide control carburetors, speed adjustment is made with engine running as follows: Remove slide control cover (Fig. T17) marked "choke, fast, slow, etc." Lock the carburetor in high speed "run" position by matching the hole in slide control member (A) with hole (B) closest to choke end of bracket. Temporarily hold in this position by inserting a tapered punch or pin of suitable size into the hole.

At this time the choke should be wide open and the choke activating

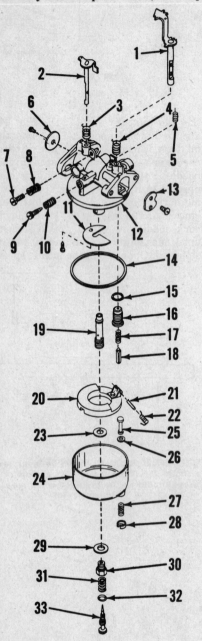

Fig. T10–Exploded view of Walbro LMG carburetor.

1. Choke shaft
2. Throttle shaft
3. Throttle return spring
4. Choke return spring
5. Choke stop spring
6. Throttle plate
7. Idle speed stop screw
8. Spring
9. Idle mixture needle
10. Spring
11. Baffle
12. Carburetor body
13. Choke plate
14. Bowl gasket
15. Gasket
16. Inlet valve seat
17. Spring
18. Inlet valve
19. Main nozzle
20. Float
21. Float shaft
22. Spring
23. Gasket
24. Bowl
25. Drain stem
26. Gasket
27. Spring
28. Retainer
29. Gasket
30. Bowl retainer
31. Spring
32. "O" ring
33. Main fuel adjusting needle

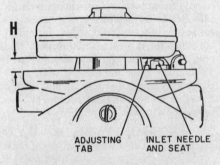

Fig. T10A–Float height (H) should be measured as shown on Walbro float carburetors. Bend the adjusting tab to adjust height.

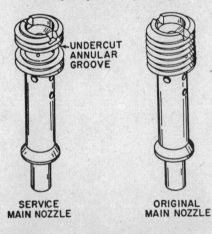

Fig. T10B–The main nozzle originally installed is drilled after installation through hole in body. Service main nozzles are grooved so that alignment is not necessary.

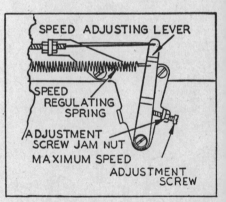

Fig. T15–Speed adjusting screw and lever. The no-load speed should not exceed 3600 RPM.

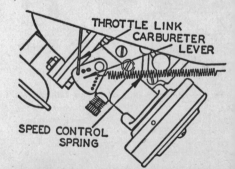

Fig. T16–Outer spring anchorage holes in carburetor throttle lever may be used to reduce speed fluctuations or surging.

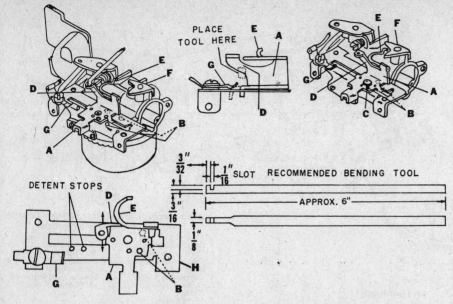

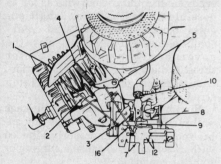

Fig. T17—When carburetor is equipped with slide control, governed speed is adjusted by bending slide arm at point "D". Bend arm outward from engine to increase speed.

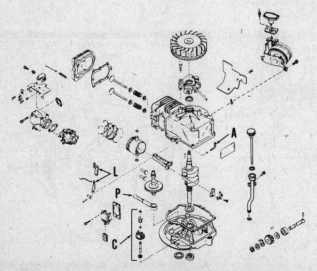

Fig. T18—View of one type of speed control with pneumatic governor. Refer also to Figs. T19, T20 and T21.

1. Air vane
2. Throttle control link
3. Carburetor throttle lever
4. Governor spring
5. Governor spring linkage
7. Speed control lever
8. Carburetor choke lever
9. Choke control
10. Stop switch
12. Alignment holes
16. Idle speed stop screw
18. High speed stop screw (Fig. T21)

Fig. T19—Pneumatic governor linkage.

arm (E) should be clear of choke lever (F) by 1/64-inch. Obtain clearance gap by bending arm (E). To increase engine speed, bend slide arm at point (D) outward from engine. To decrease speed, bend arm inward toward engine.

Make certain on models equipped with wiper grounding switch that wiper (G) touches slide (A) when control is moved to "STOP" position.

Refer to Figs. T18, T19, T20 and T21 for assembled views of pneumatic governor systems.

MECHANICAL GOVERNOR. Some engines are equipped with a mechanical (flyweight) type governor. To adjust the governor linkage, refer to

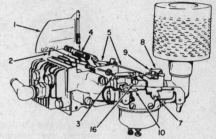

Fig. T20—Pneumatic governor linkage.

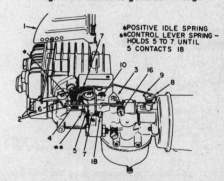

*POSITIVE IDLE SPRING
**CONTROL LEVER SPRING—HOLDS 5 TO 7 UNTIL 5 CONTACTS 18

Fig. T21—Pneumatic governor linkage.

View of Light Frame vertical crankshaft engine. Mechanical governor (A, C & L) and plunger type oil pump (P) are shown.

View of Light Frame engine typical of models ECV100, ECV105, ECV110 and ECV120. Crankcase breather valve is shown at (B).

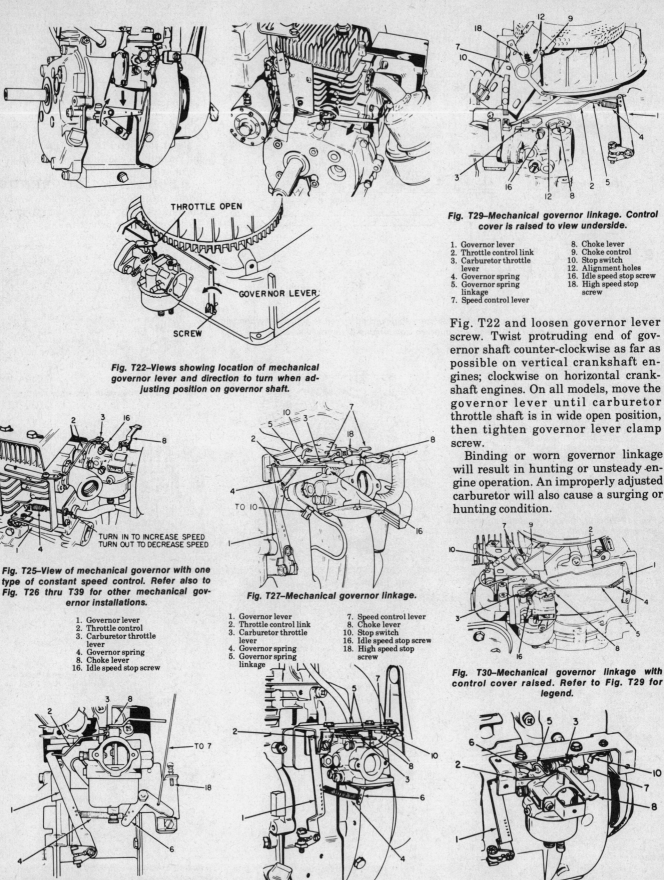

Fig. T22–Views showing location of mechanical governor lever and direction to turn when adjusting position on governor shaft.

Fig. T29–Mechanical governor linkage. Control cover is raised to view underside.

1. Governor lever	8. Choke lever
2. Throttle control link	9. Choke control
3. Carburetor throttle lever	10. Stop switch
4. Governor spring	12. Alignment holes
5. Governor spring linkage	16. Idle speed stop screw
7. Speed control lever	18. High speed stop screw

Fig. T22 and loosen governor lever screw. Twist protruding end of governor shaft counter-clockwise as far as possible on vertical crankshaft engines; clockwise on horizontal crankshaft engines. On all models, move the governor lever until carburetor throttle shaft is in wide open position, then tighten governor lever clamp screw.

Binding or worn governor linkage will result in hunting or unsteady engine operation. An improperly adjusted carburetor will also cause a surging or hunting condition.

Fig. T25–View of mechanical governor with one type of constant speed control. Refer also to Fig. T26 thru T39 for other mechanical governor installations.

1. Governor lever
2. Throttle control
3. Carburetor throttle lever
4. Governor spring
8. Choke lever
16. Idle speed stop screw

Fig. T27–Mechanical governor linkage.

1. Governor lever	7. Speed control lever
2. Throttle control link	8. Choke lever
3. Carburetor throttle lever	10. Stop switch
4. Governor spring	16. Idle speed stop screw
5. Governor spring linkage	18. High speed stop screw

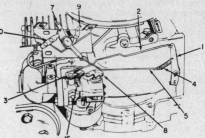

Fig. T30–Mechanical governor linkage with control cover raised. Refer to Fig. T29 for legend.

Fig. T26–Mechanical governor linkage. Refer to Fig. T25 for legend except the following.

6. Bellcrank
7. Speed control lever
18. High speed stop screw

Fig. T28–Mechanical governor linkage. Refer to Fig. T27 for legend. Bellcrank is shown at (6).

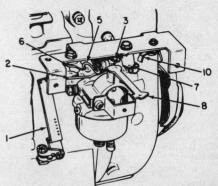

Fig. T31–Mechanical governor linkage. Governed speed of engine is increased by closing loop in linkage (5); decrease speed by spreading loop. Refer to Fig. T29 for legend.

Refer to Figs. T25 thru T39 for views of typical mechanical governor speed control linkage installations. The governor gear shaft must be pressed into bore in cover until the correct amount of the shaft protrudes (A—Fig. T40). The correct distance is 1 11/32 inches for all light frame engines (B&C); 1-7/16 inches for medium frame engines with horizontal crankshafts (D); 1-19/32 inches for medium frame engines with vertical crankshaft (E).

MAGNETO AND TIMING.

Breaker point gap at maximum opening should be 0.020 inch for all models. Marks are usually located on stator and mounting post to facilitate timing. Ignition timing can be checked and adjusted to occur when piston is at specific location (BTDC) if marks are missing. Refer to the following specifications for recommended timing.

Vertical Crankshaft Models	Piston Position Inch BTDC
8.9 & 9.06 Cubic Inch Displacement Models	0.050-0.060
ECV100, ECV105, ECV110, ECV120 & LAV40 Models	0.035
LAV50 Model	0.055-0.065
All Other Light Frame Models	0.060-0.070
Medium Frame 11.04 Cubic Inch Displacement Models	0.080-0.090
All Other Medium Frame Models	0.085-0.095

Horizontal Crankshaft Models	Piston Position Inch BTDC
8.9 Cubic Inch Displacement Models	0.050-0.060
9.06 & 10.5 Cubic Inch Displacement Models	0.030-0.040
HS50 Model	0.045-0.055
All Other Light Frame Models	0.060-0.070
Medium Frame 11.04 Cubic Inch Displacement Models	0.080-0.090
All Other Medium Frame Models	0.085-0.095

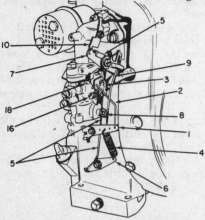

Fig. T32–Mechanical governor linkage.

1. Governor lever
2. Throttle control link
3. Throttle lever
4. Governor spring
5. Governor spring linkage
6. Bellcrank
7. Speed control lever
8. Choke lever
9. Choke control link
10. Stop switch
16. Idle speed stop screw
18. High speed stop screw

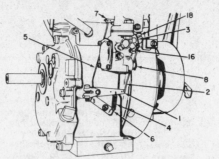

Fig. T35–Linkage for mechanical governor. Refer to Fig. T34 for legend. Bellcrank is shown at (6).

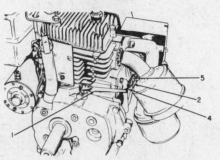

Fig. T36–Mechanical governor linkage. Refer to Fig. T34 for legend.

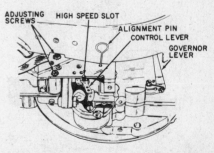

Fig. T39–Models with "Automagic" carburetor use control shown.

6. Governor spring bellcrank
7. Control lever
10. Stop switch
16. Idle speed stop screw
18. High speed stop screw

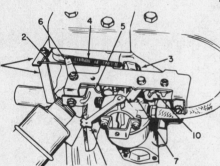

Fig. T33–View of control linkage used on some engines. To increase governed engine speed, close loop (5); to decrease speed, spread loop (5). Refer to Fig. T32 for legend.

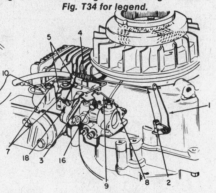

Fig. T37–Mechanical governor linkage. Refer to Fig. T34 for legend.

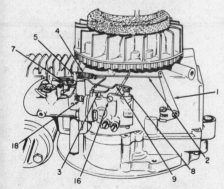

Fig. T34–View of mechanical governor control linkage. Governor spring (4) is hooked onto loop in link (2).

1. Governor lever
2. Throttle control link
3. Throttle lever
4. Governor spring
5. Governor spring linkage
7. Speed control lever
8. Choke lever
9. Choke control link
16. Idle speed stop screw
18. High speed stop screw

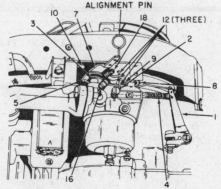

ALIGNMENT PIN

Fig. T38–On model shown, adjust location of cover so that control lever is aligned with high speed slot and alignment holes are aligned.

1. Governor lever
2. Throttle control link
3. Throttle lever
4. Governor spring
5. Governor spring linkage
7. Control lever
8. Choke lever
9. Choke linkage
10. Stop switch
12. Alignment holes
16. Idle speed stop screw
18. High speed stop screw

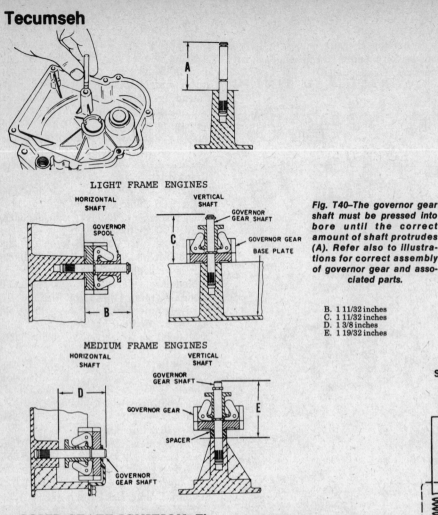

LIGHT FRAME ENGINES

MEDIUM FRAME ENGINES

Fig. T40–The governor gear shaft must be pressed into bore until the correct amount of shaft protrudes (A). Refer also to illustrations for correct assembly of governor gear and associated parts.

B. 1 11/32 inches
C. 1 11/32 inches
D. 1 3/8 inches
E. 1 19/32 inches

charge into the coil. This charge passes through resistor (6) and turns on the S.C.R. (silicon controlled rectifier) switch (7). With the S.C.R. switch closed, low voltage current stored in capacitor (4) travels to pulse transformer (8). Voltage is stepped up instantaneously and current is discharged across the electrodes of spark plug (9), producing a spark before top dead center.

Some units are equipped with a second trigger coil and resistor set to turn the S.C.R. switch on at a lower RPM. This second trigger pin is closer to the flywheel and produces a spark at TDC for easier starting. As engine RPM increases, the first (shorter) trigger pin picks up the small electric charge and turns the S.C.R. switch on, firing the spark plug B.T.D.C.

If system fails to produce a spark to the spark plug, first check high tension lead (Fig. T47). If condition of high

SOLID STATE IGNITION. The Tecumseh solid state ignition system does not use ignition breaker points. The only moving part of the system is the rotating flywheel with the charging magnets. As the flywheel magnet passes position (1A—Fig. T46), a low voltage A.C. current is induced into input coil (2). Current passes through rectifier (3) converting this current to D.C. It then travels to capacitor (4) where it is stored. The flywheel rotates approximately 180 degrees to position (1B). As it passes trigger coil (5), it induces a very small electric

Fig. T46–Diagram of solid state ignition system used on some engines.

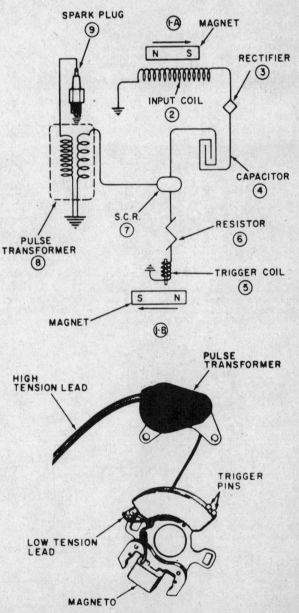

Fig. T47–View of solid state ignition system used on some engines.

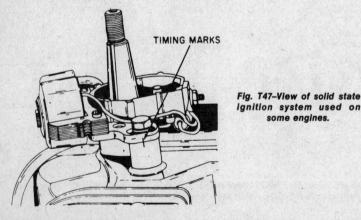

Fig. T45–Align timing marks as shown on magneto ignition engines.

tension lead is questionable, renew pulse transformer and high tension lead assembly. Check low tension lead and renew if insulation is faulty. The magneto charging coil, electronic triggering system and mounting plate are available only as an assembly. If necessary to renew this assembly, place unit in position on engine. Start retaining screws, turn mounting plate counterclockwise as far as possible, then tighten retaining screws to a torque of 5-7 ft.-lbs.

LUBRICATION. Vertical crankshaft engines may be equipped with a barrel and plunger type oil pump or a

Fig. T48–Various types of barrel and plunger oil pumps have been used. Chamfered face of collar should be toward camshaft gear if drive collar has only one chamfered side. If drive collar has a flat boss, the boss should be next to the engine lower cover, away from camshaft gear.

gear driven rotor type oil pump. Horizontal crankshaft engines may be equipped with a gear driven rotor type pump or with a dipper type oil slinger attached to the connecting rod.

The barrel and plunger type oil pump is driven by an eccentric on the camshaft. Chamfered side of drive collar (Fig. T48) should be toward camshaft thrust surface. Flat boss on side of pump drive collar should be down, toward engine lower cover. Oil pumps may be equipped with two chamfered sides, one chamfered side or with flat boss as shown. Be sure that installation is correct.

On engines equipped with gear driven rotor oil pump, check drive gear and rotor for excessive wear or other damage. End clearance of rotor in pump body should be within limits of 0.006-0.007 and is controlled by cover gasket. Gaskets are available in thicknesses of 0.005 and 0.010.

On all models with oil pump, be sure to prime during assembly to assure immediate lubrication of engine. On all models, use SAE 30 oil when operating in temperatures above 32° F. and SAE 10W oil in temperatures 32° F. and below.

REPAIRS

TIGHTENING TORQUES. Recommended tightening torques are as follows: (Values given are in inch-pounds.)

Cylinder Head	140-200
Connecting Rod Nuts	
1.7-3.5 HP Models	65-75
4 to 5 HP Light Frame Models	80-95
4 to 6 HP Medium Frame Models	86-110
Flywheel	360-400
Spark plug	180-240
Magneto stator	60-84
Mounting flange	65-110
Carburetor to intake pipe	48-72
Intake pipe to cylinder	72-96
Gear reduction housing	100-144
Gear reduction cover	65-110

CONNECTING ROD. Piston and rod assembly is removed from cylinder

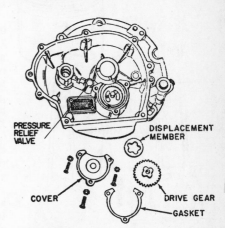

Fig. T49–Disassembled view of typical gear driven rotor type oil pump.

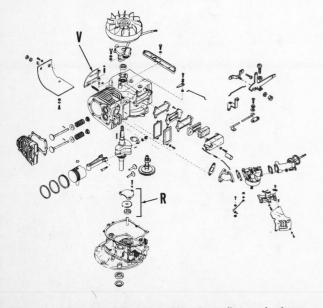

View of vertical crankshaft engine. Rotor type oil pump is shown at (R); governor air vane at (V).

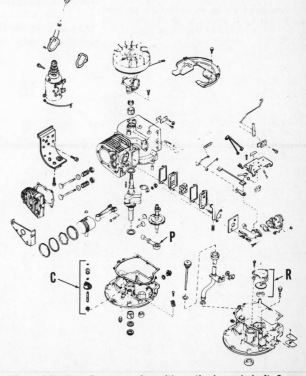

View of Medium Frame engine with vertical crankshaft. Some models use plunger type oil pump (P); others are equipped with rotor type oil pump.

head end of engine. The aluminum alloy connecting rod rides directly on crankshaft crankpin. Crankpin journal diameter is 0.9995-1.000 for 10.5 and 12.0 cubic inch displacement Light Frame engines; 0.8610-0.8615 for other Light Frame engines; 1.0620-1.0625 for Medium Frame engines. Inside diameter of connecting rod crankpin bearing should be 1.0005-1.0010 for 10.5 and 12.0 cubic inch displacement Light Frame engines; 0.8620-0.8625

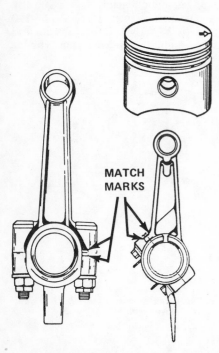

MATCH MARKS

Fig. T50–Match marks on connecting rod and cap should be aligned and should be toward PTO end of crankshaft.

for other Light Frame engines; 1.0630-1.0635 for Medium Frame engines. Align the match marks on connecting rod and cap as shown in Fig. T50. On some models, the piston pin hole is offset in piston and arrow on top of piston should be toward valves. On all engines, the match marks on rod and cap must be toward power take off (PTO) end of crankshaft. Lock plates for connecting rod cap retaining screws should be renewed each time cap is removed.

PISTON, PIN, RINGS AND CYL-INDER. Aluminum alloy pistons are equipped with two compression rings and one oil control ring. Ring end gap should be 0.007-0.020 for all models. Piston skirt clearance should be 0.0050-0.0065 for model ECV105 and 6.207, 7.35, 7.61, 7.75 and 10.0 cubic inch displacement engines; 0.003-0.005 for models LAV50 and HS50; 0.0065-0.0080 for 8.9, 9.06 and 11.04 cubic inch displacement engines; 0.0050-0.0055 for models LAV40 and HS40 and 11.0 and 12.0 cubic inch displacement engines; 0.0045-0.006 for 12.176 and 13.53 cubic inch displacement engines. Pistons and rings are available in standard 0.010 and 0.020 oversizes. On Light Frame 12.0 cubic inch displacement models, arrow on top of piston should point toward valves, and match marks on connecting rod and cap should be toward pto end of crankshaft (Fig. T50).

Cylinder should be honed and fitted with next suitable oversize piston and rings, if cylinder is scored, tapered or out-of-round more than 0.005 inch. Standard cylinder bore is 2.125-2.127 for 6.207 cubic inch displacement en-

gines; 2.3125-2.3135 inches for 7.35, 7.61 and 7.75 cubic inch displacement engines; 2.500-2.501 for 8.9, 9.06 and 11.04 cubic inch displacement engines. Cylinder bore diameter is 2.6245-2.6255 for models HS40 and LAV40; 2.750-2.751 for model ECV110; 2.812-2.813 for models HS50, LAV50 and ECV120. Cylinder bore diameter is 2.625-2.626 for all other engines with 10.0, 10.5, 12.17 and 13.53 cubic inch displacement.

CRANKSHAFT AND MAIN BEARINGS. Crankshaft main bearing journals are 0.8735-0.8740 or 0.9985-0.9990 inch in diameter when new. On some engines, the main bearing journals ride directly in the aluminum alloy bores in the cylinder block and the crankcase cover (mounting flange). A special tool kit is available from Tecumseh to ream the cylinder block and cover so that renewable main bearing bushings (also available from Tecumseh) may be installed. Other engines are originally equipped with renewable steel backed bronze bushings and some are originally equipped with a ball type main bearing at the PTO end of crankshaft.

All bushing type main bearings for 0.8735-0.8740 diameter journals should have 0.001-0.002 clearance. Clearance should be 0.0015-0.0025 between bushing bore and 0.9985-0.9990 diameter journals. Crankshaft end play should be 0.009-0.024 for models HS40, HS50, LAV40 and LAV50; 0.010-0.023 for 7.75 and 9.06 cubic inch displacement engines; 0.006-0.019 for all other Light Frame engines; 0.006-0.022 for 11.04, 12.17 and 13.53 cubic inch displacement

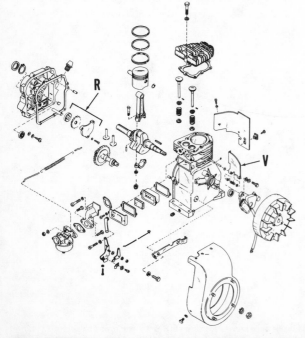

View of Light Frame engine with horizontal crankshaft. Air vane (V) type governor and rotor type oil pump (R) are used on model shown.

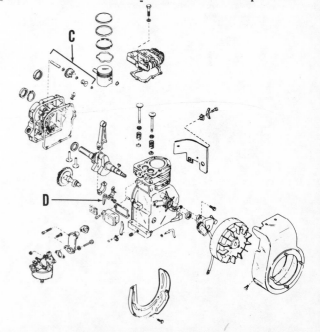

View of Light Frame horizontal crankshaft engine with mechanical governor and splash lubrication. Governor centrifugal weights are shown at (C) and lubrication dipper at (D).

Medium Frame engines.

Connecting rod crankpin diameter is 0.9995-1.000 for 10.5, 11.0 and 12.0 cubic inch displacement Light Frame engines. Crankpin diameter is 0.8610-0.8615 for all smaller displacement Light Frame engines. Crankpin diameter is 1.0620-1.0625 for Medium Frame engines. Connecting rod to crankpin bearing clearance should be 0.0005-0.0015 for all models.

CAMSHAFT. The camshaft and camshaft gear are an integral part which rides on journals at each end of camshaft. Renew camshaft if gear teeth are worn or if bearing surfaces or cam lobes are worn or scored.

Cam lobe diameter in 10.5 and 12.0 cubic inch displacement engines should be 0.9775-0.9795 for exhaust valve, 1.2939-1.2959 for intake valve. Cam lobe diameter is 0.9775-0.9795 for both

valves of other Light Frame engines; 1.258-1.262 for Medium Frame engines. Cam followers (lifters) are identical for most engines; however, parts should not be interchanged once they have been used. The exhaust cam follower is longer than the intake follower on some 10.5 cubic inch displacement and larger Light Frame engines.

On models equipped with the barrel and plunger type oil pump, the pump is operated by an eccentric on camshaft. Refer to OIL PUMP paragraph.

On engines equipped with Insta-matic Ezee-Start compression release type camshaft (Fig. T51), check compression release parts for binding, excessive wear or other damage. If any parts are damaged or excessively worn, renew complete camshaft assembly. Component parts are not serviced separately for the compression release.

When installing the camshaft, align timing marks on camshaft gear and crankshaft gear (Fig. T52) on all models except certain engines built for Sears Roebuck & Company. Refer to Craftsman engine section for identification of these engines and procedure for timing the camshaft.

VALVE SYSTEM. Intake and exhaust valve tappet gap should be 0.010 (cold). Correct tappet gap is obtained by grinding end of stems squarely. Intake and exhaust valve seats are nonrenewable. Valve seat angle for most engines is 45 degrees. Valve seat angle of 30 degrees was used on some early

production 2.25 HP models. Valve seat width should be 3/64-inch for valves with seat angles of 30 degrees or 45 degrees.

Valve stem guides are cast into cylinder block and are nonrenewable. If excessive clearance exists between valve stem and valve guide, guide should be reamed and new valve with oversize stem installed.

Valve timing is correct when timing mark on camshaft gear is aligned with timing mark on crankshaft gear. Certain engines built for Sears Roebuck & Company are timed one tooth off. Refer to Craftsman section for these engines.

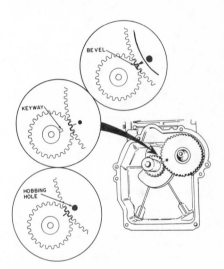

Fig. T52—The camshaft and crankshaft must be correctly timed to assure that valves open at correct time. Different types of marks have been used, but marks should be aligned when assembling.

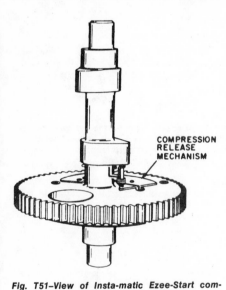

Fig. T51—View of Insta-matic Ezee-Start compression release camshaft.

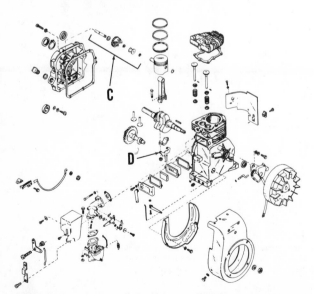

View of Light Frame horizontal crankshaft engine with mechanical governor and splash lubrication. Notice that connecting rod cap on model shown is away from camshaft side of engine.

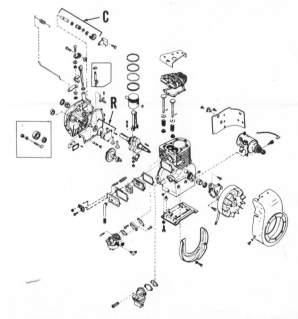

View of Medium Frame horizontal crankshaft engine with mechanical governor (C). An oil dipper for splash lubrication is cast onto the connecting rod cap instead of using the rotor type oil pump (R).

REDUCED SPEED PTO SHAFTS. A PTO (power take off) shaft that rotates at ½ the speed of the crankshaft is available by extending the camshaft through the cover (lower mounting flange). Refer to Fig. T55.

Except for the seal around the extended camshaft, service is similar to standard models.

A slow speed (8.5:1) auxiliary PTO shaft is used on some vertical shaft engines. (Fig. T56). A worm gear (W) on the crankshaft turns the PTO gear and PTO shaft. Several different versions of this unit have been used. A roll pin (Fig. T57) is used to hold the gear onto the shaft on early models. A pipe plug and a threaded boss is located as shown in center and lower views of some of these early models. The roll pin can be driven out of the gear and shaft through the threaded hole of models so equipped. Refer to Fig. T56 for order of assembly.

Disassembly and repair procedure for the 6:1 reduction will be evident after examination of the unit and reference to Fig. T58.

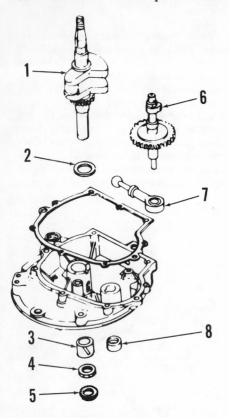

Fig. T55–An auxiliary PTO shaft that turns at ½ the speed of the crankshaft is available by using a special extended camshaft. The hole in lower cover is sealed using lip type seal (8).

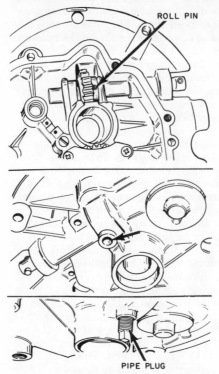

Fig. T57–The roll pin must be removed from early 8.5:1 auxiliary PTO before the shaft and gear can be withdrawn. On some models (center) the boss is closed. The boss can be drilled (⅜-inch) and tapped to accept a 7-28 N.P.T. ⅛-inch pipe plug as shown in lower view.

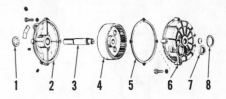

Fig. T58–Exploded view of the 6:1 gear reduction assembly. Housing (6) is bolted to cylinder block and the pinion gear is made onto end of crankshaft.

1. Seal	5. Gasket
2. Cover	6. Housing
3. Output shaft	7. Seal
4. Gear	8. Cork gasket

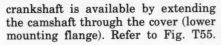

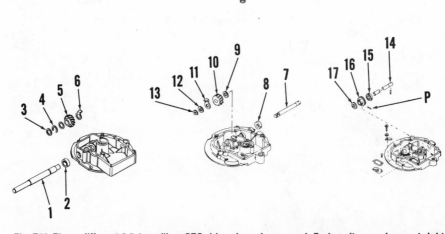

Fig. T56–Three different 8.5:1 auxiliary PTO drives have been used. Early units are shown at right. Pin (P) attaches gear (16) to the PTO shaft (14). On later units, the shaft is held in position by snap ring (4) or (13). Worm gear (W) on crankshaft drives the gear (5, 10 or 16) on all models.

1. PTO shaft	5. Gear	9. Thick washer	13. Snap ring
2. Seal	6. Tang washer	10. Gear	14. PTO shaft
3. Washers (2 used)	7. PTO shaft	11. Tang washer	15. Seal
4. Snap ring	8. Seal	12. Thin washer	16. Gear
			17. Washer

TECUMSEH 2-CYCLE

SPLIT CRANKCASE MODELS

TECUMSEH PRODUCTS CO.
Grafton, Wisconsin

MODEL	Cyls.	Bore	Stroke	Displ.
AH31, AV31	1	1⅝	1½	3.1
AH36, AV36	1	1¾	1½	3.6
AH47, AV47	1	2.0	1½	4.7
AH51, AV51	1	2.0	1⅝	5.1
AH58, AV58	1	2.09	1.68	5.80
AH61, AV61	1	2.09	1.769	6.1
AH80, AV80	1	2¼	2.00	8.0
AH81, AV81	1	2½	1⅝	7.98
AH82	1	2½	1.68	8.25
BH60, BV60	2	1⅝	1 7/16	6.00
BH69, BV69	2	1¾	1 7/16	6.90

KEY TO MODEL NUMBERS
PREFIXES
    A—Single cylinder
    B—Two cylinder
    V—Vertical crankshaft
    H—Horizontal crankshaft
NUMBER

Number in model designation represents ten times the displacement. For example 31 means 3.1 cubic inches displacement.

NOTE: The number in the model designation may not always indicate the exact displacement of the engine (i.e., the model AH81 has 7.98 cubic inches displacement).

KEY TO TYPE NUMBERS

Tecumseh two-cycle engines are distinguished by their type number for accurate identification of individual engines. Although the model number indicates the general features of the engine and is sufficient for service procedures and service specifications, the type number must be used when procuring parts, etc. The type number may be found at one of the locations shown in Fig. TP1-1. Early engines listed the type number as a suffix of the serial number. For example, if the number found on the engine is 365341 P 238, the serial number is 365341, P would indicate the engine is equipped with a Phelon magneto, and 238 is the engine type number. Another example is 1234567 1210. The serial number would be the 1234567 and the type number is 1210. The type number alone is sufficient engine identification for ordering parts, etc. Refer to the following type numbers and engine model number cross reference:

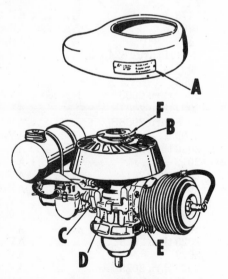

TP1-1—The engine serial number and type number may be found at one of the locations shown above.

A. Nameplate on air shroud
B. Model & type number plate
C. Metal tab on crankcase
D. Stamped on crankcase
E. Stamped on cylinder flange
F. Stamped on starter pulley

TYPE NUMBER	ENGINE MODEL
46 thru 68	AH-31
69 thru 73	AH-36
75 thru 78	AH-36
79	AH-31
80 thru 83	AH-36
84	AH-31
85	AH-36
86 thru 88	AH-31
89 thru 93	AH-36
94 thru 98	AH-47
99	AH-36
209 thru 244	AV-31
245	AV-36
246 thru 248	AV-31
249 thru 251	AV-36
252	AV-31
253 thru 255	AV-36
256 thru 261	AV-31
262 thru 265A	AV-36
266 thru 267	AV-31
268 thru 272	AV-36
273 thru 275	AV-31
276	AV-36
277 thru 279	AV-31
280 thru 281	AV-36
282	AV-31
283 thru 284	AV-36
285 thru 286	AV-31
287	AV-36
288 thru 291B	AV-31
292 thru 294	AV-36
295 thru 296	AV-31
297	AV-47
298 thru 299	AV-31
321 thru 321A	BH-60
330 thru 330B	BH-69
331 thru 332	BH-60
333	BH-69
334	BH-60
335 thru 337	BH-69
351	BV-60
353 thru 355A	BH-60
356	BV-69
357	BV-60
359 thru 363A	BV-69
364	BH-69
365 thru 366	BH-60
367 thru 368A	BV-69
369 thru 370	BH-60
371 thru 375	BH-69
401 thru 402	AH-80
403	AV-80
404 thru 406B	AH-80
407 thru 407C	AV-80
408 thru 410B	AH-80
411 thru 411B	AV-80
412 thru 423	AH-80
424 thru 427	AV-80
501 thru 509A	AV-47
601 thru 601-01	AV-47
602 thru 602-02B	AV-47
603 thru 603-23	AV-47
604 thru 604-25	AV-47
605 thru 605-18	AV-47
606 thru 606-13A	AV-47
608 thru 608C	AV-47
610 thru 610-20	AV-47
611	AV-47
614 thru 614-06A	AV-47
615 thru 616-40	AV-47
617 thru 617-06	AV-47
618 thru 618-18	AV-47
619 thru 619-03	AV-47
621 thru 621-15	AV-47

TYPE NUMBER	ENGINE MODEL	TYPE NUMBER	ENGINE MODEL	TYPE NUMBER	ENGINE MODEL
622 thru 622-07	AV-47	1233 thru 1237B	AH-58	1384 thru 1386	AH-47
623 thru 623-36	AV-47	1238 thru 1238C	AH-47	1387 thru 1388	AH-58
624 thru 630-09	AV-51	1239 thru 1243	AH-51	1389 thru 1390B	AH-47
632-02	AV-61	1244 thru 1245A	AH-58	1391	AH-58
632-02A	AV-58	1246 thru 1247	AH-51	1392	AH-51
632-03	AV-61	1248	AH-47	1393 thru 1395B	AH-47
632-04 & 05A	AV-58	1249 thru 1251A	AH-51	1396	AH-58
633 thru 633-78	AV-51	1252 thru 1254A	AH-58	1397 thru 1397B	AH-47
634 thru 634-09D	AV-51	1255	AH-51	1398 thru 1399A	AH-58
635	AV-61	1256 thru 1262B	AH-58	1400	AH-58
635A & B	AV-58	1263	AH-51	1403 thru 1404A	AH-58
635-01 thru 635-03A	AV-61	1264 thru 1265E	AH-58	1405 thru 1406A	AH-47
635-03B	AV-58	1266 thru 1267	AH-47	1407 thru 1408	AH-58
635-04 thru 635-04A	AV-61	1268 thru 1270D	AH-58	1409	AH-51
635-04B	AV-58	1271 thru 1271B	AH-47	1410 thru 1416A	AH-47
635-05 thru 635-06	AV-61	1272 thru 1275	AH-58	1417 thru 1417A	AH-58
635-06A thru 635-14	AV-58	1276	AH-47	1418 thru 1418A	AH-47
636 thru 636-11	AV-51	1277 thru 1279D	AH-58	1419 thru 1419A	AH-58
637 thru 637-17	AV-51	1280	AH-51	1420 thru 1420A	AH-47
701 thru 724	AH-47	1283 thru 1284D	AH-58	1421 thru 1421A	AH-58
1001	AH-36	1286 thru 1286A	AH-47	1422 thru 1423	AH-47
1002 thru 1002D	AH-47	1287	AH-58	1424	AH-58
1003	AH-36	1288	AH-51	1426 thru 1429A	AH-47
1004 thru 1004A	AH-47	1289 thru 1289A	AH-47	1431	AH-47
1005 thru 1005A	AH-36	1290 thru 1293A	AH-58	1433	AH-58
1006	AH-47	1294 thru 1295	AH-51	1434 thru 1436A	AH-47
1007 thru 1008B	AH-36	1296 thru 1298A	AH-58	1437	AH-58
1009 thru 1020	AH-47	1299	AH-61	1439	AH-47
1021 thru 1022C	AH-36	1300 thru 1303	AH-58	1441	AH-47
1023 thru 1026A	AH-47	1304 thru 1307	AH-51	1443	AH-47
1027 thru 1027B	AH-36	1308 thru 1316A	AH-58	1445	AH-47
1028 thru 1031C	AH-47	1317 thru 1317B	AH-51	1447	AH-47
1032	AH-36	1318 thru 1320B	AH-58	1451	AH-47
1033 thru 1034G	AH-47	1321 thru 1322	AH-51	1453	AH-58
1035 thru 1039C	AH-36	1323	AH-58	1455 thru 1456	AH-58
1040 thru 1044E	AH-47	1324	AH-51	1461	AH-58
1045 thru 1045F	AH-36	1325	AH-47	1463	AH-58
1046 thru 1054C	AH-47	1326 thru 1326F	AH-58	1467 thru 1468	AH-58
1055 thru 1056B	AH-47	1327 thru 1327B	AH-47	1477	AH-47
1057 thru 1058B	AH-47	1328 thru 1328C	AH-58	1478	AH-51
1059	AH-36	1329	AH-61	1481	AH-51
1060 thru 1060C	AH-47	1330	AH-47	1487	AH-51
1061 thru 1062	AH-36	1331	AH-51	S-1801 thru 1824	AV-47
1063 thru 1066A	AH-47	1332	AV-51	2001	AV-31
1067 thru 1067C	AH-36	1333 thru 1334A	AH-47	2003	AV-31
1068 thru 1069	AH-47	1335 thru 1342	AH-61	2004 thru 2006	AV-36
1070 thru 1070B	AH-36	1343 thru 1344A	AH-47	2007 thru 2007B	AV-31
1071 thru 1099	AH-47	1345	AH-51	2008 thru 2008B	AV-36
1101 thru 1185	AH-47	1346 thru 1347	AH-61	2009	AV-31
1185A thru 1185C	AH-51	1348 thru 1350C	AH-47	2010 thru 2011	AV-36
1186	AH-47	1351 thru 1351B	AH-58	2012	AV-47
1186A thru 1186C	AH-51	1352 thru 1352B	AH-47	2013 thru 2014	AV-31
1187 thru 1192	AH-47	1353	AH-58	2016 thru 2018	AV-36
1192A thru 1196B	AH-51	1354 thru 1355A	AH-47	2020	AV-47
1197 thru 1198A	AH-47	1356 thru 1356B	AH-58	2021	AV-36
1199 thru 1199A	AH-51	1357 thru 1358	AH-47	2022 thru 2022B	AV-47
1206 thru 1208C	AH-51	1359 thru 1362B	AH-58	2023 thru 2026	AV-36
1210 thru 1215C	AH-58	1363 thru 1369A	AH-47	2027	AV-31
1216 thru 1216A	AH-47	1370 thru 1371B	AH-58	2028 thru 2029	AV-36
1217 thru 1220A	AH-51	1372 thru 1375A	AH-47	2030 thru 2031	AV-31
1221	AH-47	1376 thru 1376A	AH-51	2032 thru 2033A	AV-36
1222 thru 1223	AH-51	1377 thru 1378	AH-58	2034 thru 2035C	AV-47
1224 thru 1225A	AH-47	1379 thru 1379A	AH-47	2036 thru 2037	AV-31
1226 thru 1227B	AH-58	1380 thru 1380B	AH-58	2038	AV-47
1228 thru 1229A	AH-51	1381 thru 1382	AH-47	2039 thru 2044	AV-36
1230 thru 1232	AH-47	1383 thru 1383B	AH-58	2045 thru 2046B	AV-47

TYPE NUMBER	ENGINE MODEL
2047 thru 2048	AV-36
2049 thru 2049A	AV-47
2050 thru 2050A	AV-36
2051 thru 2052	AV-36
2053 thru 2055	AV-47
2056	AV-36
2057	AV-47
2058 thru 2058B	AV-36
2059 thru 2063	AV-47
2064 thru 2064A	AV-36
2065	AV-47
2066	AV-36
2067 thru 2071B	AV-47
2200 thru 2201A	AV-36
2202 thru 2204	AV-47
2205 thru 2205A	AV-36
2206 thru 2206A	AV-47
2207	AV-47
2208	AV-47
2768	AV-36
40001 thru 40028	AH-81
40029 thru 40032C	AH-82
40033	AH-81
40034 thru 40045A	AH-82
40046	AH-81
40047 thru 40052	AH-82
40053 thru 40054A	AH-81
40056 thru 40060B	AH-82
40061 thru 40062B	AH-81
40063 thru 40064	AH-82
40065 thru 40066	AH-81
40067 thru 40068	AH-82
40069 thru 40069A	AH-81
40070	AV-81
40070A thru 40075	AH-81
710101 thru 710116	AV-47
710124 thru 710149	AV-47
710150 thru 710152	AH-47
710154	AV-80
710155	AH-80
710156	BH-69
710157	AH-47
710201 thru 710227	AV-47
710228	AV-80
710229	AH-47
710230 and 710231	AH-81
710232 and 710233	AH-47
710234	AH-81
710235	AV-51
710244	AH-81
710251 and 710252	AH-47
710257 and 710258	AH-58
710296	AV-51
710298 and 710299	AH-58
710302	AV-51
710303 thru 710306	AH-47
710307	AV-51
710309	AV-51
710312	AV-51
710313	AH-58
710314 and 710316	AH-47
710317 thru 710318A	AH-58
710319 thru 710323	AH-47

*Six digit type numbers beginning with 710 (such as 710101) are service replacement short block assemblies.

MAINTENANCE

SPARK PLUG. Recommended Champion spark plug numbers are shown in following chart:

Engine Identification	Spark Plug Number
AH36 Type 70	C-J8
AH47, AH58 and AH81 (Chain Saw Engines)	J-8J
Go-Kart Engines, Short Races—	
AH51 & AH82	J-4J
AH61 (Bushing Engine)	J-6J
AH61 (Std. & Super)	L-4J
AH58 (⅜ in. Reach)	J-4J
AH58 (Type 1370 & 1371)	L-7
AH58 (Other ½ in. Reach)	L-4J
Go-Kart Engines, Long Races—	
AH51 & AH82	J2J
AH61 (Bushing Engine)	J-4J
AH61 (Std. & Super)	L-57R
AH58 (⅜ in. Reach)	J-2J
AH58 (Type 1370 & 1371)	L-4J
AH58 (Other ½ in. Reach)	L-57R
All other models	J-11J

Set electrode gap on L-57R spark plugs at 0.020 inch. Electrode gap should be 0.030 for other spark plugs.

Apply a small amount of graphite grease on spark plug threads before installing. Tighten the plug to 15-20 foot-pounds torque.

If plug has been cleaned, be sure that all sand blast grit or other materials has been removed from plug prior to installation in engine.

CARBURETOR. Several different makes of both float and diaphragm type carburetors have been used. Refer to appropriate following paragraphs for servicing and adjustment information for each carburetor:

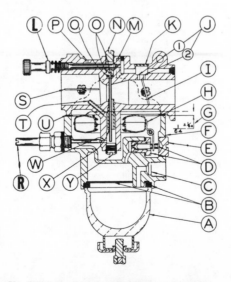

Fig. TP1-2–Section through Tillotson MD series type "B" carburetor utilizing the long idle adjusting needle (L) which leans the mixture when turned clockwise.

TILLOTSON FLOAT CARBURETORS. Early Tillotson MD and MT carburetors having the long idle adjustment needle (L—Fig. TP1-2), clockwise rotation of needle leans the idle mixture. On some series when equipped with short idle mixture needle (L—Fig. TP1-3), clockwise rotation of the needle richens the idle mixture. On all MD and MT carburetors, clockwise rotation of the main or power needle (R) leans the power mixture. Refer also to Fig. TP1-4.

Some engines use Tillotson MT carburetors with only a high speed fuel circuit. Except that these units do not have an idle adjustment needle nor idle transfer and discharge ports, they are similar to other MT models.

When disassembling Tillotson MD carburetors, remove main adjusting needle (R—Fig. TP1-2) before attempting to separate carburetor halves to prevent damage to needle.

For adjustment of float level on Tillotson MD carburetor, refer to Fig. TP1-2. Invert bowl (F) and float (H) assembly. With float tang resting against inlet valve, face of float opposite inlet valve should be 1/64-inch (dimension G) above face (U) of bowl. If float level is not within the 1/64-inch dimension, remove float and bend tang to correct float level.

Check float level of Tillotson MT carburetors as shown in Fig. TP1-5. If float level is not within limits shown, remove float and bend tang to correct float level.

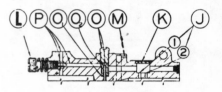

Fig. TP1-3–Some Tillotson series MD carburetors are fitted with the short air bleed type idle mixture adjusting needle (L) which enriches the mixture when turned clockwise.

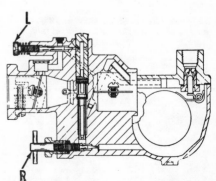

Fig. TP1-4–Section through Tillotson series MT carburetor showing idle mixture adjusting needle (L) and main needle (R) both of which lean the mixture when turned clockwise.

Initial adjustment of both idle and main fuel needles on MD and MT carburetors is one turn open from closed position. Make final adjustments with engine warm and running. Adjust main fuel needle by holding throttle half way open and turning needle in or out to obtain smoothest engine operation; then turn needle to a slightly richer position. Back-off idle speed screw and hold throttle in position to obtain slowest engine speed without stalling. Adjust idle needle for smoothest engine operation while holding throttle in this slow idle position. Adjust idle speed screw so that engine idles at 1800 RPM. (On MT-61 carburetor, no idle fuel adjustment needle is used. Adjust the one needle on this carburetor as described for main fuel needle.)

TILLOTSON DIAPHRAGM CARBURETORS (Series H, HC, HL, HN and HP). Cross-sectional view of each carburetor is shown in Figs. TP1-6, TP1-7 and TP1-8.

Clockwise rotation of both the idle and main fuel needles leans the mixture. For initial adjustment, open idle needle ¾-turn and main needle 1 to 1¼ turns. Make final adjustment with engine warm and running. Run engine at operating speed and adjust main needle for smoothest engine operation. Back idle speed regulating screw off and hold throttle so that engine runs at slowest speed possible without stalling and adjust idle needle for smoothest engine operation. Then adjust idle speed regulating screw so that engine idles at 1800 RPM.

MARVEL-SCHEBLER FLOAT CARBURETOR. On series AH Marvel-Schebler carburetors, clockwise rotation of both the idle mixture needle (24—Fig. TP1-9) and the main fuel needle (19) leans the mixture. Normal setting is 1 turn open for idle needle, 1¼ turns open for main needle. Make final adjustment as with other carburetors. Float setting is 3/32-inch.

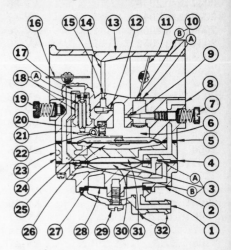

Fig. TP1-8–Cross-section view of Tillotson series HL diaphragm carburetor.

1. Fuel inlet	16. Choke shutter
2. Pump body	17. Inlet channel
3. Pump diaphragm	18. Inlet valve
3A. Pump inlet valve	19. Main needle
3B. Pump outlet valve	20. Spring
4. Gasket	21. Diaphragm lever
5. Gasket	22. Fulcrum pin
6. Metering chamber	23. Vent hole
7. Idle needle	24. Cover
8. Impulse channel	25. Diaphragm
9. Idle fuel orifice	26. Atmospheric
10A. Primary idle port	chamber
10B. Secondary idle port	27. Gasket
11. Throttle shutter	28. Screen
12. Main fuel orifice	29. Screw
13. Body	30. Fuel chamber
14. Venturi	31. Pulse chamber
15. Main fuel port	32. Strainer cover

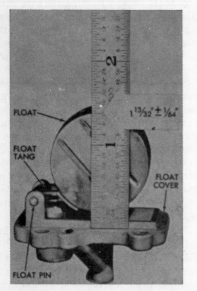

Fig. TP1-5–Checking float level on Tillotson MT carburetor.

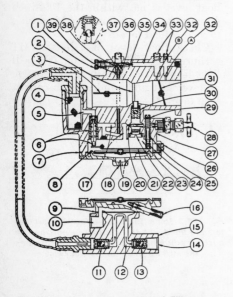

Fig. TP1-6–Cross-section view of Tillotson series H and HP diaphragm type carburetor. Carburetor may not be equipped with fuel pump.

1. Idle needle	21. Diaphragm lever
2. Venturi	22. Plug
3. Choke shutter	23. Diaphragm chamber
4. Fuel inlet	24. Tension spring
5. Inlet channel	25. Screw
6. Inlet valve	26. Drain screw
7. Gasket	27. Body
8. Diaphragm	28. Main needle
9. Fuel pump	29. Washers
diaphragm	30. Main nozzle
10. Impulse channel	31. Throttle shutter
11. Outlet valve	32A. Primary idle port
12. Inlet channel	32B. Secondary idle port
13. Inlet valve	33. Plugs
14. Fuel inlet	34. By-pass channel
15. Pump body	35. Idle orifice
16. Flushing plunger	36. Idle tube
17. Supply channel	37. Alternate check
18. Vent hole	valve
19. Vent orifices	38. Idle tube orifice
20. Main fuel orifice	39. Gasket

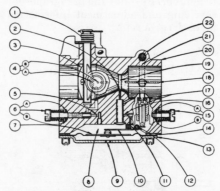

Fig. TP1-7–Cross-section view of Tillotson series HC and HN diaphragm type carburetor.

1. Throttle shaft spring	12. Fulcrum pin
2. Main fuel port	13. Cover plate
3. Throttle shutter	14. Gasket
4A. Primary idle port	15. Main needle
4B. Secondary idle port	15A. Washer
5. Idle fuel channel &	15B. Packing
orifice	16. Main fuel channel &
6. Idle needle	orifice
6A. Washer	17. Inlet valve
6B. Packing	18. Choke shutter
7. Metering diaphragm	19. Venturi
8. Fuel chamber	20. Metering body
9. Air vent hole	21. Inlet channel
10. Diaphragm lever	22. Inlet screen
11. Spring	

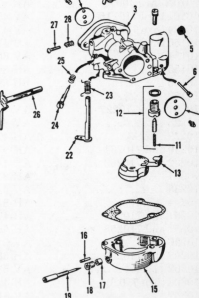

Fig. TP1-9–Exploded view of Marvel Schebler AH float type carburetor.

2. Throttle shutter	19. Main adjustment
3. Body	needle
5. Fuel strainer	22. Throttle shaft
6. Float shaft	23. Spring
9. Choke shutter	24. Low speed mixture
11. Spring	needle
12. Inlet needle and seat	25. Spring
13. Float	26. Choke shaft
15. Float bowl	27. Low speed stop screw
16. Stop pin	28. Spring
17. Packing	29. Throttle stop lever
18. Packing nut	

TECUMSEH DIAPHRAGM CAR-BURETOR. On Tecumseh carburetors (Fig. TP1-10 or TP1-11), clockwise rotation of both the idle mixture needle (L) and the main (power range) needle (H) leans the mixture. Normal setting for carburetors with knurled heads on the adjustment needles is 1-turn open for both idle mixture and power range adjustment needles. Normal setting for carburetors with smooth heads on the adjustment needles is ⅝-turn open for both the idle needle and the power range needle. Make final adjustments with engine warm and running for most satisfactory engine operation.

When overhauling, observe the following: The fuel inlet fitting is pressed in. The fuel strainer behind inlet fitting can be cleaned by reverse flushing with compressed air after inlet needle and seat are removed. The inlet needle seat fitting is metal with a neoprene seat, so fitting (and enclosed seat) should be removed before carburetor is cleaned with a commercial solvent. Diaphragm (22) should be installed with head of rivet toward inlet needle regardless of position or size of metal discs. Make certain that correct diaphragm is installed.

On carburetor models 0234-252, 265, 266, 269, 270, 271, 282, 297, 303, 327, 333, 334, 344, 345, 348, 349 and 356 the gasket (21) should be installed between cover (23) and diaphragm (22). Other models should be assembled as shown in Fig. TP1-10 or TP1-11 with gasket between carburetor body and diaphragm.

On all models, the throttle plate (3) should be installed with short line stamped on plate to top of carburetor and facing out. The choke plate should be installed with flat toward fuel inlet side of carburetor as shown.

On some models, a fuel pumping element (4—Fig. TP1-11) is used. The element expands and contracts due to changes in crankcase pressure. The pump inlet check valve is located in fuel inlet fitting (26) and outlet check valve (25) is pressed into carburetor body behind the fuel inlet fitting.

To renew the fuel pump valves, proceed as follows: Clamp inlet fitting in vise and twist carburetor body from fitting. Using a 9/64-inch drill, carefully drill into outlet valve (25) to a depth of ⅛-inch. CAUTION: Take care not to drill into carburetor body. Thread a 8-32 tap into the outlet valve. Using a proper size nut and flat washer, convert the tap into a puller to remove the outlet valve from carburetor body. Press new outlet valve into carburetor body until face of valve is flush with surrounding base of fuel inlet chamber. Press new inlet fitting about 1/3 of the way into carburetor body, coat the exposed 2/3 of the fitting shoulder with Grade 'A' Loctite, then press fitting fully into carburetor body.

TECUMSEH FLOAT CAR-BURETOR. Clockwise rotation of the idle mixture needle (12—Fig. TP1-13) and main fuel adjusting needle (34) leans the fuel mixture. Initial adjustment for both needles is 1 turn open. Final adjustment is made with engine running at normal operating temperature. Adjust main fuel needle for smoothest operation at high speed. Then, adjust idle mixture needle for smoothest engine idle. Adjust idle speed at stop screw (1) for smooth, slow idle speed.

When overhauling, check adjusting needles for excessive wear or other damage. The fuel inlet needle (22) seats against a Viton rubber seat (21) which is pressed into the carburetor body. Remove the rubber seat before cleaning carburetor in a commercial cleaning solvent. The seat should be installed grooved side first: Install

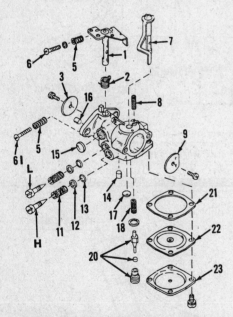

Fig. TP1-10–Some Tecumseh carburetors use low speed stop screw as shown at (6) others as shown at (61).

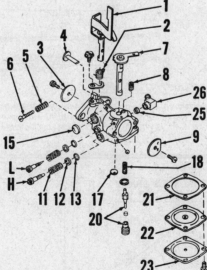

Fig. TP1-11–Exploded view of Tecumseh diaphragm carburetor with pump element (4) and check valves (25 & 26).

H. Main mixture needle	11. Springs
L. Idle mixture needle	12. Washers
1. Throttle shaft	13. "O" rings
2. Spring	14. Cup plug
3. Throttle shutter	15. Welch plug
5. Spring	16. Cup plug
6 or 6I. Low speed stop screw	17. Welch plug
7. Choke shaft	18. Fuel valve spring
8. Choke positioning spring	20. Inlet needle and seat
9. Choke disc	21. Gasket
	22. Diaphragm
	23. Cover

H. Main mixture needle	11. Springs
L. Idle mixture needle	12. Washers
1. Throttle shaft	13. "O" rings
2. Spring	15. Welch plug
3. Throttle shutter	17. Welch plug
4. Pumping element	18. Fuel valve spring
5. Spring	20. Fuel inlet valve
6. Low speed stop screw	21. Gasket
7. Choke shaft	22. Diaphragm
8. Choke positioning spring	23. Cover
9. Choke disc	25. Outlet check valve
	26. Inlet check valve

Fig. TP1-12–Exploded view of Zenith 10A5 float type carburetor.

7. Throttle stop	22. Float pivot
8. Low idle stop screw	23. Float lever
10. Low speed mixture needle	24. Float
18. Main mixture needle	26. Inlet needle and seat
19. Packing nut	28. Taper pin
20. Packing	29. Choke shaft thrust washer
21. Plugs	

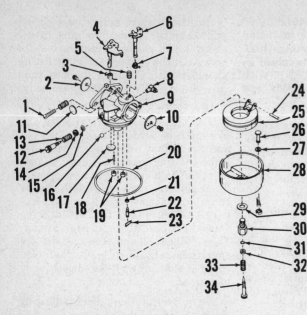

Fig. TP1-13–Exploded view of Tecumseh float type carburetor.

1. Idle speed screw
2. Throttle plate
3. Return spring
4. Throttle shaft
5. Choke stop spring
6. Choke shaft
7. Return spring
8. Fuel inlet fitting
9. Carburetor body
10. Choke plate
11. Welch plug
12. Idle mixture needle
13. Spring
14. Washer
15. "O" ring
16. Ball plug
17. Welch plug
18. Pin
19. Cup plugs
20. Bowl gasket
21. Inlet needle seat
22. Inlet needle
23. Clip
24. Float shaft
25. Float
26. Drain stem
27. Gasket
28. Bowl
29. Gasket
30. Bowl retainer
31. "O" ring
32. Washer
33. Spring
34. Main fuel needle

the flywheel. Refer to Figs. TP1-14, TP1-15 and TP1-16.

Refer to Figs. TP1-11 and TP1-20 for hookup and adjustment of air vane type governors.

To change governed engine rpm on engines having a fixed speed centrifugal governor installation like that shown in Fig. TP1-14, first remove the governor housing located on crankcase at drive end of engine. To increase speed, loosen the set screw (GS) which retains the fixed ring of weight unit to crankshaft, and move the ring toward the engine. Moving the ring 1/16-inch changes the speed approximately 250 RPM. Recommended setting is to have 3/32-inch gap at (A) when weight unit is held in compressed positions as shown. The slide ring (R) must move freely on the shaft and bellcrank and linkage to carburetor must be free to allow proper operation of the carburetor throttle.

throttle plate (2) with the two stamped lines facing out and at 12 and 3 o'clock positions. Install choke plate (10) with flat side towards bottom of carburetor. Float setting should be 7/32-inch, measured with body and float assembly in inverted position, between free end of float and rim on carburetor body. Fuel inlet fitting (8) is pressed into the body. When installing the fuel inlet fitting, start the fitting into the bore. Then, apply a light coat of Loctite (grade A) to the shank and press the fitting into position.

GOVERNOR. Pneumatic (air vane) and centrifugal type governors are used. Some early centrifugal governors were mounted on the PTO end of crankshaft; on some later installations, the governor weight elements are in

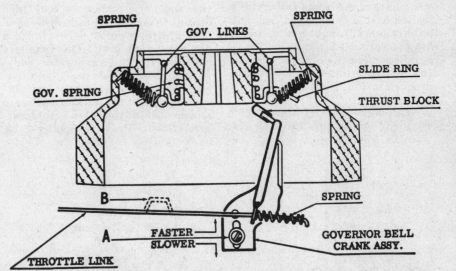

Fig. TP1-15–On some engines the centrifugal governor weight element is mounted in the flywheel. Note speed changes are obtained by raising or lowering the bellcrank assembly as indicated at (A). Bending the throttle link as shown at (B) will increase the engine speed.

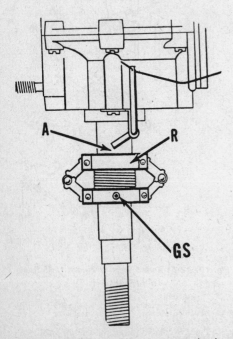

Fig. TP1-14–Normal setting of governor is when distance (A) is 3/32-inch.

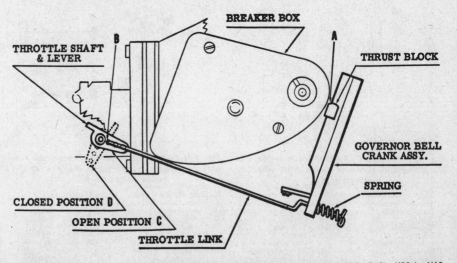

Fig. TP1-16–The gap (A) between thrust block and breaker box should be within limits 1/32 to 1/16 inch when carburetor throttle is wide open.

When governor is mounted in the flywheel, movement of the bellcrank upward as shown at (A) in Fig. TP1-15 increases the speed. A speed increase can also be obtained by bending the throttle link as shown by the dotted lines. Remove the link before bending it. When carburetor throttle is wide open (Fig. TP1-16) the thrust block must clear the breaker point box by not less than 1/32-inch and not more than 1/16-inch as indicated at (A). If throttle lever has more than one hole, place link in inside hole as shown.

Beginning in 1959, the governor slide ring of metal with a plastic follower (Fig. TP1-15) was discontinued in favor of a nylon ring with a follower arm of metal. Parts are not interchangeable in service, hence nylon slide rings must be used with metal followers and metal rings with plastic followers.

Occasionally an engine may be encountered with a governor that is operating erratically or sticking in either the low or high speed position. Likely cause of this trouble is a rough center hub in the flywheel around which the governor ring moves up and down. To correct the trouble, dismantle the governor and using emery cloth, smooth out the center hub of the flywheel so as to allow the governor ring (plastic or metal) to move up and down freely.

Two different types of ignition cut-out switches are used in conjunction with a flywheel mounted centrifugal governor to limit engine top speed by shorting out the ignition.

In Fig. TP1-17, the governor ring contacts the plunger (P) which operates the ignition cut-out switch. The factory setting on this type unit is 4400-5000 RPM. If adjustment is necessary,

loosen screw (A) and slide bracket (B) closer to flywheel to increase engine speed, or away from the flywheel to decrease speed.

In Fig. TP1-18, the governor ring contacts the plunger (5) which rides against the cut-off spring (1). The plunger is retained in a nylon block (6) which is held in a notch in the breaker box cover (7). If plunger (5) is removed, reinstall with rounded end towards governor ring. This type speed limiting device is pre-set at 4500-4700 RPM.

Both types of ignition cut-out switches are operated by a centrifugal governor similar to that shown in Fig. TP1-15. Do not adjust either type switch for engine speeds above factory setting.

On some models the flyweight (centrifugal) governor may be the type shown in Fig. TP1-19. To adjust these models, remove the flywheel, magnets and cover (4). Hold bellcrank (7) against slide (2), loosen screw that attaches lever (9) to bellcrank and hold governor lever (9) up to open the carburetor throttle valve, then tighten the lever retaining screw. To check operation, push lever (9) to throttle closed position, then release. The carburetor throttle must return to the full open position. If throttle does not return to full open position, check for binding of the linkage.

The air vane governor shown in Fig. TP1-20 is adjusted by moving the spring bracket after loosening nut (N). On some engine models, the governor air vane is attached to the carburetor throttle shaft (1—Fig. TP1-11).

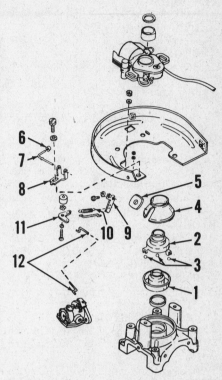

Fig. TP1-19–Exploded view of the centrifugal governor used on some models.

1. Governor cup	7. Governor bellcrank
2. Slide ring	8. Bracket
3. Governor balls	9. Lever
4. Cover	10. Governor spring
5. Cover seal	11. Bellcrank
6. Follower	12. Link

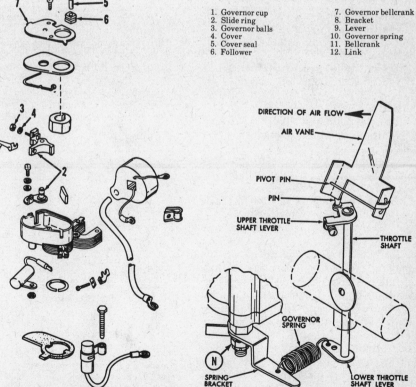

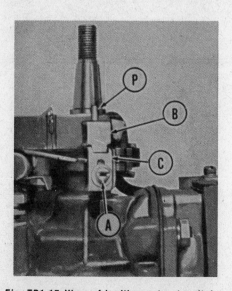

Fig. TP1-17–View of ignition cut-out switch used with centrifugal governor unit mounted under flywheel. Governor operates plunger (P) to short out ignition to limit top speed.

Fig. TP1-18–Exploded view of a second type of ignition cut-out switch used with flywheel centrifugal governor unit to limit engine top speed.

Fig. TP1-20–Drawing of air vane governor used on some models. Loosen nut (N) and move the spring bracket to vary governed speed.

MAGNETO AND TIMING.
Breaker point gap at maximum opening should be set before adjusting the ignition timing. Refer to the following specification data:

AH31 & AV31—
  Breaker point gap . 0.018-0.020 inch
  Ignition timing (piston position BTDC) .... 5/32 (0.156) inch
AH36 & AV36—
  Breaker point gap . 0.018-0.020 inch
  Ignition timing
  (piston position BTDC)—
    Aluminum rod .. 5/32 (0.156) inch
    Needle bearing rod 1/4 (0.250) inch
AV47—
  Breaker point gap . 0.015-0.021 inch
  Ignition timing (piston position BTDC) .... 5/32 (0.156) inch
AH47 (Aluminum Rod)—
  Breaker point gap . 0.015-0.019 inch
  Ignition timing (piston position BTDC)—
    Chain saws .... 11/64 (0.175) inch
    Others .... 5/32 (0.156) inch
AH47 (Needle Bearing Rod)—
  Breaker point gap . 0.015-0.019 inch
  Ignition timing (piston position BTDC)—
    Super & Slim Line
      models ...... 11/64 (0.175) inch
    Other models .... 1/4 (0.250) inch
AH51 & AV51—
  Breaker point gap . 0.017-0.023 inch
  Ignition timing (piston position BTDC) .... 11/64 (0.175) inch
AH58 & AV58—
  Breaker point gap . 0.015-0.019 inch
  Ignition timing (piston position BTDC) .... 3/32 (0.095) inch
AH61 & AV61—
  Breaker point gap . 0.015-0.019 inch
  Ignition timing (piston position BTDC) .... 0.100 inch
AH80 & AV80—
  Breaker point gap . 0.018-0.020 inch
  Ignition timing (piston position BTDC)—
    AH80 .... 1/8 (0.125) inch
    AV80 .... 3/32 (0.095) inch
AH81, AV81 & AH82—
  Breaker point gap . 0.015-0.021 inch
  Ignition timing (piston position BTDC) .... 11/64 (0.175) inch

Ignition timing should be set by moving magneto stator plate so that points just open when piston is correct distance BTDC. Piston position can be measured through spark plug hole with narrow ruled scale as shown in Fig. TP1-21. If timing is not as specified, rotate the stator plate either way after loosening the stator plate mounting screw (or screws).

On late models with Tecumseh magneto, a condenser may or may not be used in connection with the breaker points. On models without a condenser,

capacitance is built into the magneto coil, and a condenser is not required. The magneto coil furnished as repair parts for all Tecumseh magnetos may or may not require the use of a separate condenser. Specific instructions are included with the replacement coil, and should be followed carefully.

LUBRICATION. Tecumseh 2-cycle engines are lubricated with oil mixed in the fuel. Use SAE 30 non-detergent (or outboard) motor oil mixed with regular grade gasoline. Use ½-pint of oil with each gallon of gasoline for engines operating below 3600 RPM; and ¾-pint of oil with each gallon of gasoline for

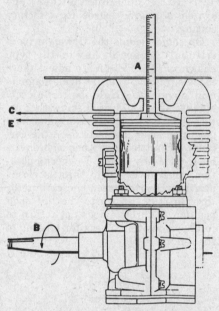

Fig. TP1-21—Recommended ignition timing can be set by measuring piston travel before top dead center as shown.

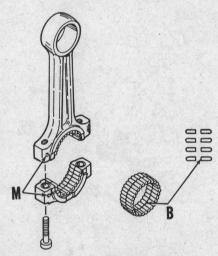

Fig. TP1-22—On some 3.1, 3.6, 4.7 and 8.0 cubic inch models, 60 short rollers are used in two rows of 30 each. On some 5.8, 6.1, 7.98 and 8.25 cubic inch models, 58 short rollers are used. When assembling, make certain that flat ends of rollers are butted together as shown at "B". Match marks (M) on rod and cap must be aligned.

engines operating above 3600 RPM. Do not use SAE 10W/30 oil and do not try to operate engines with a lean fuel mixture as this will not provide adequate engine lubrication and may result in engine seizure.

CARBON. Muffler and exhaust ports should be cleaned every 50 hours if engine is operated continuously at full load. If operated at light or medium load, the cleaning interval should be 100 to 150 hours.

REPAIRS

CONNECTING ROD. Piston and rod assemblies are removed as a unit with the crankshaft after removing the cylinders and separating the halves of the crankcase. Bronze and aluminum rods ride directly on the crankshaft crankpins but needle lower end bearings are used with the forged steel rods.

Recommended plain rod bearing running clearance on crankpin is that when the rod (without piston) is bolted to the crankpin it should not fall of its own weight when extended horizontally. Excessive running clearance of rod lower bearings is preferably corrected by renewal of the affected parts. In an emergency, the cap may be lapped slightly but in no case should more than .002 be removed from same.

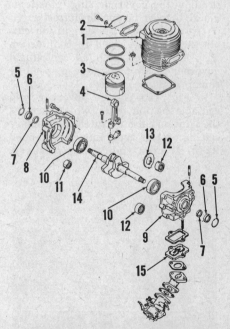

Fig. TP1-23—Exploded view typical of most 3.1, 3.6, 4.7 and 5.1 cubic inch models. Crankshaft main bearings (10, 11 & 12) may be needle roller, ball or bushing type. Thrust washer (13) is used at output end of crankshaft on some models with needle roller or bushing type main bearing. Models AH80 and AV80 are similar.

1. Cylinder	8. Crankcase (magneto half)
2. Transfer port cover	9. Crankcase (PTO half)
3. Piston	10. Ball bearings
4. Connecting rod	11. Needle roller bearing
5. Snap ring	12. Needle roller bearing
6. Seal retainer	13. Thrust washer
7. Crankshaft seal	14. Crankshaft
	15. Reed valve

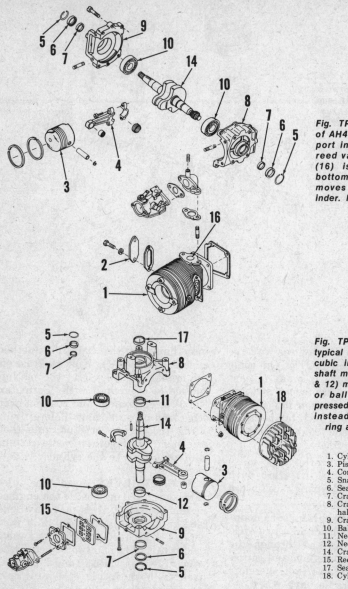

Fig. TP1-24–Exploded view of AH47 engine with third port induction instead of reed valve. The third port (16) is opened as the bottom of the piston skirt moves toward top of cylinder. Refer to Fig. TP1-23 for legend.

Fig. TP1-25–Exploded view typical of most 5.8 and 6.1 cubic inch models. Crankshaft main bearings (10, 11 & 12) may be needle roller or ball type. Seal (17) is pressed in on some models instead of retainer, snap ring and seal (5, 6 & 7).

1. Cylinder
3. Piston
4. Connecting rod
5. Snap ring
6. Seal retainer
7. Crankshaft seal
8. Crankcase (magneto half)
9. Crankcase (PTO half)
10. Ball bearings
11. Needle roller bearing
12. Needle roller bearing
14. Crankshaft
15. Reed valve
17. Seal
18. Cylinder head

On all models with deflector type piston, the long sloping side of piston head should be towards the exhaust port. Tighten the rod cap retaining screws to 40-50 inch pounds torque on bronze or aluminum rods and to 70-80 inch pounds torque on steel rods.

PISTON, PIN AND RINGS. Pistons are equipped with either 3/32-inch (thick) or 1/16-inch (narrow) piston rings. On all models, the top and second rings are interchangeable. Rings should be installed on piston with beveled inner edge towards top of piston. Recommended ring end gap is 0.005-0.010 for AH31, AV31, AH36, AV36, BH60, BV60, BH69, BV69; 0.006-0.011 for AH47, AV47, AH51, AV51, AH58, AV58, AH61 and AV61; 0.007-0.015 for AH80 and AV80; 0.005-0.013 for AH81, AV81 and AH82. Piston ring side clearance in groove should be 0.0015-0.003 for all models with 3/32-inch rings. On models with 1/16-inch rings, side clearance should be 0.003-0.005 in top groove and 0.002-0.004 in second groove. On models with pin in ring groove, make certain that ends of ring correctly engage pin when installing cylinders. Compression pressure at cranking speed should be approximately 60 psi for AH31, AV31, AH36, AV36, BH60, BV60, BH69, and BV69; 70 psi for AH47 and AV47; 80 psi for AH51, AV51, AH61, AV61, AH80 and AV80; 90 psi for AH58, AV58, AH81 and AV81; 110 psi for AH82.

On all models the piston pin is retained by snap rings located in the piston bosses. On all engines which are equipped with needle bearing in upper end of rod, the piston pin should be a press fit in heated piston. On engines without needle bearing in rod upper end, the pin should be a palm push fit in the piston and a thumb push fit in the rod eye. Oversize pins are not supplied.

Pistons are of aluminum alloy. Renew the piston and/or cylinder if skirt to cylinder clearance exceeds

No undersizes or oversizes of engine parts are supplied.

On AH31, AV31, AH36, AV36, AH47, AV47, AH80 and AV80 models with needle roller crankpin bearing, 30 long rollers or 60 short rollers are used. On AH58, AV58, AH61, AV61, AH81, AV81 and AH82 models with needle roller crankpin bearing, 28 long rollers or 56 short rollers are used. The short rollers are latest type and can be used when renewing the long rollers. When installing short rollers, two rows are used and flat ends of rollers should be toward middle of crankpin. The crankpin needle rollers should be renewed as a set if any roller is damaged. If rollers are damaged, be sure to check condition of crankpin and connecting rod carefully and renew if damaged. New rollers are serviced in a strip and can be installed by wrapping the strip around crankpin. After new needle rollers and connecting rod cap are in-

stalled, force lacquer thinner into needles to remove the beeswax, then lubricate rollers with SAE 30W oil.

On all models, make certain that match marks on connecting rod and cap are aligned. On vertical shaft models, make certain that lubrication hole in side of connecting rod is toward top.

Fig. TP1-26–Exploded view of AH58 engine with third port induction instead of reed valve. The third port (16) is opened as bottom of piston skirt moves toward top of cylinder. Gasket between cover (19) and cylinder must seal around the third port as well as the crankcase opening. Refer to Fig. TP1-25 for legend.

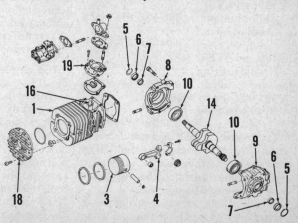

.003. On all models except AH58, AV58, AH61, AV61, AH81, AV81 and AH82, piston should be assembled to crankshaft with the sloping or exhaust side of the piston head opposite the tapered end of the crankshaft. On AH58, AV58, AH61, AV61, AH81, AV81 and AH82, engines with pinned rings, ends of rings should be away from exhaust port.

CRANKSHAFT AND CRANKCASE. Crankshaft is induction hardened and rides in two main bearings. Some engines have ball bearings, some have needle type and on others one main may be roller type and the other a plain bushing. To remove crankshaft it is necessary to separate the crankcase halves and bump shaft with soft mallet. Crankshaft journal diameters are as follows:

Main Bearing Journal Diameters
AH31, AV31, AH36, AV36, AH47, AV47, AH51, AV51, AH58, AV58, AH61, AV61, BH60, BV60, BH69 and BV69.
   Ball type .... 0.6689-0.6695 inch
   Needle roller type—
     Magneto end . 0.7495-0.7505 inch
     PTO end ..... 0.9995-1.0000 inch
   Bushing type ... 0.9995-1.0000 inch
AH80 and AV80
   Both ends,
     ball type ..... 0.9839-0.9842 inch
AH81, AV81 and AH82
   Magneto end, needle
     bearing ...... 0.7498-0.7501 inch
   PTO end, ball
     bearing ..... 0.7871-0.7875 inch

Crankpin Journal Diameter
AH31, AV31, AH36, AV36, AH47, AV47, AH51, AV51, BH60, BV60, BH69 and BV69.
   Aluminum or
     bronze rod .... 0.6860-0.6865 inch
   Needle bearing
     rod .... 0.5615-0.5618 inch
AH58 and AV58
   Aluminum rod .. 0.8115-0.8120 inch
   Needle bearing
     rod .... 0.7499-0.7502 inch
AH61 and AV61
   Aluminum rod .. 0.8740-0.8745 inch
   Needle bearing
     rod .... 0.7499-0.7502 inch
AH80 and AV80
   Needle bearing
     rod .... 0.8096-0.8099 inch
AH81, AV81 and AH82
   Needle bearing
     rod .... 0.7499-0.7502 inch

Outer races of ball and needle roller main bearings should be a tight fit in crankcase. If either bearing is loose in its seat, the bearings and crankcase assembly should be renewed.

If new ball type main bearings are to be installed, heat the crankcase when

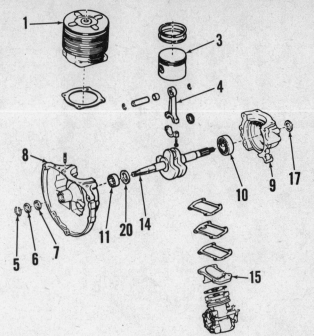

Fig. TP1-27–Exploded view typical of AH81, AV81, and AH82 models. Thrust washer (20) is used only on early models.

1. Cylinder
3. Piston
4. Connecting rod
5. Snap ring
6. Seal retainer
7. Crankshaft seal
8. Crankcase (magneto half)
9. Crankcase (PTO half)
10. Ball bearing
11. Needle roller bearing
14. Crankshaft
15. Reed valve
17. Seal
20. Thrust washer

removing the old bearings and installing new ones. NOTE: On some engines, crankcase is made of cast magnesium; therefore, when heating same do not use an open flame. Case should be heated to such temperature as will permit new cold bearings to drop into position freely.

Ball and needle roller type main bearings should be installed with printed face of the bearing race toward the center of the engine.

Main bearing oil seals must be maintained in good condition in a two cycle engine because leakage through the seals releases compression and causes loss of power. It is important, therefore to exercise extreme care when renewing seals to prevent their being damaged during installation. If a sleeve is not available, use tape to cover any splines, keyways, shoulders or threads over which the seal must pass during installation. On all models, except outboard motors, both seals should be installed with the channel groove of seal towards the inside (center of engine). On engines used on outboard motors, the crankshaft lower (PTO end) seal should be installed with lip towards outside of crankcase.

If a crankshaft thrust washer (13—Fig. TP1-23) is used on 4.7 or 5.1 cubic inch models, it should be installed on the output (PTO) end of crankshaft with grooved side toward crankshaft.

Before assembling the crankcase halves, carefully clean and inspect the mating surfaces of halves. Mating surfaces can be polished to remove slight imperfections, but the surface **must NOT be lowered.** Crankcase halves are matched assembly and must not be

interchanged with a half from another engine. Install one half of crankcase on the crankshaft, then coat the mating surface of other half with "Permatex No. 3" or equivalent and position over other end of crankshaft. Before tightening the screws or stud nuts that attach halves together, make certain joint that seals to the cylinder is perfectly flat.

REED VALVES. Reed type inlet valves are used on most of the engines in this section. Valves may have one reed petal (1—Fig. TP1-28), four reed petals (4), six reed petals (6) or twelve reed petals (12). The twelve petal reed valve (12—Figs. TP1-28 and TP1-29) is used on both single and dual carburetor models.

Reed petals should not stand out more than 0.010 inch from the reed plate and should not be bent, distorted or cracked. The reed plate must be smooth and flat. Renew petals or complete valve assembly if valve does not seal completely.

OPTIONAL EQUIPMENT. Some optional (high speed) equipment is

Fig. TP1-28–Reed valve may have one petal (1), four petals (4), six petals (6) or twelve petals (12). Reed plate is not available separately.

available from Tecumseh.

CYLINDER AND PISTON KIT. Cylinder and piston kit is available for AH81 and AH82 engines. The exhaust port is one large opening and rings are pinned to prevent end of ring from catching in exhaust port. Part number of complete kit including cylinder to crankcase gasket, piston, piston pin, rings and cylinder is 730103.

PISTONS. Pistons with narrow pinned rings are available for AH58, AH61, AH81 and AH82 engines. Part number of complete kit including piston, piston pin, rings and cylinder to crankcase gasket is 730114 for AH58 and AH61; 730107 for AH81 and AH82.

LIGHTENED ROD. A lightened connecting rod is available for AH58, AH61, AH81 and AH82. Holes are drilled through the I-beam section of rod. Part number for kit which includes rod, cylinder to crankcase gasket, piston pin needle bearing and crankpin needle bearings is 730110.

TWELVE PETAL REED VALVE. Special 12 petal reed valve assembly is available for AH81 and AH82 engines. Kit for single carburetor installation, including reed valve assembly, manifold, fuel line, gaskets and carburetor fuel pump body etc. to convert Tillotson diaphragm carburetor from inside pulsation chamber to outside hose connec-

tion, is part number 730106.

Kit for dual carburetor installation is shown exploded in Fig. TP1-29. Kit part number 730105 includes one complete Tillotson carburetor, necessary parts to convert present Tillotson carburetor inside pulsation chamber to outside hose connection, 12 petal reed plate, manifold, air cleaner, linkage and gaskets. Engine starts on one car-

buretor, second cuts in at approximately 4500 rpm.

STROKED CRANKSHAFT. Crankshaft kits including gaskets and spacers are available to increase displacement of AH58 engines to 6.1 cubic inches. Kit part number 730122 is used for counter-clockwise rotation engines; 730123 for engines turning clockwise.

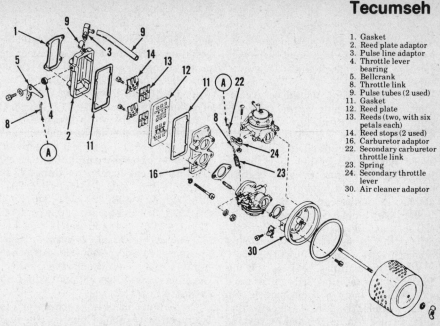

1. Gasket
2. Reed plate adaptor
3. Pulse line adaptor
4. Throttle lever bearing
5. Bellcrank
8. Throttle link
9. Pulse tubes (2 used)
11. Gasket
12. Reed plate
13. Reeds (two, with six petals each)
14. Reed stops (2 used)
16. Carburetor adaptor
22. Secondary carburetor throttle link
23. Spring
24. Secondary throttle lever
30. Air cleaner adaptor

Fig. TP1-29–Exploded view of the twelve petal reed valve assembly with dual carburetors which is available for AH81 and AH82 engines.

TECUMSEH 2-CYCLE
UNIT BLOCK MODELS

TECUMSEH PRODUCTS CO.
Grafton, Wisc. 53024

MODEL	Cyls.	Bore	Stroke	Displ.
AH440	1	2.09	1.25	4.30
AH480	1	2.09	1.41	4.85
AH490	1	2.09	1.41	4.85
AH520, AV520	1	2.09	1.50	5.16
AV600	1	2.09	1.75	6.00
AH750, AV750	1	2.375	1.68	7.50
AH817, AV817	1	2.437	1.75	8.17

MAINTENANCE

SPARK PLUG. Electrode gap should be 0.030 for AH480 and AV520 engines with the following type numbers: 638, 1494 thru 1495A, 1512 thru 1512A, 1524 and 1572. All other engine models should have 0.035 inch spark plug electrode gap. All lawnmowers and

snowblowers should be equipped with Champion J-17LM or equivalent spark plug. Recommended spark plugs for other applications are: Champion CJ-8 or J-8J for 4.30, 4.85, 5.16 and 6.00 cubic inch displacement engines; UJ-12Y for AH750 models; UJ-10Y for AV750 models; J-13Y for 8.17 cubic inch displacement models.

CARBURETOR. Tillotson HS, Tecumseh diaphragm and Tecumseh float type carburetors are used. Refer to the appropriate following paragraphs for information on specific carburetors.

TILLOTSON "HS." Initial setting is 1 turn open for idle mixture needle (6—Fig. TP2-1) and 1¼ turns open for high speed needle (5). Make final adjustments with engine warm and running. Adjust idle mixture needle (6) and idle stop screw (4) for smooth low idle speed. Adjust high speed mixture needle (5) only under load so that engine runs at highest obtainable speed without excessive smoke. Check engine for proper acceleration and open idle fuel needle (6) slightly if necessary for proper acceleration.

TECUMSEH DIAPHRAGM. Initial setting for idle mixture needle (L—Fig. TP2-2) and high speed needle (H) is 1 turn open on all models with solid adjustment needles. On some models the mixture needles are provided with a fuel passage (hole) in the inner end. If needle has a drilled fuel passage, initial setting is closed. If drilled needles are renewed, make certain the new needle has correct size hole. Clockwise rotation of both needles leans the mixture.

Final adjustment should be accomplished with engine warm and running. Adjust idle mixture needle (L) and idle stop screw (6) to provide smooth low idle speed. Adjust high speed needle (H) with engine under load so that engine runs at highest obtainable speed without excessive smoke. If engine can not be adjusted under load, adjust high speed needle (H) so that engine will accelerate rapidly without hesitation or sputtering when throttle is opened quickly.

When overhauling, observe the following: The fuel inlet fitting is pressed into bore of body of some models. On these models, the fuel strainer behind inlet fitting can be cleaned by reverse flushing with compressed air after inlet needle and seat are removed. The inlet needle seat fitting is metal with a neoprene seat, so fitting (and enclosed seat) should be removed before carburetor is cleaned with a commercial solvent. The throttle plate (3) should be installed with short line stamped on plate to top of carburetor and facing out. The choke plate (9) should be installed with flat toward fuel inlet side of carburetor as shown.

When installing diaphragm (18), head of rivet should be against fuel inlet valve (16) regardless of size or placement of washers around the rivet. NOTE: On carburetor models 0234-252, 265, 266, 269, 270, 271, 282, 297, 303, 322, 327, 333, 334, 344, 345, 348, 349, 350, 351, 352, 356, 368, 371, 374, 378, 379, 380, 404, 405 and 441, gasket (17) must be installed between diaphragm (18) and cover (19). All other models are assembled with gasket, diaphragm and cover positioned as shown in Fig. TP2-2.

On some models, carburetor is equipped with a fuel pump. The fuel pumping element is a rubber boot (20) which expands and contracts due to changes in crankcase pressure. The pump inlet check valve is located in the fuel inlet fitting (11). The pump outlet check valve (10) is pressed into the carburetor body behind the fuel inlet fitting. Engines equipped with this carburetor will operate in any position and the fuel pump will deliver fuel to the carburetor when the fuel supply is below the carburetor.

NOTE: The fuel pumping element should be installed at 45 degree angle as shown in Fig. TP2-2A. Incorrect installation may interfere with pumping action.

Two types of fuel pump valves are used. Flap type of valve may be located behind plate attached to side of carburetor body. Renew flap type valves after detaching the plate from side of carburetor. Fuel pump valves are pushed into carburetor body of some models (Fig. TP2-2). Clamp the inlet fitting (11) in vise and twist carburetor body from fitting. Using a 9/64-inch drill, carefully drill into outlet valve (10) to a depth of ⅛-inch. CAUTION: Take care not to drill into carburetor body. Thread a 8-32 tap into the outlet valve. Using a proper size nut and flat washer, convert the tap into a puller to remove the outlet valve from carburetor body. Press new outlet valve into carburetor body until face of valve is flush with surrounding base of fuel inlet chamber. Press new inlet fitting about 1/3 of the way into carburetor body, coat the exposed 2/3 of the fitting shoulder with Grade "A" Loctite, then press fitting fully into carburetor body.

TECUMSEH FLOAT. Initial setting is 1 turn open for both needles. Final adjustment is made with engine running at normal operating temperature. Adjust main fuel needle (H—Fig. TP2-

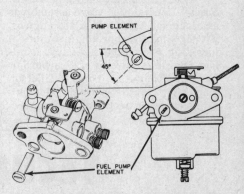

Fig. TP2-2A–The fuel pumping element should be installed at 45 degree angle as shown for Tecumseh diaphragm type carburetors (LEFT) and float type carburetor (RIGHT).

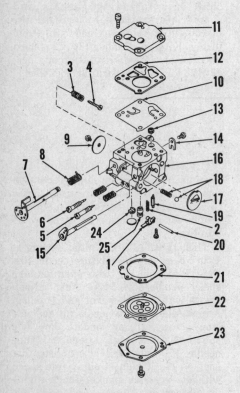

Fig. TP2-1–Exploded view of Tillotson HS, diaphragm carburetor used on some models.

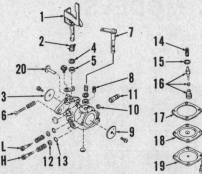

Fig. TP2-2–Exploded view of typical Tecumseh diaphragm carburetor. Some models do not use fuel pump (20) and check valve (10).

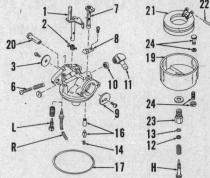

Fig. TP2-3–Exploded view of typical Tecumseh float type carburetor used on some models.

1. Inlet control lever	
2. Spring	14. Throttle shaft
3. Spring	retainer
4. Idle stop screw	15. Choke shaft
5. High speed mixture	16. Carburetor body
needle	17. Choke plate
6. Idle mixture needle	18. Choke detent
7. Throttle shaft	19. Inlet needle
8. Spring	20. Lever pin
9. Throttle plate	21. Gasket
10. Fuel pump	22. Diaphragm
diaphragm	23. Cover
11. Pump cover	24. Channel reducer
12. Gasket	25. Main nozzle and
13. Fuel screen	check ball

H. High-speed mixture	
needle	10. Outlet check valve
L. Idle mixture needle	11. Inlet fitting
1. Throttle shaft	12. Washer
2. Spring	13. "O" ring
3. Throttle plate	14. Spring
4. Felt washer	15. Gasket
5. Flat washer	16. Inlet valve
6. Idle stop screw	17. Gasket
7. Choke shaft	18. Diaphragm
8. Choke retainer	19. Cover
9. Choke plate	20. Pump element

H. High-speed mixture	12. Brass washer
needle	13. "O" ring
L. Idle mixture needle	14. Spring
1. Throttle shaft	16. Fuel inlet needle and
2. Spring	seat
3. Throttle plate	17. Seal
6. Idle stop screw	18. Fuel bowl
7. Choke shaft	20. Pumping element
8. Choke retainer	21. Float
9. Choke plate	22. Pivot pin
10. Outlet check valve	23. Bowl retaining nut
11. Inlet fitting	24. Bowl drain

3) for smoothest operation at high speed. Then, adjust idle mixture needle (L or R) for smoothest engine idle. Idle speed stop screw (6) is provided on some models.

When overhauling, check adjusting needles for excessive wear or other damage. The fuel needle seats against Viton rubber seat (16) which is pressed into carburetor body. Remove the rubber seat before cleaning carburetor in commercial cleaning solvent. The seat is removed using a 10-32 or 10-24 tap and must be renewed after removing. Install new seat using a punch that will fit into bore of seat and is large enough to catch the shoulder inside the seat. Drive the fuel inlet needle seat into bore until the Viton rubber seat is against bottom of bore. Install throttle plate (3) with the two stamped lines facing out and at 12 and 3 o'clock positions. Install choke plate (9) with flat side toward bottom of carburetor. Float setting should be 7/32-inch, measured with body and float assembly in inverted position, between free end of float and rim on carburetor body. On some models, the fuel inlet fitting (11) is pressed into body. When installing the fitting, start fitting into bore, then apply a light coat

of Loctite (grade A) to the shank and press the fitting into position. When installing float bowl (19), make certain that correct "O" ring (17) is used. Some "O" rings are round section, others are square. Fuel hole and the annular groove in retaining nut (23) must be clean. The flat stepped section of fuel bowl (19) should be below the fuel inlet fitting (11). Tighten retaining nut (23) to 50-60 inch pounds torque. The high speed mixture needle (H) must not be installed when tightening nut (23).

Some models are equipped with a fuel pump. The fuel pumping element (20) is a rubber boot which expands and contracts due to changes in crankcase pressure. The pumping element should be at 45 degree angle as shown in Fig. TP2-2A. Incorrect installation may interfere with pumping action. On early models, fuel is drawn in through a check valve in the fuel inlet fitting (11). The outlet check valve (10) is pressed into bore behind the inlet fitting. The inlet fitting (11) is removed and installed in normal manner. To renew the outlet check valve (10), proceed as follows: Drill into the outlet check valve with a 9/64-inch drill to a depth of ⅛-inch. CAUTION: Do not drill into carburetor body. Thread an 8-32 tap into the outlet valve and pull valve from the carburetor body. Press new outlet valve into carburetor body until face of valve is flush with base of the fuel chamber.

GOVERNOR. On some models, the governor air vane is located on the carburetor throttle shaft. On models

with variable speed governor, the high speed (maximum) stop screw is located on the speed control lever. On models with fixed engine speed, RPM is adjusted by moving the governor spring bracket (B—Fig. TP2-5). To increase engine speed, bracket must be moved to increase governor spring (G) tension holding throttle (T) open.

MAGNETO AND TIMING. Breaker point gap at maximum opening should be set before adjusting the ignition timing. On some models, ignition timing is not adjustable. Refer to the following specification data:

AH440—
    Breaker point gap .... 0.015 inch
    Ignition timing (piston
      position BTDC) .... 0.150 inch

AH480 & AH490—
    Breaker point gap .... 0.015 inch
    Ignition timing (piston
      position BTDC—)
      Aluminum bushing rod 0.100 inch
      Needle bearing rod .... 0.140 inch

AH520 (Aluminum Bushing Rod)—
    Breaker point gap .... 0.015 inch
    Ignition timing (piston
      position BTDC) .... 0.110 inch

AH520 (Needle Bearing Rod)—
    Breaker point gap .... 0.015 inch
    Ignition timing (piston
      position BTDC) 0.185

AV520 (type Nos. 638 & 650)—
    Breaker point gap .... 0.018 inch
    Ignition timing (piston
      position BTDC) .... 0.100 inch

AV520 (type Nos. 642 & 670)—
    Breaker point gap .... 0.020 inch
    Ignition timing (piston
      position BTDC) .... 0.085 inch

AV600 (type No. 641)—
    Breaker point gap .... 0.020 inch
    Ignition timing (piston
      position BTDC) .... 0.100 inch

AV600 (type 643)—
    Breaker point gap .... 0.020 inch
    Ignition timing (piston
      position BTDC) .... 0.085 inch

AH750—
    Breaker point gap .... 0.015 inch
    Ignition timing (piston
      position BTDC) .... 0.115 inch

AV750—
    Breaker point gap .... 0.020 inch
    Ignition timing (piston
      position BTDC) .... 0.095 inch

AH817—
    Breaker point gap .... 0.018 inch
    Ignition timing (piston
      position BTDC) .... 0.100 inch

AV817—
    Breaker point gap .... 0.018 inch
    Ignition timing (piston
      position BTDC) .... 0.100 inch

SOLID STATE IGNITION. The Tecumseh solid state ignition system does not use ignition points. The only moving part of the system is the ro-

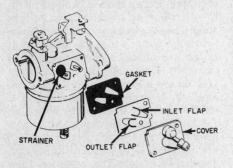

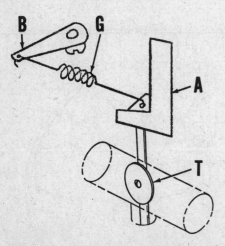

Fig. TP2-4–View of late type fuel valves. Earlier type is pressed into carburetor body as shown in Figs. TP2-2 and TP2-3.

Fig. TP2-5–On some models, the governor air vane (A) is attached to the carburetor throttle shaft and tension of governor spring (G) holds throttle (T) open.

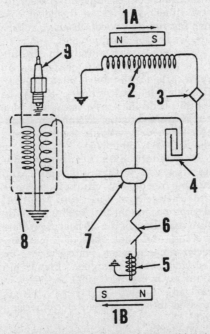

Fig. TP2-7–Diagram of Tecumseh solid state ignition system. Items (3, 4, 5, 6 & 7) are encased as shown at (10–Fig. TP2-8). Refer to text for description of operation.

tating flywheel with the charging magnets. As the flywheel magnet passes position (1A—Fig. TP2-7), a low voltage AC current is induced into input coil (2). The current passes through rectifier (3) converting this current to D.C. It then travels to the capacitor (4) where it is stored. The flywheel rotates approximately 180 degrees to position (1B). As it passes trigger coil (5), it induces a very small electric charge into that coil. This charge passes through resistor (6) and turns on the S.C.R. (silicon controlled rectifier) switch (7). With the S.C.R. switch closed, the low voltage current stored in capacitor (4) travels to the pulse transformer (8). The voltage is stepped up instantaneously and the current is discharged across the electrodes of spark plug (9), producing a spark.

If the system fails to produce a spark to the spark plug, first check the high tension lead (12—Fig. TP2-8). If condition of the high tension lead is questionable, renew the pulse transformer and high tension lead assembly. Check the low tension lead (11) and renew if insulation is faulty. The ignition charging coil, electronic triggering system and mounting plate are available only as an assembly. If necessary to renew this assembly, place the unit in position on the engine. Start the retaining screws, turn the mounting plate counter-clockwise as far as possible, then tighten retaining screws to a torque of 5-7 Ft.-Lbs.

LUBRICATION. Tecumseh 2-cycle engines are lubricated with oil mixed with the fuel. Use a good grade of SAE 30 oil mixed with regular gasoline in the following proportions: For engines operating below 3600 RPM, mix ½-pint of oil with each gallon of gasoline. For engines operating above 3600 RPM, mix ¾-pint of oil with each gallon of gasoline.

NOTE: Do not use multigrade oils such as 10W-30. Do not adjust carburetor fuel mixture too lean. A lean fuel mixture decreases the amount of oil as well as fuel and will not provide adequate engine lubrication.

CARBON. Muffler and exhaust ports should be cleaned every 50 hours if engine is operated continuously at full load. If operated at light or medium load, the cleaning interval should be 100 to 150 hours.

REPAIRS

DISASSEMBLY. Unbolt and remove the cylinder shroud, cylinder head and crankcase covers. Remove connecting rod cap and push the rod and piston unit out through top of cylinder. It may be necessary to remove the ridge from top of cylinder bore before removing piston and connecting rod.

To remove the crankshaft, remove starter housing, flywheel, and the bolts securing shroud base (bearing housing) to crankcase; then, strike drive end of crankshaft with a leather mallet to dislodge crankshaft and bearing housing.

CONNECTING ROD. On some models, the steel connecting rod is equipped with needle roller bearings at the crankpin and at the piston pin ends. On some models with aluminum connecting rod, the rod rides directly on the crankpin. On other models with aluminum connecting rod, a steel insert (liner) is used on inside of connecting rod and needle bearing rollers are used at the crankpin end.

On models with aluminum bushing type connecting rod, clearance on crankpin should be 0.0011-0.0020. Crankpin journal diameter should be 0.6860-0.6865. Only standard size parts are available. Piston pin diameter for models without needle bearing should be 0.3750-0.3751.

On models with aluminum connecting rod with steel liners and bearing needles at crankpin, observe the following: Crankpin journal standard diameter is 0.8425-0.8430. Be sure that none of the 74 bearing rollers are lost and that ends of liners correctly engage when match marks on rod and cap are aligned. Piston pin diameter is 0.4997-0.4999 and rides in cartridge needle bearing that is pressed into piston end of connecting rod.

All models with steel connecting rod are provided with loose needle rollers at crankpin end of connecting rod and a cartridge needle bearing at piston pin

end. Standard crankpin journal diameter is 0.5614-0.5618 for AH440, AH480 and AH490 models. The crankpin bearing for AH440, AH480 and AH490 models may use one row of 30 needle rollers or 60 short needle rollers placed in two rows. On AH520 models, the crankpin journal diameter is 0.5614-0.5618 and 56 short (half length) needle rollers are placed in two rows. Two different types of crankshafts, bearing rollers and connecting rods are used on AH750 and AV750 models. Early models are equipped with 0.6240-0.6243 inch diameter crankpin journal and use 32 needle rollers in the 0.7566-0.7569 inch diameter connecting rod bore. Later AV750 models are equipped with 0.6262-0.6266 inch diameter crankpin journal and use 33 needle rollers in the 0.7588-0.7592 inch diameter connecting rod bore. AV817 and AH817 models have crankpin diameter of 0.6262-0.6266 inch diameter and use 66 short (half length) needle rollers placed in two rows in the 0.7588-0.7592 inch diameter connecting rod bore.

On models with short (half length) needle rollers, bearing needles are placed in two rows around crankpin with flat ends together toward center of crankpin. On all models equipped with needle bearing at crankpin, rollers should be renewed only as a set. Renew bearing set if any roller is damaged. If rollers are damaged, check condition of crankpin and connecting rod carefully and renew if bearing races are damaged. New rollers are serviced in a strip and can be installed by wrapping the strip around crankpin. After new needle rollers and connecting rod cap are installed, force lacquer thinner into needles to remove the beeswax, then lubricate bearings with SAE 30 oil.

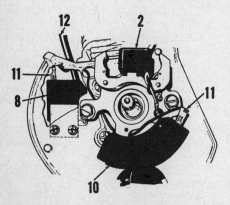

Fig. TP2-8–The solid state ignition charging coil, triggering system and mounting plate (2 & 10) are available only as an assembly and can not be serviced.

2. Charging coil
8. Pulse transformer
10. Trigger system
11. Low tension lead
12. High tension lead

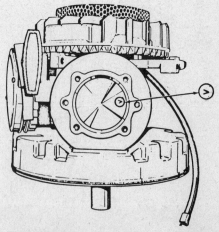

Fig. TP2-10–The "V" or "1111" mark stamped on top of piston must be toward side shown. Lubrication hole in side of connecting rod must be toward top on all vertical shaft models.

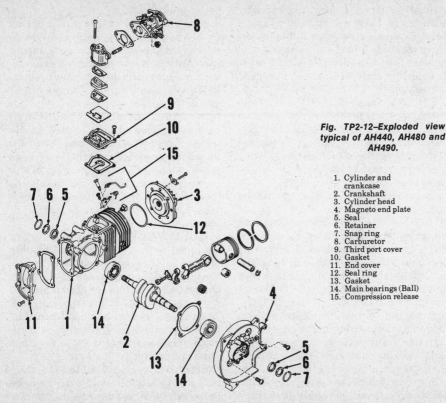

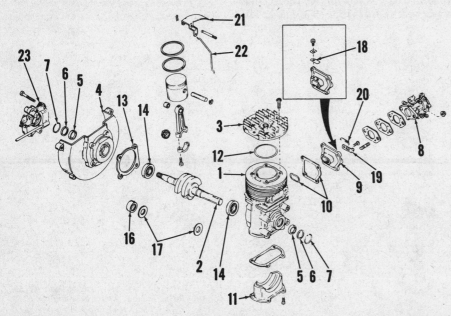

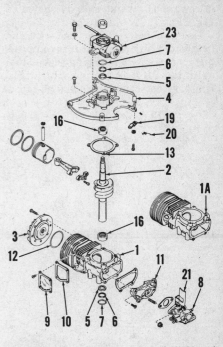

cap retaining screws (self locking) to 70-80 inch-pounds torque.

PISTON PIN AND RINGS. It may be necessary to remove ridge from top of cylinder bore before removing the piston and connecting rod. Refer to the following specification data:

AH440, AH480, AH490, AH520, AV520 and AV600

Cylinder bore
diameter .... 2.093-2.094 inches
Piston to cylinder clearance—
AV520 (type Nos. 642 &
670) .... 0.012-0.016 inch
All other 440, 480, 490, 520
& 600 Models ... 0.005-0.006 inch
Ring end gap—
AV520 type Nos. 638 &
650 .... 0.006-0.014 inch
AH520 type Nos. 1401 thru
1401F, 1448 thru 1450E,
1466 thru 1466A, 1482
thru 1482C, 1483, 1499,
1506 thru 1507A ...0.006-0.016 inch
AV600 type No. 641 0.006-0.014 inch
All other 440, 480, 490, 520
& 600 Models ... 0.006-0.011 inch
Compression pressure at
cranking speed—
AV520 type No. 642 .... 100 psi
AV600 type No. 643 .... 100 psi
All other 440, 480, 490, 520
& 600 Models .... 90 psi

Fig. TP2-12–Exploded view typical of AH440, AH480 and AH490.

1. Cylinder and crankcase
2. Crankshaft
3. Cylinder head
4. Magneto end plate
5. Seal
6. Retainer
7. Snap ring
8. Carburetor
9. Third port cover
10. Gasket
11. End cover
12. Seal ring
13. Gasket
14. Main bearings (Ball)
15. Compression release

On all models, make certain that match marks on rod and cap are aligned. On vertical shaft models, make certain that lubrication hole in side of connecting rod is toward top. Some AV520 and AV600 models are stamped with "V" or "1111" mark on piston as shown in Fig. TP2-10. On models so equipped, make certain that mark stamped on top of piston is toward the right side as shown. On all models with aluminum connecting rod, tighten rod cap retaining screws to 40-50 inch pounds torque and lock with the tab washer. On all models with a steel connecting rod, tighten the rod

Fig. TP2-13–Exploded view of AH520 engine. Supplementary reed valve is shown at (18) and governor parts at (19 thru 22).

1. Cylinder and crankcase	9. Third port cover	17. Thrust washers
2. Crankshaft	10. Gaskets	18. Reed valve
3. Cylinder head	11. End cover	19. Spring bracket
4. Magneto end plate	12. Seal ring	20. Governor spring
5. Seal	13. Gasket	21. Air vane
6. Retainer	14. Main bearings (Ball)	22. Carburetor link
7. Snap ring	16. Main Bearing (Roller)	23. Magneto
8. Carburetor		

Fig. TP2-14–Exploded view typical of AV520 and AV600 engines. The cylinder and crankcase for some AV520 and all AV600 models is shown at (1A).

1. Cylinder and crankcase	11. Reed valve
2. Crankshaft	12. Seal ring
3. Cylinder head	13. Gasket
4. Magneto end plate	16. Main bearings (Roller)
5. Seal	19. Spring bracket
6. Retainer	20. Governor spring
7. Snap ring	21. Air vane (on carburetor)
8. Carburetor	23. Magneto
9. Cover	
10. Gasket	

AH750 and AV750

Cylinder bore
  diameter .... 2.375-2.376 inches
Piston to cylinder clearance—
  AH750 .... 0.005-0.006 inch
  AV750 .... 0.012-0.016 inch
Ring end gap .... 0.005-0.013 inch
Compression pressure at
  cranking speed .... 110 psi

AH817 and AV817

Cylinder bore
  diameter .... 2.437-2.438 inches
Piston to cylinder
  clearance .... 0.005-0.007 inch
Ring end gap .... 0.007-0.017 inch
Compression pressure at
  cranking speed .... 110 psi

Piston, rings and piston pin are available in standard size only. The piston pin should be a press fit in heated piston on models with needle bearing in rod upper end. On models without needle bearing in rod upper end, the piston pin should be a palm push fit in piston and thumb push fit in rod. When assembling piston in connecting rod, observe the following. On vertical shaft engines, lubrication hole in side of connecting rod must be toward top of engine. On AV520 and AV600 models equipped with offset piston, make certain that "V" mark or "1111" mark stamped on top of piston is toward the right side as shown in Fig. TP2-10.

Use the old cylinder head sealing ring and a ring compressor to compress piston rings, when sliding piston into cylinder. NOTE: Make certain that rings do not catch in recess at top of cylinder. Always renew the cylinder head metal sealing ring. The cylinder head retaining screws should be tightened to 90-100 inch-pounds torque. Refer to the CONNECTING ROD paragraphs for installation of the connecting rods.

CRANKSHAFT AND CRANK-CASE. The crankshaft can be removed after the piston, connecting rod, flywheel and the magneto end bearing plate are removed. Crankshaft main bearings may be either ball type or cartridge needle roller. If ball type main bearings are used, it should be necessary to bump the crankshaft out of the bearing inner races. Ball and roller bearing outer races should be a tight fit in bearing bores. If new ball bearings are to be installed, heat the crankcase when removing old bearings and installing new ones. NOTE: Do not use an open flame. On all models, bearings should be installed with printed face on race toward center of engine.

If the crankshaft is equipped with thrust washers at ends, make certain that they are installed when assembling. Crankshaft end play should be ZERO for all AH480, AH490, AH817 and AV817 models. Crankshaft end play should be 0.0152-0.0172 inch for all other models with two ball type main bearings; 0.004-0.018 inch for AV520 type 638 and AV600 type 641 models with two needle roller main bearings; 0.0025-0.0157 inch for other AH520, AV520 and AV600 models; 0.0081-0.0263 inch for AV750 models with one ball bearing and one needle roller main bearing.

It is important to exercise extreme care when renewing crankshaft seals to prevent their being damaged during installation. If a protector sleeve is not available, use tape to cover any splines, keyways, shoulders or threads over which the seal must pass during installation. Seals should be installed with channel groove of seal toward inside (center) of engine on all models except for use on outboard motors. If engine is used on an outboard motor, lip of the lower seal should be toward outside (bottom) and the top (magneto end) seal should be toward inside (center) of engine.

REED VALVES. Some engines are equipped with a reed type inlet valve located in the lower crankcase cover. Reed petals should not stand out more than 0.010 inch from the reed plate and must not be bent, distorted or cracked. The reed plate must be smooth and flat. Renew petals (AV-750 only) or complete valve assembly if valve does not seal completely.

Reed petals are available separately only for AV750 models. Petals must be installed with rounded edge against sealing surface of reed plate and the sharp edge must be toward reed stop. When installing the reed stop, apply "Loctite" grade A to threads of retaining screws and torque the two screws to 50-60 inch-pounds.

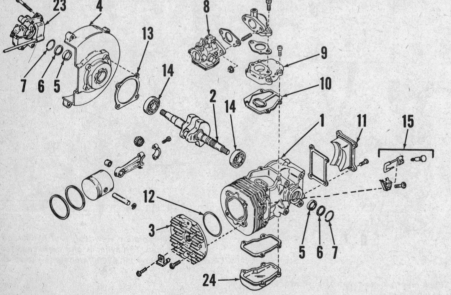

Fig. TP2-16–Exploded view of typical AV750 engine. Refer to text when assembling reed valve (11, 18 & 25). AV817 engines are similar.

1. Cylinder and crankcase	11. Reed plate
2. Crankshaft	12. Head gasket
3. Cylinder head	13. Gasket
4. Magneto end plate	14. Main bearing (Ball)
5. Seal	16. Main bearing (Roller)
6. Retainer	18. Reed valve petal (8 used)
7. Snap ring	
8. Carburetor	23. Magneto
9. Cover	24. Transfer port cover
10. Gasket	25. Reed petal stop

Fig. TP2-15–Exploded view of AH750 engine. Compression release is shown at (15). AH817 engines are similar.

1. Cylinder and crankcase		7. Snap ring	12. Seal ring
2. Crankshaft		8. Carburetor	13. Gasket
3. Cylinder head		9. Third port cover	14. Main bearings (Ball)
4. Magneto end plate		10. Gasket	15. Compression release
5. Seal		11. End cover	23. Magneto
6. Retainer			24. Transfer port cover

SERVICING TECUMSEH ACCESSORIES

12 VOLT STARTING AND CHARGING SYSTEMS

Engines of 3.5 horsepower and up may be equipped with a 12 volt direct current starting, generating and ignition unit system. The system includes the usual coil, condenser and breaker points for ignition, plus extra generating coils and flywheel magnets to generate alternating current. Also included is a silicon rectifier panel or regulator-rectifier for changing the generated alternating current to direct current, a series wound motor with a Bendix drive unit and a 12 volt wet cell storage battery.

Models LAV30, LAV35 and LAV40 may be equipped with a 12 volt starting motor with a right angle gear drive unit and a Nickel Cadmium battery pack. The "SAF-T-KEY" switch is located in the battery box cover. A battery charger which converts 110 volt AC house current to DC charging current is used to recharge the Nickel Cadmium battery pack.

Refer to the following paragraphs for service procedures on the units.

12-VOLT STARTER MOTOR (BENDIX DRIVE TYPE).

Refer to Fig. TE1 for exploded view of 12 volt starter motor and Bendix drive unit used on some engines. This motor should not be operated continuously for more than 10 seconds. Allow starter motor to cool one minute between each 10 second cranking period.

To perform a no-load test, remove starter motor and use a fully charged 6 volt battery. Maximum current draw should not exceed 25 amperes at 6

volts. Minimum rpm is 6500.

When assembling a starter motor, use 0.003 and 0.010 spacer washers (14

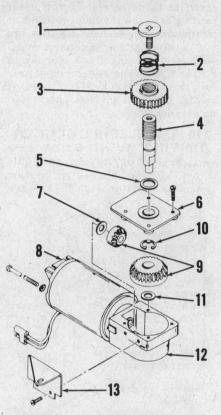

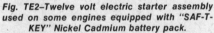

Fig. TE2—Twelve volt electric starter assembly used on some engines equipped with "SAF-T-KEY" Nickel Cadmium battery pack.

1. L.H. thread screw
2. Spring
3. Starter gear
4. Shaft
5. Thrust washer
6. Cover
7. Shim washer
8. Starter motor
9. Gear set
10. Retaining ring
11. Shim washer
12. Gear housing
13. Mounting bracket

and 15) as required to obtain an armature end play of 0.005-0.015. Tighten nut on end of armature shaft to a torque of 100 in.-lbs. Tighten the thru-bolts to a torque of 30-34 in.-lbs.

12 VOLT STARTER MOTOR (SAF-T-KEY TYPE).

Refer to Fig. TE2 for exploded view of right angle drive gear unit and starter motor used on some model LAV30, LAV35 and LAV40 engines. Repair of this unit consists of renewing right angle gear drive parts or the starter motor assembly. Parts are not serviced separately for the motor (8). Bevel gears (9) are serviced only as a set.

When installing assembly on engine, adjust position of starter so there is a 1/16-inch clearance between crown of starter gear tooth and base of flywheel tooth.

NICKEL CADMIUM BATTERY. The Nickel Cadmium battery pack (Fig. TE3) is a compact power supply for the "SAF-T-KEY" starter motor. To test battery pack, measure open circuit voltage across black and red wires. If voltage is 14.0 or above, battery is good and may be recharged. Charge battery only with charger provided with the system. This charger (Fig. TE4) converts 110 volt AC house current to DC charging current. Battery should be fully charged after 14-16 hours charging time. A fully charged battery should test 15.5-18.0 volts.

A further test of battery pack can be made by connecting a 1.4 ohm resistor across black and red wires (battery removed) or the input leads (battery installed) for two minutes. Battery voltage at the end of two minutes must be 9.0 volts minimum. If battery passes this test, recharge battery for service.

ALTERNATOR CHARGING SYSTEMS. Flywheel alternators are used on some engines for the charging system. The generated alternating current is converted to direct current by two rectifiers on the rectifier panel

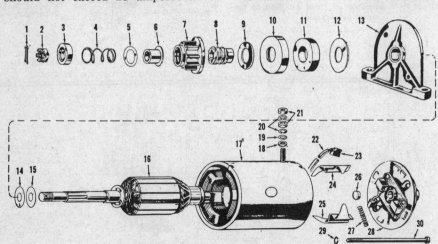

Fig. TE1—Twelve volt electric cranking motor used on some engines.

3. Pinion stop
4. Anti-drift spring
5. Pinion washer
6. Anti-drift sleeve
7. Pinion gear
8. Screw shaft
9. Thrust washer
10. Cushion cup
11. Rubber cushion
12. Thrust washer
13. Drive end cap
14. Spacer washer, 0.003
15. Spacer washer, 0.010
16. Armature
18. Insulation washer
22. Insulation tubing
23. Brush
24. Insulation
25. Insulation
26. Thrust spacer
28. Commutator end cap

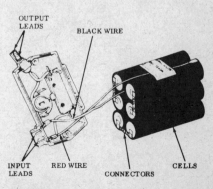

Fig. TE3—View of Nickel Cadmium battery pack connected to "SAF-T-KEY" starting switch.

OUTPUT LEADS
BLACK WIRE
INPUT LEADS
RED WIRE
CONNECTORS
CELLS

(Figs. TE5 and TE6) or the regulator-rectifier (Fig. TE7).

The system shown in Fig. TE5 has a maximum charging output of about 3 amperes at 3600 rpm. No current regulator is used on this low output system. The rectifier panel includes two diodes (rectifiers) and a 6 ampere fuse for overload protection.

The system shown in Fig. TE6 has a maximum output of 7 amperes. To prevent overcharging the battery, a double pole switch is used in low output position to reduce the output to 3 amperes for charging the battery. Move switch to high output position (7 amperes) when using accessories.

The system shown in Fig. TE7 has a maximum output of 7 amperes and uses a solid state regulator-rectifier which converts the generated alternating current to direct current for charging the battery. The regulator-rectifier also allows only the required amount of current flow for existing battery conditions. When battery is fully charged, current output is decreased to prevent overcharging the battery.

TESTING. On models equipped with rectifier panel (Figs. TE5 or TE6), remove rectifiers and test them with either a continuity light or an ohmmeter. Rectifiers should show current flow in one direction only. Alternator output can be checked using an induction ampere meter over the positive lead wire to battery.

On models equipped with the regulator-rectifier (Fig. TE7), check

the system as follows: Disconnect B+ lead and connect a DC voltmeter as shown in Fig. TE8. With engine running near full throttle, voltage should be 14.0-14.7. If voltage is above 14.7 or below 14.0 but above 0, the regulator-rectifier is defective. If voltmeter reading is 0, the regulator-rectifier or alternator coils may be defective. To test the alternator coils, connect an AC voltmeter to the AC leads as shown in Fig. TE9. With engine running at near full throttle, check AC voltage. If voltage is less than 20.0 volts, alternator is defective.

110 VOLT ELECTRIC STARTER

110 VOLT AC STARTER. Some vertical shaft engines are available with a 110 volt AC electric starting system as shown in Fig. TE11. When

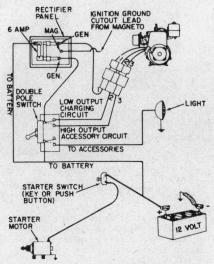

Fig. TE6–Wiring diagram of typical 7 ampere alternator and rectifier panel charging system. The double pole switch in one position reduces output to 3 amperes for charging or increases output to 7 amperes in other position to operate accessories.

switch button (6) is depressed, switch (21) is turned on and the motor rotates driven gear (23). As more pressure is applied, housing (11) moves down compressing springs (19). At this time, clutch facing (24) is forced tight between driven gear (23) and cone (30) and engine is cranked.

Electric motor (3) is serviced only as an assembly. All other parts shown are available separately. Shims (18) are used to adjust mesh of drive gear (5) to driven gear (23).

110 VOLT AC-DC STARTER. Some engines may be equipped with a 110 volt AC-DC starting motor (Fig. TE12). The rectifier assembly used with this starter converts 110 volt AC house current to approximately 100 volts DC. A thyrector (8) is used as a surge protector for the rectifiers.

To test starting motor, remove the DC output cable (9) from motor. Place an ohmmeter between one of the flat receptacle terminals and motor housing. If reading is obtained, the motor is grounded and requires repair. Connect the ohmmeter between the two flat receptacle terminals. A resistance reading or 3-4 ohms must be obtained. If not, motor is faulty.

A no-load test can be performed with the starter removed. Do not operate the motor continuously for more than 15 seconds when testing. Maximum am-

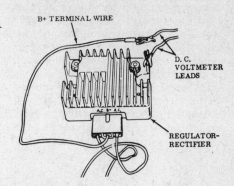

rig. TE8–Connect DC voltmeter as shown when checking the regulator-rectifier.

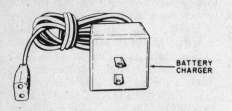

Fig. TE4–Recharge Nickel Cadmium battery pack only with the charger furnished with "SAF-T-KEY" starter system. Charger converts 110 volt AC to DC charging current.

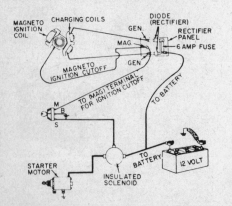

Fig. TE5–Wiring diagram of typical 3 ampere alternator and rectifier panel charging system.

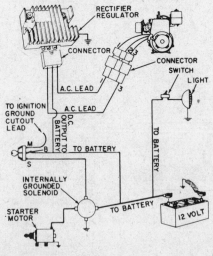

Fig. TE7–Wiring diagram of typical 7 or 10 ampere alternator and regulator-rectifier charging system.

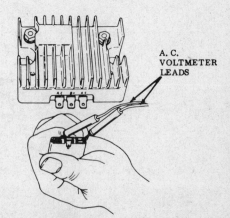

Fig. TE9–Connect AC voltmeter to AC leads as shown when checking alternator coils.

Fig. TE11–Exploded view of the 110 volt AC electric starter used on some engines.

3. Motor
4. Roll pin
5. Pinion gear
6. Starter switch button
7. Switch return spring
8. Washer
9. Screw
10. Mounting bushings (3 used)
11. Starter housing
12. Receptacle
14. Nuts (2 used)
15. Pinion bearing
16. Thrust races (2 used)
17. Thrust bearing
18. Thrust shims
19. Guide post springs (3 used)
20. Switch plunger spring
21. Switch
22. Screws (2 used)
23. Driven gear
24. Clutch facing
25. Bearing
27. Snap ring
28. Shield
29. Screws (4 used)
30. Lower cone

31. Screen
32. Cap studs (3-used)
33. Spring (3 used)
34. Acorn nuts (4 used)

35. Lock washers
36. Mounting ring
37. Reinforcing ring
40. Switch cover

pere draw should be 2 amperes and minimum rpm should be 8500.

Disassembly of starter motor is obvious after examination of the unit and reference to Fig. TE12. When reassembling, install shim washers (20) as necessary to obtain armature end play of 0.005-0.015. Shim washers are available in thicknesses of 0.005, 0.010 and 0.020. Tighten elastic stop nut (32) to a torque of 100 in.-lbs. Tighten nuts on the two thru-bolts to a torque of 24-28 in.-lbs.

To test the rectifier assembly, first use an AC voltmeter to check line voltage of the power supply, which should be approximately 115 volts. Connect the input cable (7) to the AC power supply. Connect a DC voltmeter to the two slotted terminals of the output cable (9). Move switch (3) to "ON" position and check the DC output voltage. DC output voltage should be a minimum of 100 volts. If a low voltage reading is obtained, rectifiers and/or thyrector could be faulty. Thyrector (8)

can be checked after removal, by connecting the thyrector, a 7.5 watt AC light bulb and a 115 volt AC power supply in series. If light bulb glows, thyrector is faulty. Use an ohmmeter to check the rectifiers. Rectifiers must show continuity in one direction only.

WIND-UP STARTERS

RATCHET STARTER. On models equipped with the ratchet starter, refer to Fig. TE13 and proceed as follows: Move release lever to "RELEASE" position to remove tension from main spring. Remove starter assembly from engine. Remove left hand thread screw (26), retainer hub (25), brake (24), washer (23) and six starter dogs (22). Note position of starter dogs in hub (21). Remove hub (21), washer (20), spring and housing (12), spring cover (18), release gear (17) and retaining ring (19) as an assembly. Remove retaining ring, then carefully separate these parts. CAUTION: Do not remove main spring from housing (12). The spring and housing are serviced only as an assembly. Remove snap rings (16), spacer washers (29), release dog (14), lock dog (15) and spring (13). Winding gear (8), clutch (4), clutch spring (5), bearing (6) and crank handle (2) can be removed after first removing the retaining screw and washers (10, 30 and 9).

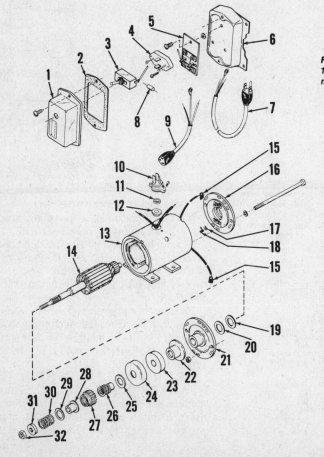

Fig. TE12–Exploded view of 110 volt AC-DC starter motor and rectifier assembly.

1. Cover
2. Gasket
3. Switch
4. Rectifier bridge
5. Rectifier base
6. Mounting base
7. AC input cable
8. Thyrector
9. DC output cable
10. Receptacle
11. Washer
12. Insulator
13. Field coils & housing assy.
14. Armature
15. Brushes
16. End plate
17. Spring insulator
18. Brush spring
19. Nylon washer
20. Shim washers (0.005, 0.010 and 0.020)
21. Drive end-plate
22. Thrust sleeve
23. Rubber cushion
24. Cup
25. Thrust washer
26. Screw shaft
27. Pinion gear
28. Spring sleeve
29. Washer
30. Anti-drift spring
31. Pinion stop
32. Elastic stop nut

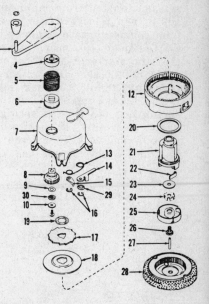

Fig. TE13–Exploded view of a ratchet starter assembly used on some engines.

2. Handle
4. Clutch
5. Clutch spring
6. Bearing
7. Housing
8. Wind gear
9. Wave washer
10. Clutch washer
12. Spring and housing
13. Release dog spring
14. Release dog
15. Lock dog
16. Dog pivot retainers
17. Release gear

18. Spring cover
19. Retaining ring
20. Hub washer
21. Starter hub
22. Starter dog
23. Brake washer
24. Brake
25. Retainer
26. Screw (left hand thread)
27. Centering pin
28. Hub and screen
29. Spacer washers
30. Lock washer

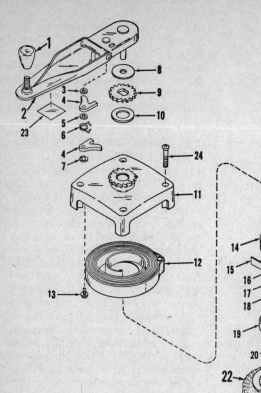

1. Handle knob
2. Starter handle
3. Dog washer
4. Dog release
5. Dog spacer
6. Dog release spring
7. Pivot retainer
8. Ratchet bearing
9. Ratchet
10. Ratchet spacer
11. Housing assembly
12. Spring and keeper
13. Keeper screw
14. Spring hub assembly
15. Starter dog
16. Spring & eyelet
17. Brake washer
18. Brake
19. Retainer
20. Screw 10-32
21. Screw 8-32
22. Hub and screen
24. Phillips screw 10-32

assembly. CAUTION: Do not remove spring from keeper. Remove pivot retainer (7), dog releases (4), spring (6), washer (3) and spacer (5) from handle (2).

When reassembling, install spring hub (14) before placing spring and keeper in housing (11). Install ratchet (9) so that teeth are opposite ratchet teeth on housing.

REMOTE RELEASE IMPULSE STARTER (SURE LOCK). To disassemble the "Sure Lock" remote release impulse starter (Fig. TE15), first release tension from main spring. Unbolt and remove starter assembly from engine. Remove centering pin (23), then unscrew the left hand threaded screw (22). Remove retainer (21), spring (20), brake (19), starter dog (17), thrust washer (18) and hub (16). Remove cranking handle (1), wind dog (9), brake band (10), lock dog spring (11) and lock dog (12). Carefully lift out spring and keeper assembly (14). CAUTION: Do not attempt to remove spring from keeper. Spring and keeper

Reassembly procedure is the reverse of disassembly. Centering pin (27) must align screw (26) with crankshaft center hole.

IMPULSE STARTER. To overhaul the impulse starter (Fig. TE14), first release tension from main spring. Unbolt and remove starter assembly from engine. Remove retaining screw (21), retainer (19), spring and eyelet (16) and starter dogs (15). Remove screw (20), brake (18), washer (17), cranking handle (2), bearing (8), ratchet (9) and spacer (10). Withdraw spring hub (14) and if spring and keeper assembly (12) are to be renewed, remove keeper screw (13). Carefully remove spring and keeper

1. Cranking handle
2. Wind dog
3. Brake band
4. Lock dog spring
5. Lock dog
6. Housing
7. Release arm
8. Wave washer
9. Release arm
10. Hub
11. Spacer washer
12. Power spring
13. Spring housing
14. Shim
15. Thrust washer
16. Brake
17. Starter dog
18. Spring
19. Retainer
20. Shoulder nut
21. Centering pin
22. Hub & screen

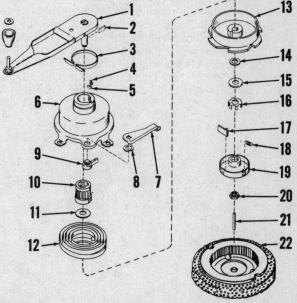

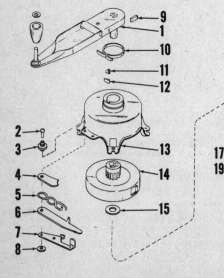

1. Cranking handle
2. Rivet
3. Pivot stud
4. Release lever
5. Release spring
6. Trip lever
7. Trip release
8. Washer
9. Wind dog
10. Brake band
11. Lock dog spring
12. Lock dog
13. Housing
14. Spring & keeper
15. Bearing washer
16. Hub
17. Starter dog
18. Thrust washer
19. Brake
20. Spring
21. Retainer
22. Screw (L.H. thread)
23. Centering pin
24. Hub & screen

are serviced only as an assembly.

NOTE: Some models use pivot stud (3), release lever (4), release spring (5) and trip lever (6). Other models use rivet (2) and trip release (7). Removal of these parts is obvious after examination of the unit and reference to Fig. TE15.

Reassembly procedure is the reverse of disassembly. Press centering pin (23) into screw (22) about ⅓ of the pin length. Pin will align starter with center hole in crankshaft.

REMOTE RELEASE IMPULSE STARTER (SURE START). Some models are equipped with the "Sure Start" remote release impulse starter shown in Fig. TE16. To disassemble

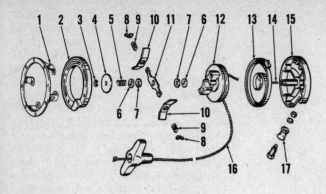

Fig. TE17–Exploded view of typical friction shoe rewind starter.

1. Mounting flange
2. Flange
3. Retaining ring
4. Washer
5. Spring
6. Slotted washer
7. Fibre washer
8. Spring retainer
9. Spring
10. Friction shoe
11. Actuating lever
12. Rotor
13. Rewind spring
14. Centering pin
15. Cover
16. Rope
17. Roller

REWIND STARTERS

FRICTION SHOE TYPE. To disassemble the starter, refer to Fig. TE17 and proceed as follows: Hold starter rotor (12) securely with thumb and remove the four screws securing flanges (1 and 2) to cover (15). Remove flanges and release thumb pressure enough to allow spring to rotate pulley

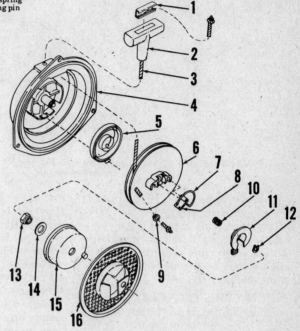

the starter, first move release lever to remove power spring tension. Unbolt and remove starter assembly from engine. Remove centering pin (21), shoulder nut (20), retainer (19), spring (18), starter dog (17), thrust washer (15) and shim (14). Remove cranking handle (1), wind dog (2) and brake band (3). Rotate spring housing (13) while pushing down on top of hub (10). Withdraw spring housing, power spring and hub from housing (6). Lift hub from spring.

NOTE: This is the only wind-up type starter spring which may be removed from the spring housing (keeper). To remove spring, grasp inner end of spring with pliers and pull outward. Spring diameter will increase about ⅓ when removed. To install new power spring in spring housing, clamp spring housing in a vise. Anchor outer end of spring in housing. Install spacer washer (11) and hub (10), engaging inner end of spring in hub notch. Insert cranking handle shaft in hub and while pressing down on cranking handle, rotate crank to wind spring into housing. When all of the spring is in the housing, allow cranking handle and hub to unwind.

To remove release lever (7) and release arm (9), file off peened over sides

Fig. TE19–Exploded view of typical dog type rewind starter assembly used on some 2-cycle engines.

1. Insert
2. Handle
3. Rope
4. Starter housing
5. Rewind spring
6. Pulley & hub assy.
7. Dog spring
8. Starter dog
9. Grommet
10. Brake spring
11. Brake
12. Retaining ring
13. Flywheel nut
14. Washer
15. Starter cup
16. Screen

of release arm. Remove lever, wave washer and arm.

When reassembling, place release arm on wood block, install wave washer and release lever. Using a flat face punch, peen over edges of new release arm to secure release lever. The balance of reassembly is reverse of disassembly procedure. Install centering pin so that end of pin extends below end of mounting legs. The pin will align the center of starter to center hole in end of crankshaft.

until spring (13) is unwound. Remove retaining ring (3), washer (4), spring (5), slotted washer (6) and fibre washer (7). Lift out friction shoe assembly (8, 9, 10 and 11), then remove second fibre washer and slotted washer. Withdraw rotor (12) with rope from cover and spring. Remove rewind spring from cover and unwind rope from rotor.

When reassembling, lubricate rewind spring, cover shaft and center bore in rotor with a light coat of Lubriplate or equivalent. Install rewind spring so that windings are in same direction as removed spring. Install rope on rotor, then place rotor on cover shaft. Make certain that inner and outer ends of spring are correctly hooked on cover and rotor. Pre-load the rewind spring by rotating the rotor two full turns. Hold rotor in pre-load position and install flanges (1 and 2). Check sharp end of friction shoes (10) and sharpen or renew as necessary. Install washers (6 and 7), friction shoe assembly, spring (5), washer (4) and retaining ring (3). Make certain that friction shoe assembly is installed properly for correct starter rotation. If properly installed, sharp ends of friction shoes will extend when rope is pulled.

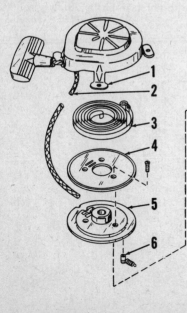

Fig. TE18–Exploded view of typical dog type rewind starter assembly. Some units of similar construction use three starter dogs (7).

1. Cover
2. Rope
3. Rewind spring
4. Pulley half
5. Pulley half & hub
6. Retainer spring
7. Starter dog
8. Brake
9. Brake screw
10. Retainer
11. Retainer screw
12. Hub & screen assy.

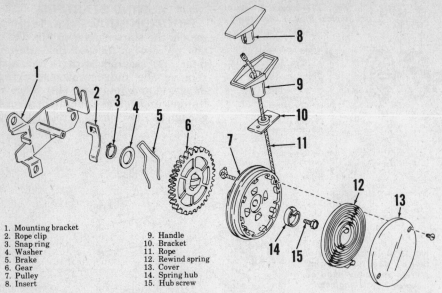

1. Mounting bracket
2. Rope clip
3. Snap ring
4. Washer
5. Brake
6. Gear
7. Pulley
8. Insert
9. Handle
10. Bracket
11. Rope
12. Rewind spring
13. Cover
14. Spring hub
15. Hub screw

Fig. TE20–Exploded view of single gear side-mounted rewind starter used on some vertical crankshaft engines

Remove brass centering pin (14) from cover shaft, straighten pin if necessary, then reinsert pin ⅓ of its length into cover shaft. When installing starter on engine, centering pin will align starter with center hole in end of crankshaft.

DOG TYPE. (4-CYCLE). To disassemble the dog type starter, refer to Fig. TE18 and release pre-load tension of rewind spring as follows: Pull starter rope until notch in pulley half (5) is aligned with rope hole in cover (1). Use thumb pressure to prevent pulley from rotating. Engage rope in notch of pulley and slowly release thumb pressure to allow spring to unwind. Remove retainer screw (11), retainer (10) and spring (6). Remove brake screw (9), brake (8) and starter dog (7). Carefully remove pulley assembly with rope from spring and cover. Note direction of spring winding and carefully remove spring from cover. Unbolt and separate pulley halves (4 and 5) and remove rope.

To reassemble, reverse the disassembly procedure. Then, pre-load rewind spring as follows: Align notch in pulley with rope hole in cover. Engage rope in notch and rotate pulley two full turns to properly preload the spring. Pull rope to full extended position. Release handle and if spring is properly pre-loaded, the rope will fully rewind.

DOG TYPE (2-CYCLE). Some engines are equipped with the dog type rewind starter shown in Fig. TE19. To disassemble the starter, first pull rope to fully extended position. Then, tie a slip knot in rope on outside of starter housing. Remove insert (1) and handle (2) from end of rope. Hold pulley with thumb pressure, untie slip knot and

withdraw rope and grommet (9). Slowly release thumb pressure and allow pulley to rotate until spring is unwound. Remove retaining ring (12), brake (11), brake spring (10) and starter dog (8) with dog spring (7). Lift out pulley and hub assembly (6), then remove rewind spring (5).

Reassemble by reversing the disassembly procedure. When installing the rope, insert a suitable tool in the rope hole in pulley and rotate pulley six full turns until hole is aligned with rope hole in housing (4). Hold pulley in this

Fig. TE21–Exploded view of multiple gear side-mounted rewind starter assembly used on some vertical crankshaft engines.

1. Shaft
2. Pin
3. Upper gear
4. Brake
5. Housing
6. Lower gear
7. Snap ring
8. Pulley & gear assy.
9. Washer
10. Rewind spring
11. Cover
12. Snap ring
13. Pin
14. Rope

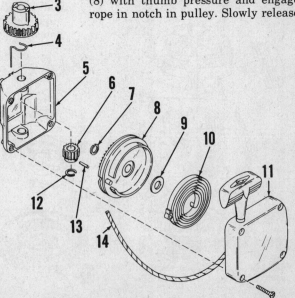

position and install rope and grommet. Tie a slip knot in rope outside of housing and assemble handle and insert on rope. Untie slip knot and allow rewind spring to wind the rope.

SIDE MOUNTED TYPE (SINGLE GEAR). To disassemble the side mounted starter (Fig. TE20), remove insert (8) and handle (9). Relieve spring tension by allowing spring cover (13) to rotate slowly. Rope will be drawn through bracket (10) and wrapped on pulley (7). Remove cover (13) and carefully remove rewind spring (12). Remove hub screw (15), spring hub (14), then withdraw pulley and gear assembly. Remove snap ring (3), washer (4), brake (5) and gear (6) from pulley. Rope can now be removed from pulley.

Reassemble by reversing the disassembly procedure, keeping the following points in mind: Lubricate only the edges of rewind spring (12) and shaft on mounting bracket (1). Do not lubricate spiral in gear (6) or on pulley shaft. Rewind spring must be pre-loaded approximately 2½ turns.

When installing the starter assembly, adjust mounting bracket so that side of teeth on gear (6) when in fully engaged position, has 1/16-inch clearance from base of flywheel gear teeth. Remove spark plug wire and test starter several times for gear engagement. A "too close" adjustment could cause starter gear to hang up on flywheel gear when engine starts. This could destroy the starter.

SIDE MOUNTED TYPE (MULTIPLE GEAR). Some engines may be equipped with the side mounted starter shown in Fig. TE21. To disassemble this type starter, unbolt cover (11) and remove items (7, 8, 9, 10, 11 and 14) as an assembly. Pull rope out about 8 inches, hold pulley and gear assembly (8) with thumb pressure and engage rope in notch in pulley. Slowly release thumb pressure and allow spring to unwind. Remove snap ring (7), pulley and gear (8), washer (9) and rewind spring (10) from cover. Rope (14) and rewind spring can now be removed if necessary. Gears (3 and 6) can be removed after first removing snap ring (12), driving out pin (13) and withdrawing shaft (1). Remove brake (4).

To reassemble, reverse the disassembly procedure. Pre-load the rewind spring two full turns.

WISCONSIN

TELEDYNE WISCONSIN MOTOR
Milwaukee, Wisconsin 53246

MODELS	Cyls.	Bore	Stroke	Displ.
AA	1	2¼	2¾	10.9
AB-ABN-ABS	1	2½	2¾	13.5
ACN-HACN	1	2⅝	2¾	14.9

Model HACN is a vertical crankshaft engine, while all other models in this section are horizontal crankshaft engines.

MAINTENANCE

SPARK PLUG. Recommended spark plug is Champion D16J, AC No. C86 Commercial or equivalent. Electrode gap is 0.030. Torque plug to 25-30 foot-pounds.

CARBURETOR AND FUEL PUMP. List below shows carburetor equipment. Note that more than one make is listed for the same model engine.

Carburetor	Engine
Marvel-Schebler—	
VH53	ABS, ACN
VH63 & VH92	AB, ABN

Carburetor	Engine
Stromberg—	
OH ⅝	AA, AB, ABN

Carburetor	Engine
Zenith—	
87B5	AB, ABN, ACN, HACN

Clockwise rotation of fuel mixture adjusting needles will lean the mixture for all carburetors. Initial fuel settings are as follows:

Marvel-Schebler
　Main fuel needle .... 1½ turns open
　Idle fuel needle .... ½ turn open
Zenith
　Both fuel needles .... 1¼ turns open
Stromberg
　Main fuel needle .... 1 turn open
　Idle fuel needle .... ¾ turn open

To check carburetor float settings on Marvel-Schebler models VH53, VH63 and VH92, remove fuel bowl and invert throttle body and float assembly. Measure distance between free end of float and body gasket surface. This space should be ¼-inch. If not, carefully bend float lever tang which contacts fuel inlet needle valve so as to obtain correct setting.

To check float setting on Zenith model 87B5 carburetor, remove fuel bowl and invert throttle body and float assembly. Distance from float tops at their free ends to machine-finished surface of throttle body should be 31/32-inch. To adjust, carefully bend float arm close to each float body until setting is correct.

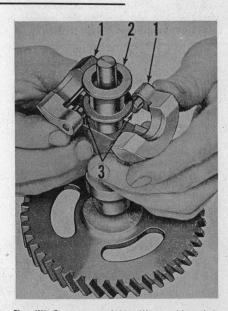

Fig. W3—Governor weights (1) are hinged to camshaft. Centrifugal force is transferred from weights to sleeve (2) through hardened pins (3). The motion of the sleeve controls the governor lever (6—Fig. W4).

To check float level of Stromberg OH5/8 carburetor, remove float chamber cover. Fuel level should be 17/32-inch below machined surface of float chamber flange. Adjust by carefully bending float lever close to float until required level is obtained.

Fuel pump, when used on models ACN or HACN is Wisconsin LP-42-B. Refer to FUEL PUMP paragraph in SERVICING WISCONSIN ACCESSORIES section for fuel pump service information.

GOVERNOR. A centrifugal weight mechanical governor (See Fig. W3) is used on all models. Governor weights (1) are hinged to the engine camshaft. Hardened pins (3) in weights transmit centrifugal force to governor sleeve (2). Movement of the governor sleeve operates the governor lever (6—Fig. W4)

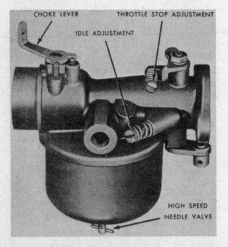

Fig. W1—Typical Marvel-Schebler carburetor used on Wisconsin engines. Note location of fuel mixture adjustment needles.

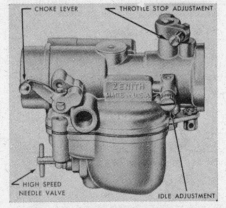

Fig. W2—Typical Zenith carburetor used on Wisconsin engines. Location of fuel mixture adjusting needles on Stromberg carburetors is similar.

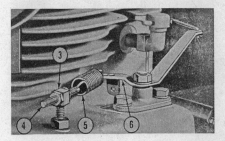

Fig. W4—Fixed speed governor controls typical of Wisconsin engine models.

3. Bracket　　　　　　　　5. Governor spring
4. Adjusting screw　　　　6. Governor lever

through a yoke.

Minor speed variations are obtained by changing governor spring tension through adjustment of screw (4). Major speed variations are obtained by repositioning hooked end of governor spring (5) in various holes of governor lever (6). Governor lever (6) has three adjusting holes—hole number one being nearest to pivot point of lever. Governed no-load and loaded speeds will vary by 100 to 350 RPM depending upon adjustment and placement of governor spring. Refer to table which follows for governed speed adjustments:

Desired RPM Under Load	Governor Spring Hole Number*	Adjust No-Load RPM to
1600	1	1930
1700	1	2015
1800	1	2060
1900	1	2110
2000	1	2180
2100	1	2240
2200	1	2340
2300	1	2430
2400	1	2535
2500	2	2650
2600	2	2750
2700	2	2860
2800	2	2950
2900	3	3160
3000	3	3200
3100	3	3260
3200	3	3445
3300	3	3525
3400	3	3595
3500	3	3670
3600	3	3735

*Governor spring holes are numbered starting with hole closest to governor arm shaft as hole No. 1, with hole No. 3 being at outer end of arm. Spring No. PM-74 is used on all models.

Rod connecting carburetor throttle arm to governor bell-crank must be adjusted for proper length as follows: With engine not running and rod attached to carburetor throttle arm and unhooked from governor bell-crank or arm, open carburetor throttle to wide open position. Move the governor bell-crank or arm towards carburetor as far as possible and adjust length of rod so that bent end of rod is in register with hole in governor bell-crank or arm end. Then turn rod into swivel block on carburetor throttle arm two turns, insert bent end into hole in end of governor bell-crank or arm and secure with cotter pin.

MAGNETO AND TIMING.

Magneto	Engine
Fairbanks-Morse—	
FMXD1B7	AA, AB, ABS, ABN
FMXD1B7S	ACN
FMXD1B7S1	HACN
Wico—	
XH1295C	AA, AB, ABS, ABN
XH2477	ACN

Magneto breaker points and condenser are accessible by removing the end cover from the magneto. Set breaker point gap to 0.015.

To time magneto on all models, remove the flywheel shroud and inspection hole plug. (Fig. W5 shows engine shroud cut-away to expose inspection hole.) Then turn engine until timing mark on cam gear is visible through inspection hole and install magneto with timing marks on magneto gear and cam gear in register as shown in Fig. W5. Reinstall inspection hole plug and flywheel shroud. Vane marked D-C on flywheel should be in register with centerline mark (2). To check timing advance, whiten vane marked D-C with chalk or paint and use power timing light with engine running at operating speed. Timing should be advanced 17° on models ACN and HACN, and 28° on models AA, AB, ABN and ABS, so that marked vane will appear in line with running timing mark (3).

When magnetos on all engine models are properly timed, the impulse coupling will snap just as the marked vane on the flywheel is in line with the centerline mark on the flywheel shroud when turning the engine slowly by hand.

On model HACN, magneto is mounted in a suspended position below timing gear train, and an oil drain tube is fitted in the magneto body to drain excess oil back to the engine crankcase.

DISTRIBUTOR AND TIMING.

Models ABN and ACN, when furnished with electric starter and generator or starter-generator combination, are equipped with battery ignition distributor (timer). Prestolite IGW-4408 distributor is used on late production engines. Earlier engines were fitted with IGW-4405 or IGW-4179 distributors. Distributors rotate at crankshaft speed. Breaker contact gap is 0.020 and should be set before timing engine. Point spring tension is 17-20 ounces.

To time the distributor after removal from engine, remove screen from flywheel air intake opening, then proceed as follows: Turn crankshaft in normal direction of rotation by hand until piston can be felt to be rising on compression stroke at spark plug hole, then gradually bring D/C marked vane on flywheel into register with static timing mark (2—Fig. W5) at top center of air shroud opening. Hold flywheel at this top dead center position. Now, with distributor removed from engine, rotate its drive gear counter-clockwise by hand until cam just starts to open the breaker points. Remount distributor on engine carefully so as not to disturb positions of either crankshaft or camshaft gear while engaging distributor drive gear. After distributor is securely remounted, loosen clamp lever screw (Fig. W6) so that running advance can be set. Automatic advance designed into distributor flyweight mechanism accounts for 15° of 17° required as running advance. Two additional degrees needed are set as initial advance on distributor body by turning it clockwise, points just starting to open. 2° is equivalent to 3/64-inch on circumference of distributor. Tighten clamp screw and use a timing light to check running advance. Note that engine must run at 1800 RPM or more for full automatic advance. If running advance does not coincide with 17° mark shown in Fig. W5, adjust as necessary and secure clamp screw.

LUBRICATION. Models AA, AB, ABN, ABS and HACN have a crankcase capacity of 1¾ pints. Model ACN requires 2 pints. Use SAE No. 30 oil for temperatures above 40°F. In temperatures ranging from +5°F. to +40°F., use 20-20W grade, and below +5°F., use SAE 10W. Manufacturer recommends that oil used be equivalent in quality to Mobiloil A or Mobiloil

Fig. W5—Magneto timing on Wisconsin models ACN and HACN. Running timing of other models is 28° BTDC. Models equipped with distributor-timer do not have inspection hole or timing marks (1).

1. Magneto timing marks
2. Centerline mark
3. Running timing mark
4. Flywheel keyway

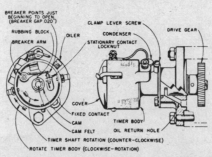

Fig. W6—Distributor-timer used on models ABN and ACN, when equipped with battery ignition. Refer to text for timing procedure.

Arctic. Horizontal crankshaft models are splash lubricated by a dipper on connecting rod cap which swings through a constant level oil trough fitted in crankcase. Oil level in this trough is maintained by a cam-operated pump in the oil sump. Vertical crankshaft model engine (HACN) is spray-lubricated by a vane-type oil pump located at lower end of crankshaft. See Fig. W8. Oil supply stores in adaptor base of engine. Oil pressure relief valve reed (5) will require renewal if bent or badly fitted to relief hole. Oil strainer screen (6) should be serviced whenever engine is disassembled for removal of sludge or contamination or for renewal if defective.

ABN and ACN models equipped with ignition timer and battery instead of magneto require that 3 to 5 drops of engine oil be applied to felt wick in cam sleeve and to shaft oiler for every 100 hours operation.

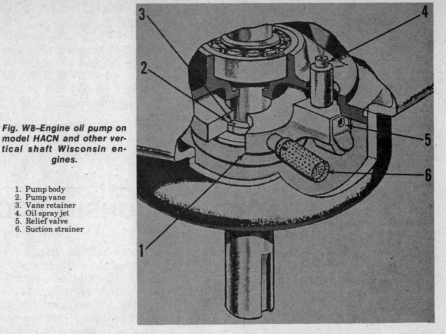

Fig. W8–Engine oil pump on model HACN and other vertical shaft Wisconsin engines.

1. Pump body
2. Pump vane
3. Vane retainer
4. Oil spray jet
5. Relief valve
6. Suction strainer

REPAIRS

TIGHTENING TORQUES: All models this section except as indicated.

Spark plug .... 25-30 ft.-lbs.
Cylinder head .... 14-18 ft.-lbs.
Connecting rod cap ..... 14-18 ft.-lbs.
Main bearing plates ..... 14-18 ft.-lbs.
Engine base to crankcase
(except HACN) .... 6-8 ft.-lbs.
Engine adapter base
(HACN) .... 24-26 ft.-lbs.
Crankcase side cover
(HACN) .... 6-8 ft.-lbs.

CONNECTING ROD. Rod and piston assembly is removed from top of cylinder bore after head is removed. Diameter of crankpin in crankshaft is 1.0 inch on all models. Crankshaft end of connecting rod is babbitted and shim-adjusted. Connecting rod bearing clearance is 0.0007-0.002 for all models. Side clearance is specified 0.004-0.010 for AA, AB, ABN and ABS models and 0.006-0.013 for models ACN and HACN. Connecting rod end and cap are indexed for reassembly with oil hole in cap installed toward oil

spray jet in model HACN; toward oil pump body in all others.

PISTON, PIN, RINGS. Model AA and some earlier production AB engines are fitted with 3 rings, 1 each of compression, scraper and oil control types. Later AB engines and all others use a four ring piston having 2 compression rings. See Figs. W9 and W10 for placement and configuration.

End gap for piston rings on all models is 0.012-0.022. On four ring pistons, stagger end gaps 90° in reassembly. Arrange 3-ring piston end gaps 120° apart.

Side clearance for all piston rings of models AA, AB, ABN and ABS is 0.002-0.003. For models ACN and HACN, top ring side clearance is 0.002-0.0035, second and third rings, 0.001-0.0025 and fourth (oil control) ring is 0.0025-0.004.

Pistons and rings are available in oversizes of 0.005, 0.010, 0.020 and 0.030 for all models. Tri-chrome rings

are available for model ACN.

Piston skirt clearance in cylinder bore is 0.0045-0.005 for models AA, AB, ABN and ABS. For models ACN and HACN, operated at 3,000 RPM and lower, piston skirt clearance is 0.005-0.0055. If these models are operated at engine speeds exceeding 3,000 RPM, skirt clearance should be increased to 0.006-0.0065.

Floating piston pin is a light press fit in piston bosses with 0.0002-0.0008 clearance in connecting rod for all models. Available oversizes are 0.005, 0.010, 0.020 and 0.030.

CYLINDER. When cylinder bores are worn to exceed 0.005, grinding to next oversize and fitting with oversize pistons and rings is required.

CRANKSHAFT. Shim-gaskets of 0.003 and 0.006 thickness are fitted in combinations between main bearing plate and crankcase to adjust crankshaft for end play of 0.002-0.004 in tapered roller main bearings. Use dial indicator set-up to measure end play.

Fig. W7–Engine timing marks on models AA, AB, ABN, ABS, ACN and HACN Wisconsin engines.

1. Magneto timing marks
2. Crankshaft gear
3. Camshaft timing marks
4. Cam gear
5. Magneto gear

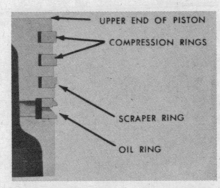

Fig. W9–Piston ring cross section. Model AA and some early production units of model AB have only one compression ring. Later AB models and models ABN and ABS are as shown. Note wiping arrangement of scraper ring and oil control ring.

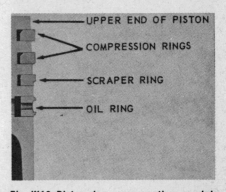

Fig. W10–Piston ring cross section, models ACN, HACN. Note position of inner chamfer (top) of compression rings and placement of scraper ring.

Timing marks of crankshaft and camshaft gears must be in proper register as shown in Fig. W7.

CAMSHAFT. Hollow camshaft with its drive gear revolves on a pin which is a drive fit in crankcase sidewalls. To remove, knock out Welch (expansion) plug and drift out the pin and opposite plug working from flywheel side of the crankcase. Renew plugs during reassembly.

VALVE SYSTEM. Valve tappet gap, cold engine, for models AA, AB, ABN and ABS is 0.011-0.013 for both intake and exhaust valves, Stellite valves included. Tappet clearance for models ACN and HACN is 0.008 for intake and 0.014 for exhaust valves, both Stellite and conventional.

Valve stem clearance in block bore or valve guides is 0.003-0.005 in. for all models. Renewable valve guides are available for models ACN and HACN, and should be installed when stem clearance reaches 0.007. Models AA, AB, ABN and ABS compensate for stem wear by use of renewal valves having stems which are 0.004 oversize.

Tappet clearance on all models, is set by careful grinding of valve stem tips. Valve seat and valve face angles are ground to 45°, then lapped to seat properly. Width of seat is 3/32-inch for all models.

SERVICING WISCONSIN ACCESSORIES

REWIND STARTER. Fig. W11 provides an exploded view of rewind starter of the type found on some model ACN engines. See Fig. W12 to identify parts. After starter is unbolted from engine shroud, disassemble as follows:

Remove retainer ring, retainer washer, brake spring, friction washer, friction shoe assembly and second friction washer as shown in Fig. W12. Hold the rope handle in one hand and the cover in the other and allow rotor to rotate to unwind the recoil spring preload. Lift rotor from cover, shaft and recoil spring. NOTE: Check the winding direction of recoil spring and rope for aid in reassembly. Remove recoil spring from cover and unwind rope from rotor.

When reassembling the unit, lubricate recoil spring, cover shaft and its bore in rotor with Lubriplate or equivalent. Install the rope on rotor and the rotor to the shaft and engage the recoil spring inner end hook. Pre-load the recoil spring four turns and install middle flange and mounting flange. Check friction shoe sharp ends and renew if necessary. Install friction washers, friction shoe assembly, brake spring, retainer ring. Make certain that friction shoe assembly is installed properly for correct starter rotation. If properly installed, sharp ends of friction shoe plates will extend when rope is pulled.

Starter operation can be reversed by winding rope and recoil spring in opposite direction and turning the friction shoe assembly upside down.

FUEL PUMP. Some special order model ACN and HACN engines are equipped with fuel pump, part No. LP-42-B. Should it become necessary to order a new crankcase assembly, be sure to specify if engine has a fuel pump so that correct crankcase unit will be furnished.

If engine performance at sustained high speed or under heavy load shows fuel pump to be at fault, a renewal kit, part No. LQ-28 is available. To service fuel pump, disconnect fuel lines at

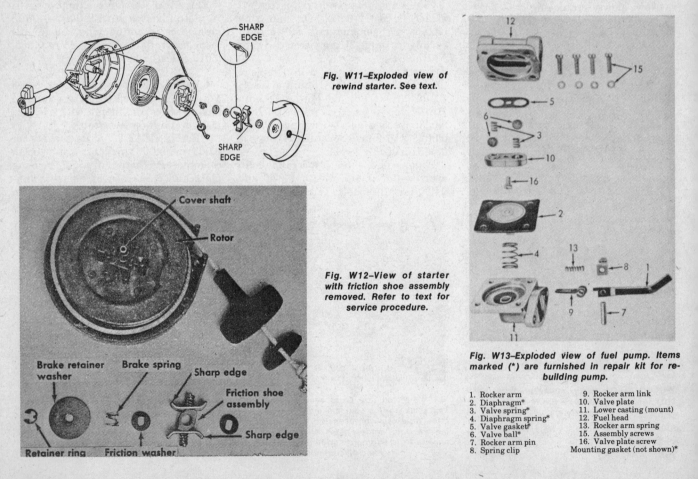

Fig. W11–Exploded view of rewind starter. See text.

Fig. W12–View of starter with friction shoe assembly removed. Refer to text for service procedure.

Fig. W13–Exploded view of fuel pump. Items marked (*) are furnished in repair kit for rebuilding pump.

1. Rocker arm
2. Diaphragm*
3. Valve spring*
4. Diaphragm spring*
5. Valve gasket*
6. Valve ball*
7. Rocker arm pin
8. Spring clip
9. Rocker arm link
10. Valve plate
11. Lower casting (mount)
12. Fuel head
13. Rocker arm spring
15. Assembly screws
16. Valve plate screw
Mounting gasket (not shown)*

pump, unbolt pump body from engine and proceed as follows:

Index-mark castings (11 & 12—Fig. W13) with a light file stroke or chisel mark at joining edges and remove four assembly screws (15) and separate fuel head (12) from lower body (11). Invert fuel head and remove screw (16), followed by plate (10), valve springs and balls (3 & 6) and gasket (5). Parts 3, 5 and 6 are provided in renewal kit. Install new valve parts exactly as old ones were positioned after thorough cleaning of fuel head casting (12) and secure valve assembly in place by securing screw (16).

Remove rocker arm spring (13) from lower (diaphragm) casting (11). Hold lower casting (11) in one hand with a thumb or finger against link (9) and press downward on metal center of diaphragm (2) to compress diaphragm spring (4) and turn diaphragm clockwise a quarter-turn to disengage diaphragm rod from link (9). Discard diaphragm (2) and spring (4). After lower casting is thoroughly cleaned, reverse removal procedure above to install new diaphragm spring (4) and diaphragm (2) from kit. Reinstall rocker arm spring (13).

Using a new mounting gasket from kit, remount lower cast-assembly in its place on the engine. Secure with pump mounting screws.

Now, slowly crank engine by hand until diaphragm (2) lies flat on surface of lower casting (11) and place fuel head (12) back in position (aligning index marks) over new diaphragm and set in and start threads of four assembly screws (15). Continue hand-turning engine until diaphragm is pulled down in lower casting then tighten assembly screws evenly and securely. Reconnect fuel lines.

STARTING MOTORS, GENERATORS, MOTOR-GENERATORS AND REGULATORS.

Of the engines covered in this section, models ABN and ACN may be equipped with battery ignition and distributor-timer. When engine is so equipped, consult wiring diagrams of Figs. W14, W15, and W16 for circuit service.

All 6-volt systems are positive (+) grounded. 12-volt systems have been changed from positive (+) to negative (−) ground beginning with engine serial No. 3985702, model ACN.

GENERATOR (6-VOLT). Prestolite GAS-4103-1 is used. Rotation is clockwise, observed from drive end, with third brush control and cut-out relay as shown in Fig. W14. Brush spring tension is 15-20 ounces and field coil draw is 3.4-3.8 Amps at 5.0-volts with current output of 7.1 Amps at 8.0-volts.

Circuit breaker teamed with this generator, Prestolite CB-4008, has these specifications: Circuit breaker contact gap is 0.015-0.045 inch with armature air gap of 0.010 inch, with contacts closed air gap is 0.030 inch. Closing voltage is 6.5-7.3 and opening current is 0.5-2.5 Amps.

GENERATOR (12-VOLT). Older, positive (+) ground units use Prestolite GJG-4007MP. Negative ground systems use GJG-4010M. Rotation is clockwise for either polarity. Brush spring tension is 12-24 ounces with current draw for field windings of 1.7-1.9 Amps at 10 volts. Motoring draw is 4-5 Amps. Maximum current output is 10 Amps (7000 RPM) at 15 volts.

VOLTAGE-CURRENT REGULATOR. A vibrating type regulator is used to control output of shunt-wound generator. Prestolite VBO-4201-Z1 is used in positive ground systems and VBO-4201-Y1 with negative ground generators. Cut-out relay opens at 3-5 Amps and closes at 12.6-13.6 volts. Current is controlled at 9-11 Amps. Operating voltage is 14.3-14.8 at 110°F. Voltage regulator specifications call for the following armature air

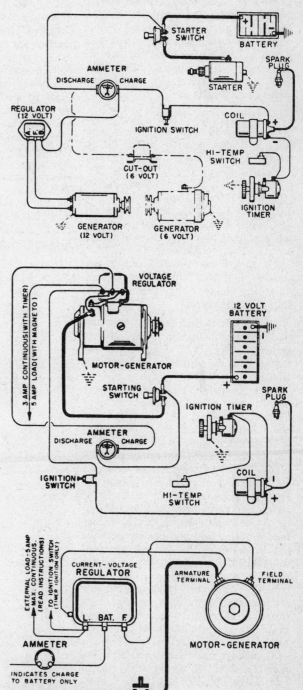

Fig. W14–Wiring circuit for models equipped with starter and generator. 12-V negative ground system is shown. Polarity is positive ground for all 6-volt systems and earlier 12-V models. Refer to text. Note high temperature switch in ignition circuit for overheating protection.

Fig. W15–Wiring layout for combination motor-generator. See text for service.

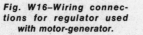

Fig. W16–Wiring connections for regulator used with motor-generator.

gaps: Circuit breaker, 0.025-0.027, voltage regulator and current regulator each at 0.048-0.052. Circuit breaker contact gap is 0.015 minimum.

STARTER (6-VOLT). Prestolite MAK-4008, which may be found on older production, is obsolete, though parts remain available. Rotation is counter-clockwise as seen from drive end. Brush spring tension is 38-61 ounces and allowable armature end-play is 0.005-0.062. No-load test is 70 Amperes at 5.0-volts and 4700 RPM. Stalling torque is 2.5 ft.-lbs. at 250 Amps and 2.0-volts. Present engine production uses starter MDH-4001M which also rotates counter-clockwise. Brush spring tension is 42-66 ounces with minimum armature end-play of 0.005 in. No-load current draw is 52 Amperes at 5.0 volts and 8100 RPM. Stall torque is 1.6 ft.-lbs. at 230 Amperes and 2.0 volts.

STARTER (12-VOLT). Prestolite MDO-4002M is used. Rotation is also counter-clockwise with brush spring tension of 42-66 ounces and minimum armature end-play of 0.005 inch. No-load current tests at 38 Amperes at 10,000 RPM and 10 volts. Stall-torque test shows 1.5 ft.-lbs. at 170 Amperes and 4 volts. Later production uses Prestolite starter MGD-4102A, which has comparable specifications.

Pinion position for both 6 and 12-volt starters is 1-25/32 inch from face of mounting flange to edge of pinion with 1/16-inch tolerance.

MOTOR-GENERATORS. Starting motor-generator-regulator circuitry is shown in Fig. W15. Fig. W16 illustrates how regulator is connected in circuits.

10 Ampere current output of generator function side of motor-generator is distributed separately at regulator terminals "L" and "BAT"—see Fig. W16. Current from "BAT" terminal is regulated to meet charging requirements for the battery. Ammeter shown in circuit indicates only battery charging rate, not the current draw for lights and accessories as in other systems. Measurement of this accessory load requires that another ammeter be set in series with load on terminal marked "L". If engine has magneto ignition, up to 5 Amps may be drawn from "L", however, if timer-distributor is furnished for ignition, accessory load must be limited to 3 Amps as 2 Amps must flow in coil-distributor circuit for engine to run satisfactorily.

Motor-generator furnished after serial No. 3985701 is negative ground (−) Delco-Remy No. 1101868, with regulator Delco-Remy No. 1118984. Earlier production, positive (+) ground

models are furnished with Delco-Remy motor-generator No. 1101972 and regulator 1118985.

These specifications apply: Model 1101868 and model 1101972 motor-generators differ only in polarity. Rotation, viewed from drive end, is clockwise. Brush spring tension is 24-32 ounces and field current is 1.43-1.54 Amps at 12 volts, checked at 80°F. Cold output is 10 Amps at 14 volts and 5450 RPM. No-load test draws an average 13 Amps (max. 18 Amps) at 11 volts and 2500-3000 RPM.

Regulators 1118984 and 1118985 also differ only in their polarity. Cut-out relay air gaps and point openings are both 0.020 inch with a closing range of 11.8 to 14.0 volts. When adjusting, set to 12.8 volts. Voltage regulator air gaps are 0.075 inch with voltage range of 13.6-14.5 volts. Setting should be adjusted to 14.0 volts.

REDUCTION UNITS. Gear drive and chain drive speed reduction units are available for Wisconsin engines in this section. Fig. W17 is typical of models available. Reduction ratios offered are 2.92:1 and 2:1 with chain-sprocket drive as shown in inset of Fig. W17. Spur gear model shown has a ratio of 3.266:1. Later model reduction units have spiral gears which may be cut at angles of 9°-12′ or 22°-38′, furnished in reduction ratios of 3¼:1, 5½:1

or 6:1. Special crankshafts are required on all reducer-equipped models and complete engine and reducer model identification is needed when ordering renewal parts.

When mounted on engine, reducer housing and main bearing plate (2—Fig. W17) is fitted in place of regular bearing plate used on basic engine and same shim gaskets and procedure for adjusting engine main bearing end play are used. Refer to CRANKSHAFT paragraph for details.

Reduction units may be mounted on engine crankcase in any of four positions, depending on requirements. Note that interchangeable oil plugs (3 and 22) and breather reducer (23) will require shifting when reduction unit is mounted in positions other than as shown in Fig. W17. Design of housing is such that a drain hole will always be in position at low side and oil check plug will be at correct oil level with breather vent slightly higher with filler hole at top regardless of position of reduction housing in relation to engine block.

Reduction gears are lubricated by oil of same type as used in engine crankcase. Gear case capacity is approximately one pint, filled to check level plug opening. Oil change interval should not exceed 500 hours operating time and should be more frequent in

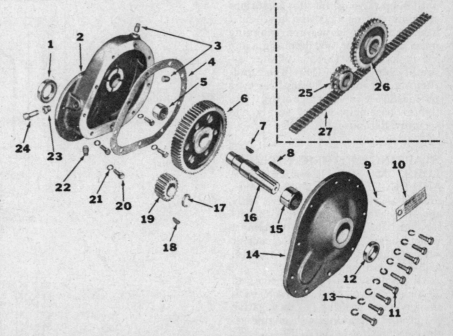

Fig. W17–Exploded view of typical reduction gear set used with Wisconsin engines. Inset shows chain-sprocket arrangement used in some models. Refer to text.

1. Crankshaft oil seal	9. Cover pin	19. Drive gear
2. Main housing and bearing plate	10. Instruction tag	20. Housing screw (same as 11)
3. Pipe plug, ¼-in. PT—same as 22	11. Cover screw (5/16-18 × ⅞)	21. Washer
4. Cover gasket	12. Take-off shaft oil seal	22. Drain plug (same as 3)
5. Inner bearing	13. Cover lockwashers	23. Reducer, ¼-in. PT × ⅛-in. PT
6. Driven gear	14. Housing cover	24. Breather
7. Woodruff key	15. Outer bearing	25. Drive sprocket
8. Key—¼-in. sq. × 1⅜	16. Take-off shaft	26. Driven sprocket
	17. Drive gear retainer	27. Drive chain (⅝-in. pitch)
	18. Woodruff key—drive gear	

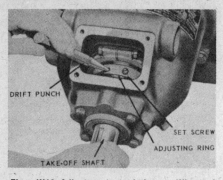

Fig. W18–Adjustment technique, Wisconsin multiple-disc clutch. See text for procedure.

1. Back clamping plate
2. Drive plate (sintered)
3. Driven plates (steel)
4. Clamping plate (front)
5. Drive plates (sintered)
6. Capscrew (2)
7. Shim (2)
8. Locknut (2)
9. Adjuster and lock
10. Adjuster set screw
11. Lock spring
12. Lever (6 used)
13. Lever rollers (9 used)
14. Collar assembly (incl. 6, 7, 8)
15. Wedge sleeve
16. Hub set screw
17. Key
18. Hub

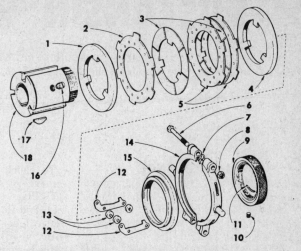

Fig. W20–Exploded view of clutch hub and disc assemblies. All parts are serviced. Collar assembly (14) may be die cast or bronze and key (17) is available in 3 styles. Furnish detailed information when ordering renewal parts.

heavy continuous duty. Maintain level by regular, periodic checks.

CLUTCH. When equipped with a clutch and power take-off assembly, engines in this section require a special crankcase, crankshaft and main bearing plate with a special seal for the clutch housing. Complete model and part number identification is stamped on engine crankcases, and must be furnished when ordering renewal parts.

Clutch is multiple-disc design, manual-lever operated and runs in oil. Service is limited to renewal of worn or defective parts, maintaining of "wet" oil level of approximately one-half pint of same oil as is used in crankcase and adjustment to overcome slippage due to normal wear of friction discs. See Fig. W18 for adjustment procedure and

Figs. W19 and W20 for parts service and assembly order.

ADJUST CLUTCH. When clutch begins to slip when engaged, adjustment should be made immediately to prevent overheating and damage. Proceed as follows:

Remove inspection plate (16—Fig. W19). Disengage clutch and rotate take-off shaft by hand until set screw of knurled adjusting collar (Fig. W18) is visible at top. Loosen set screw and turn adjusting collar clockwise

slightly, using a punch as in Fig. W18 (or comparable tool) while holding take-off shaft from turning. Engage clutch. If in proper adjustment, clutch will engage with a slight snap. If necessary, continue to rotate collar until proper adjustment is made, then retighten set screw. Replace inspection cover, replenishing clutch oil or renewing cover gasket if needed. Refer to Fig. W20 for arrangement of clutch components if renewal of defective parts becomes necessary.

1. Roll pin (2)
2. Shifter yoke
3. Shaft
4. Cork seal
5. Oil level plug
6. Screw, ⅜-16 × 1⅜
7. Washer
8. Screw, ⅜-16 × 1½
9. 1⅜ in. expansion plug
10. Street ell, ⅛ × 45°
11. Breather
12. No 4 × ¼ screw (4)
13. Clutch instruction plate
14. Washer
15. Screw, ¼—20 × ½
16. Inspection hole cover
17. Cover gasket
18. Bearing retainer screw, ¼—20 × 1¼
19. Washer
20. Oil seal, take-off shaft
21. Shift lever
22. Clamp screw (same as 8)
23. Shifter shaft
24. Shaft oil seal
25. Housing
26. Oil drain plug
27. Oil instruction tag
28. Key, ¼-in. sq. × 2½
29. Shaft bearing
30. Bearing retainer plate
31. Bearing spacer
32. Clutch assembly
33. Clutch drive hub
34. Shaft pilot bearing
35. Clutch hub key, ¼-in. sq. × 1-in.
36. Lockwasher
37. Hub set screw

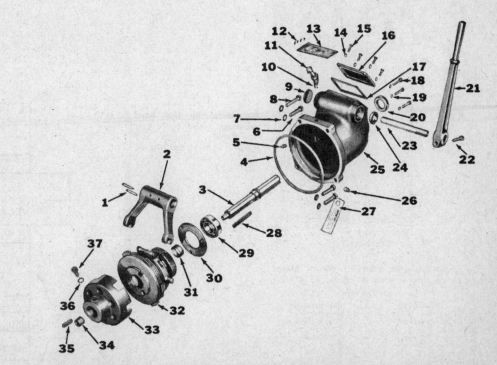

Fig. W19–Exploded view, engine side, of Wisconsin multi-disc clutch and power take-off assembly.

WISCONSIN ROBIN

TELEDYNE WISCONSIN MOTOR
Milwaukee, Wisconsin 53246

MODEL	Cyls.	Bore	Stroke	Displ.
EY18W	1	2 9/16	2 5/32	11.14

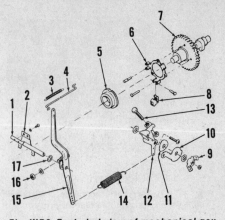

Fig. WR3—Exploded view of mechanical governor and linkage.

1. Governor lever shaft	10. Stop plate
2. Yoke	11. Wave washer
3. Link spring	12. Control lever
4. Carburetor link	13. Speed stop screw
5. Thrust sleeve	14. Governor spring
6. Governor plate	15. Governor lever
7. Camshaft assembly	16. Clamp nut
8. Flyweights (3 used)	17. Retaining ring
9. Wing nut	

MAINTENANCE

SPARK PLUG. Recommended spark plug is Champion L86, AC 44F, NGK B6HS or equivalent. Electrode gap is 0.020-0.025. Tighten spark plug to a torque of 24-27 ft.-lbs.

CARBURETOR. Mikuni model BV18H carburetor is used on model EY18W engine. Refer to Fig. WR1 for exploded view. To adjust idle fuel mixture, gently seat the idle mixture needle (1), then back needle out (counter-clockwise) 1½ turns. Main fuel is metered through main jet (19) and is non-adjustable. With engine operating, adjust idle speed stop screw (3) to obtain an idle speed of 1250 rpm. Make final adjustments on idle mixture needle and idle speed stop screw with engine running at normal operating temperature.

To check and adjust float setting, remove jet holder (20) and fuel bowl (17). Place carburetor body on end (on manifold flange) so that float pin is in vertical position. Move float to close inlet needle valve. NOTE: Needle valve is spring loaded. Float tab should just contact needle valve pin but should not compress the spring. Using a depth gage, measure distance between body flange and free end of float as shown in Fig. WR2. Distance should be 0.710-0.790. If not, bend tab on float lever to obtain correct setting.

GOVERNOR. The mechanical flyweight governor is mounted to and operated by the camshaft gear. See Fig. WR3. Engine speed is controlled by the tension on governor spring (14).

Before attempting to adjust governed speed, synchronize governor linkage as follows: Loosen clamp nut (16) and turn governor lever (15) counter-clockwise until carburetor throttle plate is in wide open position. Then, insert screwdriver in slot in end of governor lever

shaft (1) and rotate shaft counterclockwise as far as possible. Tighten governor clamp nut.

To adjust for a particular loaded rpm, hook governor spring (14) to control lever (12) and governor lever (15). Start engine, loosen wing nut (9), move control lever (12) counter-clockwise and adjust stop screw (13) until the required no-load speed is obtained. If engine is to operate at a fixed speed, tighten wing nut (9). For variable speed operation, do not tighten wing nut.

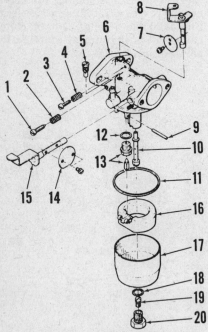

Fig. WR1—Exploded view of Mikuni model BV18H carburetor used on model EY18W engine.

1. Idle mixture needle	11. Bowl gasket
2. Spring	12. Gasket
3. Idle speed stop screw	13. Inlet needle & seat
4. Spring	14. Choke plate
5. Idle jet	15. Choke shaft
6. Carburetor body	16. Float
7. Throttle plate	17. Bowl
8. Throttle shaft	18. Washer
9. Float pin	19. Main jet
10. Nozzle	20. Jet holder

Fig. WR2—With fuel bowl removed, stand carburetor on manifold flange and measure float setting as shown.

VIEW LOOKING DOWN
Carburetor Setting on Manifold Flange

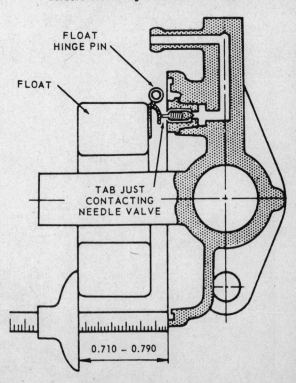

FLOAT HINGE PIN

FLOAT

TAB JUST CONTACTING NEEDLE VALVE

0.710 – 0.790

For the following loaded engine speeds, adjust governor to the following no-load speeds:

Loaded RPM	No-Load RPM
1800	2370
2000	2515
2200	2665
2400	2815
2600	2975
2800	3140
3000	3310
3200	3485
3400	3670
3600	3855

MAGNETO AND TIMING. Flywheel type magneto is used and breaker points and condenser are located under flywheel. Initial point gap is 0.014. See Fig. WR4. To check and adjust engine timing, disconnect lead wire from shut-off switch. Connect a continuity light lead to lead wire and ground other lead to engine. Slowly rotate flywheel in normal direction until light goes out. Immediately stop turning flywheel and check location of timing marks. Timing marks should be aligned as shown in Fig. WR5. If timing mark (M) on flywheel is below timing mark (D), breaker point gap is too large. If mark (M) is above mark (D), breaker point gap is too small. Carefully measure the distance necessary to align the two marks, then remove flywheel and breaker point cover. Changing point gap 0.001 inch will change timing mark (M) position ⅛-inch. Reassemble and tighten flywheel retaining nut to a torque of 47 ft.-lbs.

LUBRICATION. Crankcase capacity is 1¼ pints. Use SAE 30 oil when operating in temperatures above 40° F., SAE 20 oil in temperatures between 15° F. and 40° F. and SAE 10W-30 in temperatures below 15° F. Recommended motor oil is API classification MS or SD. An oil dipper attached to the connecting rod cap provides for splash type lubrication.

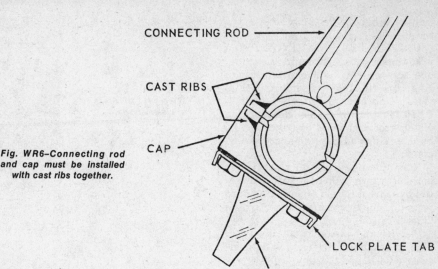

Fig. WR6–Connecting rod and cap must be installed with cast ribs together.

CONNECTING ROD

CAST RIBS

CAP

LOCK PLATE TAB

OIL DIPPER (toward flywheel end)
Mount toward gear cover if operating tilt is toward take-off end.

CRANKCASE BREATHER. A floating poppet type breather valve is located in the breather plate behind the valve cover plate. A breather tube connects breather into air cleaner. Restricted or faulty breather is indicated when oil seeps from gasket surfaces and oil seals.

REPAIRS

TIGHTENING TORQUES. Recommended tightening torques are as follows:

Spark plug . . . . 27 ft.-lbs.
Connecting rod capscrews . . . 14 ft.-lbs.
Cylinder head nuts . . . . 22 ft.-lbs.
Flywheel nut . . . . 47 ft.-lbs.
Gear cover cap screws . . . . . . 13 ft.-lbs.

CYLINDER HEAD. Always use a new head gasket when installing cylinder head. Tighten cylinder head nuts evenly in three stages; first to 12 ft.-lbs., then 18 ft.-lbs. and finally 22 ft.-lbs.

CONNECTING ROD. Connecting rod and piston assembly is removed from above after cylinder head and gear cover are removed. Connecting rod to crankpin clearance should be 0.0021-0.0031 with a maximum clearance of 0.005. Rod side clearance should be 0.008-0.0235 with a maximum clearance of 0.039. Connecting rod to piston pin clearance should be 0.0004-0.0012 with a maximum clearance of 0.0032.

When installing connecting rod and piston assembly, make certain match marks (cast ribs) on connecting rod and cap are together as shown in Fig. WR6. Install oil dipper toward gear cover end of engine if engine is to be operated on a tilt toward take-off end. Mount dipper toward flywheel end if operated on a tilt in that direction or with no tilt operation. Use a new lock plate and

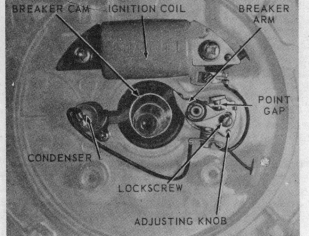

BREAKER CAM   IGNITION COIL   BREAKER ARM

POINT GAP

CONDENSER

LOCKSCREW

ADJUSTING KNOB

Fig. WR4–View showing flywheel magneto. Flywheel and breaker cover are removed.

ADVANCE TIMING MARK ON FLYWHEEL RIM

TIMING MARK ON CRANKCASE

Fig. WR5–23° BTDC timing mark (M) on flywheel aligned with timing mark (D) on crankcase.

tighten connecting rod cap screws to a torque of 14 ft.-lbs.

PISTON, PIN AND RINGS. Piston is equipped with one compression ring, one scraper ring and one oil control ring. Install rings as shown in Fig. WR7. Ring end gap should be 0.002-0.010. Piston ring side clearance in piston grooves should be 0.0004-0.003. Stagger ring end gaps 90° apart around piston.

Recommended piston to cylinder bore clearance is 0.0016-0.0032 (measured at thrust face of piston). Standard piston diameter at skirt thrust faces is 2.5567-2.5575.

Pistons and piston rings are available in standard size as well as oversizes of 0.010 and 0.020.

Standard piston pin diameter is 0.5509-0.5512. Piston pin to piston fit is 0.00035 tight to 0.00039 loose with a maximum clearance of 0.0023 loose. Piston pin to connecting rod clearance should be 0.0004-0.0012 with a maximum clearance of 0.0032.

CYLINDER BLOCK. If cylinder wall is scored, out-of-round more than 0.003 or tapered more than 0.006, the cylinder should be bored and/or honed to the nearest suitable oversize of 0.010 or 0.020. Standard cylinder bore is 2.5591-2.5599.

CAMSHAFT. Camshaft rides in bores in crankcase and gear cover. When removing camshaft assembly, lay engine on side to prevent tappets from falling out. If valve tappets are removed, identify them so they can be reinstalled in their original position. Valve tappets have an operating clearance in crankcase bores of 0.001-0.0024 with a maximum clearance of 0.004. Camshaft journal diameter is 0.5889-0.5893.

When reinstalling camshaft, install governor thrust sleeve (5—Fig. WR3) on governor flyweights. Then, slide camshaft into position, making certain that the marked tooth on crankshaft gear is between the two marked teeth on camshaft gear.

CRANKSHAFT. The crankshaft is supported in two ball bearings. Renew bearings if any indication of roughness, noise or excessive wear is found. Crankshaft end play of 0.001-0.009 is controlled by the adjusting collar located between crankshaft gear and gear cover main bearing. See Fig.

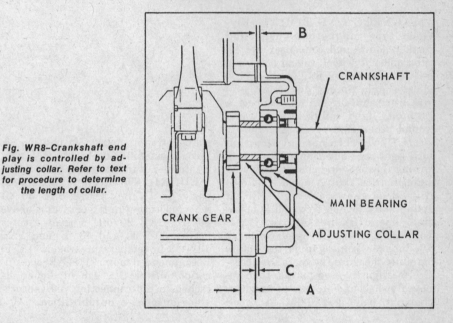

Fig. WR7–Install piston rings as shown.

Fig. WR8–Crankshaft end play is controlled by adjusting collar. Refer to text for procedure to determine the length of collar.

WR8. Three lengths of adjusting collars are available; 0.701 to 0.709, 0.709 to 0.717 and 0.717 to 0.725. To determine the correct length of adjusting collar with gear cover removed, proceed as follows: Measure distance (A—Fig. WR8) between machined surface of crankcase face and end of crankshaft gear. Measure distance (B) between machined surface of gear cover and end of main bearing. The compressed thickness of gear cover gasket (C) is 0.007. Select adjusting collar that is 0.001-0.009 less in length than the total of A, B and C. After reassembly, crankshaft end play can be checked with a dial indicator.

Standard crankpin diameter is 1.0210-1.0215. Connecting rod to crankpin clearance should be 0.0021-0.0031 with a maximum clearance of 0.005. If rod clearance is excessive or if

crankpin is out-of-round or tapered more than 0.0002, crankshaft should be renewed.

When reassembling engine, make certain that marked tooth on crankshaft gear is between the two marked teeth on camshaft gear. When renewing crankshaft oil seals, install seals with lips toward ball bearings.

VALVE SYSTEM. Valve tappet gap (cold) is 0.006-0.008. Valve face and seat angle is 45°. Desired seat width is 0.047-0.059. Valve spring free length should be 1.4173 with a minimum length of 1.3582. Stem diameter of inlet and exhaust valves is 0.273-0.274. Valve stem to guide clearance should be 0.0016-0.0039 with a maximum clearance of 0.006. Inside diameter of new guides is 0.2756-0.2769. If stem to guide clearance is excessive, renew guides and/or valves.

SERVICING WISCONSIN ROBIN ACCESSORIES

REWIND STARTER
OVERHAUL. To disassemble the rewind starter, refer to Fig. WR9 and release spring tension by pulling rope handle until about 18 inches of rope extends from unit. Use thumb pressure against ratchet retainer to prevent reel from rewinding and place rope in notch in outer rim of reel. Release thumb pressure slightly and allow spring mechanism to slowly unwind. Twist loop of return spring and slip loop

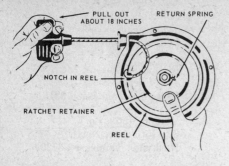

Fig. WR9–View showing method of releasing spring tension on rewind starter assembly.

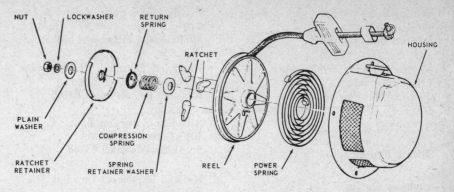

Fig. WR10–Exploded view of rewind starter assembly used on Wisconsin Robin engines.

through slot in ratchet retainer. Refer to Fig. WR10 and remove nut, lockwasher, plain washer and ratchet retainer. Reel will completely unwind as these parts are removed. Remove compression spring, three ratchets and spring retainer washer. Slip fingers into two of the cavity openings in reel hub (Fig. WR11) and carefully lift reel from support shaft in housing.

CAUTION: Take extreme care that power spring remains in recess of housing. Do not remove spring unless new spring is to be installed.

If power spring escapes from housing, form a 4½ inch I.D. wire ring and twist the ends together securely. Starting with the outside loop, wind spring inside the ring in a counterclockwise direction. NOTE: New power springs are secured in a similar wire ring for ease in assembly. Place spring assembly over recess in housing so that hook in outer loop of spring is over the tension tab in housing. Carefully press spring from wire ring and into recess of housing.

Using a new rope of same length and diameter as original, place rope in handle and tie a figure eight knot about 1½ inches from the end. Pull knot into top of handle. Install other end of rope through guide bushing of housing and through hole in reel groove. Pull rope out through cavity opening and tie a slip knot about 2½ inches from end. Place slip knot around

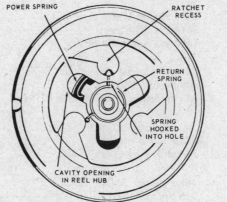

Fig. WR11–Use fingers in reel hub cavities to lift reel from support shaft.

center bushing as shown in Fig. WR12 and pull knot tight. Stuff end of rope into reel cavity. Spread a film of light grease on power spring and support shaft. Wind rope ¼-turn clockwise in reel and place rope in notch on reel. Install reel on support shaft and rotate reel counter-clockwise until tang on reel engages hook on inner loop of power spring. Place outer flange of housing in a vise and use finger pressure to keep reel in housing. Then, by means of rope hooked in the reel notch, preload power spring by turning reel 7 full turns counter-clockwise. Remove rope from notch and allow reel to slowly turn clockwise as rope winds on pulley and handle returns to guide

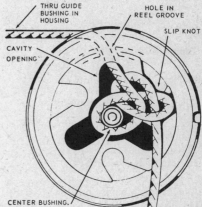

Fig. WR12–Install rope through guide bushing and hole in reel groove, then tie slip knot around center bushing.

bushing on housing.

Install spring retaining washer (Fig. WR10), cup side up, and place compression spring into cupped washer. Install return spring with bent end hooked into hole of reel hub. Place the three ratchets in position so that they fit the contour of the recesses. Mount ratchet retainer so that loop end of return spring extends through slot. Rotate retainer slightly clockwise until ends of slots just begin to engage the three ratchets. Press down on retainer, install flat washer, lockwasher and nut, then tighten nut securely.

Central Equipment Co.
4477 Garfield St.
Denver, Colorado 80216

Marine Industrial Equip. Corp.
710 Haines Street
Jacksonville, Florida 32206

P. H. Neff & Sons, Inc.
7270 Northwest 41st St.
Miami, Florida 33144

Highway Equip. & Sup. Co.
1016 West Church St.
Orlando, Florida 32802

Industrial Supply Co.
1800 Second Ave.
Tampa Florida 33605

Blalock Mach. & Equip. Co.
225 Forsyth Street SW
Atlanta, Georgia 30302

Lanco Engine Services, Inc.
3140 Koapaka St.
Honolulu, Hawaii 96819

Arnold Machinery Co., Inc.
111 East 39th St.
Boise, Idaho 83707

Industrial Engine & Parts Co.
1133 West Pershing
Chicago, Illinois 60623

Eagle Machine Co., Inc.
635 E. Market Street
Indianapolis, Indiana 46207

Port Huron Machinery Co.
301 East Court Ave.
Des Moines, Iowa 50308

Harley Sales Co.
505 South Main St.
Wichita, Kansas 67202

Womwell Automotive Parts Co.
240 Clark Street
Lexington, Kentucky 40501

Atlas Machine & Supply Co.
1326-30 W. Jefferson St.
Louisville, Kentucky 40203

Wm. F. Surgi Equip. Corp.
1149 Tchoupitoulas St.
New Orleans, Louisiana 70150

Diesel Engine Sales & Eng. Corp.
Fish Pier Road
Boston, Massachusetts 02210

R. G. Moeller Co.
44455 Grand River Ave.
Novi, Michigan 48050

Teledyne Wisconsin Total Power
6336 Lakeland Ave. N.
Minneapolis, Minnesota 55429

Klughartt-Thornhill Machinery Co.
1205 Woodswether Road
Kansas City, Missouri 64105

Allied Construction Equip. Co.
4015 Forest Park Ave.
St. Louis, Missouri 63108

Midland Implement Co., Inc.
402 Daniels
Billings, Montana 59101

Port Huron Mach. & Sup. Co.
801-813 "Q" Street
Lincoln, Nebraska 68508

Central Motive Power, Inc.
808 Second St. NW
Albuquerque, New Mexico 87101

John Reiner & Co.
94-15 150th Street
Jamaica, New York 11435

John Reiner & Co.
946 Spencer Street
Syracuse, New York 13208

King-McIver Sales, Inc.
P.O. Box 20088
Greensboro, North Carolina 27420

Northern Engine & Supply Inc.
2710 Third Ave. N.
Fargo, North Dakota 58102

Cincinnati Engine and Parts Co., Inc.
2863 Stanton Avenue
Cincinnati, Ohio 45206

Allied Farm Equip., Inc.
1066 Kinnear Road
Columbus, Ohio 43212

Harley Sales Co.
6845 E. 41st St.
Tulsa, Oklahoma 74145

Independent Distributors
2355 NW Quimby St.
Portland, Oregon 97210

Hamilton Equipment
567 S. Reading Rd.
Ephrata, Pennsylvania 17522

Joseph L. Pinto, Inc.
719 E. Baltimore Pike
East Lansdowne, Pennsylvania 19050

Contractors Equipment Service Co.
1415 Brighton Road NW
Pittsburgh, Pennsylvania 15212

Columbia Supply Co.
823 Gervais Street
Columbia, South Carolina 29202

RCH Distributors, Inc.
3150 Carrier St.
Memphis, Tennessee 38131

Wilder Motor Co.
301 15th Ave. North
Nashville, Tennessee 37203

Harley Sales Co.
8005 Sovereign Row
Dallas, Texas 75247

Harley Sales Co.
4427 West 12th
Houston, Texas 77001

Harley Sales Co.
3220 Kermit Hwy.
Odessa, Texas 79761

Harley Sales Co.
8403 Speedway Drive
San Antonio, Texas 78230

Arnold Machinery Co., Inc.
2975 W. 21st South
Salt Lake City, Utah 84119

Ronconi Equip. Co., Inc.
8815 Telegraph Rd.
Lorton, Virginia 22079

Phillips Machinery, Inc.
Staples Mill Rd. at Greendale
Richmond, Virginia 23228

Star Machinery Co.
241 Lander Street
Seattle, Washington 98134

Engine Sales & Service Co., Inc.
919 Virginia Street, East
Charleston, West Virginia 25301

Teledyne Wisconsin Total Power
2815 S. 171st St.
Milwaukee, Wisconsin 53246

CANADA

Mumford, Medland, Limited
5711 6th St. SE
Calgary, Alberta

Mumford, Medland, Limited
10809 105th Ave.
Edmonton, Alberta

Pacific Engines & Equip. Ltd.
40 E. Cordova St.
Vancouver, B.C.

Mumford, Medland, Limited
576 Wall St.
Winnipeg, Manitoba

Consolidated Engines & Machy.
Co., Ltd.
Coverdale Road
P.O. Box 848, Moncton
Riverview, New Brunswick

Seaboard GM Diesel, Ltd.
710 Windmill Road
Dartmouth, Nova Scotia

Consolidated Engine & Machy.
Co., Ltd.
3 Bestobell Road
Toronto, Ontario

Consolidated Engine & Machy.
Co., Ltd.
8550 Delmeade Road
Montreal, Quebec

Mumford, Medland, Limited
1250 St. John St.
Regina, Saskatchewan

Mumford, Medland, Limited
1729 Ontario St.
Saskatoon, Saskatchewan

NOTES